# THE PHYSICAL SCIENCES

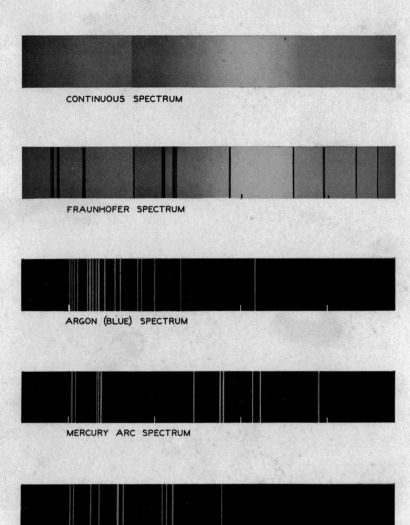

CONTINUOUS SPECTRUM

FRAUNHOFER SPECTRUM

ARGON (BLUE) SPECTRUM

MERCURY ARC SPECTRUM

COPPER SPARK SPECTRUM

4000    5000    6000    7000

*(Courtesy of Kodak Research Laboratories, Rochester, N. Y.)*

## SPECTRA

Every chemical element, whether on the earth or in a distant part of the universe, reveals
its identity by its spectrum. Besides the colored lines disclosed to the eye by means of
the spectroscope, most of the elements have many others lying beyond the visible region
in both directions.

# THE
# PHYSICAL SCIENCES

BY

## EMMETT JAMES CABLE, Ph. D.
HEAD OF THE SCIENCE DEPARTMENT

## ROBERT WARD GETCHELL, Ph. D.
PROFESSOR OF CHEMISTRY

AND

## WILLIAM HENRY KADESCH, Ph. D.
PROFESSOR OF PHYSICS
IOWA STATE TEACHERS COLLEGE

WITH REVISIONS

New York: 1941
PRENTICE-HALL, INC.

First Printing.........................May 1940
Second Printing......................October 1940
Third Printing.....................February 1941
Fourth Printing with Revisions..........June 1941
Fifth Printing.......................October 1941

# PREFACE

The aim in this book is to help the reader interpret intelligently the forces that make up the complex world in which he lives and to place at his disposal enough scientific knowledge to free his mind of prejudice and superstition. It should aid him to express himself accurately and to understand and appreciate scientific methods of arriving at the truth; also to form the habit of weighing values and reserving judgment until he knows all the facts.

The progress made in the field of science in the last quarter of a century has had a pronounced effect upon our modern life. It has influenced our existence at every turn. The individual branches of science are no longer academic entities, each cloistered in its own ivory tower; they are changing, growing fields that touch each other at a multitude of points. Their study becomes fruitful only when they are considered together so that all the interrelationships are apparent.

As the volume draws to its close, it will become evident to the reader that the various chapters are not unrelated fragments of knowledge; the individual sections, like the pieces of a puzzle, fall into their proper places and the design of the whole becomes discernible.

E. J. CABLE
R. W. GETCHELL
W. H. KADESCH

v

# PREFACE TO
# FOURTH PRINTING

The necessity for a fourth printing of this book has provided the authors an opportunity to make a number of revisions which classroom use has shown to be desirable. The phraseology has been improved in several places, particularly in the chapters on astronomy. In chapter 41 the discussion of the influence of the moon has been considerably expanded. A number of new diagrams have been substituted in the interest of greater pedagogical effectiveness. Many suggested emendations have been made.

The authors wish to take this opportunity to express their appreciation of the kindness of all readers who have pointed out inaccuracies or who have suggested modifications for the improvement of the book. In particular they wish to acknowledge their obligation to Professor Charles E. Stratton of Boston University, to Professor Henry L. Yeagley of the Pennsylvania State College, and to Doctor Hallock C. Campbell of Queens College.

THE AUTHORS

# CONTENTS

# CONTENTS

# CONTENTS

# CONTENTS

# TABLES

# CHAPTER 1

# THE DAWN OF
# SCIENCE

The birthplace of man is believed to be somewhere in the Eastern Hemisphere, but in just what region or even on what continent it is still impossible to say. It is equally difficult to determine when or where the first faint glimmerings of science appeared. The earliest notable scientific achievements are ascribed to the Egyptians and the Babylonians. It is certain, however, that the race had made enormous strides of a truly scientific nature many centuries before the great pyramids began to rise on the banks of the Nile.

Who was the first to kindle a fire, and how was it done? Who invented the earliest stone implements? Was it the Piltdown man, with whose remains some crude flints have been found? Who first used a spoken language? This achievement was both the culmination of notable intellectual development and a powerful stimulus to still further progress. By whom was a written language first developed? No greater invention than this has ever been made, for it is only by recording its thoughts and aspirations and thus making its achievements permanent that each generation has been enabled to contribute to the advancement of the race.

By the middle of the fourth millenium B. C. at least two written languages had appeared, one in Babylonia and one in Egypt. It is quite possible that two others had risen also, in India and in China. The first two countries had already made great advances in science. By 4200 B. C. the Egyptians had developed their knowledge of astronomy to such an extent that

1

they were able to devise a calendar of 365 days. By 3500 they were using a decimal number system in which each decimal unit was represented by a special symbol. The early Babylonians likewise were ardent and successful students of astronomy. They compiled lists of stars, observed the planets for astrological purposes, and were able to predict eclipses.

The learning of the Egyptians was extensive and well organized. This is well authenticated by two papyri, one dating from about the middle of the nineteenth and the other from the middle of the seventeenth century B. C. Each of these was copied from a still earlier text. Together they give evidence of remarkable intellectual activity, particularly in mathematics. Progress in this field extended back perhaps another thousand years. The seventeenth and eighteenth centuries should therefore be regarded rather as a culmination than as a beginning. However, the intellectual activities of these ancient peoples continued unabated almost down to the Christian era.

The learning of both the Babylonians and the Egyptians was passed on to the Greeks. The genius of this remarkable people employed this learning to such good purpose that the golden age of Greek civilization which followed is regarded by many writers as marking the highest level to which the race has yet attained.

The Greeks cultivated many of the sciences. Their most important contributions were made in the fields of astronomy, mathematics, botany, chemistry, physics, and medicine. At that time experimental science was still unknown. The Greeks, like other ancient peoples, relied upon observation and logic rather than upon experimentation for their results. Yet the achievements and fame of some of their scholars was so great that their views on scientific subjects were accepted without question for about two thousand years.

The rise of experimental science began in the latter part of the sixteenth century after Christ. It was during this time that William Gilbert, physician to Queen Elizabeth, performed his numerous experiments in electricity and magnetism. By means of his "terrella," he showed that the compass needle tells direction because of the magnetic properties of the earth.

It was also in this period that Galileo carried out his famous experiments on falling bodies. By dropping objects of unequal mass from the top of the tower of Pisa he showed that, except for atmospheric resistance, all objects fall at the same speed. It was he also who first used the telescope in the study of astronomy.

With Gilbert, Galileo, and their contemporaries we arrive at the beginning of the modern period of scientific development. Thenceforth the experimental method was increasingly recognized as an effective means of investigation, and considered essential in testing the merits of hypotheses. Some of the consequences of a persistent application of this method to the study of astronomy, physics, and other sciences will be described in the following chapters.

Chemistry as we know it today is one of the newer sciences. Its origin however, like that of mathematics, astronomy, and mechanics, is hidden in antiquity. Perhaps the ancient art was first nurtured in China. Its modern name harks back to "Chemia," the early name for Egypt. Articles more than fifty centuries old, of gold, silver, iron, and bronze, won from minerals by chemical methods, are now treasured in museums. The ancient Greek philosophers, mentioned above, speculated endlessly upon chemical questions, especially such mysteries as the structure of matter.

The Middle Ages witnessed the birth of alchemy, the immediate antecedent of chemistry. Practitioners of this art, the alchemists, pursued a dual search. They sought for a method or substance which would transmute the baser metals into gold. This substance was called the Philosopher's Stone, and its search consumed many centuries of time and many fortunes in money. Closely associated with this magic idea was the search for the Elixir of Life, which would insure health and longevity.

Gradually the emphasis shifted to the application of chemicals to the cure of disease. This was the period of Iatrochemistry. Since man was supposedly a composite of sulfur, salt, and mercury, illness was thought to be due to a lack of balance among these three essentials.

During the seventeenth and eighteenth centuries the mistaken ideas of the earlier devotees of the art were gradually abandoned. More and more facts accumulated. They were classified, interrelated, and unified. Then was born the science of chemistry. It early investigated the mystery of fire and created the Phlogiston theory to explain it, a theory which the discovery of oxygen undermined.

This brings us to the work of Lavoisier, Cavendish, Priestley, and their immediate successors—the fathers of a science which in the brief period of a century and a half has wrought a complete transformation in the mode of living of a large portion of the human race.

# CHAPTER 2

# MAN AND HIS MACHINES

The efforts of civilized man are largely directed toward obtaining food and clothing, providing shelter, and gaining satisfying social and intellectual experiences. In all of these activities he now makes use of a multitude of machines. While the most of these are of quite recent origin, a few simple ones have come down from very ancient times.

The bow and arrow, for example, were well known to prehistoric man. It was by hunting that he gained his food, and this machine was the chief point of advantage over his fleet, prospective meal. The wheel, one of the greatest inventions ever made by man, is also of prehistoric origin. The chariot, a two-wheeled carriage, was the vehicle of the ancient warrior, and as such is represented widely in his art and literature. The inclined plane and its uses have also long been known. It was doubtless by its use that Egyptian slaves lifted the huge stones that went into the construction of the great pyramids. The lever is probably of equally ancient origin. It is mentioned by the Greek philosopher Aristotle as a means of lifting a great weight by using a very small force. Archimedes, another great Greek who lived a century later, was so strongly impressed with this advantage of the lever that he is said to have exclaimed: "Give me a fulcrum on which to rest, and I will move the earth."

After Archimedes there was little change in the number of kinds of machines in use for nearly twenty centuries. During colonial days in America, and even later, life was hard and sim-

5

ple and moved slowly.  This condition prevailed everywhere and in everything.  Since then every activity has been speeded up again and again as one new device after another has come to displace others which were less efficient, only to give way in turn to something still faster or better.  Let us take a hasty glance at a few of these changes.

In going from his home in Mount Vernon to New York to be inaugurated as the first President of the nation, Washington traveled in a horse-drawn carriage.  The roads were unpaved and in places extremely difficult to travel.  The journey of a little over two hundred miles required seven wearisome days. During his first administration Washington made a tour through New England and one through the South.  His speed on these journeys did not vary greatly from the thirty or thirty-five miles a day made on the trip to New York.  This was typical of an era which provided only two other methods of land travel —on foot and on horseback.  Within half a century from that time a few short railroads had been built in three different parts of the country—New England, New York, and Maryland.  At first the trains were drawn by horses; in 1831 the first steam locomotive to be used in America was put in service.  Thenceforth development was rapid.  The iron horse soon proved its superiority in both speed and endurance.  New lines were projected and old ones extended.  In another thirty years the Atlantic and Pacific were connected by the first transcontinental railroad.  A speed of thirty-five miles a day had given way to regular schedules exceeding that many miles per hour.

In the first decade of the present century it was thought that the limit of desirable speeds had been reached when an eighteen-hour schedule had been introduced between New York and Chicago.  But the developments of the last few years—the substitution of Diesel for steam engines, the improvement in roadbeds, the use of light metals in the construction of cars and the streamlining of trains—have shown that much higher speeds may be safely maintained.

However, the railroad train is no longer our only means of rapid transit.  There are many young men and women in this country who have traveled widely, yet have never ridden on a railroad. In the last quarter century the greater convenience of the automobile, with its equal adaptability to long and short journeys and to almost any desired speed, has made us a nation of travelers. The great transcontinental bus lines have contributed to the same result. A journey of two hundred miles is no longer a week's ordeal, but the pleasant experience of an afternoon.

The latest and speediest type of conveyance is limited neither by rails nor by concrete or other highways. It takes to the air. In so doing it reduces the time of travel between New York and Chicago from sixteen hours to about four hours and a half, and that from New York to Los Angeles from about fifty-six hours to less than eighteen.

Facilities for transportation of goods have very naturally kept pace with those for travel. One effect of this has been to alter remarkably the diet of the entire nation. We are no longer limited to the foods produced within a small surrounding area. The vegetables served in Chicago may be grown in Idaho, California, Michigan, Missouri, or New York. The meat may come from Texas, Iowa, or Argentina. The bread may be made from wheat grown in Kansas, Montana, or Canada. The fruit may come from almost any part of the world. Nor for any of these is the housewife limited in time to the local producing season. Perishable foods such as fresh fish are kept for long periods of time in a frozen condition. New peas, green beans, and many kinds of berries are also frozen promptly after picking, and may come to the table with much of their natural fresh flavor though produced months before.

In return for the products of the soil the city furnishes to the country machinery, clothing, and other articles of manufacture. Likewise each region of the world sends the surplus of things it can produce abundantly to other regions in exchange for goods it needs but cannot well produce. Improved means of transportation greatly facilitate such a flow of goods.

The means of tilling the soil and of gathering the crops have in the last century and a half experienced a transformation no less remarkable than that exhibited by transportation. Our colonial forefathers had only the wooden plow drawn oftentimes by oxen to break the soil. They had only the sickle or at

Fig. 1.   An early reaper, one horse.

best the cradle with which to cut their bread-producing crops—wheat, barley, and rye. They had only the hand rake with which to gather them, only bands of straw applied by hand by which to hold them together, and only the ancient flail with which to beat out the grain. With such implements as these the amount of land a man could farm was very limited. Little wonder that production was small, and that about four-fifths of the population were engaged in farming in order to provide enough food for themselves and for the other fifth, who lived in towns and cities.

The days of the wooden plow, the sickle, the cradle, and the flail finally passed. The first was superseded by the steel plows of Lane, Oliver, Parlin, and Deere; the second and third by the reaper of McCormick; and the last by the thresher of Pitts. The reaper (Fig. 1), which at first only cut the grain, laid it

International Harvester Co.

FIG. 2. Combine (harvester-thresher). This machine harvests, threshes, and cleans the grain, either bagging it or collecting it in a grain tank, as desired. Width of machine in operation, about 28 ft.; width of cut, 14 to 18 ft. Harvests beans and peas, as well as grains. Capacity, 40 to 50 acres per day.

nicely upon a platform, and permitted it to be raked off by hand in bunches, was later improved by the addition of a knotter, which bound it with twine. The development of the gasoline tractor made feasible the use of a combined machine, the combine (Fig. 2), which not only cuts the grain but also threshes and bags it ready for market. Two men with such a machine can cut and thresh fifty acres of wheat in a day. With the hand implements of a hundred years ago it would have taken at least fifty men to cut and bind this amount of grain in the same length of time, and seventy-five more to thresh and bag it. Thus the production of foodstuffs has been increased enormously, and the threat of famine has been eliminated in America.

By means of machines the farmer has been enabled not only to produce much more abundantly than ever before, but to do it much more easily. This has been greatly facilitated by the rapid extension of electric lines, for electric motors instead of muscle power may now turn his grindstones, corn shellers, and cream separators, elevate his hay and grain, pump water for his livestock, and operate his milking machines.

In the means for producing clothing a similar transformation has taken place. At the beginning of the nineteenth century the arts of spinning and weaving had already undergone considerable development. The spinning wheel was a familiar object in the colonial home. The spinning machines of Hargreaves, Arkwright, and Crompton were also turning out quantities of linen and woolen thread, which the looms of the time were amply able to make into cloth. Cotton was not then an important fabric, though its fiber was highly suitable for spinning, and large sections of the country were well adapted to its production. The great obstacle to its use lay in the difficulty of separating the fiber from the seeds. This was a tedious operation which had to be done by hand. A skillful slave could clean only about four pounds of cotton per day. Then in 1792 came the cotton gin of Eli Whitney. The use of this machine increased the annual production of cotton from two million to forty million pounds in a single decade, and to seven thousand million in less than a century and a half. Faster looms operating automatically (Fig. 3) have superseded the older types, and ways of producing better or more attractive fabrics such as rayon from the same raw materials have been found. Thus we are also indebted to the development and widespread use of machines for our present abundance of excellent and inexpensive clothing.

Perhaps the greatest advancement since colonial times has been achieved in the arts of communication of ideas. When it became necessary to inform the colonists of the approach of the first invading British troops, the quickest way then available was used.  Paul Revere and others of his kind rode through the country-side on horseback, shouting the news far and wide. When in other circumstances it was desirable to give information to a large number in a less hurried way, a paper might be printed by hand, with movable type.  A permanent record of ideas, as in a book, could be made in the same way.

*Crompton & Knowles Loom Works.*
FIG. 3.  A Modern Weave Room.  Weaving rayon for women's dress goods. One weaver attends 24 big looms, each operating at about 144 throws of the shuttle per minute.   Two shuttles are used to give a crepe effect.   When filling of spools becomes exhausted, new bobbins are automatically put into shuttles without stopping or slowing the loom.   Loom is automatically stopped when warp or bobbin-filling breaks.

With the arrival of Morse's telegraph about 1844 a message could be sent, not with the speed of a rider on horseback, but with that of electric current.  It could be sent only in code, however, and required a trained operator at both the transmitter and receiver.  The telephone, which was introduced by Bell about forty years later, removed this handicap.  With such a device the patriot Revere, without moving from his desk, could have called the colonists to the defense.  But he would still have had to call them one by one.   After another forty years the radio appeared.   This removed the final limitation— the number of people it is possible for a speaker to address at one time.   With this new device in the home every colonist could have been reached with a single call.   In our own time when the President in the White House sits before the microphone, he is heard by millions of his countrymen at their own firesides in every corner of the nation.   But even this has become almost commonplace.   We are more deeply stirred when we sit

R. Hoe and Co., Inc.

FIG. 4.   A Modern, High-speed Printing Press.   Takes newsprint from huge rolls and delivers it printed and folded as complete newspapers.

as members of a world-wide audience listening to representatives of the daily press and of radio networks as they report on the troubled condition of the times from various capitals of the world.

Even that which very recently seemed the wild dream of the visionary—the hope of some day being able to see what is happening at great distances as well as to hear—has now been realized.   Television is taking its place alongside of radio to enable us not only to hear the reports of such events as baseball and football games, tennis matches, and boxing bouts, but also to see them from the most favorable positions, play by play.   Television will also bring us the performances of the theater and the music hall, and through its magic will summon great statesmen, soldiers, authors, and other famous men and women to call upon us personally in our homes.

Methods of making the printed record available to the masses have also undergone a remarkable development since colonial days. At that time a man and a boy, with the aid of the most efficient press then available, could turn out about 250 pages per hour. With the substitution of the rotary for the hand press, the speed was practically trebled. But this did not represent the limit of attainable speed in printing. Other improvements were made one after another, including the use of a cylindrical form for the type, the continuous automatic feeding of the press from a roll of paper instead of hand feeding from a pile of sheets, the multiplication of the number of cylinders and rolls, and the addition of an attachment for folding the sheets of newspapers. With these and other changes it has now become possible to turn out more than 300,000 papers per hour from a single press.

There are many such presses in daily use in the country, and thousands of others of smaller capacity. A single metropolitan paper runs off daily more than a hundred times as many copies as were issued in the entire nation a hundred years ago, each with several times as much material.

The number of copies of books has increased in proportion. There are also hundreds of weekly and monthly magazines printed, many of which are considered worthy of preservation in our libraries.

In this manner the machine has contributed greatly to the dissemination of information, the exchange of opinion, the advancement of learning.

In the home the machine has also come to occupy a conspicuous place. In the laundry the washboard and tub have disappeared and a machine driven by electric or other power has become the almost universal substitute. The electrically heated flatiron has largely displaced the fire-heated type and is itself now giving way to the more rapid and convenient mangle. The kitchen has one machine to beat the eggs or cream; another washes and dries the dishes; a third watches the oven to see that it does not become too hot or too cool; a fourth either turns off the heat or gives the signal when the roasting or baking is done; while a fifth maintains a uniform low temperature in a heat-insulated enclosure in which milk and other food may be kept fresh and wholesome for considerable lengths of time. The housewife is relieved of many physical cares and inconveniences, and is enabled not only to give attention to more than the bare physical needs of her family, but also to live a more satisfying mental and social life of her own.

Enough has been said concerning a few of the many machines which have been developed in the last hundred years to show that they have completely transformed the physical aspects of our environment, and considerably altered our mental outlook. Let us now turn our attention to their construction, to discover if possible how they operate to accomplish such remarkable results.

## THE SIMPLE MACHINES

To one unaccustomed to working with machines many of those in common use today look very complicated. A large printing press, for example, is a bewildering mass of parts. A high-grade watch, a threshing machine, a power loom, or a knitting machine looks very complicated. If any of these is taken apart, however, it is found to consist of only a small number of kinds of parts, never more than six. These are called the *simple machines*, or the *machine elements*. They have been named the *lever*, the *pulley*, the *wheel and axle*, the *inclined plane*, the *wedge*, and the *screw*. Since the more complex machines are merely combinations of two or more simple machines, a thorough understanding of these six is sufficient to enable one to understand the operation of all the others.

## THE LEVER

The lever consists of a rigid bar so arranged as to permit rotation about an axis. Examples of the lever are found everywhere. There are several used in the control of an automobile—in accelerator, gear shift, clutch, brake, and elsewhere. Any ordinary wrench such as the monkey wrench or *S* wrench is a lever. So also are fire tongs, pliers, scissors, nut crackers, the wheelbarrow, and the keys of the typewriter or piano. The movable bones of the body also act as levers. In the operation of a lever a force is applied at one point on the bar in order to raise a weight, or to move an object in opposition to frictional or other resistance, at another point on the bar. The fixed axis about which a lever turns is called its *fulcrum*. The distance from the fulcrum to the force is called the *force arm* or *effort arm* of the lever, and the distance from the fulcrum to the resistance is called the *load arm* or *resistance arm*.

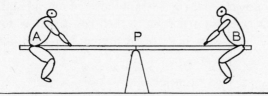

Fig. 5.   Teeter-totter—the principle of the lever.

Let Fig. 5 represent two children on a teeter-totter. The plank itself is assumed to be supported at its balancing point. If the children are of equal weight, they will balance each other if they sit at equal distances from the support. If, however, one is heavier than the other, the lighter child must sit farther from the support. Experience shows that, if one were only half as heavy as the other, the lighter would have to sit twice as far away. If one weighed 50 lb. and the other 60 lb., and if the heavier child sat 5 ft. from the fulcrum, the lighter one would have to sit 6 ft. from it. In each of these cases the product obtained by multiplying a child's weight by his distance from the support is the same for one end of the teeter-totter as for the other.

$$50 \text{ lb.} \times 6 \text{ ft.} = 60 \text{ lb.} \times 5 \text{ ft.}$$

In Fig. 5, *P* is the fulcrum. *AP* and *BP* are alternately the force arm and the load arm.

Let Fig. 6 represent a wheelbarrow in which a 100 lb. box is to be carried. If the box were placed midway between the hands and the axis of the wheel, it is evident that the weight would be shared equally by the hands and the wheel. A lifting force of 50 lb. would hold the box. If the box were placed farther forward, a greater part of its weight would be carried by the wheel. If the lift is vertically upward at points 5 ft. from the axis of the wheel and the box is placed 2 ft. from the axis, a force of 40 lb. will hold the box.

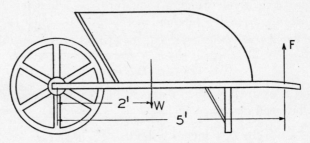

Fig. 6.   Wheelbarrow—a type of lever.

In the first case the load arm is 2.5 ft. In the second it is 2 ft. The force arm is 5 ft. It is seen that

$$100 \text{ lb.} \times 2.5 \text{ ft.} = 50 \text{ lb.} \times 5 \text{ ft.}$$
$$100 \text{ lb.} \times 2 \quad \text{ft.} = 40 \text{ lb.} \times 5 \text{ ft.}$$

Let Fig. 7 represent a fishing pole held stationary at $A$ and lifted at $B$, a point 1 ft. from $A$. If the pole is 10 ft. long and a 2 lb. fish is to be lifted, then a force of 20 lb. must be used at $B$.

$$2 \text{ lb.} \times 10 \text{ ft.} = 20 \text{ lb.} \times 1 \text{ ft.}$$

In this case the end $A$ of the pole is the fulcrum, the length of the force arm is 1 ft. and that of the load arm 10 ft.

In these examples is seen an illustration of the principle on which all levers act. This may be stated as follows:

Force × force arm = load × load arm.

For many situations a somewhat different statement of the law is more useful. Return to Fig. 5. Since in the last example cited the heavier boy sits only five-sixths as far from the fulcrum as the lighter one, his movement when they teeter will be only

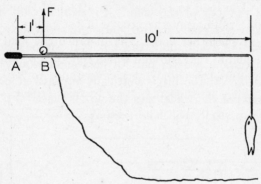

FIG. 7. Fishing rod.

five-sixths as great. Then if the 50 lb. boy rises 6 inches, the 60 lb. boy will descend 5 inches.

$$50 \text{ lb.} \times 6 \text{ inches} = 60 \text{ lb.} \times 5 \text{ inches.}$$

Again in Fig. 6, second instance, if the box is to be raised 2 inches, the hands must rise 5 inches.

$$100 \text{ lb.} \times 2 \text{ inches} = 40 \text{ lb.} \times 5 \text{ inches.}$$

And in Fig. 7, if the fish is to be lifted 10 ft., the hand at B need be raised only 1 foot.

$$20 \text{ lb.} \times 1 \text{ ft.} = 2 \text{ lb.} \times 10 \text{ ft.}$$

From these illustrations it is seen that the law of the lever may also be stated thus:

Force × distance force acts = resistance ×
distance resistance is overcome.

In this form the law can be applied not only to the lever, but to the other simple machines also.

## THE PULLEY

Another widely used device is the pulley. This consists of a wheel with its rim grooved in such a way as to permit it to carry a rope or cable. The pulley may be used in various ways. In one of these it is attached to a fixed object as shown in Fig. 8. The load to be moved is attached to one end of a rope or cable running in the groove of the pulley. The force is applied at the other end. The distance the load moves is evidently equal to that through which the force acts. Likewise the force required is equal to the resistance to be overcome. The fixed pulley is frequently used to raise objects vertically.

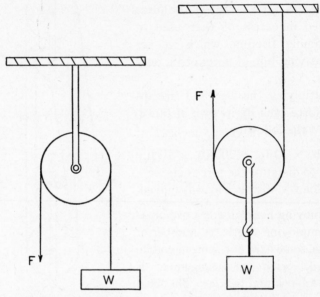

FIG. 8.   Fixed pulley.          FIG. 9.   Movable pulley.

Its merit lies in the fact that by means of it the force may be applied in a more convenient way.

In another arrangement the pulley is attached to the load to be moved, as shown in Fig. 9. One end of the rope or cable is attached to a fixed object while the force is applied to the other end. It is evident that in this arrangement the two strands which leave the pulley exert equal forces. Each carries half of the load. Hence in order to raise the load by exerting a pull upon the free end of the rope or cable, it is only necessary to apply a force equal to half of the weight of the object.

Accompanying this gain in force, there is a corresponding loss in distance. In order to raise the object 1 ft., for example, each strand must be shortened by just that amount. To accomplish this the force must act through 2 ft.

Let us suppose that such an arrangement is used in hoisting a 200 lb. barrel. If the barrel is lifted 10 ft., the force used in lifting it must act through 20 ft. However, in order to lift the barrel the force required in excess of that used in overcoming friction, which we are here leaving out of account, is only 100 lb.

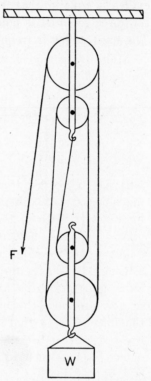

Multiplying the load and the applied force each by its own distance, we find the following:

100 lb. × 20 ft. = 200 lb. × 10 ft.
Force × distance the force acts =
    load × distance load is moved.

In moving heavy loads a combination employing a greater number of pulleys, some fixed and some movable, is used. Such an arrangement is called a block and tackle. The fixed pulleys are joined together in a single block, each pulley rotating independently of the others. The same is true of the movable pulleys, which

Fig. 10. Block and tackle.

are attached to the load. The cord or cable is then carried around the various fixed and movable pulleys in such a way that when the free end is drawn, each strand is shortened and the load thereby moved.

Let us suppose that such a system includes two fixed and two movable pulleys arranged as shown in Fig. 10. The four strands pull equally, each carrying one fourth of the load. Neglecting friction, the force that must be applied to the free end of the rope in order to raise the load is equal to one-fourth of the weight of the object to be raised.

In order to raise the object any given distance, 1 ft., for example, each strand must be shortened by this amount. The free end of the rope must be taken up 4 ft.

If the load is a 400 lb. motor, and the distance it is to be raised is 2 ft., then, if friction is neglected, the force required to raise it is 100 lb., and the distance the force must act is 8 ft.

Multiplying load and force by the corresponding distances we find the following:

$$100 \text{ lb.} \times 8 \text{ ft.} = 400 \text{ lb.} \times 2 \text{ ft.}$$

Force × distance the force acts = load × distance

load is moved.

## VELOCITY RATIO

It has been seen that the distance a load is moved by a machine is usually different from the distance through which the force acts. Thus in the case of the wheelbarrow mentioned above, the hands had to rise 5 inches in order to raise the load 2 inches. In the single movable pulley the force acted through a distance of 20 ft. in order to raise the barrel 10 ft. In the block and tackle the force acted through a distance of 8 ft. in order to raise the motor 2 ft. The ratio of the distance the force acts to that through which the load is raised (or the resistance is overcome) is called the *velocity ratio* of the device. Thus the velocity ratio of the wheelbarrow described is 5 in. ÷ 2 in. = 2.5. That of the single movable pulley is 20 ft. ÷ 10 ft. = 2. That of the block and tackle is 8 ft. ÷ 2 ft. = 4. Similarly that of the fishing pole described is 1 ft. ÷ 10 ft. = 0.1.

## MECHANICAL ADVANTAGE

In an actual working machine the force required is somewhat greater than that obtained by the sort of computation made above. Owing to friction and other causes, the force required to raise the 400 lb. motor, for example, will be greater than 100 lb. It may be 125 lb.

The ratio of the resistance overcome to the force required to overcome it is called the *mechanical advantage* of the device.

$$\text{Mechanical advantage} = \frac{\text{Resistance}}{\text{Effort}}.$$

In the case of the motor referred to above

$$\text{Mechanical advantage} = {}^{400}\!/_{125} = 3.2.$$

Pulleys and pulley systems are used in the construction of such devices as derrick cranes, steam shovels, paving machines, passenger elevators, and many others designed to handle heavy loads.

## THE WHEEL AND AXLE

A device somewhat similar to the pulley and called the *wheel and axle* is sometimes used. This often consists of a single block in the form of two pulley wheels of unequal diameter fixed together on the same axis but not in the same plane. A rope or cable runs on the rim of each wheel. The load is carried by one of the cables, as shown in Fig. 11, while the force is applied to the other. Instead of two grooved wheels fastened to-

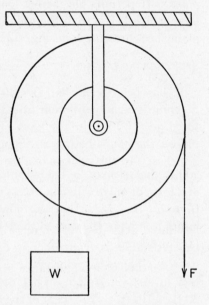

FIG. 11.   Wheel and axle.

gether in this way there may be but one such wheel, sometimes in the form of a cylinder or roller, to which a crank is attached. The force is then applied to the crank while the load is moved by the cable running over the single wheel or cylinder. This arrangement, which is called a capstan, is used for such purposes as moving buildings, raising anchors, and drawing up and lashing ships to piles at dock.

## THE INCLINED PLANE

In loading barrels into trucks or in putting heavy machines on flat cars, in drawing logs from a lake or river up into a saw mill, and in many other such operations, an inclined track is sometimes used.  In the case of barrels this track may consist simply of two planks with one end on the ground and the other on the bed of the truck.  In the case of machines it may be an incline built up of earth or concrete.  In the case of logs it may be an inclined track on which a cart is run to carry the logs.  Any such arrangement is called an *inclined plane*.  It permits the heavy load to be lifted by means of a force which is less than the weight of the object lifted.  Such a plane is represented in Fig. 12.  With fifteen-foot planks a

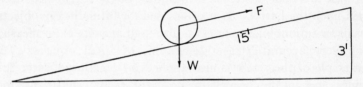

FIG. 12.    Inclined plane.

300 lb. barrel may be loaded into a truck 3 ft. high by means of a force of only 60 lbs. in excess of what is needed to overcome friction.  It is seen that the same relation applies here as was found to hold in the case of the lever and the other devices thus far considered.

Force × force distance = load × load distance.
60 lb. × 15 ft. = 300 lb. × 3 ft.

More familiar instances of the inclined plane are met with on nearly every highway.  The road rises or descends with the changing contour of the country.  Each rise or descent is an inclined plane.

## THE WEDGE

It is apparent that the wedge, which is frequently used to exert great force, consists of a pair of inclined planes placed back to back.  When the wedge is struck as with a mallet,

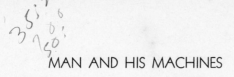

it exerts a great force tending to separate the objects between which it is driven. Such a device is often used in splitting rails or felling trees. The wedge may also be used by simple pressure instead of by blows of a mallet. We unknowingly use one in this way every time we cut a steak. Knives, chisels, blades of scissors or razors, and many other articles of everyday use are forms of this device.

## THE SCREW

Next to the lever the screw is perhaps the most widely used of all the simple machines. It may be regarded as an inclined plane wound spirally upon a cylinder or cone. It is often used for holding objects firmly together as in holding a hinge or lock to a door, fasteners to windows, or the cap of a fountain pen upon the barrel. It is often used for lifting heavy objects, as in an automobile jack. It is also used in calipers for measuring very accurately the dimensions of small objects. The principle of the screw is also applied in some large water turbines and in the propellers of motor boats, ships, dirigible balloons, and airplanes.

## COMPLEX MACHINES

More complicated machines such as steam engines, automobiles, printing presses, typewriters, and pianos consist of combinations of the simple machines mentioned above. The operation of such a machine may be understood merely by knowing clearly the operation of each of its parts. Much of the mystery attached to the remarkable work of some of the machines in use disappears when this is understood. A machine for making complicated mathematical computations may seem almost uncanny in its action until it is found that it operates on the simple principle of the devices described above. The same is true of the printing press, of knitting machines, and of whatever other complicated machine one may chance to see.

# CHAPTER 3

# ENERGY UTILIZED AND WASTED

We have seen that machines are used for doing many and varied kinds of work. Some are used in tilling the soil and cutting and threshing grain, some in processing foodstuffs, many in the manufacture of clothing or building material, a few in printing, and others in various ways in the home. Some add, multiply, subtract, and divide, or solve other more difficult problems. Many are called into service in making other machines. This last function is perhaps the most important of all. To run his machines man harnesses a wind or a waterfall, or traps the power of coal or oil. He is thus enabled to do his work more easily, and to do it many times faster. He can also do it better, for the hand cannot compare in precision with a good, modern machine.

## WORK

In common parlance the word *work* is used somewhat loosely to include almost any useful activity. In mechanics it is understood in a more restricted sense. Here it means the effect that is accomplished when a force is exerted upon some object which it moves. A boy who sits down quietly with a book to study, and without moving a muscle continues to read and think, does no work. A less studious boy who goes out with bat and ball, finds playmates, and has a lively game, does do work. The first boy may have accomplished a much more useful result. He may have conceived a new and prolific idea that may bring him wealth or fame, or may benefit man-

24

kind.   But he has exerted no mechanical force.   He has done no work.   The other boy has probably accomplished something useful, too, in terms of health and development.   But that in itself does not constitute work.   The essential difference is that he has exerted forces and overcome mechanical resistances. He has exerted them upon bat and ball and upon his own body and made them move.   He has done work.

The amount of work done in any instance depends in part upon the magnitude of the force exerted, and in part upon the distance in the direction of the force that the object moves. If a bag of grain or a box of books weighing 100 lb. is transported a vertical distance of 3 feet, an amount of work equal to 300 *foot-pounds* is done upon it.   The foot-pound is the amount of work done when a one pound force acts through a distance of 1 foot.   If a sled which requires a pull of 50 lb. to move it is drawn a distance of 30 yards, 1500 *yard-pounds* of work is done in overcoming the resistance to the motion. The amount of work done can be found by simply multiplying the force exerted by the distance the resistance is overcome.

$$\text{Work} = \text{force} \times \text{distance force acts}$$

The foot-pound is the unit most frequently used in this country in measuring mechanical work, but many others are also employed.   Among these are the *gram-centimeter*, the *kilogram-meter*, the *erg*, and the *joule*.   The names of the first two of these indicate their magnitudes.   The others are defined as follows:

The *erg* is one dyne-centimeter, or the amount of work done when a 1 *dyne* force acts through a distance of 1 centimeter.

The dyne is about $\frac{1}{980}$ part of a 1 gm. force.

The *joule* is equal to 10,000,000 ergs.

## POWER

An important feature of a machine is the rate at which it does work.   This is particularly true of such machines as water wheels, steam engines, gasoline and Diesel engines, and electric motors.   Because these are used to transport trains or other

*Marion Steam Shovel Company.*

FIG. 13.   A Giant at Work, Stripping Overburden from Coal.   Electrically operated.   Length of boom, 110 ft.; length of handle, 73 ft.   Capacity of dipper, 32 cu. yd.   Weight, 2,580,000 lb.

*Baldwin Locomotive Works.*

FIG. 14.   Steam Locomotive for Heavy Freight.   Total wheelbase, 108 ft. Weight of engine alone, 641,900 lb.   Tender, 394,000 lb.   Coal capacity, 26 tons.   Water capacity, 20,000 gal.   Tractive force, 105,000 lb.

vehicles, to run factories, to drive dynamos for generating electric current, or for other similar purposes, their value depends in part upon how much work they do per hour or per day. A steam locomotive, for example, must be able to exert a large pull upon the train and draw it at a high speed. A large force acting over a great distance every minute means that many foot-pounds of work per minute are done. Machines for doing a great deal of work very rapidly are shown in Figs. 13 and 14.

In mechanics the rate at which work is done is called *power*. A machine which is doing work at the rate of 550 foot-pounds per second is delivering 1 *horsepower* (H.P.). If working at the rate of 11,000 foot-pounds per second, it is delivering 20 H.P.

A machine will not usually be required to work at its maximum possible rate. An automobile motor, for example, though capable of driving the car at 80 to 100 miles per hour, will rarely be called upon to do so. Though rated as a 120 H.P. motor, it may still be used to deliver a much smaller amount.

Different machines are designed for very different amounts of power output. The small electric motors used in the home for running sewing machines, egg beaters, and the like may be rated at one-thirtieth of a H.P. or less, while an electric clock will take only a fraction of even this small amount. Other motors in the home may deliver $\frac{1}{8}$, $\frac{1}{6}$, or $\frac{1}{4}$ H.P. Motors used for grinding grain, running lathes of moderate size, and other similar work may deliver from a half a H.P. to one or two H.P. Automobile engines vary from 60 or 65 H.P. up to more than 150 H.P. Airplane motors may exceed 500 H.P. each, while the engine power of an ocean liner like the *Normandie* or the *Queen Mary* is of the order of 150,000 horsepower.

Electrical power is usually measured in watts or kilowatts. The watt is the power of a device which does 1 joule of work per second.

$$1 \text{ Watt} = 10,000,000 \text{ ergs per second.}$$
$$1 \text{ Kilowatt} = 1000 \text{ watts.}$$
$$1 \text{ Horsepower} = 746 \text{ watts.}$$
$$1 \text{ Kilowatt} = 1.34 \text{ horsepower.}$$

Incandescent lamps such as are used in the home range in power from 15 or 25 watts to 300 watts or more. Sizes very commonly used are those of 60 to 100 watts.

Small dynamos such as are used in home electric plants may generate as little as a fraction of a kilowatt. The large sizes

*Marion Steam Shovel Company.*

Fɪɢ. 15.  The steel piles are driven by repeatedly raising the heavy hammer and allowing it to fall.

used in central power stations, such as those at Keokuk, Niagara Falls, and elsewhere, whether driven by water power or by steam, may generate thousands of kilowatts.

## ENERGY

If a heavy object high above the ground is attached to a rope whose other end is wound about the shaft of a circular saw, a lathe, or other similar device, the object can descend and cause the saw or lathe to turn in the usual manner. The object in descending does work. It exerts a force equal to its own weight throughout the distance it descends.

**Work done = weight × distance.**

The elevated object may be the heavy hammer of a pile driver, allowed to fall freely upon the upper end of the pile. (See Fig. 15.) In this case the hammer does not begin doing

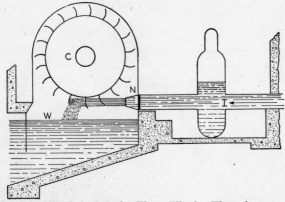

Fig. 16. Principle of the Impulse Water Wheel. Water from a great elevation flows in through $I$. It leaves the nozzle $N$ at high speed, strikes the buckets of the wheel $C$, and turns the wheel.

work until it strikes the pile. The amount done, however, depends upon the entire distance fallen, as before.

**Work = weight × distance hammer descends.**

Dammed up water may be carried down a flume to strike a water wheel, causing it to rotate and so drive other machinery, perhaps a dynamo. (See Figs. 16 and 17.) The water has done work.

In each of these cases the object had the ability to do work. This ability is called *energy*. It is measured in the same units as are used in measuring work. Assume that the object weighs 100 lb. and that it can descend 10 ft. The energy it possesses when at that height is found thus:

**Energy = 100 lb. × 10 ft. = 1000 foot lb.**

FIG. 17. Huge Impulse Turbine Wheel, with Buckets. This forms a part of the Allis-Chalmers hydroelectric unit installed at the San Francisquito Plant No. 1, Bureau of Light and Power, City of Los Angeles. A second wheel, similar to the one shown, is mounted on the same shaft at its farther end. The rotor of the dynamo which these wheels drive is mounted midway between. The unit develops 32,200 H.P.

Assume that instead of an elevated object we have a bent spring, a stretched rubber band, or air under pressure. Each of these exerts a force of reaction in opposition to the bending, stretching, or compressing force. If released, the spring and rubber will fly back; the air will expand. Each has a capacity for doing work, that is, has energy. In all of these cases, this energy may be utilized. The spring, for example, may be that of a clock, which keeps the wheels and hands in motion until the spring is unwound, that is, until the clock has run down. The stretched rubber may be that of a boy's sling shot, used to speed a pebble. The air may be that in a cash tube or a riveting hammer, in either case doing useful work.

## POTENTIAL ENERGY

The energy of all of these objects—pile driver hammer, stored water, bent spring, stretched rubber, and compressed air—is of the kind called *potential*. The potential energy of an object is the energy it possesses due to its elevated position, or to the elastic forces it exerts in opposition to distortion or compression.

## KINETIC ENERGY

An object in motion also has the ability to exert a force upon things it strikes and to overcome their resistance. That is to say, an object in motion also possesses energy. This kind, which is called *kinetic*, does not depend upon the elevation of the object nor upon its distortion, but only upon its mass (the amount of material in it) and speed.

$$\text{Kinetic energy} = \tfrac{1}{2} \text{ mass} \times (\text{speed})^2.$$

In the above formula if the mass of the object is expressed in grams and its speed in centimeters per second, its energy is found in ergs. Let us consider a 4 kg. sledge hammer moving at a speed of 5 meters per second. It is required to find the energy of the hammer. The solution is as follows:

$$4 \text{ kg.} = 4 \times 1000 = 4000 \text{ gm.}$$
$$5 \text{ meters per sec.} = 5 \times 100 = 500 \text{ cm. per sec.}$$
Then kinetic energy $= \tfrac{1}{2} \times 4000 \times (500)^2 = 500{,}000{,}000$ ergs.

The kinetic energy of such objects as hammers is useful in exerting very large momentary forces. Such forces are necessary in order to overcome the large resistance which wood offers to the penetration of a nail, or the ground to the penetration of a pile.

## OTHER FORMS OF ENERGY

There are many other kinds of energy in addition to those mentioned above. One of these is the kind stored up in coal or other fuel; another is that carried in a beam of sunlight or by the waves from a radio transmitter; a third is that existing in the region surrounding a magnet. The first of these is called chemical energy, the second radiant energy, and the third the energy of a magnetic field.

## TRANSFORMATION OF ENERGY

Perhaps the student has questioned some of the assertions made above—such, for example, as the ones stating that the raised pile-driver hammer has potential energy, but drives the pile by reason of its kinetic energy. Both assertions are true, however. The potential energy the hammer has when in its raised position is gradually transformed into kinetic as it descends. At mid-position of the hammer half the energy has been so transformed. At the instant of striking all has been transformed. We may follow a longer series of such transformations. Assume that the hammer is raised by an electric motor and that the dynamo supplying current to the motor is driven by a steam engine. Let us start with the fuel. Through combustion in the fire box, the chemical energy which the fuel possesses is transformed into heat, another kind of energy. This produces steam, which moves the piston of the engine and rotates the power wheel. The energy has now become mechanical. The engine turns the armature of the dynamo, transforming the mechanical energy into energy of the electric current. This is now transmitted to the motor which converts it again into mechanical energy—the potential energy of the elevated hammer.

# LOSSES OF ENERGY.  CONSERVATION OF ENERGY

Not all of the energy of the fuel goes through the series of transformations mentioned above.  Some of the heat goes out of the smoke stack, some is discharged through the exhaust into the condenser, while some is lost by heating the machine itself and the surrounding air.  Some of the mechanical energy derived from the remnant of heat energy that is transformed is used in overcoming friction either in the steam engine or in the dynamo.  The energy consumed by friction is turned back into heat, which is also lost to the surroundings.  Of the part of the generated mechanical energy that becomes electrical, some is lost in transmission to the motor, and some is used in overcoming friction and in other ways in the motor itself.  Energy is dissipated all along the way, so that only a small fraction of all that the fuel possesses is available to do the desired work of raising the pile-driver hammer.

In processes which are more direct there is, of course, less waste of energy, but in every transmission or transformation there is some loss.  It must not be supposed, however, that any of the energy of the fuel is destroyed.  It is simply dissipated, spilled here and there, and thus made unavailable for the work in hand.  No energy is or can be destroyed.  This is matched by an equally important circumstance; none ever is or can be created.

The two facts last stated—that energy can neither be created nor destroyed—constitute one of the most important of all physical laws—the law of the conservation of energy.

## THE EFFICIENCY OF MACHINES

It has just been pointed out that in the operation of a machine a certain amount of energy is lost.  The energy delivered by a machine in the form of useful work is therefore always less than that supplied to it.  The losses of energy are not always as great as was found to be the case in the steam engine-dynamo-motor combination mentioned above, but in all machines designed to generate power for use in other machines the loss is considerable.  In the case of the steam engine, this often amounts to upward of 90 per cent of the energy of the fuel with which the engine is supplied. In the case of the gasoline engine the loss is less. Yet even here it is 70 to 75 per cent. In this case some of the energy is purposely dissipated by means of a radiator in order to keep the motor from overheating. This is necessary because in such an engine the fuel is burned in the cylinders and not in a water-jacketed compartment as is the case in the steam engine. The amount of the energy discarded through the radiator is about 25 per cent. Another 25 per cent is unavoidably lost by way of the exhaust. This is in the form of chemical energy of unburned fuel and the heat carried by products of combustion. Still further losses occur within the engine in overcoming friction. Only 25 to 30 per cent of the energy supplied is left to run the engine and provide the power needed to run other machines.

The machines which utilize the greatest fraction of the energy supplied to them are usually electrical machines. A well-designed dynamo or motor when running at its rated load will often deliver as useful work 80 to 85 per cent of the energy supplied to it. An alternating-current transformer, which has no movable parts and consequently no friction in the usual sense, is more efficient still. Such devices frequently utilize 98 per cent of the energy with which they are supplied, or even more.

The term *efficiency* is used to indicate the fraction of the energy received by a machine which is finally delivered by it in the form of useful work. This is usually expressed as a percentage. A machine which transforms 25 per cent of the energy supplied into useful work is said to have an efficiency of 25 per cent.

## FRICTION

Sliding friction is the resistance encountered when one object slides over another. It requires energy to overcome such resistance, and that is why much of the energy supplied to a complicated machine is dissipated. The amount of energy lost in this way can be considerably reduced and the life of the machine prolonged by careful lubrication. Oils and other lubricants fill the irregularities in metal and other surfaces and in that way diminish the frictional resistance. This has the effect of improving the efficiency of the machine. Another way in which friction is reduced is by the substitution of roller or ball bearings for the earlier type of bearing in which the surfaces in contact move by sliding. Bearings of these later types are used very extensively in modern machinery.

## FRICTION OFTEN USEFUL

It must not be assumed from the cases mentioned that friction is always a disadvantage. In many instances it is highly important. Belts are often used in conveying power from one machine to another. In the absence of friction this could not be done. The driving wheel would not run the belt. Neither would the belt run the wheel to be driven. So in the absence of friction belted machinery would not be used. Again in the case of all motor vehicles friction is essential in the operation of the brake. Without friction there could be no brake. But even this does not give an adequate picture of the vital importance of friction. The vehicle could not even be started if it were not for the friction exerted between the tires and the road. We see a near approach to this condition when a car attempts to start upon a very icy pavement. The wheels may spin without moving the vehicle. Under these circumstances it may be necessary to increase the friction by means of sand or ashes thrown under the wheel. Street cars and locomotives carry a supply of sand for this very purpose. Nails hold in wood, and screws hold in either wood or metal by reason of friction, without which they would be useless. Walking is difficult enough on a very icy pavement, but it would be wholly impossible if friction between the shoe and the pavement were entirely lacking.

## PERPETUAL-MOTION MACHINES

It was a great step forward for the human race when machines were first devised for doing the heavy back-breaking labor that had formerly been done by muscular effort. The advantage was twofold. It relieved man of much of the drudgery he had formerly had to endure, thus permitting him fuller development of his mental life; and it facilitated a more abundant production of desirable goods. But to drive machines requires power. Waterfalls must be harnessed, or fuel must be provided and burned. This is a large item of expense in every factory. If this item could be eliminated, goods could be still cheaper and more abundant. Many ingenious devices have been made whose purpose was to do the work of a factory without the need of supplying steam or other power. These are called *perpetual-motion machines*. Their inventors were usually men of much mechanical ingenuity but with inadequate understanding of the laws of nature. No such machine has ever been successful. The law of conservation of energy shows very clearly that none ever will or can be.

# CHAPTER 4

# FORCE AND MOTION

To a teacher's question as to why the book he held on his open hand would fall to the floor if the hand were removed, a boy once gave the answer, "Because it has no legs." To another question, why should it need legs, the answer was less convincing.

## WHY OBJECTS FALL

One of the facts that an infant learns very early is that objects have weight—that they are drawn toward the earth. He begins to learn this when his toys slip from his hands. A little later he gleefully throws them from his crib or high chair, and when they are gone, he looks for them on the floor. He learns to use the muscles of his arms to pull himself into a standing position. As soon as he can walk, he uses them to lift and carry his cat or drum. When he then releases any object, he knows where it will go. Such events never later afford him the surprise of novelty.

When we have put the child's experiences into words, we think we have offered an explanation. The book will fall because of its weight. It has weight because the earth attracts it. Later we learn that the book also attracts the earth. We are incredulous when we are informed that the latter attraction is as great as the former, but with more experience we become convinced of the truth of that statement also.

## HOW FAR DOES THE EARTH'S ATTRACTION EXTEND?

This question arose in the mind of Sir Isaac Newton in 1666. He was then a young man of 24, home from Cambridge University to escape the plague. The attraction the earth exerts upon objects was known to be almost as great at the top of the highest building and even at the summit of a mountain as at sea level. Newton wondered whether it might not extend much farther from the earth than was commonly believed— perhaps even to the moon. He wondered whether it might not in fact be the earth's attraction that keeps the moon in its orbit.

Nearly sixty years earlier (1609) Kepler had made certain important discoveries concerning the motions of the planets. He found that each planet moves about the sun in an elliptical orbit with the sun at one focus of the ellipse. He also found that the farther a planet is from the sun, the greater the time required for it to complete a revolution. The exact relationship is as follows: The squares of the periodic times of any two planets are proportional to the cubes of their mean distances from the sun.

Newton showed that the planets would move in exact accordance with Kepler's laws if each were drawn toward the sun by a force which varies inversely as the square of the distance between the two bodies. No other reason could be given for the orbital motion of the planets, nor for the observed relations of their periodic times. It was therefore inferred that such a force of attraction is in fact exerted.

A further test of the reality of this attraction was made by applying the inverse-square rule to the movement of the moon. It was found to fit this case exactly also. The attraction of the earth does extend to the moon and holds her in her orbit. The range of the earth's attraction does not end here, however, but extends on indefinitely into space.

## THE LAW OF GRAVITATION

As stated by Newton, this law asserts that *any two particles attract each other with a force which is directly proportional to the masses of the particles, and inversely proportional to the square of the distance between them.* Larger objects attract each other because of the attractions of the particles of which they are composed. Every particle of the earth attracts and is attracted by every particle of the moon, the sun, the planets, and even of the stars.

## THE LAW FOR LARGER OBJECTS

In the absence of proof justifying such a procedure Newton was unwilling to apply the law to objects of appreciable dimensions. Because of their size they might act in some unsuspected way. Newton set himself the task of finding what this unknown manner of attraction might be. After years of study he succeeded in showing that a sphere of uniform density attracts as if its mass were all concentrated at its center. He also showed that the same is true of spheres whose densities are not uniform, provided that the density is the same at all points equally distant from the center. It was later found that an object of any shape whatever attracts as if all its mass were concentrated at a point. This point is called the *center of gravity* of the object.

## ATTRACTION OF SMALLER OBJECTS FOR EACH OTHER

The law of gravitation asserts that every particle of matter attracts every other particle. It follows then that the groups of particles which we call objects attract all other objects. Two rocks lying by the roadside have a gravitational attraction for each other. So also do the bodies of two boys on a morning hike. The law of gravitation does not say how great this attraction may be. It only says that it varies directly with the product of the masses, and inversely with the square of the distance between them.

Newton's law of gravitation, which was stated in words above, may be stated in mathematical terms as follows:

$$F = G\frac{M_1 M_2}{d^2}.$$

In this equation $F$ is the attraction, in dynes, between the two objects if $M_1$ and $M_2$ are their masses expressed in gm., $d$ is the distance in cm. between their centers of gravity, and $G$ is

$$"G" = \frac{6.66}{100,000,000} \quad \text{or} \quad 6.66 \times 10^{-8}$$

numerically equal to the attraction in dynes between two 1 gm. masses 1 cm. apart.

About one hundred and twenty-five years after Newton's announcement of the law of gravitation Sir Henry Cavendish, an English scientist, succeeded in measuring the attraction between two metal spheres of known mass at a known distance apart. The results of this experiment at once enabled him to compute the attraction of any two objects for each other when their masses and the distance between them are known. Conversely, if their attraction, the distance between their centers of gravity, and the mass of one of them is known, the mass of the other can be found.

From Cavendish's experiment it was learned that two 1 gm. masses 1 cm. apart attract each other with the very minute force of $6.66 \times 10^{-8}$ dyne. This is called the *constant of gravitation*.

Two rocks whose masses are 1000 kg. and 2000 kg. if 10 meters apart attract each other with a force which can be found by a simple computation, as follows:

$$1000 \text{ kg.} = 1,000,000 \text{ gm.}$$
$$2000 \text{ kg.} = 2,000,000 \text{ gm.}$$
$$10 \text{ meters} = 1000 \text{ cm.}$$
$$\text{Force} = \frac{6.66 \times 10^{-8} \times 1,000,000 \times 2,000,000}{(1000)^2} \text{ dyne}$$
$$= .1332 \text{ dyne} = .000136 \text{ gm.}$$

Two boys each weighing 50 kg. and walking side by side 1 meter apart have a gravitational attraction for each other given by the following equation:

$$\text{Attraction} = \frac{6.66 \times 10^{-8} \times 50,000 \times 50,000}{(100)^2} \text{ dyne}$$
$$= .01665 \text{ dyne} = .000017 \text{ gm.}$$

## WEIGHT OF OBJECTS

Insignificant as these very minute forces are for objects of ordinary size, they assume great importance for massive objects like the earth, planets, sun, and stars. The weight of an object is simply the attraction between the earth and the object. The distance between their centers of gravity is equal to the radius of the earth.

On a mountain top an object is somewhat farther from the center of the earth than at sea level. At the greater elevation it is somewhat lighter. On the top of Mount Everest a man of average size would weigh about six ounces less than at sea level. The polar radius of the earth is about 13 miles shorter than the equatorial. On this account the weight of a man at either pole would be about 12 ounces greater than at the equator.

## MASS OF THE EARTH

It is even possible from the results of Cavendish's experiment to determine the mass and average density of the earth. This may be done as follows. The attraction between the earth and a 1 gm. object at its surface is 1 gm., or 980 dynes. Then

$$980 = 6.66 \times 10^{-8} \times \frac{1 \times M}{(4000 \times 5280 \times 30.5)^2},$$

from which $M = \dfrac{980(4000 \times 5280 \times 30.5)^2}{6.66 \times 10^{-8}}$ gm. $= 6.1 \times 10^{27}$ gm.

$$= 6.1 \times 10^{24} \text{ kg.} = 6.7 \times 10^{21} \text{ tons.}$$

The average density of the earth can be computed by dividing its mass by its volume.

Density = Mass per unit volume.
Mass = $6.1 \times 10^{27}$ gm.
Volume = $\frac{4}{3}\pi r^3 = \frac{4}{3}\pi(4000 \times 5280 \times 12 \times 2.54)^3$
    = $1.117 \times 10^{27}$ cc.
Density = $\dfrac{6.1 \times 10^{27}}{1.117 \times 10^{27}} = 5.46$ gm. per cc.

Loam, clay, coal, and the like have densities of only about 1.3 gm. per cc. Limestone, marble, and granite are among the densest rocks, yet their densities range only from about 2.4 to

3.1 gm. per cc.  The interior of the earth must then be composed of materials much more dense than these.

## TIDES

Persons who live near the sea are familiar with the periodical rise and fall of the water which takes place twice in a period of about 25 hours.  These regular changes of water level are called *tides*.  In the open ocean as observed along oceanic islands the variations of level amount to only about two feet. On the shores of continents it is often much greater.  When the configuration of the shore is such as to confine the water and force it into a narrow V-shaped indentation, the tide may run to a height of 70 or even 100 feet.

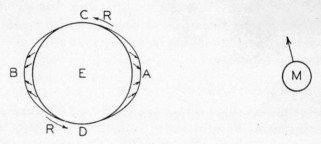

Fig. 18.   Tides.

The chief cause of tides is the gravitational attraction of the moon.  The action of the sun is chiefly to modify the effects of the moon.

How tides are produced may be understood from Fig. 18. The moon, $M$, attracts all parts of the earth, but it attracts side $A$ most strongly because it is nearest, and side $B$ least strongly because it is farthest away.  There is therefore a tendency for $A$ to be drawn away from $E$, and for $E$ to be drawn away from $B$.  This results in a slight rise of water at $A$ and $B$, and a corresponding lowering at $C$ and $D$.

The sun, though its attraction for the earth is about 175 times as great as that of the moon, is less than half as effective in producing tides.  The reason for this surprising fact is to be found in the great disparity of the distances of these bodies from the earth. The average distance between the centers of the sun and earth is about 93,000,000 miles, that between the centers of the moon and earth about 240,000 miles. The tide-producing power of either body depends in part upon the magnitude of the radius of the earth as compared with the distance of the body from the earth. For the sun the ratio is about as 1 to 2350. For the moon it is about as 1 to 60. By a fairly simple arithmetical computation in which the radius of the earth, and the masses and distances of the sun and moon are used, it is found that the tide-producing power of the moon is more than twice as great as that of the sun.

The earth rotates from west to east, as indicated by the arrows *RR*. The highs and lows therefore travel westward, following each other at intervals of a little more than six hours. This interval would be exactly six hours if it were not for the fact that the moon meanwhile moves forward in its orbit, as indicated by the arrow.

## THE VIEWS OF EINSTEIN

The attraction that bodies exert upon each other has been accounted for by Einstein on the supposition that every mass in some way affects all space around it. The magnitude of the effect is proportional to that of the mass producing it. Every object is thus influenced in its motion by the characteristics of the space in which it moves.

The forces thus far discussed may be considered as "pulls." Another class may seem more like "pushes."

## OBJECTS AT REST TEND TO REMAIN AT REST

Whenever we see an object suddenly begin to move, we assume at once that something has acted or is acting upon it to produce the change. If the object is a sled, we infer either that someone is setting it in motion, or that it is on a slope steep enough to cause it to slide under its own weight. If the object is an automobile, we assume that its engine is moving it, or that the car is on a gentle incline with the brake released. If branches or leaves begin to sway, we say the wind is blowing.

If earth and rocks suddenly fly into the air in all directions, even a deaf man will infer that there has been an explosion. Experience has taught us that objects at rest remain in that condition unless acted upon by outside forces.

## DO OBJECTS IN MOTION TEND TO CONTINUE IN MOTION?

When we see a hard-hit baseball leaving the bat clearly headed for some place outside the ball park, we do not expect it to continue for any great distance even though there may be only vacant lots for many blocks. A golf ball, no matter how hard or how well hit, soon comes to rest. A motor car is provided with brakes for making it stop quickly, but no one doubts that it would finally stop without this mechanism or

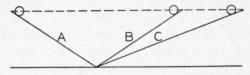

Fig. 19.   An early experiment on the laws of motion.

any other visible interference, even if traveling at high speed on the best of straight highways. We are predisposed to say that objects do not tend to continue in motion; that their natural condition is one of rest.

Certain facts, however, urge us to caution before adopting this conclusion. If the ball field is hard and bare, or the grass of the golf course short and dry, the ball travels much farther than it does under the usual conditions. It would go still farther if struck over a stretch of smooth ice. Even ice and air offer some resistance to motion. If this factor could be completely eliminated, would the ball travel on indefinitely?

Galileo undertook to solve this problem in a simple way about three and a half centuries ago. With two planes as shown in Fig. 19 he allowed a ball to roll down the plane, A. It rolled up plane B to about the level from which it started. If plane B was set at a smaller angle with the horizontal, the ball traveled a greater distance, and again rose to about the original level. This continued for still smaller angles of *B*. What would happen, Galileo wondered, if plane *B* were placed in the horizontal? His inference was that if the ball were unopposed by friction it would move on indefinitely.

Galileo's conclusion is the same as would be reached from a consideration of the motions of the baseball and golf ball. They ultimately stop, not because rest is their natural condition, but because the opposing forces of the ground and air dissipate their energy. In the absence of these frictional forces they would travel on without change of speed.

## AIR RESISTANCE

Air is light in weight and moves freely. To an object moving through it at a slow speed the resistance it offers may not be great. That it is not negligible however may easily be seen by holding a sheet of paper or a palm leaf fan at arm's length and swinging it broadside. The paper bends back. The fan veers. An automobile at high speeds meets with so much resistance from the air that the fuel consumption per mile goes up sharply. Three popular cars which at 30 miles per hour traveled upward of 20 miles per gallon of fuel consumed, showed only about 16 miles per gallon at 60 miles per hour. Falling objects, such as hailstones, rain drops, and parachutes do not increase in speed indefinitely as they descend. Each reaches a certain constant speed, which it does not exceed. This is called its *terminal velocity*. At this speed the resistance offered by the air is just equal to the weight of the object. The greater speed of airplanes at high altitudes is largely due to lessened air resistance.

## INERTIA

It may, then, be stated that an object at rest will continue at rest and that an object in motion will continue on without change of speed unless acted upon by an outside force. The property all matter has of behaving in the manner described is called *inertia*.

Inertia is utilized in many of our most useful devices. In driving a nail the hammer has so great a tendency to continue its motion that it pushes the nail before it. A pile driver acts in the same way. An ax or hatchet is effective by reason of the inertia of the entire tool.

It is because of their inertia that balls of all kinds continue their motion when thrown or struck; that long, heavily loaded trains and great ocean liners require so much time in starting and in stopping, and that heavy high-speed projectiles have their great destructive power.

## MOTION IN A CURVE

A ball tied to a string and whirled swiftly in a circle may break the string. Water flies from a grindstone, and mud from the swiftly turning wheel of a motor car. Passengers in the motor car may feel themselves thrown sidewise on a turn. Evidently an object in motion tends to continue in the direction in which it is already traveling. Its direction can be altered only by the action of a transverse force. The string pulls upon the ball, compelling it to change its direction continuously. The water clings to the grindstone and the mud to the wheel unless the speed of rotation is too great. The pull of the string and the adhesive force of the water or mud exert what is called a *centripetal force*. The reaction of the object held is just equal to the force exerted and is opposite in direction. This reaction is called a *centrifugal force*. If the string breaks or the adhesion of the water or mud is overcome, the centripetal force is removed. The object is no longer constrained to move in a curved path, and leaves it along a line tangent to this path at the point at which the break occurred.

The action just described is another manifestation of inertia. Objects in motion not only move with unaltered speed unless acted upon by some external force, but they also continue to move without change of direction.

Centrifugal forces affect us greatly in many ways. Motorists feel their influence at every bend or turn in the highway. The greater the speed and the shorter the turn, the greater the

centrifugal force.   This force is more affected by the speed of
the car than by the abruptness of the curves.   It varies directly
as the square of the speed, but only as the first power of the
curvature of the road.   At 60 miles per hour this force is four
times as great as at 30, and nine times as great as at 20.   The
highway engineer reduces the hazard of fast driving by banking
the turns, but safety lies chiefly in the hands of the driver, who
controls the speed.

Centrifugal forces are employed in many household and
industrial devices.   The vacuum cleaner produces its "suction"
by means of a centrifugal pump run by a high-speed electric
motor.   In some home washing machines the water is removed
from blankets, clothing, etc. by rotating them in a cylindrical
metal basket.   Cream is separated from whole milk by rotating
at high speed in a suitably constructed chamber.   Because the
skim milk is more dense than the butterfat the former is subjected to the greater centrifugal force and is driven farther
from the axis of rotation.   The milk is drawn off continuously
through one tube and the cream through another.

The amount of steam admitted to the cylinder of a steam
engine is controlled by a valve operated by two heavy balls
which are rotated by the engine.   If for any reason the speed
increases, the centrifugal force of the balls moves them farther
from the axis.   This partially closes the valve and reduces the
supply of steam.   If the engine speed is reduced, the balls move
in, and increase the supply of steam.   Thus a nearly uniform
speed is maintained.

## INERTIA IN THE SOLAR SYSTEM

The most nearly perfect examples of objects moving with
unvarying speeds are found in the solar system.   The earth
and the other planets revolve about the sun, each in its elliptical
orbit.   They have been doing this for millions of years.   There
is no force of any consequence tending permanently to change
their speeds; hence these remain unaltered, at least in so far as
they can be measured by the extremely accurate instruments of
the astronomer.

## HOW MASSES RESPOND TO THE ACTION OF FORCES

When a force acts upon an object, the invariable result is a change in either the rate or the direction of its motion, or both. But it must be kept in mind that the object is assumed to be free from frictional and other energy-robbing resistances. When a constant force is applied to such an object, its motion immediately begins to change. If it is not moving, it begins to do so at a uniformly increasing speed. If the force acts along the line in which the object is already moving, the speed changes at the same uniform rate.

## ACCELERATION

The rate at which the speed of an object changes is called *acceleration*. This depends upon two factors, the mass of the object and the magnitude of the force acting upon it. A section hand may push an empty hand car and cause it to gain speed at a rate of perhaps 10 feet per minute every second. With two such cars in tandem he would be able to change the speed at only half as great a rate. Acceleration resulting from the action of a given force varies inversely as the mass accelerated. If, on the other hand, two men were to join in pushing a single car, its speed would be altered at a doubled rate.

The two relationships just mentioned may be stated in a single sentence: *The acceleration of an object varies directly as the magnitude of the force producing the acceleration and inversely as the mass of the object accelerated.* This is the substance of Newton's second law of motion.

## ACTION AND REACTION

A piece of ice is suspended from a spring scale which registers 60 lb. The ice exerts a downward pull of 60 lb. upon the scale. The scale exerts an equal upward pull upon the ice.

Air is pumped into an automobile tire until the gauge reads 30 lb. The air inside exerts a pressure of 30 lb. per square inch upon the tube and the tube exerts a like pressure upon the air. If the two pressures were not equal, the tire would either expand or contract.

When the car is in motion, the rear wheels are driving it by pushing backward on the road. The road reacts with an equal forward push upon the wheels.

These are illustrations of a general law which may be stated thus: *To every force of action there is an equal and opposite reaction.* This is Newton's third law of motion.

It sometimes happens that an object fails to provide a certain reaction. A branch may break under the weight of a climbing boy. It is not strong enough to react with the force necessary to support his weight. A canoe may not provide the secure footing needed to enable one to jump ashore. Though the muscular effort was adequate, the foot was unable to exert a sufficient force because the canoe could not provide the necessary reaction. An automobile on an icy road may be unable to move forward because the wheels do not grip the pavement. The road then cannot react to push the car forward.

# CHAPTER 5

# FLUIDS AND FLUID
# PRESSURE

Historians record with admiration the achievements of the ancients in the construction of the great Pyramids of Egypt, the Walls and Hanging Gardens of Babylon, the Temple of Diana at Ephesus, and the other wonders of the ancient world. And the admiration is not misplaced. When we think of the means then available, the construction of each of these must be considered a very great achievement indeed.

Perhaps our own time will also be noted by future historians as an age of great building enterprises. In the last half century some truly remarkable structures have been created in various parts of the world. Chief among these are buildings, such as the Empire State and the Chrysler; bridges, such as the George Washington, the San Francisco-Oakland, and the Golden Gate; and dams, such as have been thrown across many great rivers in various parts of the world. In the last 30 years more than 50 of these have been completed or are under construction in the United States alone, ranging in cost from 1,000,000 to more than 100,000,000 dollars each. Among the most notable of American dams are the Boulder Dam on the Colorado River between Nevada and Arizona, the Grand Coulee on the Columbia in Washington, the Shasta Dam on the Sacramento River in California, and the Fort Peck Dam on the Missouri River in Montana. For sheer magnitude and difficulty of construction some of these far outstrip even the great Pyramid of Cheops. Their social and economic significance is also enormously greater, for they have been constructed not as monuments to the memory of a great ruler, but for the benefit of the ordinary man.

The Kensico Dam, near the lower end of the Catskill aqueduct, is built of concrete and has a maximum height of 307 feet above foundation. It is 28 feet thick at the top, and 235 feet thick at the bottom. Boulder Dam rises 730 feet above bedrock. It is also built of concrete and is 45 feet thick at the top and 650 feet thick at the bottom.

To the tourist who views these modern marvels they represent great engineering feats and miracles of applied science. To the citizen who lives within the range of their beneficent effects they stand for adequate city water supply, for rich irrigated lands, for control of the flood menace, and for almost unlimited electric power. But to the student of physics they testify to the success of man's efforts to subjugate and harness the tremendous forces of nature.

Why should the thickness of all such dams be so much greater at the bottom than at the top? And why should the bottom thickness of Boulder Dam exceed that of Kensico by more than 400 feet while its thickness at the top exceeds that of Kensico by only 17 feet?

In order to answer these questions we shall have to study the principles of fluid pressure. Let us begin this study by considering a very simple illustration.

## PRESSURE DUE TO THE WEIGHT OF A LIQUID

Let us suppose that an empty cylindrical jar with vertical sides is placed on one platform of a trip balance, and a weight just sufficient to balance it placed on the other platform. The beam will then tilt either way at the slightest touch. Now let a liquid, water for example, be poured into the jar to a depth of 10 cm. Obviously, in order to balance this, an additional weight equal to that of the liquid will have to be placed on the other platform. If the jar had been filled to a depth of 20 cm., instead of 10, then twice as much weight would have been required to balance it. In each of these cases the liquid exerts a downward force on the bottom of the jar. The force is evidently directly proportional to the depth of the liquid, and just equal to its weight.

In many cases it is more convenient to consider not the total force exerted upon a surface, but the force exerted upon 1 sq. in., 1 sq. cm., 1 sq. ft., or other area unit. The force per unit area is called *pressure*. Like the force, the pressure exerted upon the bottom of our cylindrical, vertical-sided jar is directly pro-

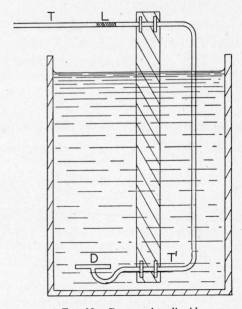

Fig. 20.    Pressure in a liquid.

portional to the depth of the liquid and is equal to the weight of the liquid lying above the unit.

Now if one dam holds back twice as great a depth of water as the other, the pressure at the bottom of the taller dam is twice as great as at the bottom of the lower. For equal lengths the taller dam sustains the pressure upon twice as great an area. There are twice as many square feet, and twice as great an average force per square foot. The force against the taller dam is therefore four times as great as against the dam of equal length which is only half as high.

To prevent it from sliding, a dam must have a secure anchorage in bedrock. To prevent it from toppling over under the great force of the water, it must have great weight and a wide base. The weight of the dam and the thickness of its base must both increase very rapidly with depth.

A good deal of additional information can be gained concerning fluid pressure by means of such a gauge as that represented in Fig. 20. Here $L$ represents a drop of liquid in a glass tube $T$ of small bore. This tube is connected with a thistle tube $T'$ by a rubber tube, as shown. The bowl of the thistle tube is closed by a light rubber diaphragm $D$. A slight pressure on $D$ drives $L$ toward the end of the tube. Removal of the pressure permits it to return to its original position. If the gauge is gradually lowered in a jar of water, $L$ gradually moves to the left. This indicates that the pressure upon $D$ increases with increasing depth in the water. In the preceding paragraph it was shown that the increase is in direct proportion to the depth.

If the gauge is moved to different positions in the jar, or if it is turned to face horizontally, vertically, or obliquely in any direction, all the while remaining at the same depth, there will be no movement of $L$. From this it is seen that in a fluid at rest the pressure is the same at all points at the same level, and that at any point it is equal in all directions.

By means of the foregoing principles the pressure at any depth in a liquid may be computed if the *density* of the liquid is known. By the density of a substance is meant its mass per unit of volume, as the number of lb. in 1 cu. ft., or the number of gm. in 1 cc.

Let us consider a few simple numerical examples.

Sea water has a density of about 64 lb. per cu. ft. A diver working 50 ft. below the surface in the sea is subjected to a pressure of

$$50 \times 64 = 3200 \text{ lb. per sq. ft.}$$

$$\text{or } \frac{50 \times 64}{144} = 22.2 + \text{ lb. per sq. in.}$$

The bathysphere, the strong metal sphere in which Dr. Beebe descended to a depth of 3028 ft. in the sea off Bermuda in order to study marine life in that region was subjected to a pressure of

$$\frac{3028 \times 64}{144} = 1345 + \text{ lb. per sq. in.}$$

Fresh water has a density of about 62.4 lb. per cu. ft. At a faucet which is 120 ft. below the level of the water in the stand-pipe of a city water system the pressure due to weight of water is

$$120 \times 62.4 = 7488 \text{ lb. per sq. ft.,}$$

$$\text{or } \frac{120 \times 62.4}{144} = 52 \text{ lb. per sq. in.}$$

Even in our blood vessels the pressure due to the weight of the fluid is quite appreciable. The pressure in the foot of a tall man in a standing position may exceed that in his head by more than two lb. per sq. in.

## ATMOSPHERIC PRESSURE

Gases also have weight, though it is small compared with that of liquids or solids. The air in a 1000 cc. flask under ordinary atmospheric conditions weighs about 1.2 gm. Near the earth's surface the atmosphere therefore has a density of about .0012 gm. per cc., or 1.2 ounces per cu. ft. The air in a moderate-sized livingroom will weigh 150 to 300 lb.

Hydrogen is only about one-fifteenth as dense as air. Carbon dioxide is about 50 per cent more dense.

It is the weight of air that gives rise to atmospheric pressure. We live at the bottom of a great sea of air. Its depth is much greater than that of the ocean, which averages perhaps less than 3 miles. The depth of the air is of course indefinite, because it becomes increasingly rarer with increasing elevation and merges by imperceptible stages into vacuous space. The depth of what may be considered atmosphere is variously estimated at 50 to 200 miles. Whatever its depth, the pressure it exerts at the earth's surface is nearly 15 lb. per square inch. This means that the air above each square inch of the earth's surface weighs nearly 15 lb.

The fact that atmospheric pressure is due to the weight of the air, and that its magnitude is as stated above, was first shown by the Italian physicist Torricelli about the year 1643. Torricelli used a quantity of mercury and a glass tube about 3 ft. long. He filled the tube with mercury, held a finger over the open end, inverted the tube, and placed this end under mercury in a dish. When the finger was removed, only a small part of the mercury flowed out, as is shown in Fig. 21. Enough remained to fill the tube to a height of about 30 inches. Torricelli attributed this to a pressure of the atmosphere upon the surface of the mercury in the dish.

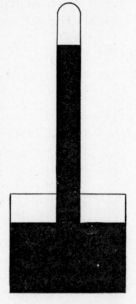

Fig. 21. The atmosphere exerts a pressure.

The French scientist, Blaise Pascal, devised another method of testing Torricelli's view that the mercury remains in the tube because of a pressure exerted by the atmosphere. He assumed that the mercury must be held in the tube by the weight of air resting upon that in the dish. He reasoned that if the tube were carried to the top of a tower, the height of the mercury column would be somewhat less. On trying the experiment, he found this conclusion verified. At Pascal's request his brother-in-law repeated the experiment on Puy-de-Dome, a mountain in southern France. The latter reported that he was "ravished with admiration and astonishment" to find that at an elevation of 3000 ft. the mercury fell about 3 in. in the tube.

## THE BAROMETER

Torricelli not only proved that the atmosphere exerts a pressure, but also provided an instrument whereby this pressure

can be accurately measured.   For this purpose it is only necessary to add to the simple tube described above a scale for
measuring the length of the column of mercury.   With this
addition the mercury tube becomes
the mercurial barometer of the
present day.   A pair of such barometers is represented in Fig. 22.

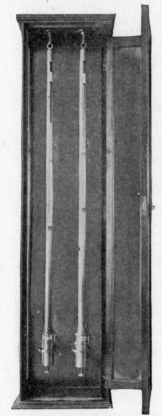

Atmospheric pressure may also be
measured by a type of gauge in
which a flexible diaphragm closing
one end of a partially evacuated,
shallow cup or cylinder is made to
move slightly by any variation in
the pressure of the atmosphere upon
it.   A system of levers multiplies
this movement and communicates it
to a hand moving over a dial and
indicating the barometric reading in
terms of inches or centimeters of
mercury.   This type, represented in
Fig. 23, is called an *aneroid barometer*.
It is widely used by geologists and
others who need a light portable
instrument that is also sensitive to
slight variations in pressure.

*United States Weather Bureau.*
Fig. 22.   Mercurial barometers.

Since atmospheric pressure varies
with altitude, the aneroid barometer
may be graduated to read in terms
of distances above sea level or above
the ground.   When so graduated, it
becomes the altimeter of the air pilot and the meteorologist.

## TRANSMISSION OF PRESSURE IN FLUIDS.   PASCAL'S LAW

If pressure is applied at any point to a fluid in a closed container, this pressure is transmitted without change to every
part of the fluid.   It is in accordance with this principle that

hydraulic presses, hydraulic lifts, and hydraulic brakes operate. Let Fig. 24 represent a vessel with two cylindrical sections, A and B. Let these cylinders be fitted with pistons, P and P'.

*United States Weather Bureau.*

FIG. 23.   Aneroid barometer.

If a pressure, say 10 lb. per sq. in., is added to the fluid by a force applied at P, this same pressure of 10 lb. per sq. in. is thereby added to the fluid everywhere.   This principle, which was first stated by Blaise Pascal about 300 years ago, is known as *Pascal's law*.

It is evident that by such a device as that illustrated in Fig. 24 any applied force can be greatly multiplied. Let P, for example, have an area of 2 sq. in. and P' an area of 100 sq. in.   If a pressure of 5 lb. per sq. in. is applied at P, this same pressure is transmitted to P'.   Here the total force exerted is

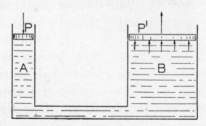

FIG. 24.   Principle of the hydraulic press.

$$100 \times 5 \text{ lb.} = 500 \text{ lb.}$$

This has been accomplished by applying at $P$ a force of only

$$2 \times 5 \text{ lb.} = 10 \text{ lb.}$$

The area of $P'$ is 50 times as great as that of $P$. The force exerted upon $P'$ is 50 times as great as that applied at $P$. However, in order to raise the load on $P'$ 1 in. it is necessary for the force applied at $P$ to act through a distance of 50 in.

Force $\times$ distance force acts = resistance $\times$ distance resistance is overcome.
10 lb. $\times$ 50 in. = 500 lb. $\times$ 1 in.

Devices of this type are used in the base of barbers' and dentists' chairs where they are operated by the foot to raise the chair. They are also used in the hydraulic brakes of our modern motor cars and in huge presses in steel mills, auto-body factories, and the like, where great forces are required.

## SUCTION

The pressure of the atmosphere is the active agent responsible for many phenomena or useful operations that are often ascribed to an indefinite something called *suction*. We drink soda through a straw, or we draw up water from a cistern by a pump. In the latter case we may have to improve the suction by priming. What is it that we call suction? By drawing on the straw we reduce the pressure within it. We do the same within the pump and in the tube leading from it to the water when we operate the pump. This reduction of pressure is what is often called suction. When the pressure is thus reduced below that of the atmosphere, the atmospheric pressure exerted upon the soda in the glass and the water in the cistern drives the soda or the water upward. If all of the pressure were removed by suction, the atmosphere would be most effective, and would raise water to the greatest height possible. If the barometer stood at 30 inches, then the height to which water would be raised would be $30 \times 13.6$ inches (since mercury is 13.6 times as dense as water), or 34 feet. If the barometric reading is less than this, water will not be raised to quite so great a height. Liquids lighter than water, such as oils or gasoline, can be lifted higher than water; denser liquids, such as acids or brines, not so high.

## BUOYANCY. THE PRINCIPLE OF ARCHIMEDES

A cork stopper or a piece of wood tossed into a pond floats without arousing even a suggestion of surprise. Would a floating rock or mass of iron do likewise? Probably not. However, both rock and iron may be floated on mercury. A loaded coal barge alongside of a dock lies low in the water. With the coal removed the barge may stand several feet higher. A bather in shallow water may find a stone which he can bring to the surface, but which even by the greatest effort he cannot lift entirely out. The bather himself may sink or float depending upon the amount of air he has in his lungs. What are the causes of these various phenomena? To understand them let us refer to Fig. 25. Here $A$ represents a cylindrical rod of uniform diameter. $S$ is a spring scale by which the rod may be weighed, and $W$ is a jar of water or other liquid into which the rod is lowered. It has been seen that a pressure exists within a liquid, owing to its weight. This is exerted perpendicularly upon any surface with which the liquid is in contact. The horizontal pressure on the side of the rod at any point is balanced by an equal pressure on the opposite side. The upward pressure on the bottom is not canceled in this

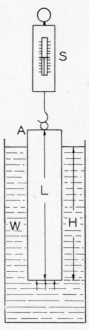

FIG. 25. Buoyancy. The liquid presses upward on the lower end of the rod.

way, however, but helps to support the weight of the rod. The greater the depth to which the rod is lowered the greater this pressure becomes, the greater the weight it supports, and the less the spring scale reads. Let us illustrate by a few numerical examples.

If a 35 gm. rod whose cross-sectional area is 2 sq. cm. is lowered 10 cm. in water, the water will exert an upward force upon the lower end of the rod amounting to

$$10 \times 2 \times 1 \text{ gm.} = 20 \text{ gm.}$$

The rod will therefore seem to lose 20 gm. in weight, and the spring scale will read

$$35 \text{ gm.} - 20 \text{ gm.} = 15 \text{ gm.}$$

The action of fluids in thus carrying or helping to carry the weight of objects is called *buoyancy*.

If the rod were lowered to the same depth in a liquid whose density is .8 gm. per cc., the lifting force upon it would be

$$10 \times 2 \times .8 \text{ gm.} = 16 \text{ gm.}$$

and the spring scale would read

$$35 \text{ gm.} - 16 \text{ gm.} = 19 \text{ gm.}$$

As the rod is lowered, the spring scale will register less and less until the rod is just submerged. Thereafter any further lowering will result in adding a downward pressure upon the top of the rod which is just equal to any further increase in the upward pressure upon the bottom. The reading of the spring scale will therefore undergo no further change.

If the rod mentioned in the above paragraphs is 12 cm. long, the lifting force exerted upon it by the water when it is just submerged will be

$$12 \times 2 \times 1 \text{ gm.} = 24 \text{ gm.}$$

The remaining 11 gm. required to support its weight must be contributed by the spring scale, which will then read just this amount. If the rod is submerged in the liquid whose density is .8 gm. per cc., the liquid pressure contributes

$$12 \times 2 \times .8 \text{ gm.} = 19.2 \text{ gm.}$$

of the 35 gm. necessary to sustain the weight. The remaining 15.8 gm. are held by the spring scale.

In each case the supporting force of the liquid is seen to be just equal to the weight of the liquid displaced. These examples illustrate an important law which, in honor of its discoverer, is called the *Principle of Archimedes.*

If the rod is of a light material, such as dry wood, its weight may not be great enough to submerge it.  In that case it will sink only until the upward force of the liquid becomes great enough to sustain the entire weight.  The weight of the displaced liquid is then just equal to that of the object itself.  This is the condition in the case of any floating object, whether it be a swimmer, a log floating down a mill stream, or a warship with its thousands of tons of steel armor.

As applied to liquids the Principle of Archimedes then states that *any object whether floating or submerged apparently loses in weight an amount which is equal to the weight of the liquid it displaces.*

The change in water line of the coal barge as the load is removed and the floating of iron on mercury are now readily understood.  So also is the fact that it is much easier to swim in sea water than in fresh, and that it is a cardinal rule for swimmers to keep the lungs well filled with air.

## THE HYDROMETER

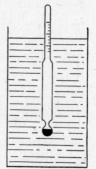

From the preceding discussion it may be seen that an object floating on a dense liquid rides high, while on a less dense liquid it sinks lower. This fact is employed in the hydrometer (Fig. 26), an instrument by which the *specific gravity* of a liquid can be easily and accurately measured. By the specific gravity of a liquid is meant the ratio of its density to that of water.  Thus

Fig. 26.  Constant weight hydrometer.

alcohol is about .8 as dense as water.  Its specific gravity is .8.

The hydrometer is a familiar object at every gasoline filling station.  There it is used to test the condition of the storage battery and of the anti-freeze solution of the patron's car. In testing the battery some of the liquid is drawn into a tube containing the hydrometer, which then floats in the liquid. If it floats high, the liquid is dense.  This indicates that the battery is well charged.   If it sinks low, the liquid is less dense. The battery may be nearly run down and need recharging.

In testing the anti-freeze solution the same procedure is followed.   The interpretation however depends upon the nature of the liquid.   If this is a mixture of alcohol and water, the lighter the liquid the greater its content of alcohol, and the lower its freezing temperature.   If it is Ethylene Glycol (Prestone), a liquid which is heavier than water, the denser the solution the lower the freezing temperature.   The mixture must be prevented from freezing, for in doing so it expands and may burst the radiator.   By noting the exact height of the liquid on the hydrometer the freezing point of the liquid and thus its measure of protection is determined.

## BALLOONS

Gases, of which the atmosphere is the most abundant, also exert a buoyant action.   It is by this means that balloons are kept aloft.   The total weight, including bag, machinery, cargo, and inflating gas, must be no greater than that of the air displaced.   If it is greater, the balloon will not rise.   If less, it will.   The lighter the inflating gas the greater its lifting power. Because hydrogen is the lightest of all gases it has been more frequently used than any other for filling balloons of all kinds. It is highly inflammable however.   This adds a large element of danger.   Helium is also light, about twice as dense as hydrogen, and noninflammable.   It is therefore admirably suited for use in dirigibles.   It occurs only in small amounts in the air, however, and for a long time this was the only known source. Since its discovery in large quantity in connection with petroleum in Texas and Oklahoma, it has been extensively used for this purpose.   It has about eight-ninths of the lifting power of hydrogen.

## COMPRESSIBILITY OF FLUIDS.  BOYLE'S LAW

One of the questions concerning which the ancient Greek philosophers speculated almost endlessly had to do with the structure of matter—whether it is continuous, or whether it is made up of very small, individually invisible natural units or particles. Modern science has discovered overwhelming evidence in support of the latter view. The very minute particles of which matter is composed are called *molecules*. All the many different substances in the world are made up either of different kinds of molecules or of molecules of the same kinds differently put together. More will be said about these tiny particles in the next few chapters.

When pressure is applied to a fluid, its molecules are forced closer together and its volume reduced. In liquids the molecules are already so close that there is little unclaimed space

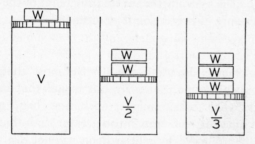

Fɪɢ. 27. The volume of a gas varies inversely with pressure.

between them. Their volume is reduced but little when pressure is applied. In the case of water at 0° C. a pressure of 1500 lb. per sq. in. reduces that volume only about one-half of 1 per cent. In alcohol the change is greater than this. In mercury it is much less.

Because the molecules of gases are much farther apart than those of liquids, added pressure reduces the volume of the former to a far greater extent. At constant temperature doubling the pressure of a gas reduces its volume to half of its former value; trebling the pressure reduces it to a third. It is seen that the volume of the gas varies inversely as the pressure. This fact may be expressed more concisely as a formula, thus:

$$\frac{V}{V'} = \frac{P'}{P} \text{ or } PV = P'V'.$$

This relationship, which is represented diagrammatically in

Fig. 27, was discovered in 1662 by the Irish physicist Robert Boyle.   It is therefore called *Boyle's law.*

The compressibility or expansive property of gases is extensively applied in devices designed to add to man's convenience and comfort.   Of these the pneumatic tire, used everywhere on bicycles, automobiles and automobile trucks, lawn mowers, tractors, and the like, is one of the most important.   Pneumatic cushions and mattresses, whether of the older types in which the air is contained in one large bag, or of the newer airfoam variety in which it is entrapped in a multitude of small pockets, also utilize this property.   The air brake operates on the same principle.   This very important addition to railway equipment enables the engineer to apply the brakes of all the cars.   Such a device places the movement of the train much more completely under his control, and has added greatly to the safety of railway travel.   Footballs, basketballs, and tennis balls all owe their elasticity to the expansive property of the inflating air.   Compressed air hammers are used as riveters in joining steel beams or plates in the construction of buildings, and in the manufacture of such equipment as steam boilers and tank cars.   They are also used in operating drills for boring into rock, tearing up old pavement, and digging into frozen ground. There are many other devices, such as air rifles, door stops, pneumatic drinking fountains, and cash tubes, all of which operate by the expansive property of a gas.   Even steam, gasoline, and Diesel engines, which supply by far the greater part of the power used in the world today, may properly be said to operate at least in part by the expansive property of gases.

In order to develop the high temperatures required by his work, the oxyacetylene welder burns acetylene gas in oxygen. These gases come to him under pressure in steel drums.   To give sparkle and flavor to his drinks the operator of a soda fountain uses another gas, carbon dioxide, which is also "packaged" and marketed in drums.   Hydrogen and helium for inflating balloons are transported in the same way.   It is the compressibility of these gases that makes it possible to confine them in quantity in containers of convenient size.

# CHAPTER 6

# MOLECULES AND
# THEIR BEHAVIOR

In the preceding chapter mention was made of certain very small particles of matter—the molecules. These are of almost unbelievable minuteness—so small that none of them has ever been seen singly or photographed; yet scientists are convinced of their existence because they provide a simple explanation of many of the observed facts of chemistry and physics which it would be very difficult to account for otherwise. The present chapter deals for the most part with their activities, for like many of the smallest beings of the animal world they are usually very busy. But let us first get as vivid an idea as possible of their number and size.

## NUMBER AND SIZE OF MOLECULES

Scientists tell us that in 1 cc. of air under ordinary room conditions there are about $27 \times 10^{18}$ molecules. This is the number 27 followed by 18 zeros. If we can think of these as spheres in regular arrangement filling a cubical box, then a single row of them 1 cm. long will contain about three million molecules. A row whose length is equal to the thickness of an ordinary sheet of paper will contain about 30,000. In 1 cc. of water there are about 1250 times as many molecules as in 1 cc. of air. In water, therefore, they are less than one-tenth as far apart. More than 300,000 water molecules side by side make a chain whose length is equal to the thickness of a sheet of paper! In common salt the corresponding number is about 280,000.

## UNOCCUPIED SPACE BETWEEN MOLECULES

It has been seen that when atmospheric air is put under increased pressure, its volume is reduced in accordance with Boyle's law. With pressure increased to one hundred atmospheres the volume is reduced to only one per cent of its original value. This indicates that in air only a small portion of the space is actually occupied by the molecules. The rest is empty. The same is true of all other gases. How small the molecules themselves must be! It is by diminishing the amount of this unoccupied space that gas volumes are reduced by pressure. In liquids and solids, on the other hand, pressure reduces the volume but little. Changing the pressure upon water from 15 lb. to 1500 lb. per square inch reduces its volume about one-half of one per cent. An equal change of pressure on nickel or steel reduces its volume less than one-tenth of one per cent. From this we infer that in these substances the molecules are very close together—approximately ten times closer than the molecules of air in a room.

## ATTRACTION OF MOLECULES FOR EACH OTHER

Notwithstanding their smallness molecules may exert forces which are surprisingly great. A steel wire one-sixteenth of an inch in diameter is strong enough to lift more than half a ton (Fig. 28). A rod of the same quality one inch in diameter would lift about 125 tons. It is the attraction of the molecules of the metal for each other that makes this possible. The tenacity of steel, that is, its ability to resist breaking by tension, is greater than that of any other metal.

We are not accustomed to thinking of liquids as having tensile strength, yet they all do. A copper disc a few centimeters in diameter suspended at its center and let down flat upon the surface of water will be held by a force of several grams. The disc when pulled away will come up wet. This shows that the attraction between metals and water is greater than the "breaking strength" of the water. It is this latter, therefore, which the experiment measures.

All gases expand to fill completely any container in which they are placed.  On this account it was long thought that their molecules have no attraction for each other.  It has been shown, however, that they do have, though the attraction is very small.  The tendency of gases to expand indefinitely is due, not to an absence of molecular attraction, but to the fact that the energy of motion of the molecules is great enough to overcome it.

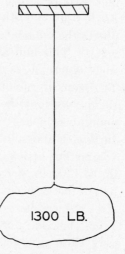

Fig. 28.   Strength of Steel.  Wire of knitting-needle size holds 1300 lb.

## SURFACE FILMS

The existence of an attraction between molecules in liquids is further shown by the formation of surface films.  By pouring very carefully a clean tumbler can be filled "heaping full" of water, as shown in Fig. 29.  The piling up is possible because of what is called a surface film.   This covers the entire surface of the water, clings to the glass, and holds the water somewhat as a sheet of cellophane over the surface might do.  The film is formed as a result of molecular attraction in the liquid.  If a drop of alcohol is let fall upon the water it causes the latter to overflow.  The drop has momentarily substituted a film of alcohol for the surface film of water.  Molecular attraction in alcohol is less than in water.  The new film is weaker than the old and therefore unable to hold the water to as high a level.

Fig. 29.   A tumbler heaping full of water.

## SURFACE TENSION

If a wire ring across which a thread is loosely tied is dipped into a soap solution, a film will cling to the wire, forming a disc-like sheet across the ring and holding the thread as shown in Fig. 30A.   If the film on either side of the thread is touched with a hot wire, it will be broken.   The portion on the other side may remain, drawing the thread in that direction as shown in Fig. 30B.   Surface films tend to contract indefinitely, exerting a force upon any objects to which they cling.   It is on this account that soap bubbles and fine raindrops are spherical.

This pull which is always exerted by the surface film of a liquid is called *surface tension*.   Its magnitude is very different in different liquids, as has already been noted.   Even in the

FIG. 30.   Loop of Wire with Thread and Soap Film.   A. Film as formed.   B. Film broken on one side of thread.

same liquid it varies somewhat with temperature.   The surface tension of water at 20 degrees C. is about .074 gm. per cm., while that of ethyl alcohol is about .022 gm.   This means that a ribbon of surface film 1 cm. wide exerts a lengthwise pull of about .074 gm. in water and .022 gm. in alcohol.   The surface tension of mercury is notably large, amounting to more than half a gm. per cm.

## CAPILLARITY

Blowing bubbles is a child's pastime, but the attraction of liquid molecules which makes them possible manifests itself in ways of greater importance.   By way of providing a basis for understanding how this may be, let us stand a clean glass tube of small diameter in a glass of water.   The water in the tube rises above the level in the glass.   If tubes of different sizes are used, it rises highest in the tube of smallest bore as shown in Fig. 31A.   If the diameter of one tube is half that of another, the liquid rises twice as high in the smaller tube. The height of rise varies inversely as the diameter. If a tube is placed in a liquid which does not "wet" it, the liquid in the tube falls below the level outside, as shown in Fig. 31B. This is the case when a glass tube is placed in mercury.

Water rises in the glass tube because the concave film, in contracting, draws the water upward with it by molecular attraction. The pressure in the liquid below the film is somewhat lowered. In the case of glass in mercury the convex film pulls downward, pushing the rest of the mercury before it. The pressure below the film is raised.

These phenomena are due to surface tension. They are examples of what is called *capillarity*, so named because they

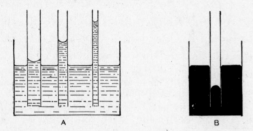

Fig. 31. Capillarity. A. Glass tubes in water. B. Glass tube in mercury.

are most easily observed and studied by means of fine "hair-like" tubes. The action is not limited to tubes, however, but takes place wherever a liquid is confined closely between solids, such as grains of sand or clay, or the fibers of paper or cloth. A drop of water or ink falling upon a handkerchief quickly spreads. A lump of sugar touched to tea or coffee in a cup is soon moistened throughout.

Capillarity is essential to the operation of many useful articles affecting our daily lives. A wick, for example, may aid in lubricating machinery by carrying oil from a supply cup to the bearing. It does so by capillary action. It is by the same means that a towel dries our hands and faces, a blotter takes up ink, and the wick used in some methods of humidification exposes a large water surface and so facilitates evaporation.

The most important instance of this type of action, however, is that in which water is brought from underground to the region near the surface, there to be taken up by the roots of plants. This is their only important source of moisture between showers in all unirrigated areas. Because the spaces between the particles of the subsoil are very small, water may be brought up in this way from depths of many feet.

## ELASTICITY OF SOLIDS

If a wire is subjected to a stretching force, it is somewhat lengthened. When the force is withdrawn, if the elongation was not too great, the wire resumes its original length. If it is bent or twisted and the distorting force then removed, it returns to its original shape. This ability of a substance to resume its original size or shape is called *elasticity*. It is evidently due to the tendency of each molecule of a solid to maintain its position with respect to neighboring molecules. They oppose any shift from their "home" positions with a force which increases directly with the amount of displacement. In such substances as steel the molecules will return to their positions after comparatively large displacements. In other substances, such as lead and copper, even relatively small twists or bends remain. The molecules of these substances have less ability than those of steel to return to positions from which they have been forcibly displaced.

The elasticity of steel adds greatly to both our comfort and technology. It is this property which adapts it so excellently for use in springs. In beds or mattresses springs contribute to our comfort while we sleep. In chairs and automobiles they perform the same service for us through our waking hours. In our clocks and watches they keep the hands moving with a precision that would seem nothing less than marvelous if we were not so prone to accept as commonplace everything to which we become accustomed. In nearly every factory and in a multitude of the devices made by factories elasticity is an essential factor in operation.

## MOTION OF MOLECULES

If a small amount of gas with a distinctive or penetrating odor is released in a room in which the air is stagnant, it is not long until the odor may be sensed everywhere in the room. If the same gas is released in an evacuated vessel, it almost instantaneously fills the entire vessel.

The cylinders of an automobile motor are completely filled with a mixture of air and gasoline vapor at every intake stroke

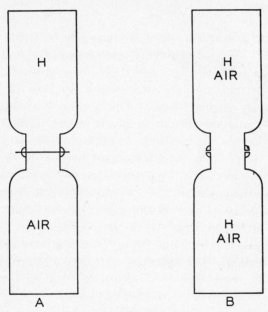

Fig. 32.   Diffusion of gases.

of the piston.   The mixture of gases follows the piston without noticeable lag, even at its highest speed.

Invert a wide-necked bottle filled with a light gas like hydrogen over a similar bottle containing air, as shown in Fig. 32A, and within a few minutes after removal of the partition the two gases fill both bottles as a uniform mixture, even though the gas originally in the upper bottle was less than one-fifteenth as dense as air.   This is represented in Fig. 32B.   All of these facts indicate that the molecules of gases are in motion at com-

paratively high speeds.   The intermingling of fluids as a result
of the motion of their individual molecules is called *diffusion*.

## CHARACTER OF MOLECULAR MOTION

In a gas the motion of a molecule is of a very irregular sort,
somewhat like that represented in Fig. 33.   At one instant
the molecule is at *O*.   At that point it is moving along a short
straight line and continues to do so until it collides with another
molecule at *P*.   From this it rebounds in some other direction
and at an altered speed.   Then it quickly collides with a third
molecule from which it rebounds in some new direction and at

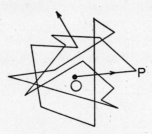

still a different speed.   So it continues.   Millions of such collisions
and rebounds occur in a fraction of
a second.   Every molecule in the gas
is doing exactly the same thing.   At
room temperatures the average speed
of the molecules of the air is about
a quarter of a mile per second.   But

FIG. 33.  Brownian movement.   the distances between molecules are
so small and the changes of direction
so frequent (about 8000 million per second) that the actual
displacements from starting point in one second are very small
indeed.   In a greatly rarefied gas, however, collisions are much
less frequent and distances traveled between collisions much
greater.   That is why a gas released in a vacuum fills the space
so quickly.

Lighter molecules move with greater speeds than heavier ones.
At the same temperature their kinetic energies are equal.   It
was shown in Chap. 3 that the kinetic energy of an object
is equal to one-half of the product obtained by multiplying its
mass by the square of its speed.

$$K. E. = \frac{1}{2}mv^2.$$

If two objects of unequal mass have the same kinetic energy,
the two masses are inversely proportional to the squares of their

speeds. The same relationship is stated by saying that the speeds are inversely proportional to the square roots of the masses. This is true of atoms and molecules as well as of objects of visible size. The molecule of hydrogen, which is only one-sixteenth as massive as that of oxygen, has a speed four times as great. The molecule of xenon, one of the rare gases of the atmosphere, is four times as massive as that of oxygen. Its speed is therefore only half as great.

The molecules of liquids move in a manner very much like that described above for gases. The number of molecules in 1 cc. is far greater, however, and the distances traveled between collisions correspondingly smaller. On this account liquids diffuse much less rapidly than gases.

In the case of solids the molecules (with few exceptions) are held in very nearly fixed positions. The motion is one of oscillation only.

## PRESSURE IN GASES

If a blast of sand is blown against a board standing on edge so far from the nozzle that the air current has no appreciable direct effect upon it, the board is subjected to an apparently steady force tending to topple it over. Each grain of sand exerts a slight impulse. The multitude of sand grains striking in such quick succession give the impression of a continuous force. An effect of the same kind is exerted by a gas upon any surface with which it is in contact. Each molecule striking the surface imparts its tiny impulse. With huge numbers of such impacts upon each sq. cm. every second, the total effect may be considerable. That is the way in which a gas exerts a pressure.

When a gas is compressed, as in an automobile tire or a pressure tank, the number of molecules in each cc. is increased. The number of molecular impacts per second is increased in the same proportion. The pressure therefore rises, varying directly with the density of the gas. Thus we find a mechanical explanation of Boyle's law.

## ORDERLY ARRANGEMENT OF ATOMS IN CRYSTALS

If a glass of water in which a spoonful of sugar has been dissolved is set aside, in the course of time the water will all evaporate. The sugar, however, will be left behind. If a small piece of sugar is attached to a thread and suspended in the solution during evaporation, much of the sugar will collect upon the string as "rock candy." On examination the sugar is found to have arranged itself in definite geometrical figures, the faces of which are inclined to each other at definite angles.

Similarly, if common salt is dissolved in water and the solution allowed to evaporate, the salt will be left behind. In this case the figures will be cubes. A solution of blue vitriol on evaporating forms blue rhombic figures of copper sulfate. Alum, saltpeter, epsom salts, and many other substances may be deposited from their saturated solution in the same way, some forming in one geometrical shape and some in another. There are however only a few general types. Solids so formed are called *crystals*.

There are two other ways in which crystals may be formed. One of these is involved in the formation of frost and snow. In these cases moisture changes from vapor into the solid state without passing through the intermediate liquid state. The beautiful tracery often seen on window panes in winter and the glittering mantle which sometimes covers trees and shrubs on a frosty morning consist of multitudes of hexagonal (six-sided) crystals built into various shapes. Some of these are represented in Fig. 34.

Sal ammoniac, a substance very similar in many respects to common salt, also passes from the vapor direct into the solid condition forming characteristic white crystals.

The third method of formation is observed when certain liquids solidify. When water freezes, crystals of the same hexagonal system are produced as are found in frost and snow. When iron, zinc, nickel, and many other metals in the molten condition are allowed to cool and "freeze," they also solidify in crystalline form. Many of the materials found in the crust of the earth occur as crystals, some of which are so beautiful as to be highly prized as jewels.  The diamond, ruby, sapphire, and emerald are among the most precious of these.  Others,

United States Weather Bureau.

FIG. 34.   Snow crystals.

like granite, marble, feldspar, quartz, and mica are more abundant and very useful.  The forms of some of these are shown in pictures in Chap. 31.

The regularity of shapes of crystals, and the fact that many of them may be readily divided along certain planes, called *cleavage planes*, show that their atoms are held together in regular arrangement. In common salt the atoms lie in definite rows and layers, atom above atom. In copper sulfate and many others the piling is somewhat inclined.

Some substances may exist as crystals of different forms depending upon the conditions under which they are produced. Crystallized sulfur, for example, may exist as rhombic octahedrons or as slender monoclinic needles. The arrangement of the atoms is different in the two types of crystals. By simple laboratory processes the chemist can readily change the substance from one of these forms to the other, or to the *amorphous* (noncrystalline) condition. Carbon also crystallizes in two forms. One of these is graphite, which is an important ingredient of the "lead" of our lead pencils. The other is the diamond. In the case of carbon the chemist has much smaller control of the type of crystal which it shall form.

A knowledge of the properties of crystals, their internal structure, and the conditions affecting their development is of great economic and scientific importance. In the alloying and tempering of steel, for example, the size and character of the crystals formed determine the qualities of the product. The properties of many other alloys and pure metals are also dependent upon the character of the crystals of which they are composed. In the case of some transparent crystals such as Iceland spar the effect upon a beam of light is such as to make them very useful in instruments for testing the purity of sugar. In quartz the mechanical and electrical properties of the crystal are utilized in providing a very accurate control of the frequencies of radio transmitters. Some high-quality microphones also operate by reason of these same crystal properties. A multitude of similarly oriented microscopic crystals spread out in a thin sheet form the new material, polaroid, which is already widely used in sun glasses, photographic screens, and study lamps to eliminate glare, and seems destined to solve the same troublesome problem in connection with the headlights of automobiles. In the realm of fundamental science, crystals have been instrumental in enabling research workers very greatly to extend our knowledge in the very important fields of $X$-rays and atomic structure.

In many solid substances the atoms are not arranged in definite positions with respect to each other, but are piled together in a haphazard, random way somewhat like potatoes in a barrel. This is true of such substances as glass, gum, wax, and fats, which are called amorphous, or noncrystalline, substances. Some substances exist in both crystalline and noncrystalline forms. This duality, as has already been noted, is true of sulfur. It also holds for carbon, of which soot or lamp black is a noncrystalline variety.

# CHAPTER 7

# BUILDING STONES
# OF MATTER

For many centuries man relied upon "Mother Nature" to supply his varied needs. From the earth he took rocks and metals for his tools; from plants he extracted various "principles" for his medicines; and from animal and vegetable sources he obtained dyes for his clothing. The products were crude and often unsatisfactory, but he did not know how to improve upon them. He knew nothing of their real nature. Their structure and composition were a complete mystery. Because of his ignorance of the nature of matter he could not fashion these crude substances into better ones. Much less could he produce them at will in laboratory or workshop.

Yet he studied and experimented. Little by little his knowledge grew; he learned how matter is "put together." He unearthed the secret of why substances behave as they do. And of late he has penetrated into the actual anatomy of the very building stones of matter. As a result the twentieth-century human enjoys comforts and conveniences of which the early experimenter dared not even dream.

## THE ATOMIC THEORY

Early in the history of science matter was conceived of as being continuous. A gold rod was a continuous mass of gold, without spaces or particles—even microscopic. This idea gradually gave way to a granular conception of matter, culminating in the work of John Dalton, English schoolmaster and scientist. Dalton, in his Atomic Theory, stated that all elements were composed of tiny, indivisible grains or atoms. If atoms of gold could be made visible, a gold rod would appear as a long strip of tiny golden spheres tightly packed together. He considered that atoms of different elements were unlike and that chemical changes, when they occurred, took place between individual atoms. Although modified in its details, the atomic theory of matter has stood the test of time. Without it, scientific invention and discovery would be lagging far behind its present attainments. In very recent times, science has probed still more deeply. It has penetrated the atom itself and observed its structure. The results will be described later in this chapter.

## IDENTITY OF THE MOLECULE

There are 92 elements. Hence it would seem that there are 92 kinds of atoms, one kind for each element. Yet it is common knowledge that there are hundreds of thousands of different substances, mostly compounds. If a chunk of some pure compound, say sodium chloride or salt, were to be subdivided in the extreme, there would finally be obtained the tiniest particle of salt which could exist. This particle would be called a *molecule*. True, this molecule is, in turn, made up of one atom of sodium and one of chlorine; but these atoms do not have the properties of salt. The molecule of salt still retains the properties of salt. Likewise a molecule of table sugar is the smallest particle which exhibits the characteristic properties of sugar. Analysis shows that its molecule, in turn, is composed of 12 atoms of carbon, 22 atoms of hydrogen and 11 atoms of oxygen. *A molecule, then, is the smallest particle of a substance which retains the properties of the substance.*

## KINDS OF MOLECULES

The last statement will bear further analysis. A molecule of a *compound* contains whatever number and kind of atoms are necessary to form the compound, as shown by analysis. What can be said of molecules of *elements?* Consider the gaseous element, oxygen. According to definition, a molecule must retain the usual properties of the substance. How many atoms make up the oxygen molecule? Molecules of oxygen containing only one atom each are seldom met with. Our only contact with them comes with the use of such substances as ozone, hydrogen peroxide, and chlorine for bleaching and sterilizing. Evidently, one-atom molecules of oxygen are a very unusual sort and not at all like the oxygen which supports respiration and combustion. Actually, a molecule of ordinary oxygen contains two atoms, and hence is said to be *diatomic.* This state applies also for most of the gaseous elements, such as nitrogen, hydrogen, and chlorine.

Exceptions to the rule are gaseous elements at high temperatures and more especially, the so-called rare gases of the atmosphere such as helium, neon, and argon. They actually have only one atom to the molecule—they are *monatomic.* Their atom and molecule, then, are identical. Most liquid elements, such as mercury and bromine, and solid elements, such as sulfur, phosphorus, iron, and copper, are also monatomic.

## CHEMICAL SYMBOLISM

Short cuts are popular. They save time and energy. Even the names of the elements have, for centuries, been simplified by symbolic expressions. The early chemical symbols were hard to draw and difficult to remember (Fig. 35). Gradually they evolved, and in 1811 Berzelius proposed our present system. His proposal was to use the initial letter or the initial and one other letter of the English or Latin name. Hence we have C for carbon, Ca for calcium, Cl for chlorine and Cu for copper (cuprum).

A symbol may merely stand for the substance. Cu may represent copper, regardless of form or quantity. As commonly employed, however, a symbol means more than just the substance. It expresses one atom and one atomic weight. Thus, Cu usually stands for one atom of copper and for the atomic weight of copper (63.57 parts by weight; see later section in this chapter).

Molecules, as well as atoms, possess a chemical symbolism. The molecule of table salt contains one atom each of sodium and chlorine. This is expressed by writing the symbols of sodium and chlorine, one after the other, thus: NaCl. It is called a *formula*. A formula is a symbol or a combination of symbols used to represent the composition of a molecule. Pure iron oxide—iron rust—contains two atoms of iron and three of oxygen in its molecule. Its formula is expressed by writing the symbols of iron and oxygen, one after the other, and employing subscripts to indicate the number of atoms of each

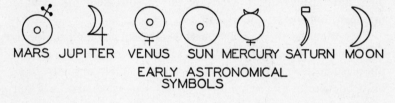

MARS JUPITER VENUS SUN MERCURY SATURN MOON
EARLY ASTRONOMICAL
SYMBOLS

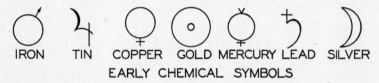

IRON TIN COPPER GOLD MERCURY LEAD SILVER
EARLY CHEMICAL SYMBOLS

Fig. 35. Chemical Symbols Derived from Astronomical Signs. Elements were associated in the minds of early chemists with the heavenly bodies.

element, thus: $Fe_2O_3$. The formula of sugar, before referred to, is $C_{12}H_{22}O_{11}$. If this same system is applied to the molecules of elements, it is evident that the previously mentioned molecules would be expressed as follows: $O_2$ for oxygen; $N_2$, nitrogen; $H_2$, hydrogen; $Cl_2$, chlorine; He, helium; Ne, neon; S, sulfur; P, phosphorus; Fe, iron; and Cu, copper. Formulas may represent just the substance, or one molecule or a molecular weight.

## ATOMIC WEIGHTS

It was stated in a previous paragraph that the symbol Cu may represent an atomic weight of copper, or 63.57 parts by weight. The meaning of the value will now be explained. Large masses of substances are made up of molecules and

TABLE 1

INTERNATIONAL ATOMIC WEIGHTS

| | Symbol | Atomic Number | Atomic Weight | | Symbol | Atomic Number | Atomic Weight |
|---|---|---|---|---|---|---|---|
| Aluminum | Al | 13 | 26.97 | Molybdenum | Mo | 42 | 95.95 |
| Antimony | Sb | 51 | 121.76 | Neodymium | Nd | 60 | 144.27 |
| Argon | A | 18 | 39.944 | Neon | Ne | 10 | 20.183 |
| Arsenic | As | 33 | 74.91 | Nickel | Ni | 28 | 58.69 |
| Barium | Ba | 56 | 137.36 | Nitrogen | N | 7 | 14.008 |
| Beryllium | Be | 4 | 9.02 | Osmium | Os | 76 | 190.2 |
| Bismuth | Bi | 83 | 209.00 | Oxygen | O | 8 | 16.0000 |
| Boron | B | 5 | 10.82 | Palladium | Pd | 46 | 106.7 |
| Bromine | Br | 35 | 79.916 | Phosphorus | P | 15 | 30.98 |
| Cadmium | Cd | 48 | 112.41 | Platinum | Pt | 78 | 195.23 |
| Calcium | Ca | 20 | 40.08 | Potassium | K | 19 | 39.096 |
| Carbon | C | 6 | 12.010 | Praseodymium | Pr | 59 | 140.92 |
| Cerium | Ce | 58 | 140.13 | Protactinium | Pa | 91 | 231 |
| Cesium | Cs | 55 | 132.91 | Radium | Ra | 88 | 226.05 |
| Chlorine | Cl | 17 | 35.457 | Radon | Rn | 86 | 222 |
| Chromium | Cr | 24 | 52.01 | Rhenium | Re | 75 | 186.31 |
| Cobalt | Co | 27 | 58.94 | Rhodium | Rh | 45 | 102.91 |
| Columbium | Cb | 41 | 92.91 | Rubidium | Rb | 37 | 85.48 |
| Copper | Cu | 29 | 63.57 | Ruthenium | Ru | 44 | 101.7 |
| Dysprosium | Dy | 66 | 162.46 | Samarium | Sm | 62 | 150.43 |
| Erbium | Er | 68 | 167.2 | Scandium | Sc | 21 | 45.10 |
| Europium | Eu | 63 | 152.0 | Selenium | Se | 34 | 78.96 |
| Fluorine | F | 9 | 19.00 | Silicon | Si | 14 | 28.06 |
| Gadolinium | Gd | 64 | 156.9 | Silver | Ag | 47 | 107.880 |
| Gallium | Ga | 31 | 69.72 | Sodium | Na | 11 | 22.997 |
| Germanium | Ge | 32 | 72.60 | Strontium | Sr | 38 | 87.63 |
| Gold | Au | 79 | 197.2 | Sulfur | S | 16 | 32.06 |
| Hafnium | Hf | 72 | 178.6 | Tantalum | Ta | 73 | 180.88 |
| Helium | He | 2 | 4.003 | Tellurium | Te | 52 | 127.61 |
| Holmium | Ho | 67 | 163.5 | Terbium | Tb | 65 | 159.2 |
| Hydrogen | H | 1 | 1.0081 | Thallium | Tl | 81 | 204.39 |
| Indium | In | 49 | 114.76 | Thorium | Th | 90 | 232.12 |
| Iodine | I | 53 | 126.92 | Thulium | Tm | 69 | 169.4 |
| Iridium | Ir | 77 | 193.1 | Tin | Sn | 50 | 118.70 |
| Iron | Fe | 26 | 55.84 | Titanium | Ti | 22 | 47.90 |
| Krypton | Kr | 36 | 83.7 | Tungsten | W | 74 | 183.92 |
| Lanthanum | La | 57 | 138.92 | Uranium | U | 92 | 238.07 |
| Lead | Pb | 82 | 207.21 | Vanadium | V | 23 | 50.95 |
| Lithium | Li | 3 | 6.940 | Xenon | Xe | 54 | 131.3 |
| Lutecium | Lu | 71 | 175.0 | Ytterbium | Yb | 70 | 173.04 |
| Magnesium | Mg | 12 | 24.32 | Yttrium | Y | 39 | 88.92 |
| Manganese | Mn | 25 | 54.93 | Zinc | Zn | 30 | 65.38 |
| Mercury | Hg | 80 | 200.61 | Zirconium | Zr | 40 | 91.22 |

molecules are made up of atoms.  Since masses have weight, their component atoms must have weight.  But an atom is such a tiny object, we have no convenient unit in which to express its weight.  All that is really needed, however, is a standard of comparison and for that standard, oxygen has been chosen and the weight of its atom fixed at sixteen.  Originally, sixteen was selected because the atoms of the lightest element, hydrogen, are about one-sixteenth as heavy as oxygen atoms. The lightest element would thus have an *atomic weight* of at least one if oxygen is assigned the value sixteen.  A further justification for the standard—oxygen equal to sixteen—will be presented under the topic, Properties of Atoms (page 86).

The statement that the atomic weight of copper is 63.57 merely asserts that an atom of copper is nearly four times as heavy as an atom of oxygen.  Mercury, with an atomic weight of about 200 is two-hundred sixteenths as heavy as oxygen, atom for atom.  An international committee has agreed upon a system of atomic weights and the "International Atomic Weight" tables are now used the world around (Table 1).

## MOLECULAR WEIGHTS

We are on familiar ground when we read that "a formula expresses the composition of a molecule."  The formula $NaCl$ represents a molecule made up of one atom of sodium and one of chlorine and hence of one *atomic weight* of sodium (22.997) and one *atomic weight* of chlorine (35.457).  It is evident that the weight of the molecule, the *molecular weight*, is the sum of the atomic weights (58.454).  The molecular weight of iron oxide—$Fe_2O_3$—is the sum of two atomic weights of iron and three atomic weights of oxygen or 159.68 $(2 \times 55.84 + 3 \times 16)$. The molecular weight of oxygen $(O_2)$ is 32; of hydrogen $(H_2)$ 2.0162; of helium (He) 4.003.  The atomic weight and the molecular weight would be identical for monatomic elements.

## PERCENTAGE COMPOSITION

A knowledge of atomic and molecular weights makes it possible to study a simple type of chemical problem: percentage composition. It might be stated: Given, the formula of a compound and the atomic weights; required, the percentage composition. Suppose it is desired to know the percentages of iron and oxygen in pure iron oxide. As described above, the formula indicates that in 159.68 parts by weight of $Fe_2O_3$, there are 111.68 parts by weight of iron and 48 parts by weight of oxygen. The per cent by weight of iron, then, is (111.68 ÷ 159.68) × 100, or 69.9%. Of oxygen, it is (48 ÷ 159.68) × 100, or 30.0%. The rule for computing percentage composition is: Divide the total atomic weights of each element by the molecular weight and express the quotients as per cents.

## BUILDING STONES OF ATOMS

Dalton's fertile imagination conjured up atoms which were hard, indestructible spheres. His theory marked a great advance and opened new fields in chemical theory. The twentieth-century scientist, equipped with research tools of which Dalton never dreamed, has dissected the atom and found it to be a veritable universe in itself. Research in this field is so difficult and is undergoing such rapid development, that we dare not reach dogmatic and final conclusions. At least four kinds of building stones appear to be present in the atom: (1) tiny particles of positive electricity called *protons;* (2) particles of positive electricity called *positive electrons* or *positrons;* (3) particles of negative electricity called *negative electrons* or *negatrons*, and (4) closely bound proton-negatron pairs, called *neutrons*. For the sake of simplicity—and with a certain sacrifice of accuracy—we shall visualize the atom as a complex of neutrons, protons, and negative electrons (sometimes called merely electrons).

The proton is relatively dense, being over eighteen-hundred times as heavy as the negative electron. The mind cannot conceive of the extreme minuteness of such tiny particles of matter. It is computed that a magnification which would enlarge an atom to pinhole size would make a pinhole appear over a mile in diameter. And in such a tiny atom it is estimated that the proton and negative electron are as far apart, *in proportion to their size,* as two toy balloons with one resting in the center of the Yale Bowl and the other on the uppermost row of seats in the stadium.

## ARCHITECTURE OF THE ATOM

Such tiny universes are beyond the range of the most powerful microscopes. Man can only build an atom model in imagination by observing the behavior of atoms under various

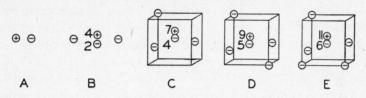

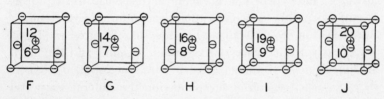

FIG. 36.   Octet Structure of the Atom.   The Lewis-Langmuir octet structure theory is here applied to the ten lightest elements.   They are, in order, hydrogen, helium, lithium, beryllium, boron, carbon, nitrogen, oxygen, fluorine, and neon. The number of protons—positive charges—represents the atomic weight.   The number of planetary electrons increases regularly from one to ten.

conditions.   For a fairly accurate picture of atoms we are indebted to such scientists as Gilbert N. Lewis and Irving Langmuir, who proposed an "octet" structure (Fig. 36) and to Niels Bohr, who favors an orbital structure.

The former theory assumes that all of the protons and some of the electrons are grouped in the center of the atom as a nucleus and the rest of the electrons, like little planets, occupy corners of imaginary, concentric cubes which have the nucleus as their center.   The Bohr theory, which is probably more correct but less easy to visualize, considers that the "planetary" electrons are not at the corners of stationary cubes but are moving in orbits around the nucleus.   An atom of aluminum (atomic weight about 27), according to both theories, contains in its nucleus 27 protons and 14 electrons. Outside of the nucleus, like planets around a central sun, are 13 more electrons. The 14 electrons in the nucleus are paired with 14 of the protons. The remaining 13 protons of the nucleus are called "unbound" or "free" because their electron mates are "out in space" as planetary electrons. This complex structure of the aluminum atom can best be visualized by drawing a sketch based upon the above description.

## PROPERTIES OF ATOMS OF DIFFERENT ELEMENTS

Since all of the heavy protons are in the nucleus of the atom, it can be stated that the *mass of the atom* is determined by the number of protons it contains. This conception justifies the older system of atomic weights. *Each unit of atomic weight is due to a proton.* The aluminum atom with its 27 protons would obviously have an atomic weight of 27. Oxygen, of atomic weight 16, contains 16 protons in the nucleus. Hence the originators of our system of atomic weights "hit the mark, though shooting in the dark."

The nuclear structure accounts for the differences in the masses of atoms of different elements. But how account for the variations in all of the other properties of different elements? The answer is comprehended in this all-inclusive statement: "All of the properties of elements, except mass, are due to the *number* and *arrangement* of their planetary electrons." It seems incomprehensible that copper, zinc, gold, sulfur, carbon, hydrogen, and radium atoms differ so greatly merely because of the number and configuration of their planetary electrons, but such is the explanation. No two elements, according to this theory, could contain the same number of atomic planetary electrons.

One very logical question presses for answer here. If each proton contributes one unit of atomic mass and there are no fractional protons, why are not all atomic weights whole numbers? In this brief discussion this question (and many others) cannot be answered satisfactorily. There are two causes for this apparent discrepancy—"the packing effect" and "isotopes." Comprehensive texts in chemistry explain those terms in more detail.

## THE REASON FOR FORMULA SUBSCRIPTS

The formula for salt is $NaCl$; "chloride of lime," $CaCl_2$; "chloride of iron," $FeCl_3$; and for iron oxide, $Fe_2O_3$. Why do atoms unite in varying ratios, as indicated by the subscripts? In order to answer this question, our solar system may be used as an analogy. The sun is the center of our solar system— the "nucleus." At some distance from the sun, the planet Mercury revolves around it in a definite orbit. At a greater distance Venus is revolving about the sun and its orbit must be larger than that of Mercury. Our earth is at a still greater distance from the sun, with a correspondingly larger orbit.

In the cases of atoms of different elements, the nuclei are their "suns." But the maximum number of electrons (planets) which can revolve about the nucleus *in any given-sized orbit is not one*, as in the case of our solar system. Actually two electrons can move in the smallest-sized orbits, eight in the next larger orbits, eight in still larger orbits, and so on. The three sets of orbits here described are designated as the K, L, and M "energy levels" or "shells." No two elements contain the same number of planetary electrons, hence most elements do not have the proper number of planetary electrons to form complete "shells," namely two, or two plus eight, or two plus eight plus eight. And here we meet an interesting fact. The most stable, inactive elements are those with atoms whose energy levels are completely "filled" with electrons. Such atoms contain two planetary electrons or ten $(2 + 8)$ or eighteen $(2 + 8 + 8)$ and the like. Atoms of other elements, when they take part in a chemical reaction, tend to attain this same atomic-energy balance or symmetry. To accomplish it they may lose excess electrons to other elements; they may receive electrons to supply their deficiency; or they may share electrons with other atoms which would likewise profit by the deal.

A complete survey of these possibilities is too technical to present here. Two illustrations must suffice. The sodium atom contains eleven planetary electrons. This means that its K shell is complete with two electrons; its L shell is complete with eight electrons; and just one lone electron is occupying the M shell. Evidently sodium would readily lose this electron. A fluorine atom carries nine planetary electrons—two in the K shell and seven in the L shell. Its outer shell is, therefore, short one electron. Now suppose sodium and fluorine atoms are allowed to form the compound sodium fluoride. We can imagine that a sodium atom would readily lose its one electron of the M shell to a fluorine atom and that a fluorine atom would as readily receive that electron to complete its M shell. So the deal is made; they unite; and the compound NaF, sodium fluoride, is formed. One atom of each element is required to form the compound because they need to transfer only one electron.

Consider, next, the case of magnesium and fluorine. Magnesium contains twelve planetary electrons—two in the K, eight in the L, and two in the M shells. It is evident that magnesium, in order to attain to symmetrical structure, must either receive six electrons to fill its M shell or lose the two which it has. The latter course is the simpler. Since fluorine needs only one electron for its L shell, as described above, it will require two fluorine atoms to accept the two electrons from the magnesium atom. Two atoms of fluorine must therefore unite with one atom of magnesium to give a compound whose formula is $MgF_2$, magnesium fluoride.

## VALENCE

The number of electrons which an atom loses or receives is called its *valence*. In the cases above, sodium and fluorine have a valence of one, and magnesium of two.

Loss of electrons leaves an atom with an excess of protons or positive charges. Hence it is said to have a *positive valence*. Likewise, a gain of electrons by a neutral atom will produce a negative charge on it. It then has a *negative valence*. Applying this reasoning to sodium fluoride and magnesium fluoride, sodium has a positive valence of one, magnesium a positive valence of two, and fluorine a negative valence of one.

## ATOMIC KNOWLEDGE AT WORK

A knowledge of molecular and atomic structure has made it possible for science to provide us with a multitude of comforts and conveniences. The natural anesthetic, cocaine, contains in its molecule a group of atoms which are toxic. A reconstructed cocaine, with this grouping removed, has been prepared. It produces insensibility to pain without the toxic effect. Of still more interest, it is possible to build (synthesize) products in the laboratory which are similar to but more efficient than cocaine. These laboratory products are called novocaine, eucaine, and so forth.

Dyes were at one time obtained only from animal and vegetable sources. They were very expensive and unsatisfactory. Then the chemist took dye molecules apart, as it were, and learned how to construct them. Dyes are now synthesized chemically, and they are cheap and efficient. The proton-electron structure of the atom finds application in $X$ rays, in the radio, and in other fields.

It would be difficult to point to any modern convenience or to any useful product of modern science which could have been perfected without knowledge of the complex architecture of Nature's atoms and molecules.

# CHAPTER 8

# SOME SIMPLE HEAT
# PHENOMENA

The mention of heat suggests at once a little instrument found in almost every household. Its purpose may be to record the temperature out of doors, indoors, or in the mouth of a member of the family who is ill. It may serve as a guide in making jelly or fudge. It may show whether the proper degree of "coldness" is being maintained in the refrigerator. In any case the instrument is likely to consist of a short glass tube of small bore with a bulb at one end containing mercury or colored alcohol.

## GALILEO'S THERMOMETER

The thermometer has not always had its present form. The first instrument for comparing temperatures was made by Galileo in 1593. This device consisted of a glass bulb an inch or two in diameter, with a long tube as a stem. To prepare the thermometer for use, the bulb was slightly heated and the end of the tube immersed in water in a small bottle. When the bulb cooled, the water rose to a small height in the stem. Galileo's thermometer indicated higher temperatures by a falling of the water in the tube, and lower ones by a rise. It had the serious disadvantage of responding to changes in atmospheric pressure, as well as to changes in temperature.

Notwithstanding this defect it was very useful, especially to physicians. By putting the bulb first in his own armpit and then in that of his patient the physician could determine whether the former had "a temperature," and roughly how much. No temperature scale had then been adopted.

## IMPROVEMENTS

The first improvement in the thermometer was made by a French physician, Jean Rey. In 1639 Rey reported that he filled the bulb and part of the stem with water and pointed the stem upward. Changes of water level in the stem indicated any changes in temperature. Water expands and contracts much less than air with change of temperature. Rey's thermometer was therefore far less sensitive than Galileo's. It had the great advantage, however, of eliminating the effect of atmospheric pressure, though it introduced another error—that of evaporation of water from the stem. This defect was corrected a quarter of a century later by sealing the upper end of the tube. A further improvement was made by using alcohol or mercury, not water, as the thermometric substance.

## THERMOMETRIC SCALES

Various temperatures have been taken as fixed points for the establishment of thermometric scales. As first used by Fahrenheit in 1724 the lowest temperature obtainable with a mixture of ice, water, and sea salt was taken as zero, and that of the mouth or armpit of a healthy person as 96°. Basing his temperature scale upon these fixed points Fahrenheit found the boiling point of water at normal atmospheric pressure to be 212°, and the melting point of ice 32°. These two values proved to be most suitable as fixed points on a thermometric scale. Their adoption gave us our present Fahrenheit thermometer.

Celsius in 1742 used a scale on which the boiling point of water was marked 0° and the freezing point 100°. In 1750 Stromer interchanged the 0° and 100° of Celsius, giving us the centigrade (sometimes called Celsius) scale. This scale is used throughout the world in scientific work, and in continental Europe for all purposes.

In America, where both the Fahrenheit and centigrade scales are used, it is often necessary to find what reading on one scale corresponds to a given reading on the other. The method will be easily understood from Fig. 37. There are 180 Fahrenheit divisions between the freezing and boiling points of water, and only 100 centigrade divisions in the same range. Hence

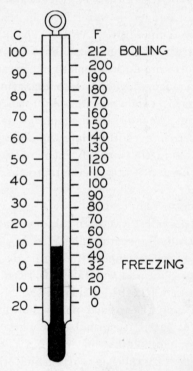

FIG. 37.   Mercurial thermometer, C. and F.

180 Fahrenheit divisions are equivalent to 100 centigrade divisions. One Fahrenheit division equals $\frac{1}{180}$ of 100, or $\frac{5}{9}$ centigrade division. One C. division equals $\frac{1}{100}$ of 180, or $\frac{9}{5}$ F. divisions. To find what reading on the centigrade scale is equivalent to a given reading on the F. scale, the number of F. degrees between the given temperature and the freezing point is multiplied by $\frac{5}{9}$. To find the Fahrenheit temperature

that corresponds to a given centigrade temperature, the latter with its algebraic sign retained is multiplied by $\frac{9}{5}$, and the product is added algebraically to 32°.   These processes may be expressed by means of formulae as follows:

$$C = \frac{5}{9}(F - 32).$$
$$F = \frac{9}{5}C + 32.$$

## EXTREMES OF TEMPERATURE

The zero of temperature adopted by Fahrenheit as one of the fixed points on his scale was not the lowest then known. About 1702 Amontons devised an air thermometer by means of which temperatures were measured by the pressure of a fixed quantity of air.   The pressure rose or fell approximately in proportion to the changes in temperature at all points on the scale.   Amontons inferred that the temperature might be reduced to such an extent that the air in his thermometer would exert no pressure.   This would represent the limit of coldness— the absolute zero of temperature discussed in Chap. 9.   Later observations of a similar kind have shown that this condition is reached at about 273 centigrade degrees below the freezing point of water.   The temperature on the absolute scale may therefore be found by adding 273° to the centigrade reading.

The absolute scale has the advantage that its zero marks an actual physical zero, the temperature at which objects are entirely devoid of heat.

While it is not possible to conceive of a temperature lower than the absolute zero, there is no such limitation at the other extreme.   We think of boiling water as hot, and so it is—100° C. Molten tin is hotter (melting point 232° C.).   Molten iron is hotter still—1530° C. or more.   Tungsten, the most refractory of all metals, melts at 3400° C.   It can barely be melted in the 3500° C. temperature of the oxy-acetylene flame or the electric arc furnace.   Even this last temperature is cold compared with those existing in the sun and many other stars.   Astronomers have reported surface temperatures which range from about 2000° C. in the dull red stars to about 20,000° C. in the bright blue ones.  The sun has a moderate surface temperature of about 6000° C.  The interiors of stars are a great deal hotter than their surfaces, in many instances probably reaching millions of degrees.

## THE DIAL THERMOMETER

The thermometers above described depend for their operation upon the fact that the liquids used expand more than glass

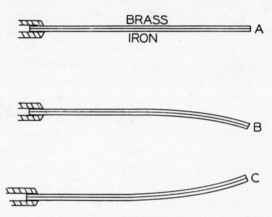

FIG. 38.   Unequal expansion of metals.

when heated, and contract more when cooled.   Thermometers may also be constructed entirely of solid materials.   If strips of

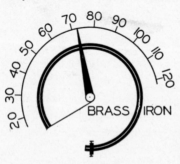

FIG. 39.   Dial thermometer.

two different metals such as brass and iron are soldered or riveted together as shown in Fig. 38, they will bend when heated or cooled, because the expansion or contraction of brass is much greater than that of iron.   The effects of heating and cooling are represented in Fig. 38, B and C respectively.   The slight movement of the free end of the bar may be multiplied to any extent by means of a cord which is given a turn about a little hub to which a pointer is attached, or by a system of tiny levers and gears. The cords or levers move the pointer over a scale graduated in degrees. This is the principle of the dial thermometer, Fig. 39. The sensitivity of this type of instrument may be greatly increased by the use of a long compound bar formed in the shape of a spiral.

## COEFFICIENTS OF EXPANSION

The expansion of various materials when heated differs widely. Steel expands about 50 per cent more than ordinary glass, aluminum about twice as much as steel, and ebonite almost four times as much as aluminum. The expansibility of a substance is expressed as a coefficient of linear expansion for solids, and as a coefficient of cubical expansion for liquids. The former is the elongation per unit of length and the latter is the expansion per unit of volume when the temperature rises 1 C. degree. Thus 1 cm. of steel at $0°$ C. increases to about 1.000012 cm. when its temperature rises to $1°$ C. Its coefficient of linear expansion is about .000012. One cc. of mercury at $0°$ C. increases to about 1.00018 cc. when its temperature rises to $1°$ C. Its coefficient of cubical expansion is about .00018.

## EXPANSION OF WATER

Most substances expand continuously with rise of temperature, though not usually at a uniform rate. There is one

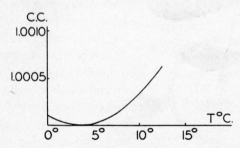

FIG. 40.   Volume of 1 gm. of water at different temperatures.

interesting exception to this rule. Water at $4°$ C. expands when heated. It expands also when cooled. It has its maximum density at $4°$ C. The volume of 1 gm. of water at temperatures between 0° and 15° C. is represented by the graph in Fig. 40. This exceptional behavior of water has important effects in nature, chief of which is the fact that in winter ice forms at the surface of lakes and rivers. In deep lakes the water often remains at 4° C. at the greater depths during even the coldest

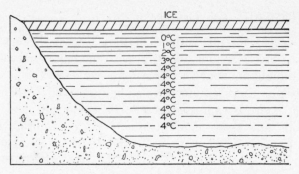

FIG. 41.   Temperature of water in a pond in winter.

winter. The temperature is 0° C. immediately below the ice. This condition is represented in Fig. 41.

## EXPANSION OF ROADS AND BRIDGES

Concrete and steel expand almost equally when heated. (Coefficient about .000012). In middle latitudes a thirty-foot length of railroad steel or of concrete highway is nearly half an inch longer during the hottest day of summer than during the coldest night of winter. Allowance is made at the time of construction for this change in length by leaving a little space between rails, and by inserting tarry separators between slabs of concrete. In long suspension bridges such as the George Washington bridge across the Hudson at New York or the great Golden Gate bridge at San Francisco, the variation in length amounts to several feet.

## A CONSTANT TEMPERATURE FOR ROOMS AND REFRIGERATORS

The fact that different metals expand unequally when heated makes possible a fairly close regulation of any temperature which is maintained by artificial heating or cooling. This is accomplished by means of a *thermostat*. The principle of one such instrument is represented in Fig. 42. Here $M$ represents an electric motor which supplies fuel to a furnace. When the temperature of the room in which the thermostat is located is too low, the brass-iron bar makes contact with the point $P$, and the

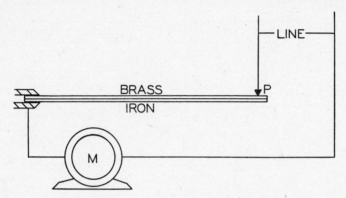

FIG. 42.   Principle of the thermostat.

motor runs. When the temperature has risen sufficiently, the bar breaks contact at $P$, and the motor stops. When later it has fallen a little, the bar makes contact again, and the motor starts.

A low temperature is maintained in mechanical refrigerators by the alternate liquefaction and vaporization of some such gas as ammonia or sulfur dioxide. The liquefaction is accomplished by cooling and compression as described in Chap. 9. The pressure pump is usually operated by an electric motor. To adapt the thermostat to maintain the desired low temperature it is only necessary to place the contact point below the compound bar instead of above it. When the temperature rises to a certain point, the bar makes contact with $P$. This completes the electric circuit and starts the motor and compression pump. The temperature inside then drops to the desired point, the bar bends away from $P$, and the motor stops.

Such thermostats allow a fluctuation in temperature amounting to two or three degrees. Greater constancy may be secured with more refined devices.

Thermostats operating by the unequal expansion of different substances are used to regulate the temperature of ovens and of the cooling fluid of automobile radiators; to control the evaporation in some types of humidifiers, and for many other purposes.

## A CONSTANT RATE FOR WATCHES

The frequency of oscillation of the balance wheel determines the rate of the watch.   If this wheel expands with rise of tem-

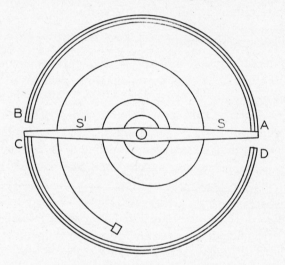

FIG. 43.   Balance wheel of a watch.

perature, its frequency is reduced and the watch loses time.   In order to compensate for changes in temperature, balance wheels are made as represented in Fig. 43.   The rim of the wheel is a bimetallic strip made in two or more parts, as $AB$ and $CD$.   The metal having the greater expansion is on the outside, so that when the temperature rises the free ends $B$ and $D$ will be brought somewhat closer to the center of the wheel.   This compensates for the increase in the distance of the ends $A$ and $C$ from the center, which results from the expansion of the spokes, $S$, $S'$.   Thus the rate of oscillation remains the same regardless of changes of temperature.

## HEAT AND TEMPERATURE

If a small pan of water and a large bucketful are heated over exactly similar burners, the panful will begin to boil long before the bucketful. The latter has required more heat. If the two quantities of boiling water are now used to warm two equal quantities of cold water, the bucketful will be far the more effective. The temperatures of the boiling water are the same in both cases, but the amount of heat the bucketful contains is much the greater. The amount of heat a body contains is something quite different from its temperature.

## MEASURING STICKS FOR HEAT

Amounts of heat, like other physical quantities, are measured in definite units. Those most commonly employed are the following:

1. The *calorie*. This is the amount of heat required to raise 1 gram of water 1 centigrade degree. It is the unit in which heat is measured in scientific work throughout the world and in engineering and commerce everywhere except in English-speaking countries.

2. The *great calorie* or *kilogram calorie*. As the latter name signifies, this unit is equal to 1000 calories. It is used by dieticians in stating the energy values of foods.

3. The *British thermal unit* (B.t.u.). This is the amount of heat required to raise 1 lb. of water 1 Fahrenheit degree. It is the unit employed in engineering and commercial work in the United States and the British empire. 1 B.t.u. = 252 calories.

## HEAT VALUES OF FUELS

When buying sugar or potatoes by the bag, the purchaser wishes to know the number of pounds a bag contains. When buying fuel, he should be no less interested in the number of calories or B.t.u.'s each pound or gallon will liberate. Different grades of coal differ widely in their heating values; different grades of fuel oil vary much less in this respect. The following table (Table 2) illustrates this difference, and shows the heat content of some of the more common gaseous fuels.

TABLE 2

FUELS

*Coal*

| | |
|---|---|
| Anthracite..................... | 10,500 to 11,600 B.t.u. per lb. |
| Semianthracite................ | 11,000 " " " |
| Bituminous.................... | 10,000 to 14,500 " " " |
| Subbituminous................ | 9,000 to 10,000 " " " |
| Lignite....................... | 6,000 " " " |

*Oils*

| | |
|---|---|
| Gasoline...................... | 20,000 B.t.u. per lb. |
| Kerosene..................... | 20,000 " " " |
| Benzene...................... | 18,000 " " " |
| Petroleum.................... | 20,000 " " " |

*Gases*

| | |
|---|---|
| Blue water gas................ | 285 B.t.u. per cu. ft. |
| Coal gas..................... | 560 " " " " |
| Coke oven gas................ | 475 to 540 " " " " |
| Natural gas.................. | 950 to 2250 " " " " |

## SPECIFIC HEATS

In defining the heat units water is chosen as the standard "receptacle" for the heat. At temperatures around 20° C. it requires only about one-fifth of a calorie to raise 1 gm. of aluminum 1° C., one-ninth of a calorie for iron, and about one-thirtieth of a calorie for lead or mercury. Few other substances have as great a capacity for heat as water. Numerically the amount of heat required to raise the temperature of 1 gm. of a substance 1° C. is its *specific heat*.

Because of the high heat capacity of water, the ocean and even large lakes have a marked effect in moderating the climate of regions adjacent to them. By absorbing and storing up heat during the hot seasons and returning it to the air during the cold ones, they tend to prevent the extreme and sudden changes of temperature so often observed in regions far removed from such a stabilizing agency.

## HEAT REQUIRED TO MELT A SOLID SUBSTANCE

When the weather turns warm after a long period of cold and heavy snow, it may require many days of sunshine before all the deep drifts disappear. Even after the snow has been warmed

to the melting point a great deal of heat must still be supplied
to convert it into water—about 80 calories for each gram.    All
this is added without causing any change in the temperature of
the snow.    When ice melts from streams and lakes, the same
amount of heat—80 calories per gram—is also required to
change the ice, already at the melting point, into water at the
same temperature.    The amount of heat required to change one
unit of mass of a substance from the solid into the liquid condition is called the *heat of fusion* of the substance.    Thus the heat
of fusion of ice is 80 calories per gram.

Just as water is formed from ice by the addition of heat without change of temperature, so ice is formed from water by the
withdrawal of heat, also without change of temperature.    Both
processes take place at the same temperature—0° C.    Which
process will occur is determined entirely by the surroundings.
A well-stirred mixture of ice and water is always at 0° C.    If
the mixture is in a region whose temperature is above 0°, heat
is absorbed by the mixture and there is melting.    In a region
whose temperature is below 0° C., heat of the mixture is lost to
the surroundings, and there is freezing.

As compared with that of ice, the heats of fusion of most
solids are quite low.    That of tin, for example, is 14 calories
per gram.    Those of lead and grey cast iron are about 5.8 and 5.5
calories per gram respectively while that of mercury is less than
3.    In solidifying, each of these metals liberates the same
amount of heat it absorbs in melting.

The high heat of fusion of ice is another important reason
why autumn weather does not change suddenly into winter nor
winter into spring in the neighborhood of large bodies of water.

## HEAT REQUIRED TO VAPORIZE A BOILING LIQUID

Just as heat is required to change a substance from the solid
into the liquid state, so also heat is required to change it from
liquid into gas or vapor.    The amount of heat needed to bring
about the latter change is in some instances surprisingly great.
Here again water is a notable example.    A pan of water over a
large gas burner may be brought to boiling quickly.    A much

Ice        80 cal/gr
Iron .      23-33   "
Lead       5.86    "
Mercury    2.82   "
Sulphur    9.37   "
Zinc       28.1   "

longer time is required to boil it all away. When water has reached the boiling point, an additional 540 calories must be supplied to each gram to convert it into steam without causing any further rise in the temperature. It requires about 204 calories to vaporize 1 gm. of alcohol at the boiling point, and only about 65 calories for 1 gm. of mercury.

The amount of heat required to vaporize a unit mass of a liquid without changing its temperature is called the *heat of vaporization* of the substance. Thus the heat of vaporization of water at its normal boiling point is 540 calories per gram. That of mercury is 65 calories per gram.

Bathers may feel distinctly cool when coming out of the water. This is due to rapid evaporation of water from the skin, the heat for which is supplied largely by the body. Evaporation of perspiration during vigorous exercise enables the body to maintain its normal temperature. Evaporation from the leaves in an extensive grove in summer may be sufficient to reduce the temperature noticeably below that in an unwooded region. Gangs of workmen often keep food or water in a tight box or can covered with wet burlap. The arrangement is a simple but fairly effective "refrigerator," kept cool by evaporation.

When a vapor condenses, it gives off the same amount of heat as the liquid absorbed when it vaporized. The effect is sometimes observed in summer when a shower is followed by a rise of temperature. The heat of vaporization was released in the condensation of the moisture, and warmed the air. The same effect is often noticed accompanying or following a gentle snow storm. In this case the vapor is converted directly into a solid, in which process both the heat of vaporization and the heat of fusion are released.

## HEAT CAN BE TRANSMITTED

In order to be useful, heat must be carried from the device in which it is generated to the place where it is to be used. If the heat in the firebox of a steam boiler could not reach the water in the boiler, it would produce no steam. The earth would now be a cold, dead mass if the heat from the sun could not reach it.

## HOW HEAT IS TRANSMITTED

A spoon dipped in hot soup or coffee soon becomes warmed throughout.  Heat has been carried by the metal from the parts that touch the liquid to the parts that do not.  The outside of the fire box of a furnace becomes hot from the fire inside.

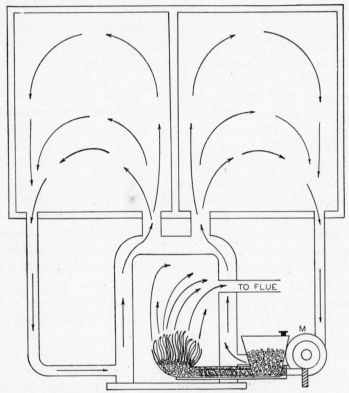

TO FLUE

M

FIG. 44.   A warm-air heating plant.

Heat is carried by the metal from the inside surface to the outside.  In each of these cases the molecules of metal next to the source of heat are set in more lively motion.  They then plunge more swiftly against the molecules adjacent to them, giving them an increased speed.  These in turn collide more vigorously with those next farther from the source.  Thus the entire spoon or fire box wall is soon heated. This method of heat transfer is called *conduction*.

Silver and copper are the best of all heat conductors. Aluminum is also an excellent conductor—much better than iron. For that reason the bottom of an aluminum pan is more uniformly heated by a burner than that of an iron pan.

An entire room may be heated by a single radiator, or a house by a single furnace. Air is warmed by the radiator and driven upward by heavier cooler air. This causes a circulation which carries heat to all parts of the room. Air or water heated by the furnace is driven upward by the cooler and heavier fluid and carried by pipes to the various parts of the house as shown in Fig. 44. Thus the entire house is heated. This process in which heat is carried by a movement of the heated fluid is called *convection*.

A third method of heat transfer is called *radiation*. It is by this method that the heat of a bonfire reaches the people standing near by, and that the earth receives its heat from the sun. Radiant heat is transmitted with the speed of light (about 186,000 miles per second). The energy is carried by electromagnetic waves. These speed up the molecules of any objects upon which they fall and by which they are absorbed, that is, they heat the object. This is true of light as well as of the longer waves by which the greater part of the energy received from the sun is carried.

## LIMITING THE FLOW OF HEAT

A ready flow of heat is not always desirable. In handling a heated object such as a flatiron, a soldering iron, or a baking dish, precautions are taken to limit the amount of heat reaching the hand. The flatiron and soldering iron are provided with wooden handles. The baking dish is held by a cloth or pad.

Wood and cloth are poor conductors of heat. There are many others, notable among which are asbestos, blotting paper, cork, cotton, wool, hair, felt, leather, rubber, sawdust, silk, almost all liquids, and all gases.

## INSULATING THE REFRIGERATOR

In a refrigerator it is important to reduce as far as possible the amount of heat flowing in from the outside. This is accomplished by making the walls of very poor conductors. Porous

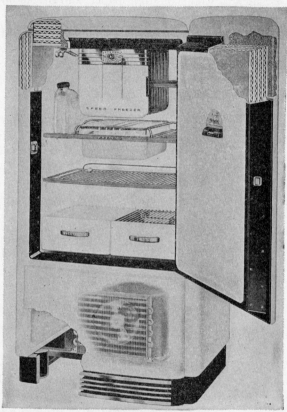

*Edison General Electric Appliance Company, Inc.*

FIG. 45. Heat Insulation of a Refrigerator. Insulation is contrived: (1) by building fibrous material of low conductivity into the walls; (2) by corrugation of this material to enclose air in small compartments; (3) by placing air channels in horizontal position to reduce convection.

or corrugated mineral or fibrous materials are especially good for filling the space between inner and outer walls, because they enclose a great deal of air and by their form prevent any but the minutest of convection currents.

## INSULATING THE DWELLING

For year-round comfort it is important to prevent all unnecessary loss of heat through walls and windows in winter, and entrance of heat through the same channels in summer.   Nonconductors, such as wood, building paper, and bricks have long been used in dwelling-house construction.  Of more recent development is the practice of filling the air spaces with loose nonconducting materials such as rock wool to prevent the transfer of heat across these spaces by convection currents.

Storm windows greatly reduce the loss of heat by providing a nonconducting air space between the panes.

It is estimated that about $100,000,000 worth of fuel could be saved in the United States each year by adequate heat insulation of all dwelling houses.

## CLOTHING

The body, like other self-operating machines, is heated by its own internal "fires."   One of the functions of clothing is to conserve this heat.   Complete heat insulation is neither possible nor desirable.   Enough heat should be permitted to escape to enable the body easily to maintain its normal temperature. When oxidation is rapid, as during vigorous exercise, the amount of heat dissipated must be greater than during repose.   Because of the large amount of air they contain, furs and loosely woven garments are warmer than firmer and harder ones.  For the same reason two light garments are likely to be warmer than a single heavy one.   In general, wool is warmer than cotton and cotton warmer than linen.

## COLD

A good deal has been said here concerning heat, but very little concerning cold.  The reason is that "cold" is negative. It implies the comparative absence of heat.  We say that cold in winter comes in through a window.  What really happens is that heat readily passes out that way.

# CHAPTER 9

# STATES OF EXISTENCE

## STATES OF MATTER

It is a cold winter morning. A half pan of water was thoughtlessly left out of doors the evening before. The water is now solid ice and partly fills the pan. When the pan is placed on a hot stove, the ice changes to a liquid which still fills the lower half of the pan. While the cook's attention is absorbed, perhaps by a radio program, the water boils merrily and she returns to the kitchen to find an empty pan. The water has been changed to a gas, which now fills every part of the room.

The water has passed through the *three states of matter*—solid, liquid, and gas. In the first state it *retains* the shape of the pan and occupies only the space needed for its bulk. In the second state it takes the shape of the container and occupies a small space. In the third state it fills all space available and takes the shape of that space. Such considerations characterize the three states of matter.

## MOLECULES IN MOTION

We should like to understand as students of science just what has happened to the water. The atomic theory provides the answer. In the *solid* state—ice—the molecules are resting close together, perhaps touching each other. Furthermore, much of the heat which they possessed at higher temperatures has been withdrawn into the cold winter air and their motion is inhibited. Thus, crowded close together and apparently motionless, the molecules of water form a hard, rigid mass of small volume.

107

The molecules upon being heated begin to receive that which they lost to the cold air—energy. Energy produces motion. The molecules show increased mobility; they pull away from their fellows; they roll and "flow" over each other easily. Yet they are still packed closely together. In this state, with its

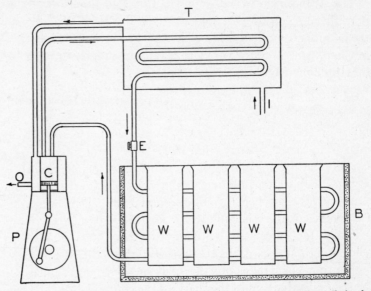

Fig. 46. Ice Manufacturing Plant. Gaseous ammonia from the coils in the refrigerating tank B is highly compressed in the cylinder C by means of the pump P. The gas, heated by compression, is cooled in tank T by means of circulating water and liquefies. The liquid ammonia sprays through the expansion valve E, to enter the pipes which are immersed in the brine tank B. These pipes are at low pressure; hence the liquid ammonia vaporizes and cools the pipes and the brine in which they are immersed. Water, placed in portable tanks W, is frozen to give "artificial" ice. The vaporized ammonia is again compressed and liquefied to repeat the cycle endlessly. The water from tank T circulates through the water jacket of the compresser, then passes to the drain at O.

molecules mobile, the water takes the shape of the container but it occupies only a small space.

While the water is boiling, it is receiving large quantities of heat. The molecules absorb it and become tremendously energetic. They kick loose from the attractions of their neighbors and go sailing off into the air. They fly to the farthest corners of the room and dash madly about like a great swarm of gnats. This conception of flying gas molecules, as given in detail in an earlier chapter, explains why a gas completely fills its container, regardless of size and shape.

## THE BATTLE FOR HEAT

The phenomena of molecular motion find practical application in the mechanical refrigerator, the liquid-air machine, and the manufactured-ice plant. The first two devices are described in Chap. 10. Manufactured ice is rapidly superseding the natural product from rivers and lakes because of its sanitary qualities

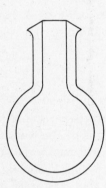

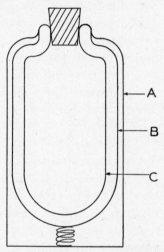

Fig. 47.  Dewar flask.

Fig. 48.  Vacuum Bottle. Bottles *B* and *C* are sealed together, their surfaces silvered, and the space between them evacuated. For protection they are supported in metal case *A*.

and the convenience of production. The stages in its manufacture are illustrated in Fig. 46.

When Dewar, of England, was working with liquid air, he wished to preserve the liquid and yet have it accessible. He recognized that two principles were involved here. (1) Heat energy must be kept from the liquid air. (2) Heat will not pass through a vacuum. Accordingly he constructed a double-walled bottle, sealed air-tight the space between the two walls, and exhausted the air from this space. Liquid air was then poured into the bottle and a stopper inserted. Very little heat could now penetrate into the bottle and the liquid air vaporized very slowly. To exclude any heat energy which might enter from outside sources, he silvered the walls of the vacuum space to reflect it outward again (Fig. 47).

Seizing upon the idea of the "Dewar flask," manufacturers have perfected the "vacuum bottle" to keep hot things hot and cold things cold, providing a useful accessory to the picnic basket and dinner pail. Like the Dewar flask, it is a double-walled bottle with a vacuum space (Fig. 48).

The most modern application of the gas-to-solid-to-gas cycle is the extensive use of "dry ice." This substance is carbon dioxide which has been frozen by cooling and compression. It is at a temperature of 112 degrees below zero, Fahrenheit. As it abstracts heat from its surroundings, the solid passes directly into the gaseous state.

## THE GAS LAWS

The behavior of gases with changes in pressure and temperature is so consistent that it can be expressed by mathematical laws. The derivation and explanation of these laws are too technical for this discussion. They will merely be stated, for reference purposes. Boyle's law (see Chap. 5) states that "the volume of any sample of a gas, the temperature being steady, varies inversely as the amount of pressure applied." The mathematical expression of this law does not designate pressure in weight per unit area, such as grams per square centimeter. Instead, it applies the manometer principle (see page 55) and measures, in centimeters or millimeters, the height of a column of mercury, under a vacuum, which the gas can support. For example, at sea level our atmosphere presses with sufficient force to support a column of mercury 76 centimeters high. Hence 76 centimeters represent the pressure of "one atmosphere." It is called "standard" or "normal" pressure.

According to Charles' law, "the volume of any sample of gas, the pressure being kept constant, varies directly with the *absolute* temperature applied." "Absolute zero" is 273 degrees below centigrade zero. Hence zero on the centigrade scale is 273 on the absolute scale; twenty above zero C. is 293 absolute; and thirty below zero C. is 243 absolute. "Standard" or "normal" temperature is zero C. or 273 A.

## DALTON'S LAW OF PARTIAL PRESSURES

Gases exert certain pressures when they are in the pure form, depending upon how closely the molecules are crowded into a given space. How are the pressures affected if two or more different gases are crowded into the same space? If the gases tend to react chemically, the results are complicated. But gases that are indifferent to each other follow a very simple law. Imagine two strong steel cans of identical size. Into one oxygen is forced under a pressure of 200 centimeters. The other is charged with nitrogen under 600 centimeters' pressure. Now assume that the nitrogen is forced into the oxygen can. The total pressure in this can will now register 800 centimeters. The original pressure of each gas is unaffected by the pressure of the other gas. The part of the total pressure which each gas exerts is called its "partial pressure." *In a mixture of gases*, then, *each gas exerts the same pressure which it would exert if the other gases were removed;* and the sum of the partial pressures of the gases is the total pressure of the mixture.

## RESTLESS MOLECULES

Perfumes give off a gas of pleasant odor. If a few drops of perfume are spilled in one corner of a room, its fragrance is observed in all parts of the room. This effect, as explained on page 71, is caused by molecular motion. It is true of all gases that their molecules are in ceaseless, perpetual motion. They move in straight lines, collide, rebound, and never lose their energy. Unlike larger masses, they exhibit perpetual motion. This concept is referred to as the *Kinetic Theory* of gases. From their constant motion, the molecules are continually bumping against the walls of their container and producing pressure. In fact, all gas pressures, such as the pressure of the atmosphere or of air inside a rubber tire, are due to the incredibly rapid bombardment of the moving molecules of the gas. This motion of gases from place to place, as a result of their molecular energy, is called a *diffusion* process. The rate of such motion can be measured by allowing the gas to diffuse through a small opening. Expressed as a law, *the rates of diffusion of different gases are inversely proportional to the square roots of their densities.*

Molecular motion is not limited to the gaseous state. A layer of alcohol carefully poured upon water, will eventually mix uniformly with the water. Diffusion of liquids is much slower than that of gases because the molecules are packed so much closer.

## ADSORPTION

An interesting application of molecular motion is encountered in certain devices used for igniting kitchen gas stoves and for lighting cigars. To understand their operation, consider a piece of porous rock having a pore space of one cubic inch. When exposed to the air, it can take up one cubic inch of that gas. The molecules of the gas scatter through the pore space, maintaining their usual inter-molecular distances. We call the process *absorption*. An entirely different result is observed when a jet of cold illuminating gas or hydrogen gas is directed against a mass of spongy platinum. The temperature of the metal rapidly rises to red heat, and it ignites the gas. Our knowledge of gases offers an explanation. The internal surface of the platinum, due to its numerous pores, is very extensive. As the gas enters these pores, the platinum has a peculiar effect upon its molecules. Instead of scattering through the spaces as air would through a rubber sponge, the molecules of gas settle upon the pore walls, one molecule deep and "shoulder to shoulder." In this way a very large volume of gas *condenses* into a very small space. Now, when a gas is condensed or compressed, it gives out heat as we have seen. Hence the temperature of the metal is raised. This effect of spongy platinum upon certain gases is called *adsorption*. It is a surface effect whereas *absorption* is a space effect. A number of substances with large surfaces exhibit adsorptive action toward certain gases.

## AVOGADRO'S OBSERVATION

The phenomena of adsorption and of gas pressures indicate that the molecules of a gas are countless in number. Actually the finite mind cannot comprehend the figures in which we must express the number of molecules in just one cubic centimeter of a gas. It is over a billion billion. To count them one by one is an impossibility. Several different methods are available for estimating their number and these diverse methods give such concordant results that we feel assured of their reliability.

Long before we were able to estimate the actual number of molecules in a gas, an Italian physicist, Amadeo Avogadro, announced a far-reaching discovery. Although molecules of different gases vary widely in density, size, and velocity, he stated that *equal volumes of all gases*, at the same temperature and pressure, *contain the same number of molecules*. Announced a century and a half ago, its validity has withstood every test and its applications are numerous—even to freshman chemistry problems.

## THE DISSOLVED STATE

Breakfast coffee is improved, for some, by dissolving sugar in it. The fizzy drinks of the soda fountain contain dissolved carbon dioxide. Gold jewelry is really a solution of copper in gold. The air we breathe is made up of oxygen dissolved in nitrogen. Strictly speaking, solutions are not one of the conventional states of matter. At any rate, they are first cousins and may properly be considered here. In the simple kinds of solutions to be studied here, one substance is so completely scattered or dispersed throughout another that the resulting mixture appears completely uniform. The entire product is homogeneous. Based upon states of matter, there are nine types of solutions: gases in gases, liquids, or solids; liquids in gases, liquids, or solids; and solids in gases, liquids, or solids.

Of these nine types, solutions of solids in liquids are most commonly encountered. One such case will now be examined in some detail.

Drop a lump of sugar in water and, in imagination, watch the molecules. While resting in the sugar bowl, the molecules stick fast together, for how could molecules of sugar break loose and sail through the air? Technically expressed, the air is not a suitable medium for the dispersion of molecules of solids. Now watch as the lump is dropped into water. We are reminded of a grade school full of restless boys and girls at afternoon dismissal as they burst from every door and scatter in every direction literally to fill the landscape. So the molecules of sugar tear loose from their fellows and (in accordance with the kinetic theory) scatter throughout the water. Water is a medium in which molecules of sugar can move about freely. We call this product a *solution*. Several characteristics are to be observed. (1) The liquid is perfectly *clear*. If copper sulfate is dissolved, the solution will be blue in color, but it will be clear—not cloudy. (2) After once stirring it thoroughly, it will be entirely homogeneous. Every drop will contain the same amount of sugar. (3) This homogeneous condition is permanent. The sugar will never settle out. (4) The molecules of sugar are no longer joined together. Each is a separate particle, moving about in the water. The dissolved substance —the sugar—is called the *solute* and the dissolving liquid is the *solvent*. If the solvent contains a relatively small amount of solute, it is said to be *dilute;* if a large amount, it is *concentrated*. A solution which contains all of the solute which it can hold under ordinary conditions, be that little or much, is described as *saturated*.

## FACTORS INFLUENCING SOLUTION

For some reason, not entirely clear, solutions are rather "choosy"—they are *selective*. Salt will dissolve in water but not in ether. Fat will dissolve in ether but not in water. Ether and water will dissolve in each other to a limited extent. Saltpeter is very soluble in water. Salt is less so. Gypsum will dissolve but little and iron not at all.

Temperature plays a large part in solubility. At the freezing point, water will dissolve about fifteen grams of niter per hundred cubic centimeters. At 30 degrees it will dissolve 45 grams, and at 60 degrees, 110 grams. If the 60 degree solution is cooled to zero, the extra 95 grams will crystallize out. Salt is only slightly more soluble at the boiling point of water than at the freezing point, and gases become less soluble in water as its temperature is raised (Fig. 49).

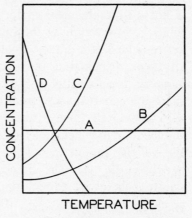

Pressure has a marked effect upon the solubility of gases. Nearly everyone enjoys some form of cold, foamy drink. But why does it foam? If it is a fermented drink, it was tightly stoppered and allowed to ferment. Carbon dioxide formed and produced a pressure inside the bottle that kept the gas dissolved. If it is a carbonated drink, the liquid was poured in, then carbon dioxide was forced in under

Fig. 49. Solubility Curves. Variations in solubility with temperature changes can be shown very compactly by means of curves. Increase in temperature is shown from left to right on the horizontal axis, and increasing concentration or solubility is plotted along the vertical axis. With rise in temperature of the solvent, the solubilities of the solids $A$, $B$, and $C$ become more and more marked. Gases decrease in solubility with rise of temperature as typified at $D$.

pressure and the bottle was immediately sealed. Under these high pressures the gas remains dissolved. Then the cork is pulled and instantly the gas bubbles or effervesces from the liquid. When the bottle is opened, it is under a much lower pressure, and less gas can be held in solution. Water cannot dissolve so much gas under low pressures as under high. The formal law (Henry's) states that *the solubility of a gas in a liquid is proportional to the pressure applied.*

## EFFECTS OF DISSOLVED SUBSTANCES

Solutes, especially dissolved solids, affect the freezing point and the boiling point of their solvent liquids quite noticeably. A cook sometimes puts salt into the water in which a vegetable is to be boiled in order to hasten the cooking process. Dissolved solids raise the boiling point of water and at the higher temperature food cooks more rapidly. Why do we use salt with the ice in preparing ice cream? Water freezes, and ice melts, at zero C. (32° F.). But solutions freeze at temperatures below zero. The more concentrated the solution, the lower the freezing point. When salt is added to ice, it dissolves in the surface moisture on the chunks. This gives a solution whose freezing point is *below* zero. The ice, then, which is at zero degrees is *above* the freezing point of the solution which covers it. Hence the ice melts. To melt, it must absorb heat. This heat it takes from the cream—and the cream freezes. For a similar reason, salt thrown upon an icy sidewalk will cause the ice to melt. The tanks of water for making "artificial" ice are immersed in a water solution of calcium chloride whose freezing point has been greatly lowered by the dissolved calcium chloride.

## SEPARATION OF SOLUTES FROM SOLVENTS

Liquids can be separated from their dissolved contents by a variety of methods. A common example is the preparation of pure water. Ordinary well water contains mineral matter dissolved from the rocks in the earth. Since these will not vaporize—are nonvolatile—the water can be boiled and the steam condensed. This is a *distillation* process. On a large scale the water is boiled by means of steam pipes immersed in it. The pure steam from the boiling water passes through long coils of pipe around which cold water flows, in a *water jacket*. The cooling action causes it to condense into drops of distilled water and these are collected. Neither the condensing coils nor the tank may be made of any material which can be dissolved by the distilled water. Coils are often made of pure tin (Fig. 50).

When a mixture of two liquids of different boiling points is distilled, the liquid of lower boiling point tends to come over first. It is not possible, however, to separate the liquids completely by simple distillation. Government "grain" alcohol is purified by a distillation process, giving a product containing about 94 per cent alcohol and six per cent water. It is said to

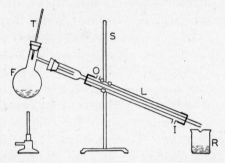

FIG. 50. Laboratory Distillation Outfit. The liquid in the distilling flask $F$ is heated to boiling as registered by the thermometer $T$. The vapor passes into the Liebig condenser $L$ and is condensed on the walls of the tube which are cooled by water entering the water jacket at $I$ and leaving at $O$. The receiver $R$ catches the distillate.

be "188 proof," the proof value being twice the per cent of alcohol. Whisky is 100 proof if it contains 50 per cent alcohol.

## COLLOIDS

Another condition of matter is found in *colloids*. Colloid materials are in a size group just above molecules. They range in size from the largest molecules to the smallest particles just visible under a high-power microscope. Like true solutions, their particles do not settle out, and they are homogeneous. Unlike solutions, they tend to be cloudy and their particles in some cases can be observed in an ultramicroscope. An ultramicroscope is an ordinary compound microscope with a special illuminating device. Colloid particles may be tiny grains, drops, and bubbles. Or they may be filaments suggestive of a single spider-web thread or films similar to a soap-bubble film.

Colloidal materials may be divided into *emulsoids* (lyophilic colloids) and *suspensoids* (lyophobic colloids). The former include such substances as glue, boiled starch, white of egg, gelatine jelly, and fruit jellies. The latter are mostly mineral compounds and elements which have been converted into the colloidal state. The emulsion of a photographic film, synthetic silk, glue, glass, rubber, lubricants, soap, and a host of other materials are colloids. Even the living cells of our bodies are largely colloidal. Colloid chemistry of the brain is being intensively studied at present in the war against certain types of insanity. The colloid field is large and has only been mentioned here.

# CHAPTER 10

# HEAT AS A FORM OF ENERGY

## HEAT IS NOT A SUBSTANCE

The nature of heat was quite unknown a century and a half ago. Many scientists thought of it as a fluid which could pass from one object to another. This imaginary fluid was called *caloric*. All objects were assumed to possess a certain amount of it. If more was added, the temperature rose. If some was lost, the temperature fell. If two blocks of iron at different temperatures are placed in contact with each other, the cool one becomes warmer and the hot one colder. Soon they are both at the same temperature. According to the caloric theory these changes were due to the passage of the fluid from the hot block to the cold one.

One difficulty with this theory was the fact that, though considered as a fluid, caloric must be assumed to have no weight. An object is no heavier when hot than when cold. Another difficulty was the fact that the supply of caloric that could be derived from an object by rubbing or abrading it seemed almost unlimited. Either the object in its normal condition must possess an unbelievably large store of the fluid, or it was created in the rubbing or abrading process.

Count Rumford, in Germany, found that in the boring of cannon the amount of heat developed depended markedly upon the condition of the drill. If it was very dull, the amount seemed to be unlimited, and to depend only on the amount of work done in boring. The advocates of the caloric theory accounted for the heat generated by assuming that the finely

119

divided bronze was less able to contain caloric (had a smaller specific heat) than the original block.  The specific heat of the borings, however, was found to be exactly equal to that of the bronze from which they came.  No caloric should have been liberated.

Sir Humphry Davy, an English scientist, succeeded in melting ice to which no heat was allowed to flow by merely rubbing two pieces of ice together.  The amount melted seemed to depend only on the amount of work done in rubbing. In this case the evidence against the caloric theory is even more convincing.  The specific heat of water is double that of ice. Caloric should have been absorbed.

## HEAT IS ENERGY

Rumford and Davy were agreed that heat is not a fluid, nor anything material, but that it is a form of motion.  We now call it energy.  The work of later investigators has completely confirmed their views.  James Prescott Joule, another Englishman, succeeded in showing not only that heat is generated whenever work is done in overcoming frictional resistances, but also in finding just how much energy must be converted into heat to yield 1 calorie.  According to Joule

$$1 \text{ calorie} = 41,800,000 \text{ ergs.}$$
$$1 \text{ B.t.u.} = 778 \text{ foot-pounds.}$$

Rowland, an American, arrived at almost exactly the same result.  Heat is not a fluid, but a form of energy.

## THE ENERGY OF MOVING MOLECULES

It was mentioned in Chap. 6 that the molecules of all kinds of materials are in constant irregular motion.  This has been shown to account for diffusion in fluids, pressure in gases, and other important natural phenomena.  It is now accepted by scientists everywhere that heat is the energy that molecules possess by virtue of their rapid motion.  Heating an object, then, means imparting higher speeds to its molecules.

## TEMPERATURE

Two objects are at the same temperature if neither of them imparts heat to the other when they are near each other or in contact. This means that the molecules of the one give no energy to those of the other. The average energies of the molecules of the two objects are equal. If the molecules of one of the objects are lighter than those of the other, the lighter molecules will have the greater average speed.

## CONDUCTION OF HEAT

It is now easy to understand the nature of heat conduction. When a spoon is dipped in tea or one end of a poker put into a furnace, the molecules at the inserted end are beaten upon and set into swifter motion by the molecules of the tea or of the fuels and gases in the furnace. The molecules thus speeded plunge with greater vigor against their neighbors, setting them into more rapid motion. These, in turn, impart some of their increased motion to molecules still farther from the source of heat. And so, in conduction, heat is carried along or through the object by this progressive speeding up of molecules.

## FRICTION, CONCUSSION, AND COMPRESSION

A person coming in from the cold out-of-doors will sometimes rub his hands together. He is warming them by friction. A poorly lubricated bearing becomes hot—even smoking hot— by friction. It is friction that makes it possible to light a match, or to make a fire without one. When one surface rubs against another, the molecules of both are set into more rapid motion. Heat is generated.

A piece of metal, if struck a few sharp blows with a hammer while lying on an anvil, will feel warm. So also will the hands after prolonged applause. The hammer blows have speeded the molecules of the metal. The impacts of the hands have speeded those of the skin.

A bicycle or automobile tire pump is warmed with use. Some of the heat is due to the friction between the piston and the barrel. A greater amount results from the repeated compression of the air. This appears chiefly near the bottom of the pump, as indicated in Fig. 51. The device known as a fire syringe consists of a tube about fifteen inches long provided with a closely fitting piston. A piece of tinder placed inside the tube may be ignited by a vigorous movement of the piston.

In the cylinders of a Diesel engine, air drawn in from the outside is quickly subjected to so great a pressure that it is heated to a point above the kindling temperature of the fuel. This is then sprayed in under still higher pressure and burns during the power stroke. No other provision is made for its ignition.

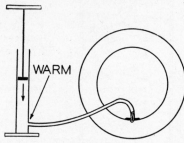

FIG. 51. Heat by compression of a gas.

In all of the cases cited above, mechanical energy has been converted into heat. We are familiar with other transformations. Chemical energy, for example, is converted into heat when fuel burns or when food is oxidized in the body. Electrical energy is transformed into heat in electric lamps, toasters, and flatirons. Radiant energy is converted into heat when sunlight strikes an object by which it is absorbed. Energy of whatever kind can be thus transformed. In all such cases all of the energy involved in the change may be converted into heat.

## EXPANSION OF A GAS

If a gas at any pressure is permitted to expand, its temperature falls. The process is the converse of that taking place in the bicycle pump and fire syringe. The gas in expanding does work upon its surroundings. The energy used is supplied by the gas at the expense of the kinetic energy of its molecules. Heat energy is used, and the temperature falls.

This action occurs on an extensive scale in nature when a mass of air rises, as on the windward side of a mountain. As the wind goes up the mountain slope, the diminishing pressure at increasing altitudes permits an expansion and progressive cooling of the air, often below the saturation point of the water vapor, producing rainfall.

The cooling effect of expansion along with that of evaporation is employed in liquid-air machines, ice machines, refrigerators, and air conditioners. The operation of the ice machine was discussed in Chap. 9. In the liquid-air machine atmospheric

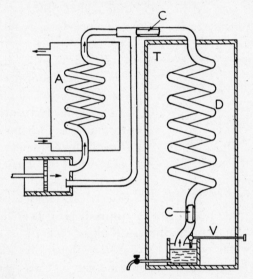

FIG. 52.    Liquid-air machine.

air is compressed and run through cooling coils as shown at A in Fig. 52. These remove the heat of compression. The gas is then carried through a second coil, C, and allowed to pass through a needle valve, V, into a low-pressure tank. The gas in expanding is cooled. It then returns to the compression pump by way of a coil D which surrounds C. This further cools the air in C, which is thus gradually reduced to the temperature of liquefaction.

The construction of a modern electric home refrigerator is represented in Fig. 53. Its operation is as follows:

An electric motor and rotary compression pump (bottom, center) compress the refrigerant, and drive it into the condenser (bottom, left). There it is cooled and liquefied. The liquid is driven upward, and passes through a spiral channel into the freezing chamber. This is connected by a pipe with the

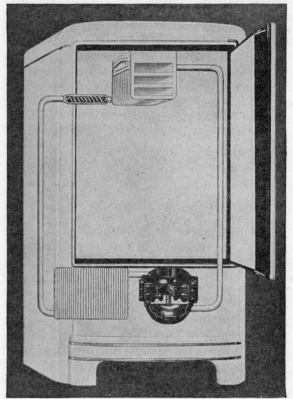

*Frigidaire Division, General Motors Sales Corporation.*
FIG. 53.  Cooling by evaporation and expansion.

low-pressure side of the compression pump. On entering the freezing chamber, therefore, the liquid evaporates and the resulting vapor expands. In both of these processes the refrigerant takes heat from its surroundings, that is, from the chamber, which is thereby cooled to a freezing temperature.

## CONVERSION OF HEAT INTO MECHANICAL ENERGY

We have seen that mechanical energy may be converted into heat, and that in any instance all of the energy involved may be so transformed. Heat may also be converted into mechanical energy. A simple arrangement for accomplishing this is illustrated in Fig. 54. A cylinder containing air is provided with a closely fitting piston, $P$. At room temperature the arrangement is as shown at $A$. If the air is now heated, it expands, pushing the piston upward and lifting a weight $W$, as shown at $B$. A part of the heat has been converted into potential energy of the raised weight.

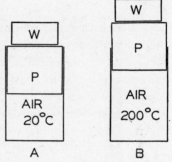

FIG. 54.  Work done by heating air.

## THE STEAM ENGINE

Several machines have been invented whose sole purpose is to convert heat into mechanical energy. One of these is the steam engine. As a toy this has been known for about two thousand years, but as a machine of industrial importance it dates back only about two hundred. The construction of the first working steam engine is credited to Thomas Newcomen, of England. This machine was built in 1711, and was installed in a coal mine to pump out the water. The Newcomen engine was unwieldy and inefficient, however, and on this account never came into extensive use. James Watt, of Scotland, about half a century later, succeeded in making improvements of so great importance that he is often called the inventor of the steam engine.

The principle of Watt's engine is illustrated in Fig. 55. Steam from a boiler is led by a pipe $P$ into a steam chest, $C$, and thence through channel $M$ into one end, $A$, of the cylinder. There it exerts a pressure upon the piston-head, $H$, driving it to the farther end of the cylinder.   The spent steam in end $B$ is meanwhile expelled through channel $N$ and exhaust pipe $E$. Wheel $W$ rotates in the direction of the arrow.   By means of a rod $R$, connected to $W$ by an eccentric (a type of crank), the slide valve $V$ meanwhile is moved far to the right.   Channel $N$ is thus connected with the steam chest $C$, while $M$ is connected with the exhaust pipe $E$.   Steam then enters end $B$ of the cylinder, driving the piston to the right, and expelling the spent steam from end $A$.   Valve $V$ is meanwhile moved to the left, connecting $N$ to $E$ and $M$ to $C$ as in the beginning.   This completes one cycle of operations of the engine, and one rotation of the wheel.   These movements are repeated as long as steam continues to be supplied to the cylinder.

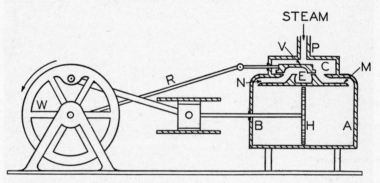

FIG. 55.   Principle of the steam engine.

The present-day reciprocating steam engine operates according to the same general plan.

In the steam turbine there are neither cylinders nor valves. The steam is driven at high speed against blades set in a wheel somewhat in the manner of the vanes in a windmill.   This drives the wheel.   A portion of the blading of a steam turbine is represented in Fig. 56.

An exterior view of a large steam turbine and the dynamo it drives is shown in Fig. 57.

The steam turbine is more efficient than the reciprocating engine, which it has largely displaced for service in large stationary power plants.   Its chief disadvantages for other uses are that it will operate satisfactorily only at high speed, and as yet only in large units.

The steam engine is one of the most important inventions ever made.  It is doubtful whether any other has had a more

Allis-Chalmers Mfg. Co.

Fig. 56.   Low-pressure blading on spindle of 25,000 kw. steam turbine.   Speed 1800 r.p.m.

profound effect upon the social and economic conditions of mankind.  It is not too much to say that it went into the cottages of the poor, gathered up the spinning wheels and looms, put them together in factories, and relieved women and children of the long hours of wearisome labor necessary to supply the family requirements of thread, yarn, and cloth.  It went into the smithies, took the forges, hammers, and anvils; gave them new forms better adapted to rapid and precise fashioning of metals; and set them to work supplying buckets, pans and cutlery, saws, axes, hammers, plows, harrows, drills, reapers,

*Allis-Chalmers Mfg. Co.*

Fig. 57.  135,000 H.P., 80,000 Kw. Turbo-generator of Milwaukee Electric Railway and Light Co., at Port Washington, Wis.   Overall size of unit, 33 × 96 ft. Weight, about 860 tons.   Steam pressure, 1230 lb. per sq. in.   Temperature at throttle, 825° F.   Turbine has more than 42,000 special alloy blades.   Speed of tip of longest blade, 600 miles per hr.   Efficiency of machine, 31 per cent.

and threshing machines, and latterly automobiles, trucks, and tractors.   It also travels over land and sea to carry both goods and persons everywhere.   In doing these things it has completely transformed the mode of life of perhaps one-third of the people of the world, and in some measure has altered that of nearly all the rest.

## THE GAS ENGINE

Another important machine for converting heat into mechanical energy is the gas engine.   Though commonly run by gasoline it may be adapted to use alcohol or other easily vaporized liquid fuels. The operation of a four-stroke cycle engine is represented in Fig. 58. In diagram *A* the piston is moving downward. Valve *V* is open, and the mixture of air and gasoline vapor is being taken in. The gas and air are mixed by an auxiliary device called a carburetor in about the proportions needed for complete combustion. When the cylinder is filled and the piston is at its lowest point, valve *V* closes. The piston now moves upward, compressing the mixture of air and gasoline vapor in the upper part of the cylinder, as shown in *B*. When the compression is complete, an electric spark between the metal

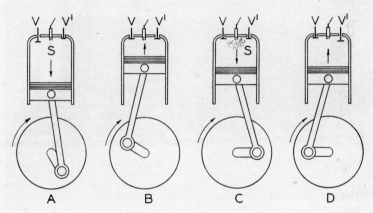

Fig. 58. Principle of gasoline engine.

points at *S* ignites the gas. This is shown in diagram *C*. The heat of combustion of the vapor greatly increases the pressure, driving the piston downward. This is the power stroke. It is during this movement that the fuel delivers energy. At the end of the power stroke, valve *V'* is opened, the piston moves upward, and the spent gases are discharged. The fourth or exhaust stroke completes the cycle, and a new cycle begins with the next intake stroke, as in *A*.

Because power is supplied only one-fourth of the time, the speed is irregular unless kept uniform either by means of a flywheel, or by having several cylinders operating upon the same shaft, and arranged to fire at different times. For example, if four cylinders are used, they are so related that one of the four fires at each half-turn of the shaft.

The internal-combustion engine has several advantages which have combined to bring it into almost universal use in automobiles, airplanes, tractors, home lighting and power plants, and for many other purposes.  One of its advantages is that it consumes fuel only when in operation.  Another is that no special preparation is necessary to make it ready to run, as is the case with the steam engine, in which the water must first be brought to boiling under high pressure.  A third advantage is that it gives great power with comparatively small weight.

American Locomotive Company.

FIG. 59.  Diesel Electric Locomotive.  This locomotive is driven by electric motors which are supplied with power from a dynamo run by a 600 H.P. Diesel engine.  Weight of locomotive is 216,000 lb.  Tractive force in starting, 64,800 lb.  Maximum speed, 40 miles per hour.  Used in switching service.

Furthermore, the gas engine uses a convenient kind of fuel, and is relatively efficient.

Another type of internal-combustion engine which is meeting with increasing favor is the Diesel (see page 122).  This also uses liquid fuel, which is sprayed into the cylinder under high pressure.  The Diesel engine is especially well suited for use in larger installations, such as central power plants and railway locomotives.  It is widely used also in marine craft, automobile trucks, and to some extent in airplanes.  A Diesel-driven locomotive is represented in Fig. 59.

## THE WASTE OF ENERGY IN HEAT ENGINES

We have seen that energy exists in many forms—mechanical, chemical, heat, radiation, and others.  We have also learned that these may all be transformed one into another. In any such transformation the total amount of energy is left unchanged. If mechanical energy is converted into heat, each gram-centimeter, erg, or foot-pound yields its definite fraction of a calorie —no less, no more. The same is true of other types of transformations. One calorie or B.t.u., when transformed into any other form of energy, yields a definite and constant amount. These facts are summarized in the law of the conservation of energy stated in an earlier chapter: in any transformation of one type of energy into another the total amount of energy remains unchanged. Or, stated in another way, the law asserts that energy can neither be created nor destroyed.

Though energy cannot be destroyed, it can be wasted. By this it is meant that energy can be dissipated and rendered incapable of being recaptured and utilized. All machines waste energy. Some waste a large fraction of all they handle. The reciprocating steam engine, for example, ordinarily wastes 80 to 85 per cent of the energy of the fuel, and converts only about 15 to 20 per cent into useful work. The best steam locomotives utilize only 12 to 13 per cent of the energy supplied. In stationary engines run at higher pressures the performance is considerably better.

In steam turbines and in gasoline and Diesel engines the losses are usually smaller than in stationary reciprocating engines. The efficiency of the best of these, however, has not exceeded 33 per cent.

## WHAT BECOMES OF THE WASTED ENERGY?

In the usual steam power plant not all of the chemical energy of the fuel is converted into heat. Some of the fuel escapes unburned as black smoke. This is finely divided carbon. Even if the smoke is of light grey color, it may still contain incompletely oxidized fuel in the form of an invisible gas, carbon monoxide.

Of the heat that is generated, a large amount is lost through the chimney, from which flows a constant stream of highly heated gases. Some is lost from the surface of the engine.

This is carried through the walls of the firebox or boiler and dissipated chiefly by the processes of convection and radiation. Still other quantities of energy are used in overcoming friction in the machine itself, at the various bearings, at slide valves, or wherever one part impinges or slides upon another. This frictional loss is immediately reconverted into heat, and dissipated as other heat losses are.

As another illustration, observe a bit of gasoline going through an automobile motor. It is taken into the cylinder with several times its own volume of air, as already mentioned. In the power stroke it is burned, though incompletely, and a large amount of heat is generated. This heats both the gases themselves and the engine. In order to keep the latter from overheating, a liquid is kept flowing about it and through the radiator. This carries away and wastes about one-third of all the heat generated. In the exhaust stroke the spent gases are expelled. These include not only the products of combustion, but a certain amount of unburned gas—carbon monoxide—all at a high temperature. Through this channel another third of the energy of gasoline is carried away and lost. Of the remaining third some is used in operating the valves, cams, shafts, and other moving parts of the motor, leaving only 25 to 30 per cent of the energy of the fuel available to drive the car.

All of these various losses, great as they are, do not in any way contradict the law of conservation of energy. If it were possible to measure all of the energy lost in either the steam power plant or in the automobile motor and add it to the amount delivered by the machine in the form of useful work, the sum would be found to be exactly equal to the chemical energy of the fuel consumed.

# CHAPTER 11

# OUR ATMOSPHERE

## INTRODUCTION

No part of the earth is more essential to life than is our atmosphere. Without it life could not exist. It is so subtle that most of us go about our daily tasks little realizing that we actually live at the bottom of a vast sea of tasteless, odorless, and colorless gases. Withhold them a short time from the lungs, and one will struggle desperately to obtain the life-giving fluid. The atmosphere dominates man's activities. What we eat, what we wear, and what we produce is largely a question of climate. If it is too cold, man's needs are more difficult to satisfy; if it is too hot, his energy is stifled, and his desire to supply his physical needs is lessened.

The atmosphere serves as a blanket to protect us from too severe (1) sunlight and high temperatures, and (2) loss of heat during night time. Without an atmosphere there could be no clouds, no rain, no running water, and no wind. The surface of the earth would become intensely hot by day and unbearably cold at night.

## PROPERTIES OF THE AIR

Of what is air composed? Is it a mixture or a compound? The four major constituents are: nitrogen (N) 78.03; oxygen (O) 20.9; argon (A) .93; and carbon dioxide ($CO_2$) .03. In addition to these four, there are rarer gases, as krypton (Kr), helium (He), and some hydrogen (H). When liquid air is allowed to boil, some of the gases escape more quickly than others, and the percentage changes. If the various components are mixed together, no change in temperature or volume occurs as would be the case if air were a compound. If we were to mix equal amounts of dry sand, salt, and sugar together, each one of the ingredients would keep its original identity. Thus air is a mixture, not a compound.

Dust and water vapor are also found in the air, but they are usually considered impurities, and not a part of the air.

## USES OF THE CONSTITUENTS

It is impossible to determine which is the most important gas. All of them in about the proportion in which we find them are necessary for life on the earth. The inert gases, with the exception of nitrogen, seem to have little or no effect upon life. The composition of the air remains remarkably constant, the chief reason being that as a gas it is very mobile, diffuses readily, and is mixed and transported great distances by the wind.

## SOURCES AND USES OF THE GASES

Nitrogen is an inactive element. When breathed into the lungs, it appears to have no physiological effects. Its chief use is to dilute the oxygen and lessen the rate at which oxidation occurs. It is also used in the formation of many food substances which both plant and animal life need.

Oxygen is the active element and is the part of the air that concerns us most. We breathe air, but make direct use of the oxygen only. The oxygen consumed in this and other ways is returned to the air chiefly by green plants, although some is obtained from the earth through volcanoes, vents in the earth, and from weathering of rocks. Combustion on the earth would not be possible if this element were absent.

Carbon dioxide, although but a small percentage of the air, plays a very important role in life on the earth. Without it plants could not thrive, and plant life is essential to animal life. The green cells of plants have the property of combining $CO_2$ from the air chemically with water which the plants have absorbed from the soil to form carbohydrates. As a result, proteins are formed which serve as food for both plants and animals. In this complex process, oxygen is liberated from the $CO_2$.

Carbon dioxide is supplied to the air from many sources: fires, decay of organic matter, respiration of plants and animals, and from the earth.

The rarer gases, argon, helium, krypton, neon, and xenon, seem to have no real functions so far as it is possible to determine.

Dust, an impurity in the atmosphere, performs a very important function. The tiny particles scatter the light rays and help give color to the sky. If dust particles were absent, the sun would shine from a black background instead of a blue one. Dust particles also offer surfaces on which moisture collects and thus aid in rainfall. Dust also helps to produce the colors of our morning and evening twilight.

Dust is of two kinds: organic and inorganic. The former consists of bacteria, pollen, and spores of plants, all of which are invisible. The latter consists of finely weathered rock material in suspension in the air. Inorganic dust may come from volcanic explosions, the fusing and disintegration of meteors, from combustion, and from the evaporation of ocean spray. Dust is one of the chief causes of haze.

The amount of water vapor in the air is never large, rarely exceeding four per cent. Its chief function is to sustain life, wash the air of its impurities, and to act as a blanket around the earth.

The atmosphere has mass and is therefore held to the earth by gravity. Since air is not a compound but a mixture of the various components, each component behaves as if the others were absent. This means that the heavier gases such as carbon dioxide, oxygen, argon, and nitrogen will be held near to the earth's surface, while the lighter gases, helium and hydrogen, occupy the upper portion of the atmosphere. These components would thus arrange themselves about the earth according to their density, assuming there was no mixture produced by the wind.

## PARTS OF THE ATMOSPHERE

Until recently it was assumed that the air grew colder as elevation above the earth's surface increased until the temperature became that of outer space. Thus only the atmosphere within a few miles of the earth's surface influenced terrestial affairs. Recent study has proven that the air, especially the upper portion, presents a very definite structure somewhat similar to a several-story building. It has been divided into layers, each layer possessing its own peculiar features.

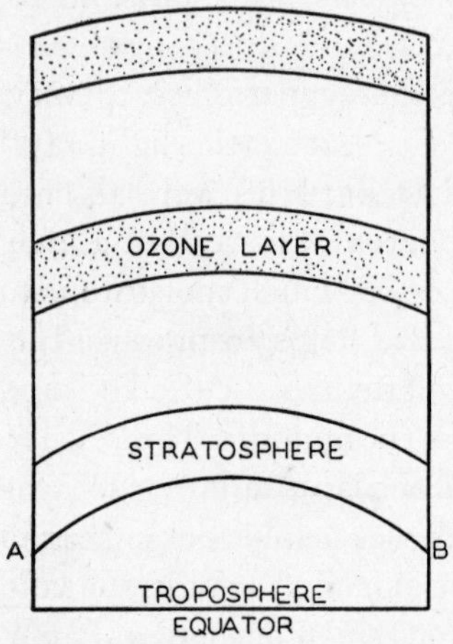

Fig. 60.    Structure of the atmosphere.

## THE TROPOSPHERE

This portion of the atmosphere extends upward from the earth's surface to an average height of about seven miles, below *AB* (Fig. 60). The prefix "tropo" means a "turning over of the air." In this portion of the atmosphere, the air is never quiet. Convection produces a rising of the warm air and a sinking of the cooler dense air. It is in this portion of the air that our moisture is present, and our winds occur.

## THE STRATOSPHERE

That portion of the atmosphere above the troposphere is known as the *stratosphere* (Fig. 60). Upper-air soundings made by hydrogen balloons have shown that except for the layers of air near the earth's surface in high latitudes, there is a rather uniform decrease in temperature of 0.6° C. for each 100 meters of elevation over the entire surface of the earth. This temperature decrease, except for various seasons and latitudes, ceases suddenly at a certain elevation. Above this elevation the temperature remains about the same, −67° F., and ceases to drop with further elevation. This region of rather uniform temperature is the stratosphere. Here the air remains quiet, and there is no up-and-down movement as in the troposphere. The level at which the temperature drop ceases with increased elevation is known as the *tropopause*. Little water vapor is present in the stratosphere, and winds are absent.

The first adventure into the stratosphere by a heavier than air machine was made by Lieutenant Appolo Soucek on June 4, 1930. He attained an altitude of 43,166 feet. On April 12, 1934, Lieutenant Donati of Italy succeeded in attaining an altitude of 47,672 feet, the highest elevation ever reached thus far by airplane.

The real exploration of the stratosphere, however, has been left for the balloon. This thrilling work was first begun by Mr. and Mrs. J. Piccard. On October 23, 1934, they ascended in their gondola to a height of 57,579 feet. Their first adventure was soon followed by others. Fedoseinko, Vatenko, and Usyskin of the U. S. S. R. ascended to an altitude of 72,176 feet, but all lost their lives before reaching the ground. One of the most noted explorations of the stratosphere was that of the *Explorer II*. In 1933, Captains Orvil A. Anderson and Albert W. Stevens of the U. S. Army attained a height of 72,392 feet, the highest point ever reached by man. At this height the air was calm and bitter cold, −80° F. The sun shone with a brilliant whitish color from an almost black sky. The gondola was constantly bombarded from above and on all sides by the cosmic rays from space. These rays registered their tracks on photographic plates which had been wrapped in black paper. Death to humans from the deadly cosmic and intensely burning ultraviolet rays would be certain in the rare air unless adequately protected by well-constructed gondolas. What the future holds for man in the realm of the stratosphere is as yet problematical. It seems quite certain that in the near future transatlantic flights in airships will be made in the lower part of the stratosphere.

One of the recent discoveries in the upper portion of the air is that there are certain layers which cause temperatures to change and that the rise may, in some cases, become comparable with the temperatures found near the earth's surface.   One of these layers at a height of about 12 to 30 miles is known as the ozone layer (Fig. 60).   No doubt the ultraviolet light of the sun is responsible for this layer.   The large amount of ozone may absorb great amounts of heat and thus cause a rise in temperature.   This gas acts as a filter for the absorption of much of the ultraviolet rays which come from the sun.   Were it not for this filter, man would probably be burned to death.   If it were thicker, it might absorb all of the ultraviolet light, and the health and vigor of man would be seriously impaired.   The ozone layer is not the only one that has been discovered.   Two other layers have already been detected.

## AIR PRESSURE

Why does the air have weight?   We learned that air is composed of many gases, and since gases are matter, they must have weight.   If an electric vacuum bulb is placed on a balance pan and weighed, and then an opening made in the bulb with a blow pipe and the bulb again weighed, it will be found to be heavier than without the air.   This is evidence that the air has weight.

We are living at the bottom of an ocean of air many miles in thickness.   Thus a pressure is exerted on every portion of our bodies.   It amounts to 14.7 pounds per square inch.   This means that if it were possible to place on a balance pan a column of air one square inch in cross section and as high as the air extends above the earth, it would weigh 14.7 pounds if the weighing were made at sea level.

The weight of the air decreases as elevation above the sea level increases.   At a height of six miles the pressure will drop to about four pounds per square inch, and at ten miles, it will have decreased to about two pounds.

The pressure of the air is measured by means of an instrument called a *barometer* (see Chap. 5).

## SOURCES OF ATMOSPHERIC HEAT

The earth has several sources of heat.   Some is obtained through combustion, some comes from the interior of the earth, some from distant stars, but the chief source is the sun. All other sources besides the sun would not raise the temperature one-fourth of a degree Fahrenheit. The sun is our chief stove. It has a surface temperature of about 10,000° F. and is close enough to us to furnish abundant heat to support all forms of life.

The direct method of heating the atmosphere is known as *insolation*. Heat in the form of radiant energy is transmitted from the sun through space to our atmosphere. When the heat waves reach the atmosphere, they speed up the motion among the gaseous molecules. A transformation of radiant energy into heat energy results.

The amount of insolation varies with the time of year, latitude, and the length of the sunshine period. The earth's orbit is not a circle but an ellipse with the sun at one of the foci (Fig. 272). From the figure it will be seen that the earth is nearest the sun on January 1, *B*, when its distance is about 91,500,000 miles.

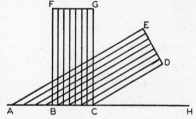

FIG. 61. Energy of the sun received from vertical and oblique rays.

On July 1, *A*, it is about 94,500,000 miles distant. The amount of heat received from the sun varies inversely as the square of the distance of the earth from the sun. Since the earth is 3,000,000 miles nearer the sun on January 1 than it is on July 1, the total amount it receives should be greater. This variation of insolation has been estimated at about seven per cent.

Latitude determines the directness of the sun's rays. A high summer's sun permits the rays to strike the surface more directly than a low winter's sun. When the sun is near the horizon in winter, the rays will strike the earth's surface very obliquely and their heat will be scattered over a large area *ABC* (Fig. 61). When the sun is high during a long summer's day, the heat scattering will be much less, *BC* (Fig. 61), and the temperature will be higher.

The length of the period of sunshine has also a decided effect upon the amount of heat received on different portions of the earth's surface. The length of sunshine in any latitude is intimately associated with seasons (Chap. 39).

After the heat from the sun has been received by the earth, it is redistributed to some degree, with the result that portions of the earth which get a large amount share with those portions which receive less. The three ways in which the atmosphere receives, loses, and transfers its heat are radiation, conduction, and convection. To understand fully the nature of these processes, turn to Chap. 8. In addition to these processes of heat redistribution, we should not omit the effect of the winds and ocean currents, which aid greatly in the redistribution of the sun's heat over the earth.

## THE MOISTURE OF THE ATMOSPHERE

Moisture is supplied to the atmosphere from a number of sources. About three-fourths of the earth's surface is covered with ocean. In addition to the ocean, which is the chief source of water vapor, are lakes, rivers, vegetation, and the ground itself. When heat is applied to a body of water, the water particles near the surface break away from their neighbors and make their way into the air. This requires a large amount of heat energy. The heat energy used in this process is transformed into what is known as latent or insensible heat. Evaporation then is a cooling process and lowers the temperature of the region in which it takes place (Chap. 8).

The rate at which evaporation goes on is influenced by temperature, winds, and the amount of water already in the air.

## ABSOLUTE HUMIDITY

Humidity is the condition or state of the air as regards moisture. When the air is dry, the humidity is said to be low; when moist, the humidity is high. Absolute humidity is the exact amount of moisture in the air at any given time. It is generally expressed in terms of so many grains per cubic foot of air at a given temperature.

## RELATIVE HUMIDITY

The amount of moisture the air has at any given time in comparison to what it would hold at the same temperature and pressure is known as *relative humidity*. If, for example, the capacity of a given volume of air is 20 grains, and its absolute humidity is only 10 grains, the relative humidity is 50 per cent. That is, the air space has only 50 per cent as much water vapor as it can contain. Relative humidity is always expressed in terms of *per cent*. The humidity in furnace-heated homes should be about 40 to 50 per cent for temperatures around 70 degrees.

Lowering of temperature increases the relative humidity, while an increase of temperature decreases it. When temperatures are decreased, the capacity of the air to hold moisture is lowered so that what moisture is present in the air may more nearly saturate it. When the temperature is raised, the capacity of the air to hold moisture is increased, and the relative humidity drops.

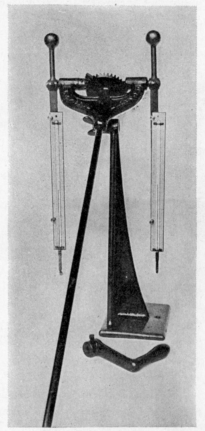

*United States Weather Bureau.*

Fig. 62. Whirled Psychrometer. A wet muslin jacket surrounds one bulb. The psychrometer is whirled by means of a crank.

Humidity is measured by an instrument called a *psychrometer* (Fig. 62). This consists of two thermometers mounted on a frame. One thermometer has its bulb inclosed in a wick which is kept moist by an immersion in water, while the other is dry. Since evaporation takes up heat, the wet bulb will record a lower temperature than the dry bulb. The difference between the dry and wet bulbs may be used with tables which have been prepared from laboratory experiments to determine the quantities desired: the dew point, relative humidity, and absolute humidity.

Another instrument which may often be seen in homes and public places is the hair hygrometer. This instrument reads directly the relative humidity. A delicate hand is actuated by a human hair from which all of the oil has been carefully removed. When the moisture of the atmosphere increases, the hair lengthens; when it decreases, the hair shortens. The change in the hair's length actuates a pen which moves over a cylinder making a continuous record of the relative humidity.

## SATURATION POINT

That temperature of the air reached when air space has all the water vapor it can hold is known as the *saturation point*. It is not possible to saturate air, as air is matter, and two bodies cannot occupy the same space at the same time. If we were to pour oats into a carton containing eggs, the oats would not penetrate the eggs but would find their way into the spaces around the eggs. In a similar way when water is placed in the air, it finds its way into the air spaces between the air molecules.

## DEW POINT

*Dew point* is that temperature reached when air space has all the water vapor it can hold. Any further cooling would cause some to condense and become visible. This principle may be simply illustrated by filling a tumbler with water and then placing in it a few small pieces of ice. In a short time, tiny droplets will collect on the outside of the tumbler. These tiny droplets of water did not pass through the glass. The cool water in the tumbler lowered the temperature of the air surrounding the glass to the dew point, and further condensation produced visible water drops.

## FORMS OF MOISTURE

Condensation is the opposite of evaporation; it is the passage of the invisible moisture of the air into a visible form either as a solid or a liquid.  There are many forms of visible water vapor with which one should be familiar.

## CLOUDS

Condensed moisture in a visible state suspended some distance above the earth's surface is called *clouds*.  They may be

*United States Weather Bureau.*

FIG. 63.   High cirrus clouds.

composed of either droplets of water or spicules of ice or snow. These small liquid or solid particles tend to fall, but owing to their minute size, descend very slowly because of the resistance offered by the air.

Clouds are classified according to their appearance and methods of formation.

## CIRRUS CLOUDS

Feathery, fluffy, flocculent, veil-like or plume-like masses that are found high in the sky on fair days are known as *cirrus clouds* (Fig. 63). The word cirrus means *curl* or *ringlet*. They occur at heights ranging from five to six miles and are composed of small spicules of ice or snow crystals. These clouds always have an easterly movement in the prevailing westerly wind belts. When a cirrus cloud passes between an observer and sun or moon, rings or halos (Chap. 17) are formed around the sun or moon. If the clouds are high, the ring is small; if low, the ring is large. They are often the forerunners of approaching cyclonic storms somewhere to the west of the observer's position.

## CUMULUS CLOUDS

These clouds are characterized by having even or horizontal bases (Fig. 64). Their tops are rounded, dome-like summits.

FIG. 64. Cumuliform clouds.

When seen near the sun, they appear dark with brilliant white borders; when seen in the sky opposite the sun, they appear whitish with dark centers. When viewed near the horizon, they often appear to be arranged in parallel rows or belts. Cumulus clouds are generally warm-weather clouds. They may be seen in the afternoon during the hottest part of the day.

Their height averages from two to three miles from the ground to their bases. Their thickness may be equal to or greater than the height of their bases above the surface.

## NIMBUS CLOUDS

Clouds from which moisture comes are known as *nimbus clouds*. The word nimbus means *storm*. They are of variable heights; the average is usually less than a mile. Nimbus clouds are of a dark-grayish color, and they often overcast the entire sky.

## STRATUS CLOUDS

*Stratus clouds* are any low-lying horizontal cloud masses with nearly uniform thickness. They present a rather flat, structure-

FIG. 65.   Stratus or fog cloud in a valley.

less form of wide extent. They are quite often a night cloud common to water bodies and valley lowlands (Fig. 65).

## FOG

Visible water vapor suspended at or near the earth's surface is called *fog* (Fig. 65).

In addition to the above distinct cloud forms, there are many modified forms. The United States Weather Bureau gives the following classification:

Cirrus, Cirrocumulus, Cirrostratus, Altostratus, Altocumulus.

Cumulus, Stratocumulus, Cumulonimbus, Cumulostratus.

Nimbus, Nimbostratus.

Stratus.

## DEW

Condensation of water vapor at temperatures above freezing on objects at or near the earth's surface is called *dew*. The air near the earth's surface cools rapidly at night and the vapor in the cooling air reaches the dew point. Dew never falls, but gathers or collects. It generally forms on clear, calm, cool nights.

## FROST

Condensation of water vapor at freezing temperatures on objects at or near the earth's surface is *frost*. Frost is not *frozen dew*. The air moisture condenses directly from the gaseous state to the solid in the form of white crystals or hoarfrost. Frosts are generally classified by the Weather Bureau as heavy or light. A heavy frost is severe enough to kill growing vegetation. After the freeze the green vegetation turns black, and the expression *black frost* is applied. Frost usually occurs first in low areas, since the cold heavy air from the surrounding regions accumulates in low places and remains stationary. Like dew, it forms on clear, cool, calm nights.

## RAIN

Condensation of water vapor at temperatures above freezing some distance above the earth's surface in sufficient quantities to fall in the form of drops is called *rain*. If the drops are small, air resistance is sufficient to prevent them from falling rapidly, and the term *mist* is applied.

Rainfall is measured by means of a rain gauge.  Any open
vessel of uniform cross section will suffice.  The Weather
Bureau uses an 8-inch rain gauge (Fig. 66).  It consists of an
outer can eight inches in diameter on the top of which is fitted
a funnel-shaped bottom.  This funnel conducts the rain into

*United States Weather Bureau.*
FIG. 66.   Standard 8-inch rain gauge.

an inside brass cylinder 20 inches in length and 2.53 inches in
diameter.   A special graduated ruler is then used to measure the
amount of precipitation.   For a given length, the volume of
the brass cylinder is one-tenth the volume of the receiver.   The
depth of the rainfall is, therefore, magnified ten times.   A
depth of ten inches of water in the brass cylinder equals one inch

of rainfall, while one-tenth of an inch is only 0.01 of an inch.

When the moisture falls in the form of snow or sleet, the funnel is removed and the 8-inch receiver is then inverted and forced downward through the layer of snow representing the average depth of the fall. It is then melted and the water poured into the brass cylinder and measured as in the case of rainfall. Several measurements of the snow should be made in different places since the depth varies from place to place. Each depth should be accurately measured as to the amount of moisture and the average of all the cases taken to represent the precipitation.

## SNOW

Condensation of water vapor some distance above the earth's surface at freezing temperatures in sufficient quantities to fall to the earth in the form of flakes (Chap. 6) is called *snow*.

## SLEET

Often rain drops form in clouds high above the earth's surface and start their downward descent. In their downward journey they often pass through thick masses of cold air with freezing temperature. The liquid drops are quickly frozen and fall as *sleet*.

## ICE STORM

It often happens that rains or mists occur after a severe cold period. During the continued cold spell the air near the earth's surface as well as the ground itself and all other objects are still below the freezing point. When the rain strikes the ground and the objects on it, these are coated with a layer of ice. This is known as an *ice storm*, not a sleet storm. One of the great dangers to aviation is the forming of ice on airplanes.

Icing of aircraft is a subject that has received very careful study within the last few years. While the mechanics of the cause are quite well understood by the physicist and the meteorologist, the dynamics are not clear. It is a well-known fact that liquid droplets are present in certain forms of clouds, especially those of the cumuliform type. They are also met with in the stratiform in less amount, but are entirely absent in the high cirriform cloud. Liquid droplets may exist at temperatures ranging from $-14°$ F. or $-16°$ F. to as low as $-22°$ F. The liquid condition of the droplets is apparently contingent upon their remaining in a quiet or undisturbed state. Agitation caused by the airplane's striking them produces their immediate solidification.

Icing of airplanes occurs in three distinct types: namely, clear *compact ice*, *rime*, and *hoarfrost*. Clear amorphous ice is the most serious for pilots. It forms on the blunt nose of the wings and adds weight, reduces the resistance of drag, lowers the aerodynamic efficiency of the wings, and thereby reduces the lifting power of the plane. Rime is an opaque, whitish ice consisting of a granular structure. It is not so tenacious in its formation on the airfoil and does not, therefore, interfere with the lifting property of the wings as does clear ice. Ice may form at freezing or below freezing temperatures. It often happens that heavy coatings of ice on aircraft consist of both clear and rime ice in a laminar structure somewhat similar to summer hailstones. Frost is of little importance in icing of aircraft, since it is light and easily blown off.

The size of the droplet determines the type of ice produced. When the larger droplets of super-cooled water are struck by the airfoil, they spread a film of water over the surface which quickly passes into ice, since the wing surface is at freezing or below freezing temperatures. When the droplets are small, the low temperature causes an immediate freezing and the solid product is rime.

Several methods are now employed to de-ice the plane. The exposed parts of the plane may be heated by electrical resistance or by heat from the engine's exhaust gases. Only the small mechanisms such as the exposed portions of flight and navigational instruments and the radio antenna may be protected by this means since the amount of heat required by the larger surfaces is prohibitive. De-icing is also accomplished by employing a pneumatic covering for the leading edges. Alternate inflation and deflation of the rubber covering causes the ice to crack and be blown away by the wind. Sometimes the surface of the plane is coated with a thick oil or varnish which prevents the adherence of ice. This principle is employed chiefly to prevent the ice from forming on propellers and cockpit windshields. Small vents in the propeller hub permit a small stream of de-icing fluid to stream over the propeller blades. More accurate weather forecasting has made it possible to inform the pilot of certain zones in which there is danger of icing. These reports issued to the pilot before he sets out give accurate information as to the height of the isothermal layer of freezing temperature in relation to the cloud layers. All of these improvements have led to safer flying.

## HAIL

It is not easy to define hail. It consists of hard, round pellets of ice, or of ice and compact snow combined. Hail which occurs during the cold winter months consists of clear pellets of ice. Summer hail is associated with thunderstorms and is formed in the front portion of the cumulonimbus cloud where there is a pronounced rising and falling, or convectional movement of the air. In the lower portion of the cloud, the rising air soon reaches the dew point and raindrops are formed. The drops do not fall but are carried up by the strong ascending currents into the upper portion of the cloud where freezing temperatures prevail and snow is forming. The raindrops are frozen and acquire a coating of snow and frost. This rising and falling will continue until the hailstone becomes large enough to fall to the ground as summer hail.

# CHAPTER 12

# WINDS AND WEATHER

## WINDS

Wind is air in motion essentially parallel to the earth's surface. All other movements of the air are considered as air cur-

*United States Weather Bureau.*

Fig. 67. Robinson cup anemometer.

rents. Winds are always named from the direction from whence they come; if air moves from the east toward the west,

151

it is called an east wind. The term windward is used to designate the direction from which the air comes, and leeward the
direction to which it blows. Where winds follow the direction
of the hands of a clock, they are called *veering winds;* where the

*United States Weather Bureau.*
FIG. 68. Weather Bureau anemoscope.

direction changes to a counterclockwise direction, they are
termed *backing winds*.

Wind velocity is the rate at which the air moves over the
surface. It is measured by an instrument called an *anemometer*
(Fig. 67). This consists of two arms at right angles to each
other on the ends of which are hemispherical aluminum cups to

catch the wind. The crossarms to which the cups are attached have a vertical screw shaft which meshes with cog wheels to record the revolutions of the cups upon two dials. From these dials it is possible to determine the wind velocity.

Wind direction is obtained from the *anemoscope*, or weather vane (Fig. 68).

If the wind velocity can be determined, it is possible to compute the pressure exerted upon a unit area of surface. It is always expressed in so many pounds per square foot. Wind pressure is expressed by the formula $P = .005V^2$. $P$ represents the pressure exerted by the wind on a unit area of surface and $V$ the wind velocity. A wind velocity of 60 miles per hour exerts a pressure of 18 pounds per square foot.

## REASONS FOR AIR MOVEMENT

Air movement is intimately related to pressure. When pressure varies from place to place on the earth, there must be a movement of air, since air is a gas and is mobile. There are three factors which affect the weight of the air: temperature, moisture, and altitude.

When air is heated, it expands and becomes less dense. A column of warm air will weigh less than a column of cold air, if both are of the same height and cross section. Water vapor has a lower density than dry air, and when present, makes the air lighter.

Air is a gas, and gases are compressible (Chap. 5). The lower layers of the atmosphere are dense because of the weight of all the layers above them. At high altitudes the air becomes rarer and lighter until at an elevation of 17,500 feet more than one-half of the atmosphere by weight is below this level.

## DISTRIBUTION OF PRESSURE ON THE EARTH

A study of Figs. 69 and 70 shows the horizontal, sea level distribution of pressure on the earth for January, the coldest month, and July, the warmest month. Near the equator, where the temperature throughout the year is highest, a low-pressure belt exists. This belt shifts with the seasons, moving north-

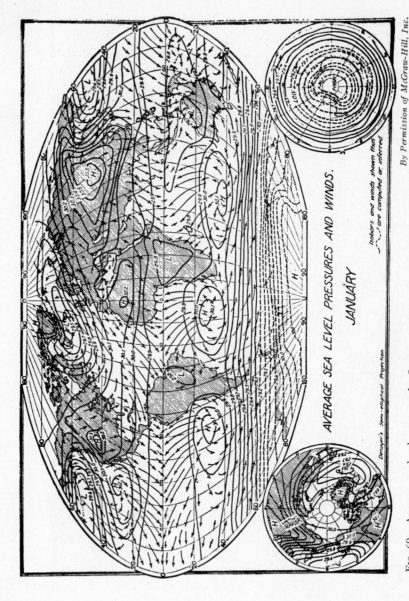

AVERAGE SEA LEVEL PRESSURES AND WINDS.
JANUARY

Isobars and winds shown thus _____
are computed or inferred ˙˙˙˙

Denoyer's Semi-elliptical Projection

By Permission of McGraw-Hill, Inc.
(From An Introduction to Weather and Climate by Trewartha.)

Fig. 69.   Average sea level pressures for January.

154

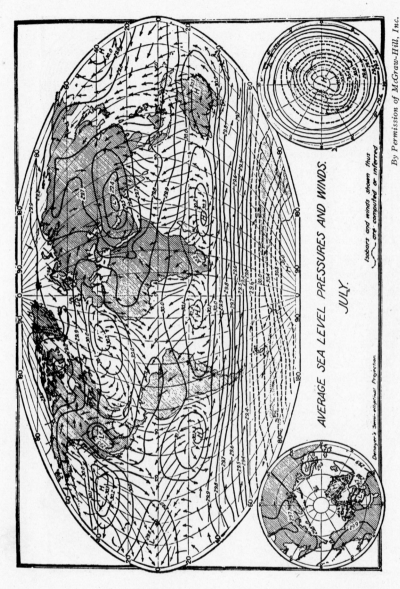

AVERAGE SEA LEVEL PRESSURES AND WINDS.
JULY.

*Isobars and winds shown thus ~~~ are computed or inferred*

Denoyer's Semi-elliptical Projection

*By Permission of McGraw-Hill, Inc.*

Fig. 70.   Average sea level pressures for July.   (From *An Introduction to Weather and Climate* by Trewartha.)

155

ward when the vertical rays of the sun shift north, and migrating to the south during the winter time. Land heats up more quickly than water but loses its heat by radiation more rapidly than water. Since the larger percentage of land is found in the northern hemisphere, this heat belt extends farther north of the equator than it does south.

A further study of Figs. 69 and 70 will reveal that there are high-pressure belts, extending around the earth, just outside the tropics, somewhere between latitude 30° and 40° N. and S. These high-pressure belts are known as the *subtropical highs*. From them the pressure decreases as the poles are approached, until low-pressure belts are again in evidence in the vicinity of 60° to 70° N. and S. Beyond these high-latitude low-pressure belts are found high-pressure areas around the poles. It will be noted from Figs. 69 and 70 that the pressure at the South Pole is in a large land mass which is still covered with ice, while land is absent near the North Pole.

It will be observed that in middle latitudes in the northern hemisphere there are great land masses, such as North America and Eurasia. Since land heats up more quickly than water during summer, low pressures of a semipermanent nature develop over land, while high pressures exist over the oceans, and vice versa during the winter. The lowest pressure in summer is found over Asia, the largest land mass.

## PRESSURE AND WINDS

Winds result because of horizontal differences in pressure on the earth. If there were no pressure gradient, there could be no movement of the air. Air movement is always from high pressure to low pressure. Pressure lines are called *isobars*. The change in barometric pressure with horizontal distance is called *the barometric slope* or gradient.

The winds of the earth may be classified into three great divisions:

    I. Planetary or Permanent Winds
        (a) Prevailing westerlies
        (b) Trades

      (c)  Antitrades

      (d)  Polar easterlies

  II. Periodical or Regular Winds

    1. Seasonal

      (a)  Migrating winds of calm belts

      (b)  Monsoons

    2. Diurnal Winds

      (a)  Land and sea breezes

      (b)  Mountain and valley breezes

III. Nonperiodical or Irregular Winds

    1. Storm winds

      (a)  Cyclones

          1. Tropical cyclones $\begin{cases} \text{Typhoons} \\ \text{Hurricanes} \end{cases}$

          2. Extratropical cyclones

      (b)  Thunderstorms

      (c)  Desert whirlwinds

      (d)  Tornadoes

    2. Accidental winds

      (a)  Waterfall breezes

      (b)  Landslide and avalanche breezes

      (c)  Volcanic winds

## THE PLANETARY WINDS

The wind systems of the earth are quite complex. It is not easy to make clear the reasons for the high-pressure areas on the earth just outside the tropics.

Let us assume a nonrotating earth having an all-land or an all-water surface and with a continuous vertical sun at the equator. The temperature would decrease gradually from the equator to the poles but would always be high at the equator and low at the poles. The colder dense air from the poles would flow toward the equator, while the warmer, lighter, expanding air at the equator would flow aloft to the poles and descend to continue its backward journey to the equator as surface winds. We would experience two large air-mass movements, one in the southern hemisphere from the south, and one in the northern hemisphere from the north. But such a simple circulation is not found on the earth.

The first attempt to explain the effect of the earth's rotation on air movement was made by Hadley in 1735. He set forth the principle that air moving from the tropical calm belts, 30 ± degrees north and south of the equator, directly toward the equator would pass over regions having a greater easterly velocity of movement due to the speed of the earth's rotation than have the regions from which it started. As a result the air would lag behind the earth's rotation and be deflected to the right of the meridian (a meridian is a line drawn from pole to pole) in the northern hemisphere, and to the left of the meridian in the southern hemisphere. Hadley's explanation was only partially correct.

The true deflective effect of the earth's rotation on moving air masses was later explained by Ferrel in 1856, who proved that it makes no difference in what direction air moves; it will be deflected to the right of the meridian in the northern hemisphere and to the left of the meridian in the southern hemisphere.

Air starting from the equator at high altitudes and moving poleward toward higher latitudes under the influence of rotation is deflected more and more to the east. By the time it reaches a point somewhere between latitudes 30° to 40° N. and S., it becomes almost a west wind. A large part of the air can no longer go poleward, but piles up in the vicinity of 30° to 40° N. and S., creating subtropical high pressures because of the large amount of air. A second reason for high pressure in these latitudes is due to centrifugal force on high poleward-moving air. Rotation of the earth produces a force which throws bodies away from the center. If a circular washbowl is filled with water, the drain stopper removed, and the water given a rotary movement, it will escape slowly from the bowl. The rotary motion of the water near the top of the bowl is slow at first, but as the water in the bowl lowers, the speed of the rotation increases. The more rapidly rotating water piles it up around the sides of the bowl and a hollow core is seen where the water is escaping through the opening. The force which causes the piling up of the water around the sides of the bowl is called *centrifugal*, that is, away from the center.

Poleward-moving air from the equator at high altitudes spirals in toward the pole, like the water toward the opening in the basin, and as its distance from the pole decreases, its velocity of rotation increases. This action would keep much of the air away from the poles and produce low pressure there if the air movement were not interfered with. But this is not what we find. The extremely low temperatures at the poles, however, make the air there dense and heavy, and this results in high pressure at the poles, surrounded by subpolar troughs of low pressure in latitudes 60° ± N. and S. These low-pressure

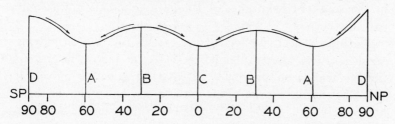

FIG. 71.   A pressure profile from pole to pole, showing air movement.

troughs surrounding the polar high-pressure areas result, according to Trewartha, "from a compromise between thermal and centrifugal forces in the polar regions."

High-pressure regions are thus found at the poles and on either side of the equator, *DD*, *BB* (Fig. 71), while low-pressure regions are found near the equator, *C*, and 60° ± N. and S., *AA*. Air flowing along a meridian over such an irregular barometric surface will move from high to low pressure as shown by arrows (Fig. 71).

## THE PREVAILING WESTERLIES

Air starting from the subtropical regions and moving toward the poles is deflected to the right of the pressure gradient in the northern hemisphere and to the left in the southern (Fig. 72).

## THE TRADES

Air moving from the subtropical calms toward the equator is deflected to the right of the gradient in the northern hemisphere and to the left in the southern.   These winds are known as the *northeast* and *southeast trades*.

Air currents moving poleward high above the trades are called *antitrades*.   The planetary winds are ever present on the

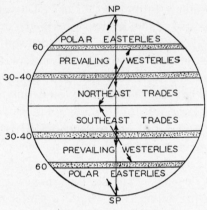

FIG. 72.   Law of wind deflection.

globe.   They may shift somewhat in latitude with the seasons, but they never disappear.

## PERIODICAL OR REGULAR WINDS

These winds which appear at definite seasons of the year are largely influenced by the migration of the sun northward in summer and southward in winter.   The distribution of land and water masses in the northern hemisphere produces thermal effects that cause a shifting of pressure gradients between land and water.   Land heats up quickly and cools rapidly; water heats slowly but retains its heat a long time after being warmed. Thus, in summer, land masses are warm and water masses are cool.   In winter the reverse is true.   This shifting of pressure in the planetary winds gives rise to certain seasonal winds that should be clearly understood.

## MONSOONS

Winds that appear on the earth at definite seasons of the year are known as *monsoons*.   They change their direction with the coming and going of the seasons.   The earth's surface is composed of both land and water which, as we have just seen, have quite different heating and cooling qualities. Thus, in summer, there develops over the interior of the heated land masses in low latitudes a semipermanent low-pressure area, while a high-pressure is found over the cooler water area. This produces a pressure gradient from sea to land causing movement of cooler air from the water to the land called summer monsoons. These summer monsoons, coming from the oceans, are highly charged with water vapor. When they reach the high lands, they are forced to rise. The sudden rise results in a rapid cooling and drenching rains.

In winter a reversal of pressure conditions results. A high-pressure area develops over central Asia which becomes semi-permanent. Over the warmer seas to the south and east, low-pressure areas develop. The air thus moves from the land to the sea. This prevailing land wind is a winter monsoon and is always a dry wind. Monsoons are present in India, Gulf of Guinea, the Mediterranean Sea, along the eastern coast of Asia, the Gulf of Mexico, and in many other localities on the earth.

## MIGRATING WINDS OF CALM BELTS

In summer and winter, the pressure and wind belts migrate slightly, five or six degrees, to the north and south of their average positions. This causes the planetary winds to migrate also. In summer the region of greatest heat is north of the equator. In the center of this belt, which is called the *doldrum belt*, is the heat equator (the broken line, Fig. 73).

The doldrums are the equatorial belt of calms. The warm trade winds blow to these regions highly charged with moisture. The air is forced to rise, and on rising, cools; thus overcast skies and heavy rains in the form of afternoon thunderstorms are common. When the doldrum migrates northward, there is an overlapping of wind along the subtropical belts of high pressure and on either side of the equator. In Fig. 73 you will observe that along the subtropical belts of high pressure, *B*, the winds shift somewhat in latitude. In summer the westerlies as well as the trades are shifted northward, while in winter they are

shifted southward. This causes an overlapping of winds in
these areas. In Fig. 73 northeast trades are present as shown

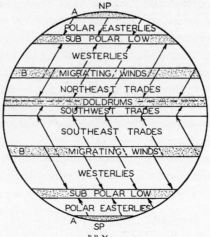

FIG. 73. Wind circulation for July.

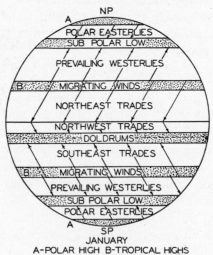

FIG. 74. Wind circulation for January.

by the continuous arrows through this belt *B*, but westerlies
as indicated by the dotted arrows are absent. In the southern

hemisphere the westerlies are present, while the absence of southeast trades is shown by the dotted arrows.

When the doldrum belt shifts north of the equator, the southeast trades are forced to cross the geographical equator and in so doing are deflected to the right of the pressure gradient, where they are known as the southwest trades (Fig. 73).

When the doldrum belt migrates south of the equator in winter (Fig. 74), the northeast trades are forced to cross the equator and are deflected to the left of the pressure gradient to become northwest trades. At this time of the year, as in summer in the northern hemisphere, there is a migration of the trades and westerlies along the subtropical high-pressure areas, B (Fig. 74). See if you can find the chief differences from the winds shown in Fig. 74.

## LAND AND SEA BREEZES

During the day, the land along the seashore heats up more rapidly than does the water. This gives rise to an air movement from the sea to the land called a *sea breeze*. At night the land cools more quickly than the adjacent water and the air flow will then reverse itself and move from land to water causing a *land breeze*.

## MOUNTAIN AND VALLEY BREEZES

Where long, narrow valleys from mountain areas emerge on a large, open plain, there is often a strong movement of air from the mountain tops down the valley. The mountain tops cool more rapidly than do the valleys, and the heavier air moves down into the valley as a *mountain breeze*. During the day, the air of an enclosed valley and the slopes adjacent to the valley receive more direct rays from the sun and become intensely heated, causing the air to move up the valley and mountain slopes. An air movement of such a nature is called a *valley breeze*.

## IRREGULAR OR NONPERIODICAL WINDS

These winds may rightly be thought of as a secondary circulation, that is, a circulation within a circulation. They are air movements which result from traveling disturbances within the primary wind system. Cyclones are of two types: the violent, or tropical cyclone; and the nonviolent, or the extratropical.

## THE TROPICAL CYCLONE

This storm is confined to the tropics. It is a large, traveling, destructive inward movement of air, counterclockwise in the northern hemisphere, clockwise in the southern, which is accompanied by high winds and torrential rains. In the West Indies they are known as *hurricanes*, while along the eastern coast of Asia and in the Indian Ocean they are called *typhoons*. They have their origin in or on the polar margins of the doldrum belts. The warm, moist trade winds blow toward these belts and on reaching them are forced to rise. The more probable impulse for vigorous convective action in starting these rotary storms results from lofty, cold polar air meeting warm, moist rising air, thus creating a marked unstability, with cold air above warm moist air. The cold air over the warm air is capable of supplying the energy to start cyclonic action. Cyclones first move in a westerly direction until they encounter the westerlies, when they change to the east.

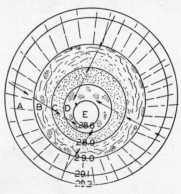

FIG. 75. Tropical cyclone showing rain area, wind, and eye of storm.

Tropical cyclones are more or less circular in shape, averaging from 300 to 500 miles in diameter (Fig. 75). In the center of the storm the pressure is low, the air is calm, and the sky is clear. This central area is known as the *eye* of the storm. Its average diameter is from 2 to 30 miles. Tropical storms are not always destructive. They frequently are, however, the wind often reaching speeds of 100 to 150 miles per hour. Clouds and rain are found around the entire storm.

The signs of approach of a tropical storm are found in both sky and sea. The sky becomes covered with a thin cirrus cloud $A$ (Fig 75) which causes the lurid red sunrises and sunsets before the coming of the storm.   It is these same clouds that produce halos around the moon by night and the sun by day. The barometer is high, the winds calm, and the moisture-laden air is sultry and oppressive.   As the storm center is approached, the pressure begins to drop, the winds increase in intensity, and the cirrus clouds thicken into cirrostratus or cirrocumulus, $B$. Soon the sky becomes overcast, the barometer drops rapidly, nimbus clouds fill the sky, the sea is lashed into fury by the strong winds, and torrential rains descend, $C$.   After some time, the rain ceases, the winds decrease in velocity, and the nimbus clouds break through and give place to cirrus, $D$.   When $E$ has been reached, the air becomes calm, the sky clears, and the only evidence of the surrounding hurricane winds and torrential rains are the high ocean swells.

The tropical cyclone is a water-convectional storm and travels at the rate of 10 to 30 miles per hour.

## EXTRATROPICAL CYCLONES

These storms occur outside of the tropics.   They are large, easterly moving, nondestructive, inward movements of the air, counterclockwise in the northern hemisphere and clockwise in the southern hemisphere.   They are usually accompanied by warm, cloudy, rainy, or snowy weather.   They are found in the westerlies in middle latitudes and must move from west to east.   They are represented on a weather map by a series of closed isobaric lines which are more or less concentric and roughly oval in shape (Fig. 76).   The pressure is low at the center and increases toward the margins.   Some winter cyclones may carry as much as an inch difference in pressure between the center and the outside, though the difference is generally much less than this.   Their average size in the United States is from 1000 to 1200 miles, although individual storms may be larger or smaller.   Unlike the tropical cyclone, the winds are not destructive, the average velocity being about 25 miles per hour.

The approach of this storm is generally preceded by high, lofty cirrus clouds, $A$ (Fig. 76), which move in from the west.

They rise from the horizon to the zenith as thin streamers or veil-like clouds producing quite frequently a halo about the sun by day and the moon by night. Later on these clouds pass into cirrostratus, altostratus, or fractostratus, *B*, and finally into nimbus, *C*. In summer these veil-like clouds often become cirrocumulus, altocumulus or stratocumulus, and finally nimbus. Rain or snow may fall for several hours. The wind

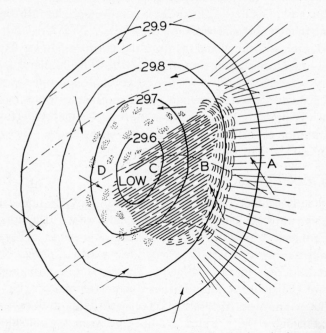

FIG. 76. Extratropical cyclone showing winds, cloud, and rain areas.

will then shift suddenly from an easterly to a westerly direction. The nimbus clouds soon become fractonimbus, *D*. The barometer begins to rise, the temperature lowers, and soon the sky clears, and cool, fair weather will prevail.

The rain area is generally confined to the south-southeast portion of the storm. Cyclones may originate over either land or water, and at any time of the year. Their average rate of travel is from 20 to 30 miles per hour.

These storms have many tracks across the continent, and each individual storm seems to select its own path as it travels eastward. Cyclones that have their origin in the western Pacific generally move northeastward along Japan to west Alaska. From here they move southeast, where they enter the North American continent as "Alberta lows." In their eastward journey across North America the most frequented tracks are: (1) along the northern and southern boundary of United States and Canada; (2) southeastward into the Mississippi basin, thence northeast to the Great Lakes, New England, and St. Lawrence Valley; and (3) from the southwest to the Mississippi basin, thence northeast across the New England states. Many of these storms cross the Atlantic Ocean and enter the European continent, traveling as far as Siberia, where most of them disappear. Without these storms the major portion of the interior of North America would be a desert. They are our moisture distributors.

## THE ANTICYCLONE

An anticyclone is a very large, easterly moving, nondestructive, outward movement of the air, clockwise in the northern hemisphere, counterclockwise in the southern. They are usually accompanied by clear, cool, fair weather, except on the front and rear margins. Unlike the cyclone, the pressure is high at the center and diminishes toward the margin (Fig. 77).

The winds near the storm center are light, and calms are frequent since the pressure gradient between the outside and the center is less than in the cyclone. On the east side of the storm, stratocumulus clouds of the passing low (dotted area of Fig. 77) may still be seen. On the west margin cirrus and cirrostratus clouds (straight and wavy line areas of Fig. 77) of the approaching low may have already made their appearance. It will be observed that the wind directions experienced by the observer will depend upon his location with reference to the center of these two storms.

These storms follow about the same tracks as the cyclone. The anticyclone is a very large storm, often covering as much as one-third of the entire North American continent. The rate of travel is about 20 to 30 miles per hour.

The sudden changes of temperature experienced in the interior of the United States are the direct result of the passage of these two storms.

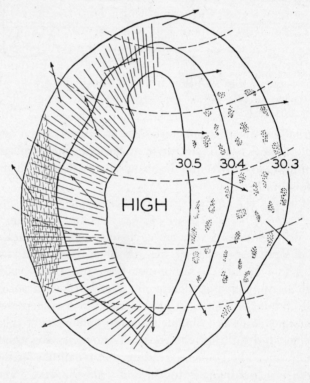

Fig. 77. Extratropical anticyclone showing winds, cloud, and clear sky area.

It should now be clear why the movement of the air in the cyclone and anticyclone may be thought of as a secondary circulation within the primary. The air from one storm center supplies the air to the other. A study of Fig. 78 will show the relation of air movement along the surface and higher up as these storms cross the United States. The large arrow indicates the primary circulation, the westerlies.

No two similar storms can follow one after the other on the same track.   A cyclone must be followed by an anticyclone.

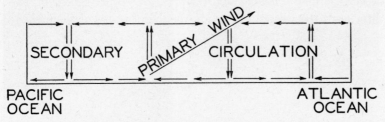

FIG. 78.   Diagram showing horizontal surface movement of air in cyclones and anticyclones together with vertical and lofty winds.

## THE TORNADO

A tornado is a very small, very local, very destructive inward whirl of the air, counterclockwise in the northern hemisphere. The word is derived from a Latin word, *tornare,* which means *to twist.*

The tornado is a storm that is peculiar to the United States, although it may occur in other parts of the world in a modified form.   To the ordinary layman, cyclone and tornado mean one and the same thing.   They are, however, very different in nature.   The cyclone is not destructive, but the tornado is.

These storms are most commonly associated with an extra-tropical cyclone.   Often a well-developed low may depart from the normal oval shape.   In the southern quadrants of the low, a so-called wind-shift line develops.   The oval isobars assume a *v*-shaped, bulge-like pocket extending in a northeast-southwest direction.   Such a bulge is known as a *wind-shift line.*   On the east margin of this line the wind continues from the south, the velocity decreases, rainfall disappears, and nimbus clouds are replaced by cirrus.   On the west side of the line strong northwest winds prevail.   It is along this line that violent thunderstorms often occur with which a violent tornado may develop. Tornadoes have a funnel-shaped cloud which forms from the low squall cloud of a cumulonimbus cloud.   The funnel may rise and descend and twist about in a rather violent fashion. At (a) (Fig. 79) the funnel may be seen forming from the squall

(a)                                        (b)

(c)                                        (d)

*United States Weather Bureau.*

FIG. 79(a, b, c, d).   The development of a tornado from its beginning until the spout reaches the ground.

170

cloud; at (b) it is approaching the ground; at (c) it has almost reached the surface; and at (d) great clouds of dust are seen rising from the ground. When it reaches the ground, it leaves complete destruction in its path. The wind velocity may reach 200 to 400 miles per hour. Tornadoes advance across the surface at the rate of 20 to 40 miles per hour. In the United States, they generally move from the west-southwest to east-northeast.

Wind is not the only destructive force in these storms. When the spout reaches the ground, the violent whirling of the air around the spout forces much of it away, leaving at its center a partial vacuum. The sudden reduction of pressure on the outside of buildings as the spout passes over them will often cause an explosion.

These storms are small and generally occur in the hot part of a summer's afternoon. If the tornado is seen in time, one may take a course at right angles to the storm and escape injury. The safest place is an excavation made in the ground with a substantial roof and located some distance away from buildings.

Tornadoes originate over land and are caused by cold air underrunning warm, moist air.

## THUNDERSTORMS

Local, moving storms of short duration accompanied by lightning and thunder are called *thunderstorms*. They are usually only a few miles wide at their origin but may spread until they cover a path of from 30 to 40 miles in width, over a length of 75 to 100 miles. The summer thunderstorm is characterized by a strong upward current of warm, moist air which in time forms an overgrown cumulus cloud from which heavy rains may fall for a short time.

## ORIGIN OF CYCLONES AND ANTICYCLONES

No one yet seems to know the true origin of these storms. It was once thought that they might be convectional, but later study seems to indicate that few are of this nature. It is now known that these storms may originate over water as well as over land. They are more numerous and better defined in winter than in summer and originate in areas of strong winds rather than in calms. If convection is the cause of origin, we should not find them in winter as the land is cold and the air currents are much stronger than in summer. Since water has a more uniform temperature than land, there would be little cause for convection over water.

The most recent theory for the origin of cyclones and anticyclones is the *polar front* conception of Bjerknes, a noted Norwegian meteorologist. He conceived these traveling disturbances to be the result of a reciprocal action between two

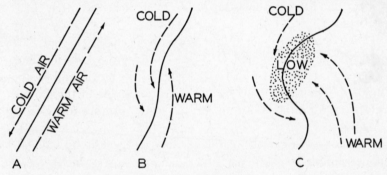

Fig. 80. Diagram showing: *A*, inception, *B*, growth, and *C*, development of an extratropical cyclone.

masses of air of different temperatures. One is a cold, dry polar air moving equatorward; the other, a warm, moist tropical air mass moving poleward. From Fig. 73 it will be observed that the westerlies are bounded on the equatorward side by subtropical high-pressure belts. This gives rise to a poleward movement of warm, moist air. On the high latitude margins (Fig. 73) of the westerlies are found the polar and continental high-pressure areas. Warm, moist air flows poleward from the tropical highs and is met by cold, dry air moving equatorward. The zone separating the warm and cold air front is called the "polar front" (heavy lines in *A*, *B*, and *C* of Fig. 80).

The warm, moist air of low latitudes expands and starts poleward at the upper levels. There must be a compensating movement equatorward of the polar air near the surface. This transfer of air is not a uinform frontal movement. The cold polar front often breaks out in the form of great lobes extending down into the westerlies and even into the subtropics. Thus there appear along the margin of the cold, equatorward-moving air wave-like disturbances. These small waves or bulges are the beginning of cyclones. The colder tongues extending equatorward into the warm air are the anticyclones. In Fig. 80 the heavy line represents the boundary between the warm, moist polar-flowing air and the cold, dry equatorward-moving air. At *B*, the starting of the wave or bulge in the warmer,

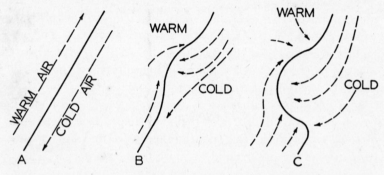

FIG. 81.  The start, growth, and development of an extratropical anticyclone.

moist air is seen. The bulge results possibly from some local irregularity in the air movement. *C* shows the bulge well developed. As soon as the wave is well initiated, the deflective force resulting from the earth's rotation, together with the movement of the two air masses, produces a cyclonic center with spirally inward-moving air. The dotted area indicates the region of cloud and precipitation.

The anticyclone is produced in a manner similar to the cyclone. The warm air at *A* (Fig. 81) is moving poleward on the west side of the cold equatorward-moving air. At *B*, a bulge is formed in the cold air mass, and at *C*, the initial wave is aided by the deflective force of the earth's rotation, and an anticyclone with outward, spirally flowing winds is inaugurated.

# CHAPTER 13

# WEATHER FORECASTING

## WEATHER AND CLIMATE

The condition of the atmosphere for any particular time and place on the earth is a result of six things: temperature, pressure, winds, clouds, relative humidity, and precipitation. These six factors are known as the weather elements. To give a statement in regard to weather, one would need to know the relative values of each of these elements.

Weather may be defined as the average succession of the weather elements over a short period of time. It is the weather of today, this week, this month, this year—and not climate. Climate, on the other hand, is more than "average weather," for the variations from the average are in themselves of significance. Climate is a composite of the varying day-to-day changes.

There are three weather-conditioning factors: normal weather, that is, the conditions of the atmosphere that would exist if there were no local influences or disturbances of any kind; local influences, such as land and sea breezes and mountain and valley breezes; and the passing of cyclones and anticyclones. To forecast the weather is to evaluate in advance the importance of each of the weather elements. This would be simple in a region with none of the above-mentioned weather-conditioning factors.

Weather forecasting is not easy. It requires a thorough understanding of the science of meteorology. Long training as an apprentice is required by the Weather Bureau before one is permitted to make forecasts. In addition to a knowledge of the physics of the air, a person entering the Weather Bureau Service must be endowed with an alert and comprehensive mind and an accurate and retentive memory.

## HISTORY OF THE UNITED STATES WEATHER BUREAU

In the earlier history of weather forecasting, it was a common occurrence to find peoples of all classes ridiculing anyone who made an honest attempt to forecast weather.   Today, however, the Weather Bureau is held in high esteem and few there are who cast sneers or jokes at men who have carefully trained themselves for a serious, scientific task.   The Weather Bureau saves the people of the United States annually ten times its cost of operation.   The public of today is interested because weather affects it at every turn.   The farmer, the fruit grower, the stock shipper, and the transportation agencies by water and air are dependent upon its daily forecast.

The first attempt to forecast weather for a local area was made in 1869 by Abbe, Director of the Astronomical Observatory in Cincinnati.   At the request of the Board of Trade of that city, he accepted the responsibility of forecasting approaching storms.   The Western Union Telegraph Company agreed to transmit the messages from the surrounding cities free.   Abbe's forecasting was so successful that it gained national recognition almost instantly.   A bill to appropriate $20,000 to make weather forecasting a national undertaking was written by Professor I. A. Lapman of Milwaukee and introduced into Congress in 1870 by Hon. H. E. Pain of Wisconsin.   The bill was passed February 9, 1870, and the weather service of the United States was placed under the War Department with Albert J. Meyer, Chief Signal Officer, as its head.   It was the Chief's duty to collect weather observations at the army stations and elsewhere and to give notice of approaching storms. The first weather map was made January 1, 1871.

The weather service developed rapidly under General Meyer; he was a man of excellent executive ability, though not much interested in the scientific side of weather forecasting.   Upon his death, January 16, 1887, General William B. Hagen of the

Signal Service was made head. Under his administration marked advance was made in a scientific attempt to interpret weather changes.

The Weather Service was divorced from the army in July, 1891, and placed under the Department of Agriculture, with Professor M. W. Harrington, Director of the Astronomical Observatory of Michigan University, as its head. He was later succeeded by Willis S. Moore, July 4, 1895, as Chief. The present Chief is Francis W. Reichelderfer.

## PRESENT ORGANIZATION

The central station of the United States Weather Bureau is located in Washington, D. C. Its work is administered by a Chief, who is selected because of scientific preparation and executive ability. The appointment is nonpolitical and is made by the President. The tenure of service is for life with Civil Service status. All other commissioned persons are selected only after rigid Civil Service examinations.

Closely associated with the Chief in both executive and scientific work are an assistant chief, a chief clerk, professors of the divisions into which the work of the central station is divided, and inspectors for the various divisions. About 260 men and women are employed in the central station and 1,000 outside of Washington.

Scattered throughout the country are many other stations, as: general or first-order stations, airport stations, display stations, snowfall stations, crop stations, and cooperative stations.

## GENERAL STATIONS

There are at the present time about 190 of these stations, usually located in the larger cities throughout the United States. Each station is manned by one or more professional and subprofessional employees, the number depending upon the importance of the station. Every regular station is required to have certain standard Weather Bureau instruments: maximum and minimum thermometers, wet- and dry-bulb thermometers for securing relative humidity, rain gauge, Robinson cup anemometer, electric sunshine recorder, mercurial barometer, and a contact-making anemoscope. They may also have thermographs and barographs for keeping continuous temperature and pressure readings. Each station must collect data on maximum and minimum temperature, wind velocity, wind direction, relative humidity, amount of precipitation, forms of clouds, pressure reduced to sea level reading of the stations, and any other data that might be useful in forecasting weather.

## AIRPORT STATIONS

No other method of transportation is more influenced by weather than is air navigation. Pilots of great planes weighing many tons must have intimate knowledge of the behavior of the air along their routes. The Weather Bureau, together with the Department of Commerce, has located stations along the main arteries followed by transportation planes, by means of which the pilots are kept informed the entire 24 hours of the day as to pressure, wind direction, wind velocity, temperature, sky conditions, height of visibility, and other information that might be of value to flying pilots. For example, the following is a pilot's coded message for Omaha, Nebraska, on November 27, 1939:

X 03/4GF 217/40/40  /3 016 VSBY E8 FOG VERY SHALLOW

## COOPERATIVE STATIONS

These stations are manned by volunteers selected by a regular station under whose supervision they work. They receive no pay, nor are they required to take Civil Service examinations. Each cooperative station must make a monthly report to the regular station. The reports are primarily concerned with the collection of climatological data. There are thousands of these stations scattered throughout the United States.

## GATHERING WEATHER DATA

Each regular station is required to observe weather data at 8:00 A. M., and 8:00 P. M., Washington, D. C., time and to telegraph the same to Washington, together with such data as may have been secured in early-morning airplane flights. Before a message is sent from a station, it must be reduced to cipher code containing a series of code numbers. Here is an example of such a message sent to Washington from Omaha on the morning of November 27, 1939 (a teletype code report from three stations, sent to the Omaha Weather Bureau Station):

CA06 04204 40624 24402 2238
LS55 26204 39628 26301 00597 27
EF05 32204 38923 22103 2342

These cipher codes, when translated from the code book with which each station is supplied, give accurate information as to the weather elements from all over the United States, southern Canada, Alaska, Puerto Rico, and the Hawaiian Islands. All weather messages are coded to save expense and to prevent people along the way from securing incorrect information about the weather.

The messages are first collected in Washington, and then selected lists are sent to district forecasting centers and to some of the regular stations where weather maps are made or bulletins are published.

## FORECASTING DISTRICTS

The country is divided into seven forecasting districts. In each district is a station which supervises the forecasts for that district. These districts and forecasting centers are: New England and Middle Atlantic States—Washington, D. C.; the South Atlantic States—Jacksonville; North Central States—Chicago; South West Central States including Kansas, Missouri, and Oklahoma—Kansas City; Lower Mississippi or Gulf States—New Orleans; Rocky Mountain States—Denver; and the Pacific Coast States—San Francisco.

The official in charge of a general station in a forecasting district has the privilege of changing or modifying the district forecast for his region if he so desires.

## THE WEATHER MAP

As soon as weather telegrams come into the station, they are sent to the room of the forecast division where the code messages are translated and the data transferred to an outline map.

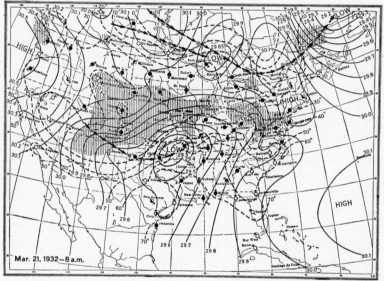

*United States Weather Bureau.*

FIG. 82. The daily weather map.

Beside and between each station, symbols and data are placed to show sky conditions, wind directions, precipitation, temperature, and pressure (Fig. 82). When all the data which have been received from all the regular stations have been transferred to the outline map, the isobars and isotherms are drawn in and the high- and low-pressure areas are located (Fig. 82). What is the meaning of "High" and "Low"?

A weather map gives a picture of the possible weather conditions which prevail in different parts of the country.

## METHODS OF FORECASTING

Long, continued training is required of any Weather Bureau official before he is permitted to make forecasts. An official who cannot make a high percentage of his forecasts accurate is not retained long in the service.

The expert forecaster first locates the storm center which appears after the morning data have been placed upon the map. He must then decide which track the storm will probably follow across the country. If the storm center is a low that has just appeared on the map for the first time, the forecaster has no way of knowing which one of the many tracks the storm center may take. In this case, he will probably place it upon the most frequented storm track.

After the storm center is located, the forecaster will then project it ahead twenty-four and forty-eight hours, at the same time taking into consideration modifications that may occur in rate of movement and changes that might occur in the weather elements. Every forecaster has certain empirical rules which he has observed after long years of experience and which he applies to each storm center.

Many unknown factors enter into determining the track taken by the storm: the rate of movement, sudden changes in the weather elements, the path followed by a storm, and its intensity are a resultant of, (1) the direction and speed of the upper drift of the atmosphere, (2) the nature of surface over which the storm passes, (3) relation to water areas, and (4) the influence of surrounding meteorological formations.

After the storm center has been located and projected ahead twenty-four to forty-eight hours on its track, the forecaster determines the probable distribution of the weather elements about the storm. He gives a detailed statement as to wind direction, condition of the sky, temperature, pressure, clouds, moisture, and precipitation in different parts of the storm.

Each district forecaster issues two forecasts daily, one at 10 A. M., and the other after 7:30 P. M. The first is based on station observations made at 7:30 A. M. Washington time and covers a twenty-four hour period from 7:30 A. M. of Wednesday, for example, to 7:30 A. M. Thursday. The second, sometimes called "tonight," includes the period from 7:30 P. M. Thursday night until 7:30 P. M. Friday.

The Weather Bureau makes extensive distribution to the general public of daily thirty-six to forty-eight-hour forecasts of weather conditions that might be expected to occur over specified areas. This distribution is accomplished by various means such as the mailing of weather maps, bulletins, and forecast cards from Weather Bureau offices and substations which are located at advantageous points over the country; by direct broadcast from Weather Bureau offices over commercial radiophone stations, or included in programs broadcast direct from commercial radio stations by their own personnel; and also by special bulletins broadcast from government-owned and commercial radiotelegraph stations. A large amount of information is also furnished press associations for publication in daily newspapers throughout the country. Every agricultural community, however remote it may be from ordinary facilities, is now on equal terms with the more populous centers in securing accurate data and warning about weather conditions.

## CYCLONIC WEATHER

We have learned that a cyclone (Fig. 76) is characterized by having low pressure at the center. Air must, therefore, move from the border of the storm toward the center. Since the earth is turning, the air moves in a counterclockwise fashion and a little to the left of the center. The direction of winds around the storm will be determined by the observer's position with reference to the storm's center. If he is situated to the east, the winds will be easterly; if to the south, air will move from a southerly direction; if to the north, northerly winds will prevail; and on the west margins, the air will be moving in from the west. In the south-southeast portion of the storm, warm winds with a high relative humidity are moving northward. On the north, cool, dry winds are coming to meet the southerly, warm, moist air. As they approach the center of the low, the air is forced to rise. As the air rises, it is suddenly cooled and

the dew point is reached, the sky becomes overcast, the temperature rises, and the pressure falls.   If the air carries sufficient
moisture, the cloudiness will be followed by rain or snow.

In the western part of the cyclone the cool, dry, northerly air
becomes warmed; thus evaporation rather than condensation
takes place, resulting in clearing skies.

The direction of the wind in the storm is determined by the
path of the cyclone's center.   If the storm center goes to the
south of the observer, backing winds will be experienced; if to
the north of the observer, veering winds will prevail.   The next
time one of these storms passes over your position, see if you
can detect whether a backing or veering wind prevails.

## ANTICYCLONIC WEATHER

The anticyclone has high pressure at its center (Fig. 77)
instead of low.   Thus, the air moves clockwise from the center
outward, or a little to the right of the center.   The weather
elements, temperature, moisture, and clouds which prevail
about the anticyclone are the reverse of those found about the
low.   The anticyclone has westerly winds on its front margins,
and easterly winds on the back side.   The air coming into the
anticyclone is from above.   It is cool, dry air, and as it settles
near the center of the storm, it is warmed and results in evaporation of moisture and clearing sky.

## THE AMERICAN BLIZZARD

A cold wave is generally defined as a sudden drop in temperature below a certain minimum within a twenty-four hour
period.   This minimum varies, depending upon the location
within the continent, and the time of year.

A blizzard often occurs when a well-developed cyclone with
abnormally low pressure passes over the country followed by a
well-developed high-pressure area, carrying a large mass of cold,
dry air.   With the passing of the low storm center, the wind
shifts suddenly to the northwest and the cold air drives in on
the west side of the storm with considerable velocity, causing

a further precipitation and drifting of the snow with rapidly falling temperature.

## WHAT IS NEW IN WEATHER FORECASTING?

The last five years have brought to the front a new method of weather analysis called the Air-Mass Analysis. The term *air mass* is given to an extensive portion of the atmosphere which is relatively homogeneous throughout.

The term *air mass* is given to an extensive portion of the atmosphere which is alike throughout in temperature, pressure, and moisture. When a large portion of the atmosphere remains stationary for some time over a more or less uniform surface, the air takes on the properties of the surface over which it rests. If the surface is a cold one, as northern Greenland, northern Canada, and outlying islands, the atmosphere in time will take on the temperature of the region over which it rests. If, on the other hand, the source region is warm, as the Gulf of Mexico, the air mass will become warm and will contain a large amount of water vapor.

Air-mass analysis involves a detailed study of the structure of the air, not only at the earth's surface but at high altitudes. It might well be thought of as the "third dimension" in weather forecasting. To determine the structure of the air at high altitudes is not easy. Airplane flights in different portions of the United States are being made daily, when atmosphere conditions permit. Planes with weather instruments attached to their wings ascend to a height of three miles and make a recording of temperature, pressure, wind direction, wind velocity, and moisture at thousand-foot intervals. Upon landing, these records are immediately sent to the Washington Weather Bureau where they are used in making weather forecasts. Hydrogen balloons are now being used.

The cold air masses entering the United States are from high northern latitudes and have various names, depending on their source regions. The cold masses are designated as follows: the Polar Canadian or Continental, Pc; Polar Pacific, Pp; and Polar Atlantic, Pa. The warm, moist air masses originate in low latitudes and for the most part over water.  They are: Tropical Gulf, Tg; Tropical Atlantic, Ta; and Tropical Pacific, Tp.

The high-latitude air masses are dry and cool, while the tropical are warm with high relative humidity.

When a cold air mass enters the country from the north and meets a warm air mass moving northward, there are likely to be rapid changes in weather along their margins.

To forecast weather by the air-mass analysis, for a period of twenty-four to forty-eight hours, the forecaster must know where the cold and warm fronts are and about where they will meet.  He receives this information from the weather elements which are obtained by pilot balloons and from airplane flights. Is it too much to anticipate that, in the near future, more accurate and longer range forecasting will become a reality?

## WEATHER LORE

Are you one of the great throng that believes in superstition? Do you look with gloom and foreboding upon future weather if on groundhog day this harmless animal should be so fortunate as to see his shadow and hie himself away underground for another six weeks' nap? Do you think it makes any difference if you plant certain kinds of garden seeds in the dark of the moon or lay shingles in moonlight?  Does the extra large house of the muskrat, the commodious nest of the timber squirrel, the extra thick husks on the ear of corn, or the thick onion skin portend long, cold winters?  Do you believe that aching corns and bunions and crowing cocks at eventime are sure signs of changing weather?  Do you think that if it rains on Easter Sunday it will rain on the four following Sundays?  If you are a believer in the above, you belong to that large family of weather lore disciples.

Weather lore is made up of both good and worthless statements.  Weather proverbs may, for convenience, be grouped into various classes: seasonal; sky signs; winds; barometric; halos; beasts and birds; hair and fibers; smoke; springs and wells; plants and animals; and the moon.

"Ice in November
Brings mud in December."

"A year of snow, a year of plenty."

"January wet, no wine you get."

"When it rains on Candlemas, the cold is over."

"If Candlemas Day is fair and bright,
Winter will have another flight."

Seasonal forecasting is as yet beyond a scientific possibility.
Most proverbs relating to seasonal changes are of no real
merit and should be given no serious consideration.

"Evening red and morning gray,
Helps the traveler on his way.
Evening gray and morning red,
Brings down rain upon his head."

"The sun sets weeping in the lowly west,
Witnessing storms to come, woe and unrest.
If the sun goes pale to bed,
'Twill rain tomorrow, it is said."

These are a few of the many sky proverbs in which sky colors
have been used to forecast coming weather. Some are fairly
good and some are worthless. Colors tell something of moisture
and dust in the air. Space will not permit a detailed discussion
of the proverbs.

"When the wind backs and the weather glass falls,
Then be on your guard against winds and gales."

"When smoke goes west,
Gude weather is past;
When smoke goes east,
Gude weather comes neist."

"The wind from the northeast,
Neither good for man or beast."

"The wind in the west suits everybody best."

"When the wind is in the south,
The rain is in the mouth."

The prevailing wind in middle latitudes is westerly.   Shifting winds usually signify the approach of a cyclonic center. Cyclones, we learned, move easterly bringing with them warm, cloudy, rainy, or snowy weather.   A thorough knowledge of cyclones and anticyclones will enable one to place a certain significance in changing winds.

The shape of clouds, as well as their height, is determined by temperature, air movement, and the relative humidity of the air.   Knowing the effect of these factors in cloud formation, cloud proverbs have been used to forecast coming weather changes:

"Mackerel sky and mares' tails,
Make lofty ships carry low sails."

"The higher the clouds, the fairer the weather."

"When the mists begin to nod,
Fisher then put up your rod."

"When the clouds appear like rocks and towers,
The earth's refreshed by frequent showers."

Halos are arcs and circles of rather large diameters showing the rainbow colors, and often appear around the moon and sun. They are caused by light from the sun or moon passing through small spicules of ice or snow.   The clouds are of the cirrus type and are generally the overflow clouds of cyclonic storms to the west of the observer.   The size of the circle is always the same, although it may appear small at times and larger at others. If the clouds are high, the ring appears small; when low, the circle is large. The size has nothing to do with the nearness or remoteness of the storm.

"A moon with a circle brings water in its beak."

"The bigger the ring, the nearer the wet."

"When the wheel is far, the storm is n'ar;
When the wheel is n'ar, the storm is far."

The behavior of animals and birds has often been used to forecast coming weather. A careful observation, however, will convince the most critical that all such proverbs are groundless. While various states of atmosphere may affect life, is it not more probable that all such actions may indicate hunger or a state of suffering from the effects of overindulgence?

"When a cow endeavors to scratch its ear,
It means a shower is very near.
When it thumps its ribs with angry tail,
Look out for thunder, lightning, hail."

"If the cock crows going to bed,
He will certainly rise with a watery head."

"When the peacock loudly bawls,
Soon we'll have both rain and squalls."

"If the cat washes her face over her ear,
'Tis a sign the weather will be fine and clear."

Many hygroscopic substances, both organic and inorganic, absorb moisture readily. Where the moisture content of the air is high, which is often the case with the approach of a cyclonic storm, hairs and vegetable fibers shorten and curl, thus:

"Curls that kink and cords that bind;
Signs of rain and heavy winds."

Smoke from chimneys in olden times was used as a sure
weather sign.   When the air is dry and cool, the ascending
smoke particles condense little or no moisture upon themselves.
The particles, lighter than the air, rise and are soon dispersed.
If the air is moist, condensation on the smoke particles takes
place rapidly and they settle to the ground, thus:

"The smoke from chimneys right ascends,
Then speeding back to earth it bends."

Cyclonic storms, which are moving areas of low pressure,
often make possible the escape of fetid odors from the ground,
marsh, or pond.   Mud-imprisoned bubbles of putrid gas, which
were unable to escape when the anticyclone was present, come
to the surface of the marsh or pond, rendering offensive the surrounding air.   Likewise underground caverns and tunnels during dry weather become filled with water and gases.   When the
surface pressure just balances the underground pressure, there
is no flow of water to the surface.   With the approach of a low-
pressure area, the surface pressure is reduced and the wells
or springs begin to spout.

"When the ditch and pond affect the nose,
Then look out for rain and storm blows."

"Very well we know,
When a well doth well,
A rain and blow
It doth foretell."

Often weather forecasts are based on certain peculiarities of
certain kinds of vegetable life.   Plant signs are not to be taken
seriously as guides to approaching weather.   Moisture, temperature, and soil condition affect plant life more than do
atmospheric conditions.

"When the ash is out before the oak,
Then you may expect a drought."

"When the oak is out before the ash
Then you ought to see it rain."

"Onion skin thick and tough,
Come winter cold and rough."

Rainbows, more than any other signs, are used to forecast coming weather. They are always seen on the opposite side of the observer from the sun. Thus an evening rainbow means that the storm has passed and the morrow is coming fair; a morning bow, the storm is to the west and may mean rain and storm.

"A rainbow in the morning,
Is the shepherd's warning;
A rainbow at night,
Is the sailor's delight."

"Rainbow to windward, foul weather the day;
A rainbow to leeward, damp sun away."

These are but a few of the many weather lore sayings that have been handed down from ancient times. Some have suggestions of truth, while others are highly fantastic and nonscientific.

No forecast extending beyond twenty-four or forty-eight hours should be taken seriously at this time.

# CHAPTER 14

# SOUND

From time immemorial man has spontaneously expressed his feelings in song, whether of joy or sadness, exaltation or despair.  It has not been necessary for his song to be in words, nor even that it have a thought content.  Words and ideas may even hamper the free flow of feeling that often wells over in song.  Tones and cadences have been an adequate vehicle for the expression of both the heights and the depths of human emotion.  But for this purpose man has not been content to rely upon the voice alone.  He has fashioned musical instruments of many forms.  Some of these have been as simple as the pipes of Pan, some so complex as to be mastered by only the few of great ability.  Whether simple or intricate, their effectiveness as means of expression depends less upon their own inherent qualities than upon the genius of the musician to whose hand they respond.

Even more important than the sounds of music are those of speech.  True, many of these are also musical, but not all. The vocal sounds most important in music are the vowels. Those most important in speech are the consonants, the vowels serving chiefly as connecting links for consonants.

It is impossible to say at what stage of his development man began to use a definite spoken language.  One can be certain, however, that this event marked a distinct upward turn.  Language not only facilitates the mental growth of the hearer by adding a store of contributed ideas, but also stimulates mental activity in both hearer and speaker, thus establishing the condition necessary for the conception of still other ideas.  Mental development operates on the principle of compound interest. Each new achievement helps in making still further gains.

Let us turn to the distinctly physical aspects of sound.

## HOW SOUNDS ORIGINATE

We shall begin our study by asking the question, "By what means are sounds produced?" and shall attempt to answer by referring to a few simple examples. If a finger is touched to the larynx while a vowel is intoned in a clear voice, a rapid vibratory motion is felt. This increases in vigor with the loudness of the sound. A similar movement is felt if any musical instrument, such as the violin, is touched while it is sounding a clear, sustained note. The string of a violin when bowed seems to spread out into a fuzzy band. A stylus attached to the prong of a sounding tuning fork and drawn over a piece of smoked or whited glass traces a wavy line. All of these observations indicate that a sounding object is in rapid vibratory motion. To extend the study to such instruments as horns and organ pipes merely confirms the conclusion already reached, that sounds originate from vibrations. In the latter type of instrument the vibrating body is the column or mass of included air.

## HOW SOUND REACHES THE EAR

If a sounding object such as an electric bell is supported by springs or by a pile of soft cotton under a bell jar and an air pump applied, the sound becomes steadily more faint as the evacuation proceeds. When the air has been nearly all removed the sound is scarcely audible. When air is readmitted, it resumes its original intensity. If the bell jar is now filled with some other gas, carbon dioxide for example, the sound is heard distinctly, as before. Gases are thus shown to be able to transmit sounds, while empty space is not.

If a disk of some light material is attached to the handle of a vibrating tuning fork and the disk held in contact with the surface of oil, water, or any other liquid in a tumbler as shown in Fig. 83, a distinct sound is heard issuing from the table upon which the tumbler stands. The vibration has been transmitted to the table through the liquid. If the handle of the fork is held against one end of a light rod the other end of which stands upon the table, the sound is heard coming from the table as before. The vibration has been transmitted by the rod.

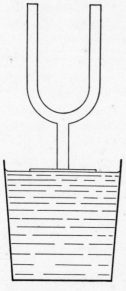

That sound may be carried by both solids and liquids is well known to the schoolboy who places his ear to one rail of a track to hear a distant train, or who strikes two stones together under water while his friends dive down to listen.

## THE SPEED OF SOUND

In watching a foot race, persons at the finish line of the 100 yard dash will see the smoke of the starter's pistol a short time before hearing the report. Persons a mile or so from a locomotive approaching a crossing will see the steam from the whistle a few seconds before hearing the sound. The time elapsing between the seeing and the hearing is

Fig. 83. Transmission of sound by a liquid.

that required for the sound to travel the intervening distance. The speed of sound may be found by measuring the time required for it to travel a measured distance. In air at 0° C. it is about 1087 feet per second. At higher temperatures it is greater, increasing at the rate of about 2 feet per second for each centigrade degree. In water the speed is about 5000 and in steel about 16,500 feet per second, or roughly about 1 mile and 3 miles per second respectively. In both cases the speed increases with rise of temperature.

## SOUND IS A WAVE PHENOMENON

Let Fig. 84 represent a tall narrow jar with a sounding tuning fork held close above it. If the length of the air column is altered by changing the amount of water in the jar, the intensity of the sound will vary, and for a certain length of column it will reach a maximum. The fork and air are then said to be in *resonance* with each other. The air column has a natural frequency exactly equal to that of the fork. If the fork is now rotated slowly about the axis of the handle, the sound will again vary in loudness, and for certain positions of the fork will dis-

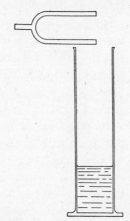

FIG. 84.   Reenforcement of sound by resonance.

appear. It may be made to appear again, however, without further rotation of the fork by placing a small tube around the upper prong, without touching it.

These two surprising effects, that of the disappearance of the sound when the fork is rotated, and its reappearance when one of the prongs is surrounded by a tube, may be explained as

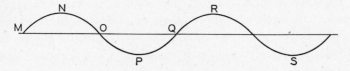

FIG. 85.   A water wave.

follows: The fork has in reality sent out two trains of waves, one from each prong. If these were waves on the surface of water, each would look somewhat like the wavy line in Fig. 85. In a symbolic way this line may also represent a sound wave. If in entering the jar one of the trains is half a wave length behind the other, as shown in Fig. 86, they will everywhere tend to neutralize each other's effect.   If they are of equal intensity, they will completely destroy each other, and no sound will be heard.   If one of the wave trains is prevented from entering

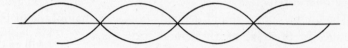

FIG. 86.   Waves in opposite phase.

the jar, as was done when the tube was placed over one of the prongs, the other enters alone and is reenforced by resonance.

## THE NATURE OF SOUND WAVES

Let Fig. 87 represent a strip of steel clamped at one end, and vibrating to and fro at the upper end.   During the move-

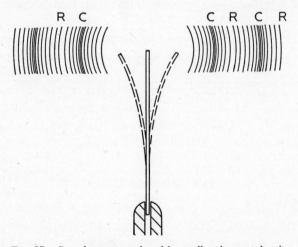

FIG. 87.   Sound waves produced by a vibrating metal strip.

ment to the left, the air to the left of the strip is somewhat compressed, that to the right of it somewhat rarefied.   During movement to the right, the compression is to the right of the strip and the rarefaction to the left.   These disturbances in the air, repeated at each vibration of the strip, travel outward in all directions.   In Fig. 87 $C$, $C$, $C$, represent regions of greatest compression, while $R$, $R$, represent regions of greatest rarefaction. If Fig. 85 is taken to represent a sound wave, such points as $N$ and $R$ on the curve will represent regions of maximum compression, while such as $P$ and $S$ will represent regions of maximum rarefaction.

The loudness of a sound depends upon the magnitude of the changes in pressure as the sound wave passes. The greater the variation, the louder the sound. In general the larger the vibrating object and the greater its movement, the greater these variations will be.

## WAVE LENGTH

The length of a water wave is the distance from one crest to the next, that is, the distance from $N$ to $R$ in Fig. 85. In the same way the length of a sound wave is the distance from one point of maximum compression to the next, that is, from one $C$ to the next in Fig. 87.

The length of a sound wave evidently varies with the vibration frequency of the sounding object, and with the speed at which the sound wave travels. If a piano string whose frequency is 200 vibrations per second is struck and the speed of sound in the surrounding air is 1130 feet per second, at the end of one second the space around to a distance of 1130 feet will be filled with these 200 waves. The length of one wave is therefore

$$1130/200 = 5.65 \text{ feet.}$$

If the same number of waves per second is made in water in which the speed is 5000 feet per second, the wave length is

$$5000/200 = 25 \text{ feet.}$$

## PITCH

If the vibration frequencies of two tuning forks giving tones of the same pitch are measured, it is found that they are the same. If the notes are of different pitch, the one of higher pitch is emitted by the fork making the greater number of vibrations per second. If a fork and a piano string emit tones of the same pitch, the fork and string are found to have the same vibration frequency. If one emits a higher tone than the other, the one of higher pitch is found to have a greater frequency. It appears, therefore, that the pitch of a sound depends only upon the vibration frequency and not upon the character of the sounding object.

The same conclusion will be drawn if we observe the sounds made by a siren disc. This instrument consists of a disc in which rows of equally spaced holes are arranged in circles, as shown in Fig. 88. If a jet of air is blown against one of the rows while the disc is rotated, a sound is made whose pitch

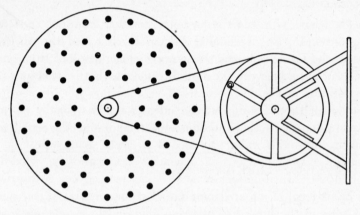

FIG. 88. Siren disc.

rises as the speed of rotation is increased. If the speed is such that the siren emits the same note as a fork or string, it is found that the number of puffs of air per second made by the holes of the siren is just equal to the number of vibrations per second made by fork or string. Each puff made as a hole passes the jet gives rise to one sound wave.

## SOUNDS THE EAR CANNOT HEAR

If the siren disc is rotated at a diminishing speed with the air jet directed at one of the rows of holes, the pitch of the sound goes steadily lower. When the number of puffs of air falls below about 15 or 16 per second, it ceases to be a continuous musical note. The disturbance is heard as a series of individual puffs. If the siren is speeded up, the continuous musical character of the sound begins again at about 16 puffs per second. From this point the pitch continues to rise until at a frequency of about 20,000 waves per second it is too high for the ear to hear.

## MUSICAL INTERVALS

The numbers of holes in the various circles of the siren disc described above are commonly 24, 30, 36, and 48. If the disc is rotated at a speed of ten rotations per second and the air jet directed against these various rows in succession, sounds are made whose vibration frequencies are 240, 300, 360, and 480 per second. The ratio 300/240 or 5/4 is called the *interval* between the first note and the second. The ratio 360/240 or 3/2 is the *interval* between the first note and the third. If the speed of rotation of the disc were doubled, the vibration frequencies would all be doubled, but the ratio of the frequencies of the various notes to each other would remain unchanged. The musical intervals would still be 5/4, 3/2, etc., as before.

## HARMONY AND DISCORD

If air jets are directed simultaneously at any two of the rows of holes in the siren disc, the combination of tones is pleasing. This is true of any three, and of all four. If there were another row, with 31 holes, for example, the effect of sounding this row with any of the others would not be pleasing. The first four tones are said to be *harmonious*. The last, with any of the others, is not harmonious, but *discordant*. It is found that in any case in which the interval can be expressed as a ratio of small whole numbers the tones are harmonious. If they cannot be so expressed, the tones are discordant.

For example, two tones whose frequencies are 240 and 300 vibrations per second harmonize with each other. The interval between them, 300/240, may be expressed as the ratio of the small whole numbers 5 and 4. Tones whose frequencies are 240 and 265 do not harmonize with each other. The interval

265/240 cannot be expressed as a ratio of whole numbers smaller than 53 and 48.

## MUSICAL SCALES

Students of the physics of sound use a scale composed of eight notes whose vibration frequencies are proportional to the following numbers:

24, 27, 30, 32, 36, 40, 45, and 48.

In this scale it is usual to take middle C as having a frequency of 256 vibrations per second. The notes of the gamut then have frequencies as follows:

| C | D | E | F | G | A | B | C |
|---|---|---|---|---|---|---|---|
| 256 | 288 | 320 | 341.33 | 384 | 426.67 | 480 | 512 |

These eight notes constitute what is called an *octave*, and the scale they represent is called the *diatonic scale*. The intervals between successive notes are not equal, but have the values

9/8, 10/9, 16/15, 9/8, 10/9, 9/8, and 16/15.

The first, third, and fifth notes have vibration frequencies in proportion to the numbers 4, 5, and 6. Any such group is called a *major triad*. Because the ratio is one of small whole numbers, the notes are harmonious. The fourth, sixth, and eighth notes also constitute a major triad. The fifth, seventh, and the octave above the second constitute a third such triad. Such combinations are of very frequent occurrence in music.

Because of the inequalities in the intervals, the diatonic scale is not suitable for use in most musical instruments. On this account an entirely different scale is used. In this scale there are thirteen notes in the octave, the last note of one octave being the first note of the next. The twelve intervals all have the same value. This is therefore called the *equally tempered scale*. In the piano keyboard there are thirteen keys in each octave. Eight of these are white, for the tones that correspond approximately to those of the diatonic scale. The other five are black, one to divide each of the larger intervals.

## BEATS

In studying the nature of sound waves we found that two waves of the same frequency may unite in such a way as to produce a wave of greatly reduced intensity, and even to annul each other entirely.   Complete extinction of the sound occurs if the two tones are of equal intensity and meet in *opposite phase*, that is, if the crest of one wave falls exactly in the trough of the other.   This is illustrated in Fig. 86.   Two such sound waves may also combine to produce a greatly intensified sound.   This occurs when the waves travel together in the same phase, that is, crest on crest.   If two tones of slightly

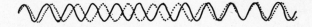

Fig. 89.   Beats.

different frequency travel together, a new phenomenon known as *beats* appears.   This is illustrated in Fig. 89.   Let us suppose that one of the tones is the result of 256 vibrations per second and the other of 260.   In this case the crests of the two waves fall exactly together four times per second.   The combination then gives a greatly intensified sound.   Likewise the crest of one falls upon the trough of the other four times per second. The result is then a greatly weakened sound.   This rise and fall of intensity is the effect referred to above as beats.   The frequencies 256 and 260 when sounded together give rise to four beats per second.   If the frequencies 256 and 258 or 258 and 260 are sounded together, there are two beats per second. The number of beats made per second is equal to the difference between the frequencies of the two tones combining to produce them.   Two strings may be easily tuned to exact unison by slowly changing the tension and hence the frequency of one of them until all beats disappear.

## BEAT TONES

Let us suppose that two similar whistles with movable pistons are sounding the same note. No beats are heard. If one of the pistons is now slightly moved to raise the pitch a few vibrations per second, just that number of beats will be heard. As the piston is moved still farther, the number of beats steadily increases, as described above. What is to be expected when the number exceeds 16 per second? It is found that to the ear the effect is the same as if a new tone were sounded whose frequency is that of the number of beats produced. At such frequencies these are no longer called beats, but *beat tones*.

## MUSICAL INSTRUMENTS

The instruments most highly regarded are those whose notes are made by the vibrations of air columns or of strings. The pipe organ, flute, bugle, horn, piccolo, clarinet, cornet, trombone, and tuba are representatives of the first group. The piano, harp, violin, viola, violoncello, mandolin, and banjo are of the second group.

Every schoolboy who has made willow whistles knows that a long whistle gives a low-pitched note, while a short one gives a high note. At the closed end of the whistle cavity no air movement is possible but only changes in pressure. This marks the location of a *node*. At the open end of the tube there is a maximum movement of air. This marks the location of a loop, or *antinode*. From node to loop is one-fourth of a wave length. The length of the sound wave made by the whistle is therefore about four times the length of the whistle cavity. Since sounds of different pitch all travel at the same speed, the longer the wave the fewer of them the whistle will make in a second, and hence the lower the pitch. The same principle applies to all musical instruments in which the sounds are made by vibrating air columns. In the pipe organ the tones of different pitch are produced by tubes of different length. In order to cover the

range of notes desired the organ must have many tubes, some of
which are quite long in order to register the low notes. To
give a note as low as 20 vibrations per second, the tube, if closed
at one end, must have a length of about

$$\frac{1130}{4 \times 20} = 14.1 \text{ ft.}$$

In what is called an open tube (open at both ends) there is
an antinode at each end. The length of the tube is therefore
half that of the sound wave it emits. To produce 20 vibrations
per second an open tube would be 28.2 ft. long. In other wind
instruments, such as the flute, cornet, trombone, etc., different
notes may be sounded by changing the length of the enclosed
air column. In many instruments this is accomplished by
opening or closing holes in the side of the tube. Such is the
case in the flute, piccolo, clarinet, bassoon, and many others.
The effective length of the air column is the distance from the
lip or mouthpiece to the nearest open orifice. In some cases
the length of air column is changed by altering the length of the
tube, as in the slide trombone.

## STRINGED INSTRUMENTS

The harp has a frame upon which are stretched strings of
various length and thickness. This is also true of the piano.
In these instruments the low notes are given by the long heavy
strings, the high notes by the short thin ones. The strings are
of such length and thickness that when put under proper tension
they give the successive notes of the musical scale.

In many other stringed instruments such as the violin, the
cello, the mandolin, and banjo, the strings are all of equal length
though not of equal weight. The number of strings also is
very limited. The violin has only four. Since the number of
strings is small, each string must be made to give notes of
different pitch. This is accomplished by varying its effective
length. By pressing a string against the finger board the player
uses only that portion of it which lies between the finger and the

bridge.　It is this selection of proper lengths of string that keeps the left hand so busy when lively music is played.

In certain instruments like the banjo, strips of metal are fixed across the finger board in such a way as to enable the player to use only strings of certain definite length.　The player of this instrument is therefore less able than the violinist to secure notes whose frequencies differ from each other by very small amounts.

## OTHER INSTRUMENTS

Still other instruments set up sound waves by the vibrations of other types of objects.　The triangle, for example, is a metal rod bent into triangular form.　Rods are likewise the sounding elements of the xylophone.　Here they are of wood.　Short thick pieces vibrate at a high rate and give notes of high pitch. Longer pieces vibrate less rapidly and give notes of lower pitch. The wooden rods are so made and so arranged that they give in order the various notes of the musical scale just as is done in the piano.　A tube of proper length is placed under each rod to reenforce its note by resonance.

In drums the sound is set up by vibrating diaphragms; in cymbals by thin metal plates.

## QUALITY OF SOUND

We have seen that when properly interpreted such a curve as that of Fig. 85 may represent a sound of which the distance from $M$ to $Q$ or from $N$ to $R$ represents one wave length.　This is the simplest type of musical sound.　It is the type emitted by a tuning fork.

If one of two forks has a vibration rate just double that of the other, the notes these forks emit may be represented by the curves $A$ and $B$ of Fig. 90.　However, when sounded together the two notes combine to make a wave form which is different from that represented by either $A$ or $B$.　The resultant note may be represented by the curve $C$.

If one of the forks has a frequency three times that of the other, the separate notes and their resultant may be represented by the three curves of Fig. 91.

It is seen that the wave length and the frequency of the combination tone are in each case the same as those of the fork of
lower pitch.    The ear can detect no change in this respect because
of the sounding of the other fork.    The character of the tone

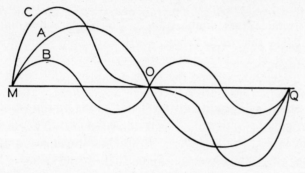

FIG. 90.    Two Harmonious Sounds.    Ratio of frequencies, 1 to 2.

however is very different, so that the ear can readily distinguish between the resultant and the single low-pitched tone.
It can also distinguish between the two resultant tones obtained
as just described.    The forms of the two resultant waves are
different both from the original waves and from each other.

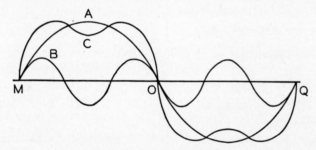

FIG. 91.    Two Harmonious Sounds.    Ratio of frequencies, 1 to 3.

It is on this account that they make such widely different
impressions upon the ear.    The characteristic of a tone that
enables the ear to distinguish it from other tones of the same
intensity and pitch is called its *quality*, or *timbre*.

Although a tuning fork makes a sound that may be represented
by a simple curve such as that of Fig. 85, this is not true of many

other sounding objects. Strings, for example, do not give such simple tones. The modes of vibration of violin, piano, and other strings have been very carefully studied. It has been found that each string vibrates not only as a whole but also as if composed of two equal parts. Each part gives rise to a note whose frequency is double that of the string vibrating as a whole. The tone of the whole-length string may be represented by curve *A* of Fig. 90, that of the segments by curve *B*. The former is the lowest tone the string produces, and is called the *fundamental*. The latter is called an *overtone*. If, as here, the overtone has a frequency which is an exact multiple of that of the fundamental, it is also called a *harmonic*. The combined effect of the two tones may be represented by curve *C*.

While vibrating as a whole and as halves, the string may also vibrate in three, four, five, and greater numbers of equal parts. The segments then give rise to overtones whose frequencies are three, four, five, etc., times that of the fundamental.

In Fig. 91 curve *A* may represent the fundamental of a string and curve *B* its first odd overtone (frequency three times that of the fundamental). Curve *C* will then represent the combined effect of the two simple tones.

By means of an ingenious instrument called a *phonodeik*, Professor Miller of the Case School of Applied Science discovered many interesting things concerning the tones produced by various musical instruments. In almost every case the tone consisted of the fundamental and several harmonics. The violin and flute each gave about half a dozen overtones, the oboe gave about a dozen, and the clarinet twenty or more. The horn gave the greatest number of all, its low notes including the entire series of harmonics up to thirty.

The wave forms of sound may also be studied by means of a microphone connected with an oscillograph. Fig. 92 is a curve obtained in this way. This wave form was produced by a female voice intoning the vowel ō at a fundamental frequency of about 300 vibrations per second. From such curves it is possible to determine what overtones are present, and what their relative intensities are. The curve of Fig. 92 indicates the presence of a very strong first overtone.

The striking of a single tuning fork produces a sound which is rather barren and uninteresting. If four tuning forks whose frequencies are in the ratio of four, five, six, and eight are struck at the same time, the pitch is the same as if only the lowest fork were struck. The tone given by the four, however, is much more pleasing. The quality has been changed by the presence of the higher tones.

We prize such instruments as the violin, cello, piano, and harp partly because their notes are rich in overtones. We are

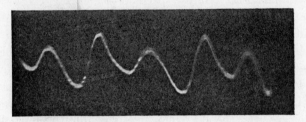

FIG. 92.   The vowel ō intoned by a female voice.

delighted by what we call a pleasing voice. Its overtones are also many and harmonious. It is largely because of differences in the number and relative intensities of overtones that we are able to distinguish between different instruments sounding the same note, and between different voices, whether in singing or in speaking.

## THE ORCHESTRA

In your favorite orchestra there are several instruments, perhaps several dozen, all playing at the same time. Each instrument is giving forth its characteristic tones, many of which are composed of the fundamental and several overtones. The total number of tones and overtones emitted at any instant by all of these instruments may be very great. Even the best trained ear may not be able to catch them all. Yet they all blend together and are all essential in producing the total pleasing effect.

## SOUNDS FROM MOVING OBJECTS

If two cars pass each other on the highway while the horn of one is sounding, the occupants of the other notice a change of pitch as the two cars approach each other, pass, and separate. While they are approaching each other, the pitch is higher than that corresponding to the vibration frequency of the horn. When they are receding from each other, it is lower. This change from what we may call the normal pitch is directly proportional to the relative speeds of the cars.

The apparent change of pitch from the relative motion of the hearer and the sounding body is known as the *Doppler effect*. It results from the fact that when the distance between them is diminishing, the number of waves entering the ear per second is greater than the number emitted by the sounding object. When the distance between them is increasing, the number entering the ear is less than the number emitted.

The same effect occurs in the case of light waves. The importance of this will be pointed out in Chap. 17.

## SOUND RECORDING

A radio audience is frequently told that it has been hearing a program of recorded music, or that the speech or play has been given by sound transcription, or that a recorded announcement will now be made. From this we may infer that the phonograph record is still in active service.

The phonograph is one of Edison's great inventions. In the original method of recording sound, a diaphragm was made to vibrate in accordance with the variations of pressure in the sound wave. A stylus attached to the diaphragm had its point resting upon a rotating cylinder of wax, and thus engraved a fine spiral line of varying depth. The louder the sound, the greater the movement of the diaphragm and the greater the variations in the depth of the groove. To reproduce the sound it was only necessary to reverse the process. The cylinder was rotated as before.   A steel or fiber needle, which was substituted for the stylus, was allowed to travel in the groove, rising and falling as the stylus had done.   The movement thus given to the needle was transmitted to the diaphragm, which then set up sound waves like the ones by which the record was made.

The phonograph disc of the present day represents an improvement over the early wax cylinder in several important respects.   It is a more convenient form of record to store and to handle.   Because of its suitability to receive an impression on both surfaces it is also more economical of both space and material.   By its form it facilitates easy, exact, and almost unlimited duplication; for a master record may be made in metal and then used as a die to stamp in wax as many copies as may be desired.   But the greatest improvement lies in the fact that the recording is now done by a stylus driven by electrical impulses which correspond much more closely to the characteristics of the original sound than the movements of the diaphragm-driven stylus could be made to do.

In reproducing the sound, greatly improved methods are also available.   Instead of the diaphagm a small coil of fine wire in a strong magnetic field is used.   When moved by the needle, this operates as a tiny dynamo to generate a small electric current which is almost indistinguishable in character from the one actuating the recording stylus.   This current is then amplified and passed into a loud speaker, which gives a very faithful reproduction of the original sound.

Many radio broadcasting stations maintain libraries of standard phonograph records, chiefly of music.   When it is desired to put one of these selections on the air, the record is run as described, the electric current taken from it being carried to the broadcast transmitter instead of to a loud speaker. Many programs broadcast in this way, whether of band, orchestra or chorus, or of a vocal or instrumental soloist, are so faithfully reproduced as to be hardly distinguishable from the original performance.

Programs or announcements to be broadcast from several widely separated stations are sometimes supplied to them in the form of phonograph records. Another procedure is for the station itself to make a recording from the original broadcast. The material may then be run later in the usual way. Speeches, news broadcasts, and the like are well adapted to be handled in this manner.

## SOUNDS IN BUILDINGS

If the hands are clapped a single time in a large empty auditorium, the probability is strong, unless special care has been taken in the design or construction of the room, that the sound will continue to be heard with diminishing intensity for several seconds. The sound waves are reflected from ceiling, floor, and walls, and continue traveling about the room, but lose a certain fraction of their energy at each reflection. If this fraction is large, the energy is soon dissipated and the sound quickly dies away. If the fraction is small, the energy is dissipated slowly and the sound continues for a longer time. The persistence of sound in such a case is called *reverberation*. If the reverberation time in an auditorium is long, the sound of one syllable may still be strong when the next is spoken. The result is confusion.

The science of acoustics has now been developed to such a point that in any new auditorium good acoustic properties can be planned for and attained with almost as much certainty as other desirable features. The room will be so designed as to avoid large regular reflecting areas. The walls and ceiling will probably be covered in part with soft materials such as felt or fabricated cork board which strongly absorb the energy of the sound. Seat cushions and an audience also help to absorb the sound and reduce reverberation. All of these factors contribute toward improving the acoustics.

In the studios of radio transmitting stations special care is taken to avoid reverberation, and thus assure that each sound or syllable will reach the microphone with the greatest possible distinctness. The need for this is often painfully clear to the radio audience when the broadcast is made from an inadequately insulated auditorium.

# CHAPTER 15

# ILLUMINATION

## ILLUMINATION IN COLONIAL DAYS

To our colonial forefathers the problem of illumination was a fairly simple one. For the most part this was provided almost exclusively by the great luminary—the sun. Franklin's philosophy of early to bed and early to rise suggests a mode of life whose wisdom lay largely in necessity. After sunset was darkness, and the most effective means for dispelling it consisted of nothing better than a tallow dip or candle.

## LATER SOURCES OF LIGHT

A distinct improvement in artificial lighting came with the development of the kerosene lamp. Its wick could be made wide and could be turned high. The resulting high, broad flame, rich in particles of solid carbon made luminous by the heat, gave several times as much light as the ordinary candle. A little later natural gas and gas made by the distillation of coal or in other ways came into use for illuminating purposes. At first the gas light was merely a broad open flame, scarcely superior except in convenience to the kerosene lamp.

In 1885 Auer von Welsbach, an Austrian scientist and inventor, conceived the idea of using a Bunsen burner as a means of producing better illumination. This type of burner, which mixes air with the gas before passing it into the flame, gives an intense heat but, as ordinarily used, almost no light. At the temperature of the Bunsen flame certain oxides glow brilliantly. By making a screen-like mantle of such oxides and supporting it in the hottest region of the flame, Welsbach suc-

209

ceeded in developing a lamp which gave a steady light of remarkably high illuminating power. Because of its convenience, its powerful light, and its freedom from soot and odor, the Welsbach lamp rapidly displaced kerosene wherever gas was available. Many persons in middle life will well remember its advantages.

Even before the advent of the Welsbach mantle, great strides had been made in developing methods of lighting by means of an electric current. Though the basic discoveries of both arc and incandescent filament lighting had been made by Sir Humphry Davy as early as 1810, no practical electric lighting system for general use was developed until the latter part of the century. The long delay was due chiefly to the lack of suitable methods of producing the necessary current. This was supplied by Gramme in 1870 by the invention of a new type of dynamo. A system of arc lighting for the illumination of streets and large buildings was developed by Brush, and introduced in 1878.

Meanwhile Edison had been searching the world for a material that could be formed into a filament, enclosed in an evacuated bulb, and heated by an electric current. This he succeeded in finding in 1879. The material used was carbon obtained from a particular type of bamboo. The carbon filament lamp was less brilliant but more convenient than either the electric arc or the Welsbach gas lamp. It rapidly displaced the latter wherever electric power became available.

Research in the laboratories of the General Electric Company led to the discovery of methods by which tungsten can be fashioned into filaments of any required length and fineness. These withstand much more intense heating than carbon without undue evaporation and glow more brilliantly. The permissible temperature and hence the brilliancy is raised still farther by filling the bulb with an inert gas, nitrogen or argon. This is the most efficient of the incandescent lamps in use today.

Several other types of lamp are of still more recent development. One of these is the Cooper-Hewitt mercury arc. Another is the familiar neon glow lamp. A third is the sodium lamp, recently put on the market, and recommended as especially well suited for highway lighting.

The mercury arc lamp consists of an evacuated tube two or three feet long and an inch or two in diameter, with an electrode in each end. The lamp operates with the tube in a slightly inclined position. The electrode in the low end of the tube is a pool of mercury. When the arc is started, some of the mercury is vaporized, and it is this vapor that carries the current and emits the light. For general illumination the mercury vapor lamp has the disadvantage of casting a sickly yellow-greenish hue. Because of the strong actinic properties of its light this lamp is widely used for illumination in photographic work.

In the neon glow lamp, neon gas fills the tube at a pressure of a few millimeters of mercury, and is made luminous by the electric discharge. The result is a moderate intensity of light from a large source. By the addition of small amounts of other gases, such as helium and the vapor of mercury, various colors are obtained, which contribute considerably to the value of the sign as an advertising means. The neon lamp operates at a rather high voltage, 8000 to 12,000 volts, and has a high illuminating efficiency.

The sodium lamp, like the mercury arc and the neon glow lamp, emits light throughout its volume due to the incandescence of the enclosed vapor. The bulb contains neon at a low pressure, and a small amount of metallic sodium. When the light is first turned on, the neon carries the entire current until enough heat has been developed to vaporize the sodium. The latter then becomes luminous and thereafter contributes nearly all the light. The sodium lamp is well adapted to street and highway lighting because of its very high light-giving power. The amount of light it emits per watt of electrical power used is about three times as great as that of the best incandescent filament lamp.

By these more modern types of lamp the darkness has been largely dispelled not only from our homes, factories, offices, and public buildings, but also from our city streets, and to some extent from suburban thoroughfares.

## THE POWER OF A LAMP

One important question concerning any lamp is that of its light-emitting power. This is often expressed in terms of how much light it will give as compared with that given by a *standard candle*. Such a standard is the light given by a candle of spermaceti burning at the rate of 120 grains (7.776 gm.) per hour. A lamp giving ten times as much light as a standard candle is said to be of ten *candle power*.

## INTENSITY OF ILLUMINATION

A more important question than that of candle power, though closely related to it, concerns the intensity of light falling

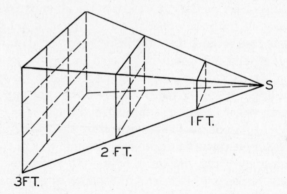

FIG. 93. How illumination varies with distance from lamp.

upon the object we wish to see. The intensity is directly proportional to the candle power of the source. It also diminishes with increasing distance from the source. If the light is too faint, one obvious remedy is to move closer to the lamp. It is seen from Fig. 93 that at a distance of two feet the area over which a beam of light from $S$ is spread is four times as great as at one foot, while at three feet the surface is nine times as great as at one foot. At two feet from the lamp the amount of light falling upon one square inch of surface is therefore only one-fourth as great, and at three feet only one-ninth as great as at one foot. Expressing this as a general law we may say that the illumination varies inversely as the square of the distance from the source. The intensity of illumination on a surface perpendicular to the beam at a distance of one foot from a standard candle is called a *foot-candle*. The intensity at 2 ft. from a 10 candle power lamp is $10/2^2 = 2.5$ foot-candles. At 10 ft. from a 100 candle power lamp it is $100/10^2 = 1$ foot-candle.

## MEASURING THE CANDLE POWER

Oil or molten paraffine spread thinly over heavy clear white paper renders it translucent. Light passes through it readily but is diffused in the process, so that objects, if seen through it at all, are not distinctly outlined. If the oil or paraffine is applied to the paper in a small spot and a light placed on one side, the spot seems dark if seen from the illuminated side, but bright if seen from the opposite side. The spot appears dark in the one case because there the light passes through the paper, while all around the spot it is reflected to the eye, causing the surrounding paper to appear bright. It is the oil spot that appears bright when the paper is viewed from the opposite side because there the light comes through and reaches the eye, while all around the spot the light is cut off by the paper.

The facts just mentioned provide a simple way of comparing the intensities of two sources of light. An instrument for this purpose is called a *photometer*. If a paper with a small paraffined spot is placed between the two lights, the action described above takes place for each of them. If the paper is moved away from one of the lamps and toward the other, the spot will grow brighter or darker depending on which side is viewed. For one position of the paper it will practically disappear. In that position the paper is equally illuminated on the two sides. If the distances of the lamps from the paper are then measured, their relative candle powers may be easily computed. Since the intensity of light at different distances from the source varies inversely as the square of the distance, it follows that the candle powers of the lamps compared in this way will be in the same ratio as the squares of their distances from the paper. This may be stated as an equation thus:

$$\frac{P_1}{P_2} = \frac{d_1^2}{d_2^2}.$$

If one of the lamps must be placed 1 ft. from the paper in order to illuminate it as strongly as the other does at 2 ft., the second lamp is four times as powerful a source as the first.

$$\frac{P_2}{P_1} = \frac{d_2^2}{d_1^2} = \frac{2^2}{1^2} = \frac{4}{1}.$$

If $P_1$ is a lamp of 1 candle power, then $P_2$ is of 4 candle power.

The candle powers of kerosene lamps vary with the height and width of the wick—that is, with the rate at which the fuel is consumed. The candle powers of incandescent electric lamps depend upon several different factors. The most important of these are the amount of electrical power used, the kind of filament and its temperature, and the kind of glass in the bulb, whether clear or colored. A 40 watt, clear glass lamp with bulb evacuated will give about 25 candle power, while a 1000 watt, nitrogen-filled lamp may give as much as 1500 candle power. In the first case it requires about 1.6 watts of electrical power to yield 1 candle power, in the second only .66 watt.

## AMOUNT OF LIGHT NEEDED

Different persons require different amounts of light. An older person is very likely to need more than a younger one. The amount of light required also depends greatly upon the nature of one's activity. Lighting intensities for the home approved by the Illuminating Engineering Society include the following: For general work in the kitchen and elsewhere, 5 to 10 foot-candles; for ordinary reading and writing and for sewing on light goods, 10 to 20 foot-candles; for prolonged reading of fine type or prolonged sewing on light goods either by hand or with a sewing machine, 20 to 50 foot-candles; for fine needle work on dark goods, 100 foot-candles or more.

Much of the work in factories and stores requires only a moderate amount of light—10 to 15 foot-candles. For typing and other comparable work in an office, 20 to 30 foot-candles is recommended. Fine mechanical work of any kind such as mechanical drawing, or watch assembling or repairing, requires as much light as the reading of script or fine type.

## MEASURING ILLUMINATION

The *photoelectric* cell (see Chap. 19), popularly known as the *electric eye*, is called upon for many kinds of service in many different fields. Among these is the field of illumination. When light shines upon such a cell connected into an appropriate circuit, an electric current is produced. If the light is faint, the current is small; if intense, the current is greater. A

*Weston Electric Instrument Corporation.*
FIG. 94.   Universal exposure meter.

galvanometer (described in Chap. 19) connected in circuit with such a cell will measure the current it yields and thus give a measure of the illumination. The galvanometer scale may be marked to read in foot-candles. The combination is then called a *foot-candle meter*. To the illuminating engineer it is indispensable.

Such an instrument is of great value to the photographer also. He calls it an *exposure meter*, and uses it to obtain accurate information which guides his camera adjustment and his exposure time. An instrument of this type, which also indicates the intensity of the light in foot-candles, is represented in Fig. 94.

## GLARE AND SHADOWS

In designing a lighting system, whether for a home, an office, or a factory, an approach to uniformity of illumination is very desirable. Sharply contrasting regions of strong and faint illumination, as in the case of sharp shadows, are very detrimental to clear vision. Frosted electric bulbs are much better than bulbs of clear glass because the light is then diffused and comes to the eye from the entire bulb and not directly from the intensely luminous filament. Indirect lighting, in which a large portion of the light is diffused from ceiling and walls, is still better.

Glare results when too much light enters the eye, or when there are sharp differences in the amounts reaching the eye from different points or objects close together. This condition unfortunately exists in many a study where the table top is well polished and the papers white and shiny. Strong automobile headlights on the highway, showing as intense spots shining out of the darkness, may cause acute discomfort. The same lights would hardly be noticeable during the day. The brilliancy of summer sunlight shining on a pavement or that of a clear winter sun on snow may be almost blinding. A table lamp in which the light shines through a sheet of the recently developed material known as polaroid greatly reduces glare from polished surfaces. Colored glasses, which absorb a portion of the light, may furnish distinct relief from an intense sun. The recently introduced polarizing spectacles, in which polaroid is used instead of glass, are better. The hope also seems near that polaroid may make it possible greatly to reduce the hazards and discomforts of automobile headlights, or perhaps even to eliminate them. This will require, however, that a sheet of the material be used on every headlight and windshield, that lamps be made more powerful since such a sheet absorbs not less than half of all the light that enters it, and that means be provided for keeping the polarizers cool.

## USE OF REFLECTORS

In many cases the efficacious use of the light emitted by a lamp may be greatly improved by means of suitable reflectors. When a street lamp, for example, is allowed to throw its light unhindered in all directions, much of it will pass upward as shown in Fig. 95A, and serve no useful purpose. If a suitable reflector is placed above the lamp, this light will be turned downward helping to illuminate the street and objects upon it, as shown in Fig. 95B.

The automobile headlight is provided with an excellent reflector which forms the rear wall of the lamp housing and directs the light forward. It is so shaped that the light emitted from any point on the lamp filament leaves the reflector along

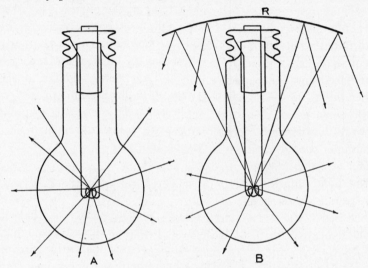

FIG. 95.   Use of reflector.

lines which are nearly parallel.   All of the light is thus confined to a small region ahead.

## LAWS OF REFLECTION

The best reflectors found in everyday use are our ordinary mirrors.   In these the reflecting surface is one of untarnished metal, usually a thin layer of silver or of an alloy of mercury spread on glass and covered with some kind of protective coating.   The glass serves to hold the metal and to give it a very smooth surface without the necessity of grinding or polishing.

Light from a lamp or candle striking a mirror perpendicularly is reflected perpendicularly as shown at $A$, in Fig. 96.   If it strikes obliquely, it is reflected obliquely, as shown at $P$ and $Q$.

If *MP* and *NQ* are perpendiculars to the mirror at *P* and *Q*, the points of incidence of the beams, then

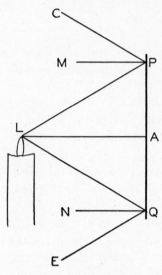

FIG. 96.    Plane mirror.

angle *LPM* = angle *MPC*, and angle *LQN* = angle *NQE*.

In each case the angle between the reflected ray and the line perpendicular to the mirror is equal to the angle between the incident ray and the perpendicular.  It is also found that the incident and reflected rays and the perpendicular to the mirror all lie in the same plane.

The two relationships last stated are called the laws of regular reflection of light.

## REFLECTION FROM UNPOLISHED SURFACES

When such a surface as that of smoothly planed wood or unsized paper is viewed through a magnifier, it is seen to consist of fibers apparently thrown together irregularly, between which there are great irregular chasms leading deep into the body of the wood or paper. Somewhat the same thing is true of apparently smooth stone, brick, concrete, flat paint, and many other surfaces. If a beam of light strikes one of these, it is evident, as shown in Fig. 97, that different parts of the beam meet the surface at very differ-

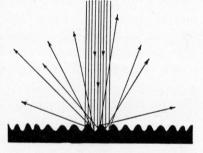

FIG. 97.—Reflection from an unpolished surface.

ent angles.  The light is therefore reflected in many different directions.  This scattering of light by unpolished surfaces is called *diffuse reflection*.  This type of reflection is of great importance, for it is only by this means that a nonluminous object may be seen. Even a mirror is seen, if at all, by the small amount of light that it reflects diffusely.

## REFRACTION AS AN AID

Whenever a ray of light passes from one transparent substance into another, its speed is altered, with the result that its direction is also changed. This effect is called *refraction*. There is one exception to the rule just stated. If the original direction of the ray is exactly perpendicular to the surface of contact of the two bodies, the ray passes from the one into the other without change of direction.

In vacuous space, such as that between the sun and the earth, or between stars, or in the vacuum of a radio tube, light advances at the tremendous speed of about 186,000 miles per sec.— equal to one and a half times around the world at the equator during a single tick of a watch. In the atmosphere the speed is only slightly less than this. In water it is about three-fourths, and in ordinary glass about two-thirds of the speed in empty space. In a diamond the speed is scarcely more than two-fifths of that in a vacuum—a mere 75,000 miles per second.

Substances in which light travels at slower speeds are said to be optically more dense. Those in which it travels at higher speeds are optically less dense, or more rare. Thus water is optically more dense than air, glass more dense than water, and diamond more dense than glass.

In passing from a rarer into a denser medium the beam takes a new direction which lies closer to the perpendicular to the surface at the point of passage. This is shown in Fig. 98. In this, the line $AB$ represents a ray of light striking a plate of glass at $B$. $PQ$ is perpendicular to the surface of the glass at that point. In passing into the glass the beam changes its course, now following the line $BC$. This line makes with the perpendicular $PQ$ an angle $CBQ$ which is smaller than the angle $ABP$. In entering the rarer medium the reverse change of direction occurs. In Fig. 98 the ray is represented as passing from glass into air at $C$. $RS$ is perpendicular to the second glass surface at that point. The new direction of the ray is *CD*. The angle *DCS* is greater than the angle *BCR*. In entering the rarer medium the ray has been "bent" away from the perpendicular.

A beam in passing from air into water or from water into air changes its direction in exactly the same way, but to a lesser

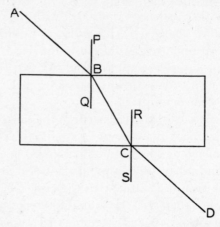

FIG. 98. A beam of light traversing a plate of glass.

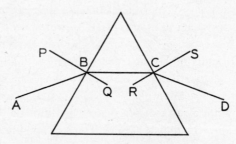

FIG. 99. A beam of light traversing a prism.

degree. This is because the change of speed is not so great in passing from one of these into the other as in going from air into glass or the reverse.

If the surfaces through which the light passes in entering and leaving the glass are not parallel with each other, the final direction of the ray may differ widely from the original direction. This may be seen from Fig. 99. A ray whose original direction is *AB* on entering the glass at *B* takes a new direction, *BC*. The perpendicular to the surface of the glass at *B* is *PQ*. As before, angle *CBQ* is smaller than *ABP*. On leaving the glass at *C*, the beam is "bent" away from the perpendicular. Its new direction *CD* makes with the perpendicular *RS* an angle *DCS* which is greater than angle *BCR*.

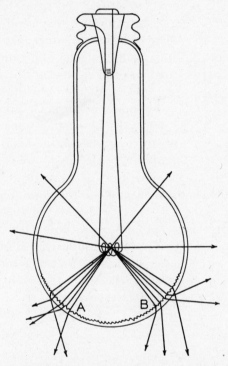

FIG. 100.  Frosted bulb scatters the light.

Most of the electric bulbs in use today are "frosted." They have been roughened over a part or all of the inside surface by the action of hydrofluoric acid. The wall of the bulb no longer has its inner and outer surfaces practically parallel, as in clear glass bulbs. The wall acts as if it were composed of a multitude of variously oriented tiny prisms whose action is similar to that of the prism shown in Fig. 99. The net effect on the light advancing from the filament is somewhat as represented in two regions, *A* and *B*, of Fig. 100. Thus the light is scattered, leaving the bulb as if emanating from its entire frosted surface. This greatly reduces the blinding effect of an intensely luminous small filament, which is directly seen in bulbs of clear glass.

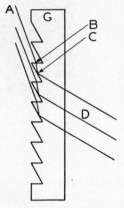

FIG. 101.   Prism glass.

Globes of milk glass are extensively used to scatter the light still more. By their greater size they tend to eliminate sharp shadows, reduce glare, and thus improve the quality of illumination. The amount of light passing through a bulb is not greatly altered by frosting.

In some circumstances prism glass is useful. If a window opens near an obstructing building or high wall a large portion of the light that reaches the window from a skyward direction can be brought in by means of glass of the form represented in Fig. 101. A beam *AB* strikes a shoulder of the glass almost perpendicularly, and continues on with only slight change of direction to *C*. There it meets the surface at so small an angle (large angle with the perpendicular) that none of the light is able to emerge. It is totally reflected at that point in the direction of *CD*, and passes on into the room.

# CHAPTER 16

# THE EYE.   OPTICAL
## INSTRUMENTS

The eye is one of the most highly specialized organs of the body.   Like many other organs and mechanisms with specialized functions, it is delicate, and frequently in need of aid.   This need may arise from an impairment of vision.   Remedial measures are then necessary.   It often happens that even a perfect eye is in need of aid because the inherent limitations of the organ render it inadequate for the task to be performed. Some type of optical instrument will then be used.   For example, the astronomer uses a telescope to gather as much light as possible from a faint distant star.   The biologist uses a microscope to magnify to the point of distinct visibility objects which are too small to be seen by the unaided eye.   The tourist uses his binoculars to get a better view of a distant scene, and his still or motion-picture camera to secure a permanent record of it.   The enthusiast with a hobby and the omnipresent news reporter may each carry a candid camera to "shoot" the scene or the persons concerned in any occurrence of personal or public interest.   On the theory that one good picture is worth a thousand words, entirely new types of news magazines have been founded in which the words are few and the pictures many and colorful.

## THE EYE AND THE CAMERA

The instrument that most closely resembles the eye is the camera.   Each admits the light through a small round aperture. In the eye this aperture, called the pupil, automatically varies in size according to the intensity of light, contracting as the intensity increases and dilating as it diminishes. In the camera the size of the aperture is adjustable, and controlled by the photographer. The eye and camera both include a surface on which the light registers its effects. In the eye this is the retina; in the camera it is the sensitized plate or film. In the

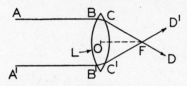

eye, the effects of light are transitory, lasting but a fraction of a second. In the camera they are permanent, and cumulative. The eye has its crystalline lens for focusing the light upon the retina. The camera has a lens also, for focusing the light upon

FIG. 102. Light from a very distant object.

the plate or film. The crystalline lens, by a reflex muscular action, is adjusted for distinct vision of objects at different distances. This adjustment, called *accommodation*, is accomplished by slight changes in the thickness and curvature of the lens. The camera is also adjustable to give clear definition. This is done by altering the distance between the lens and the film.

The action of such a lens upon the light from a nearby object will be evident from a study of Figs. 102 and 103. The disc-like form, *L*, represents the lens. In Fig. 102, *AB* and *A'B'* represent two parallel rays of light. The portions of the lens through which these pass may be considered as prisms whose bases face each other. By the principles developed in the preceding

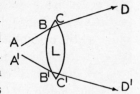

FIG. 103. Object very near the lens.

chapter the upper ray will be bent downward at *B* on entering the lens, and downward again at *C* on leaving it. By the same principles the lower ray will be bent upward at *B'*, and again at *C'*. The two rays thus made convergent meet at *F*. The distance *O* to *F* is called the focal length of the lens. The rays *AB* and *A'B'* of Fig. 103 will be bent in a similar way, though not enough to bring them to a focus.

The lens of the camera is more complex than those here illustrated, but its focusing effect on light rays is similar. The action of such a lens in forming an image is shown in Fig. 104.

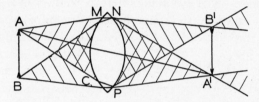

FIG. 104. Formation of real image by a convex lens.

*A* and *B* represent the extremities of an object. Light from *A* reaches the lens as a cone, the limits of which may be represented by the lines *AM* and *AC*. After passing through the lens the light forms another cone, converging to its apex at *A'*.

FIG. 105. Scene in the Bad Lands. Left. Camera in good adjustment. Right. Camera out of focus.

Light that leaves *B* and enters the lens converges to *B'*. Likewise rays from every other point on *AB* converge to corresponding points on *A'B'*. Hence *A'B'* is an image of *AB*. For a sharply defined photograph the camera must be adjusted to make $A'B'$ fall exactly on the sensitized plate or film.   This is illustrated in Fig. 105.

Such images as $A'B'$ of Fig. 104 are known as *real* images. They are formed by the convergence in them of rays that left the object, $AB$.

## SELECTING YOUR EYEGLASSES

First make sure that your eyes need this assistance.   If you can look at a page of ordinary print held about ten inches from

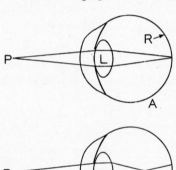

the eyes and see it clearly everywhere within a three or four inch circle, the chances are that you do not need glasses.   If you find it necessary to hold the page much closer to the eye than this, or much farther away, or if the type looks fuzzy anywhere, you probably do.   In case of doubt consult your oculist.   Do not buy a pair of glasses at a store.

For distinct vision it is necessary that light from each point on the object within the field of view shall be sharply focused on the retina.   A condition of such focusing is represented in Fig. 106A.   If the light is focused in front of the retina, as shown in Fig. 106B, or reaches the retina without coming to a focus, as in

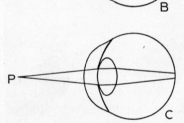

Fig. 106.   The eye.

106C, the object will not be clearly seen.   In the first case vision will be improved by holding the page closer to the eye, for then the rays will be more divergent before reaching the eye, and less convergent after entering it.   This represents an instance of nearsightedness.   The crystalline lens is too powerful, or the eyeball too long from front to back.

In the case represented in Fig. 106C vision will be improved by holding the page farther from the eye. The light will then be less divergent before reaching the eye and more convergent after entering it. At arm's length the print may be seen distinctly. This is an instance of farsightedness. It is due to a lack of power in the lens, or shortness of the eyeball.

For the first of these defects the oculist will prescribe lenses which will cause the light to diverge somewhat more sharply before entering the eye. This kind of lens and its action on a beam of light are represented in Fig. 107. For the second defect he will prescribe lenses which help to converge the light. This kind of lens is represented in Figs. 102 and 103.

The third defect referred to above, that of indistinctness of vision along some line through the center of the field of view is called *astigmatism*. Focusing is defective along this line. The two eyes may not both have the same defect, or if the same in

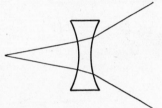

Fig. 107.   Diverging lens.

kind, the defects may be different in degree. The oculist will determine by scientific test just what the defects of vision are and will prescribe the exact kind and power of lens required for each eye.

## HELP FOR THE NORMAL EYE

It has already been stated that in many circumstances the eye requires the help of an optical instrument. In examining a small flower, for example, the botanist can more easily observe the details of its structure if he uses a simple magnifier. The zoologist uses the same device in studying small beetles and other still smaller animal forms. In assembling or repairing delicate machines, such as fine watches, the workman would be helpless without his magnifier. In examining the minute structure of both plants and animals, ranging down to the individual cells, a more powerful aid than the simple pocket lens is required. The compound microscope is used for such studies.

In the realm of larger things, on shipboard at sea for example, it is necessary to keep a constant lookout all around, all the way to the horizon.   The purpose is to discover other craft which may be in distress, or to see icebergs or other objects that may present an element of danger.   The unaided eye is poorly adapted for an effective survey of this wide expanse of sea. The telescope affords the needed assistance.

The person most in need of the telescope is the astronomer. The objects of his study are not a few miles or even a few scores of miles away.   In some cases they are at distances that seem to reach well toward the other side of the universe.   That is why he builds his telescopes so large and powerful.

## HOW THE MAGNIFIER OPERATES

Looking through a reading glass at a printed page, one sees the print considerably magnified, and apparently farther from

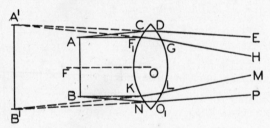

Fig. 108.   Simple magnifier.

the glass than it really is.   Fig. 108 shows how these effects are brought about.   *A* and *B* represent the top and bottom respectively of the letter *I*.   If the letter is between the lens and its principal focus (between *O* and *F*), the light that reaches the lens from any point on *I* will be so divergent that it will not be brought to a focus.   The cone of rays from the point *A* and included between *AC* and $AF_1$ will, after passing through the lens, be included between the rays *DE* and *GH*.   This new cone diverges as if originating at *A'*.   To an observer looking through the lens from the right, *A* appears as if it were really at *A'*, and *B* as if at *B'*.   Thus the letter *I*, which actually extends from *A* to *B*, seems to be lengthened to extend from *A'* to *B'*.   The magnification is in the ratio $A'B'/AB$.   The width of the object is magnified in the same way.   The smaller the focal length of the lens the greater is the magnifying power.   This usually does not exceed twelve to fifteen diameters, though it may be considerably more.

Such images as $A'B'$ of Fig. 108 are called *virtual* images. Light from the object does not traverse them, but enters the eye as if originating in them.

## THE COMPOUND MICROSCOPE

This instrument is used for viewing very small objects.   It consists of two lenses (lens groups) cooperating to give great magnifying power.   One of the lens groups is called the objective; the other is called the eyepiece.   The objective is sharply curved (has a small focal length) and, in use, is placed at such a distance from the object that it forms a greatly magnified real image in the upper end of the tube.   The action of the objective is similar to that of the simple lens of Fig. 104.   The eyepiece is used as a simple magnifier to view the image formed by the objective.   The action of the compound microscope is shown in Fig. 109.   $AB$ represents the object, $A'B'$ the real image formed by the objective, and $A''B''$ the magnified image of $A'B'$ seen by an eye with pupil at $P$.

The magnifying power of a compound microscope depends upon the focal lengths of the two groups and

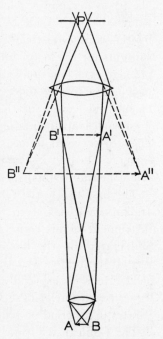

Fig. 109.   Compound microscope.

upon the length of the tube.   The smaller the focal lengths and the longer the microscope tube, the greater will be the magnification.   If the objective gives a magnification of 25 diame-

ters and the eyepiece a magnification of 10, the combination
will have a magnifying power of 250.

$$M = 25 \times 10 = 250.$$

The magnifying power of compound microscopes varies from
30 or 40 diameters to more than 1000.

## THE TELESCOPE

Telescopes are made in various forms, and are used for many
different purposes.  The surveyor's transit includes such an
instrument as one of its essential parts.  In the ordinary opera
glass two low-power telescopes of the Galilean type described
below are placed side by side.  Both instruments are focused
by the same adjusting screw.  Telescopes are in universal use
as sights for the heavy guns of fighting ships, and are becoming
popular even for small firearms.  The periscope is a telescope
in which a totally reflecting prism is placed near each end to
change the course of the beam of light through 90 degrees.
Two such instruments, one of which contains a thin wedge of
glass to serve as a measuring device, are used in the range-
finder.  The best-known use, however, and the one for which the
telescope was originally developed, is in the study of astronomy.

The first to use the telescope for this purpose was the great
Italian scientist Galileo.  Early in the year 1610 with a small
instrument of his own construction he discovered mountains
and craters on the moon, saw several of the satellites of the
planet Jupiter, viewed the rings of Saturn, and examined the
sun.  He was especially interested in sun spots, which he
observed to move in such a way as to indicate that the sun
rotates in a period of about one month.

The Galilean telescope consists of a convex object lens, Fig.
102, and a concave eyepiece, Fig. 107.  Objects seen through
this instrument appear erect, that is, not inverted.  This
accounts for its use in opera glasses.  The refracting telescope
used in the study of astronomy has two convex lenses.  One of
these, the objective, is large and of great focal length.  The

other, the eyepiece, is small, and of short focal length. Telescopes of this kind are in use in most of the great observatories of the world. The largest is in the Yerkes Observatory of the University of Chicago, at Williams Bay, Wisconsin. The diameter of the object lens of this instrument is 40 inches. The tube in which it is carried is more than sixty feet in length. The second largest lens is in the Lick Observatory of the University of California, on Mount Hamilton. (See page 538.) The diameter of its object lens is 36 inches.

It is thought that larger lenses than these will probably not be practicable. There is a slight distortion of a large lens as a result of its own weight. This leads to imperfection in the image which nullifies the gain to be achieved by the greater light-gathering power of a larger diameter.

## REFLECTING TELESCOPES

Another type of telescope uses a concave mirror for collecting light and forming the first image. This type of instrument may be made in much larger sizes than those employing lenses for objectives. There are many such telescopes in various parts of the world. The largest of these now in use is in the observatory of the Carnegie Institution of Washington, on Mount Wilson, California. The mirror of this instrument has a diameter of 100 inches, and a light-collecting power more than six times that of the 40 inch lens of the Yerkes telescope. There is now in course of construction an even greater reflector to be located on Mount Palomar, in California. The mirror of this telescope will have a diameter of 200 inches, and a light-gathering power four times that of the great reflector on Mount Wilson. This mirror, which alone weighs twenty tons, was cast in Corning, New York. It is the largest single piece of glass ever cast. It was shipped to Pasadena, California, where in the astronomical shops of the California Institute of Technology, its upper face is being slowly ground to the exact curvature required. Meanwhile other parts of the instrument are being constructed. This work is now nearing completion. It is expected that this giant telescope will be in service some time in the present year (1940), gathering information concerning more distant galaxies than have yet been discovered.

Telescopes are an invaluable aid for the feeble eye of man. Without such instruments the great science of astronomy could probably not have progressed far beyond the point reached even before the days of Galileo.

## RETURN TO THE CAMERA

Galileo's astronomical discoveries were made by looking through his telescope at the heavenly bodies just as one looks through a field glass or opera glass at a landscape or the stage. This method is still used by hundreds of amateur astronomers the country over who make their own telescopes, study the heavens with delight and enthusiasm, and often make valuable discoveries.  The technique of making observations with the large instruments of the observatories is somewhat different. There a special form of camera takes the place of the eye. This method loses something of the romantic flavor we may associate with the lone astronomer scanning the heavens through the night with his telescope, but it adds enormously both to the efficiency of operation and to the reliability of the observations.  In the first place the camera serves as a tireless secretary to record the messages, leaving the astronomer free to think about the records and to discover their significance. This, after all, is his most important function.  In the next place the camera is thoroughly unbiased—has no favored hypothesis.  Again, because the chemical effect of light on the photographic plate is cumulative, it is possible by increasing the exposure time to secure a distinct record of stars so faint that they can not be detected by visual means.  And finally, the record so obtained is permanent.  It does not vanish in the fraction of a second as visual sensations do, leaving only a memory with the astronomer, or the imperfect record that he may make by hand.

It is, therefore, from his photographic plates, which are preserved and catalogued with the greatest care, that the astronomer learns of the appearance of an unfamiliar comet, of the character of new or unstudied stars, or of the existence of universes hitherto unknown.

The astronomer may sometimes have to expose his plate for many hours in order to secure a satisfactory photograph of a faint star, a process which introduces complications.

*A. G. Spalding & Bros.*

Fig. 110.   A Multiple-flash Photograph of Bobby Jones with a Driver.   The interval of time between pictures is 1/100 second.   The exposure of each picture is 1/100,000 second.   Measured from this photograph:
  The ball velocity is 225 feet per second.
  The club velocity before impact is 166 feet per second.
  The club velocity after impact is 114 feet per second.

Because of the rotation of the earth, the sun and moon move across the sky from east to west.   So also do the stars.   If a telescope were pointed in a fixed direction with reference to the observatory, the stars would move across the field making streaks upon the photograph.   In order to make the long exposure which is sometimes necessary, the telescope at every instant must focus the light of the desired star at the same point on the plate.  The telescope must be rotated from east to west at exactly the rate at which the earth rotates from west to east.  This slow, steady motion of the instrument is maintained by means of clockwork.  The rate of the clock is first controlled by a mechanical governor, which keeps it almost constant.  For finer control a pendulum is provided which closes an electric circuit at each swing.  This brings into action a mechanism which slightly accelerates the motion if it is too slow, and slightly retards it if too fast.

In contrast with the long exposure the astronomer may sometimes need to make, the motion picture cameraman and the flash photographer often secure very vivid pictures in a tiny fraction of a second.  See Fig. 110.

## THE PICTURE PROJECTOR

If the object $AB$ in Fig. 104 were moved a little closer to the lens, its image $A'B'$ would recede to a somewhat greater distance and would become larger.  By placing an object close to the lens, but still outside of the principal focus, its image may be greatly magnified.  This is how it is possible for the motion picture projector to throw so large a picture on the screen from so small a one on the film.

It is seen from Fig. 104 that the image is inverted.  To bring the players upon the screen in their normal postures the film is inverted in the machine.

The eye retains an impression for about one-fifteenth of a second after the light ceases to fall upon the retina.  This is an essential factor in the projection of motion pictures.  The film consists of a succession of pictures, each with characters in the positions they occupy and the poses they assume at instants about one-twentieth of a second apart.  After one of these has been flashed upon the screen, the light is interrupted for an instant while the next picture is brought into position to be shown.  Then the light is flashed on again.  The shift is made while the eye still retains something of the first impression. The arrangement of objects in each picture differs so little from that of the one preceding it that the motion seems to be uniform and continuous.

In motion pictures a surprising effect is often seen in which the wheels of a moving vehicle seem to be turning backward. This results from the same general causes that give apparent motion to the vehicle as a whole and to other objects. If at the instant a picture is taken each spoke is exactly in the position with reference to the car that was occupied by a spoke at the times of previous exposures, the wheel will seem to move forward without turning. If the spokes fall just a little short of these positions, however, the wheel will seem to be turning backward.

# CHAPTER 17

# COLOR. SPECTRA

Looking eastward at sunset toward a passing shower, who has not been thrilled by the splendor of the arch of color spanning the summer sky? Appreciation of the beauty of other objects is often emphatically expressed by the phrase "all the colors of the rainbow." Popularly this "all" means seven. The names of the seven in order beginning at the bottom are violet, indigo, blue, green, yellow, orange, and red. Where one color ends and another begins no one is able to say. Each merges into those on either side of it by imperceptible degrees.

When a second bow appears outside the first, as often happens, the second is much the fainter. Its colors also appear in the reverse of the above order.

A rainbow appearing in the early morning is always seen in the west. If one appears when the sun is a little higher, it is distinctly shorter and lower.

The same colors can be produced by means of a prism and a beam of sunlight. But to spread them out into an arch as is done by the summer shower requires more extensive apparatus.

## NEWTON'S EXPERIMENTS

One of the first to spread light into a band of color was the great English scientist, Sir Isaac Newton. He did this by means of a simple triangular prism of glass. When a beam of sunlight entering a darkened room through a small hole in a window shade fell upon the prism in the way indicated in Fig. 111, the same colors appeared upon the wall as in the rainbow. Isaac Barrow, Newton's professor at Cambridge, and many others, believed that the colors were created by the prism, the red end of the band by reason of a "condensation of the light,"

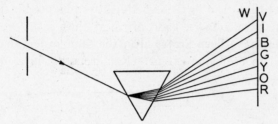

FIG. 111.  Sunlight through a prism.

the violet end by a rarefaction of it.  Newton disagreed with this view.  By placing another prism behind the first as in Fig. 112 he brought the colored rays together again.  The colors vanished.  A spot of ordinary sunlight fell upon the wall. He also placed the second prism behind an opening in a small screen upon which the band of colors was projected, as in Fig. 113.  The second prism bent again the ray that fell upon it, but produced no new color as it should have done according to the views of Barrow.  Newton concluded, therefore, that the

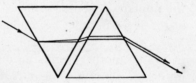

FIG. 112.   Colors reunited by second prism.

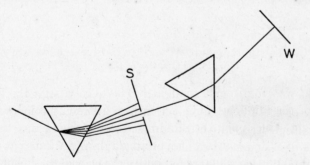

FIG. 113.   Transmission of a single color.

prism did not produce the colors, but only separated those that were already present in the sunlight.

## THE RAINBOW

If Newton had used a triangular bottle filled with water instead of the prism in the experiment represented in Fig. 111, he would have found a band of colors, just as before. They would also have been arranged in the same order, though not separated to the same extent. Raindrops act in a somewhat

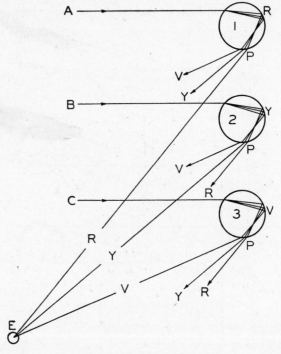

FIG. 114.　Formation of the rainbow.

similar way to disperse sunlight. This accounts for the formation of the rainbow. The action is as represented in Fig. 114. Sunlight shines upon the raindrops, some of the rays striking as shown by $A$, $B$, and $C$. On entering a drop the different colors are refracted by different amounts. The violet is bent most and the red least. Some of the light is internally reflected, as shown at $R$, $Y$, and $V$, while some emerges and is scattered. The part that is reflected travels within the drop to $P$. There some of it emerges while some is again reflected internally. The ray that emerges is spread into a band of colors. The violet, yellow, and red leave the drop in some such directions as those shown in the figure, while the other colors take directions according to their wave lengths. A person at *E* will receive the red ray from a multitude of drops in the position represented by drop 1 in Fig. 114. These drops may be anywhere on the arc of a circle. He will receive the violet ray from drops which at

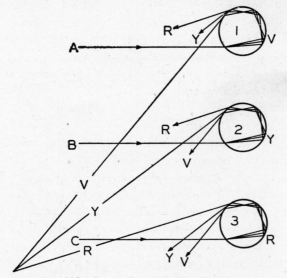

FIG. 115.  Formation of the secondary bow.

the moment are in positions represented by drop 3. These drops may also be anywhere on the arc of a circle—a smaller circle than the first. Other drops, represented by 2, will send yellow to the eye. Thus the rainbow is formed.

The second bow is formed in much the same way, by light that reaches the eye after two internal reflections in the drop, as shown in Fig. 115.

## HALOS

A circle of light called a *halo* is sometimes seen around the sun or moon. The most common halo is a ring or portion of a ring of about 22° radius. One of 46° radius may also sometimes be seen.  Halos are red on the inside and shade off to a pale yellow on the outside.  They are formed by the action of minute columnar ice crystals in the upper atmosphere.

The crystals are regular hexagonal prisms.  A beam of light from the sun or moon which passes through two alternate faces is deviated from its original direction by a minimum angle of about 22°.  Such beams form the smaller halo.  Light passing through a base of the prism and one side is deviated by a minimum angle of about 46°.  It is such beams which form the larger halo.

Regions of color sometimes appear on opposite sides of the sun at about the distance of the smaller circle.  These regions are called *parhelia*, or *sun dogs*, and are also due to the refraction of light by ice crystals.

## LIGHT AS A WAVE EFFECT

The colors of soap bubbles and oil films also result from a separation of the components of ordinary light.  Colors exhibited in this way are usually less clearly defined than those of the rainbow.  A more regular and permanent arrangement of colors may be seen by reflecting a beam of light as shown in Fig. 116.  $P$ and $Q$ are two plates of optical glass held together at one end, and separated by a single thickness of paper at the other.  Or they may be the two surfaces of a soap film in the end of a large glass tube.  A portion of a beam of light striking these plates is reflected from $P$, and another portion is reflected from $Q$.  The light that is seen by such reflection will show a succession of bands of color somewhat similar to those of the rainbow.  This series may be repeated several times.  If the light shining upon the plates is of a single color, the appearance is that of a succession of bright and dark bands.  The number of each may be a dozen or more.  The width of the bands depends upon the minuteness of the angle between the glass plates $P$ and $Q$.  (A piece of asbestos dipped in salt water and held in the flame of a Bunsen burner gives a yellow light suitable for use in this experiment.)

The colors seen in the experiment just described are due to a cause quite different from that which produces the rainbow. The colors of films can be accounted for not as the result of different amounts of deviation of the different colors, but as the result of the interaction of two beams of light upon each other. It was mentioned in Chap. 14 that two sounds may combine to produce silence. From the experiment just described it appears that two rays of light may also combine in such a way as to produce darkness. Consider first the alternation of light and dark bands seen when the plates are illuminated by the yellow Bunsen flame. The beam reflected from $P$ unites with the beam reflected from $Q$. If light, like sound, is a wave phenomenon, then wherever these two beams meet in opposite phase, that is, the crest of one on the trough of the other, the light will be greatly reduced in intensity or even eliminated. In regions where they meet in the same phase, that is, crest on crest, the light will be intensified. The wedge shape of the space between the plates facilitates the formation of the bands. At one

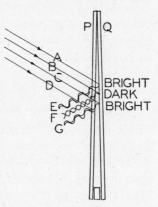

FIG. 116. Reflection from a pair of plates.

level the beam that is reflected from $Q$ will traverse a distance which is a whole number of wave lengths greater than that of the beam reflected from $P$. The two waves will then meet in the same phase, and will give a bright yellow band. Just below this level the beam reflected from $Q$ traverses an additional half wave length—an odd number of half wave lengths farther than that reflected from $P$. The two beams then oppose each other when they unite. The result is darkness. A little lower still the ray from $Q$ traverses one more half wave length excess distance. Crest is now on crest and another bright band is formed. The formation of such bands is evidence that light is a wave phenomenon.

If the plates are illuminated by sunlight or light from a projection lantern, the result is somewhat more complicated.  There is then a series of colored bands instead of a succession of dark and bright ones.

Various methods have been devised for measuring the wave length of light of any color.  It is found that those of red are greatest and those of violet smallest.  The wave length of the longest red ray is about .000076 cm., that of the shortest violet ray about .000038 cm.  It would require the combined lengths of about 130 waves in the red, or about twice that number in the violet, to make a length equal to the thickness of a single sheet of note paper.

## LIGHT, ELECTRICITY, AND MAGNETISM ALL IN ONE

Though light is a wave phenomenon, unlike sound it is not a mechanical wave motion dependent upon the elastic properties of the material through which it passes.  It is an effect of combined electrical and magnetic fields, and travels most freely in regions most nearly devoid of what is known as matter.  We have seen in Chap. 15 that the speed of light in air is more than 30 per cent greater than in water and more than 50 per cent greater than in glass.

The single octave of waves capable of producing the sensation of sight comprises only a tiny fraction of all of the known electromagnetic waves.  Even in the rays of the sun there are many waves both longer and shorter than those of light.  Those of greater wave length are called infrared.  It is these that carry the most of the heating power of sunlight.  Rays having smaller wave lengths than those of light are called ultraviolet. It is these that are most largely responsible for the growth of plants, for sunburn, and for various other chemical effects, such as the fading of dyes and the destruction of bacteria.

Electromagnetic waves shorter than the ultraviolet are also well known.  The $X$ ray is one of these.  Its wave length varies from about one one-thousandth to one ten-thousandth part of that of the shortest violet.  The gamma rays of radioactive substances, referred to in Chap. 21, are even shorter than the X rays.

Longer electromagnetic waves are familiar to us all. It is by means of these that radio amateurs communicate, that our broadcast programs reach us, that radio telegraphic messages are sent, and that airplanes are guided in the densest fog.

The entire range of known electromagnetic waves covers about 60 octaves.

## OPTICAL SPECTRA

A band of colors such as is formed when a beam of light is spread out by a prism is called a *spectrum*. An instrument

FIG. 117. Prism spectrometer.

for studying spectra, called a *spectrometer*, is represented in Fig. 117. The prism and two lenses of the spectrometer, and their action on a beam of light, are represented in Fig. 118. If the beam is from an incandescent electric lamp, the mantle of a Welsbach gas lamp, or any other white-hot liquid or solid, the colors spread without break over the entire visible range, merging into each other imperceptibly. This is called a *continuous spectrum*. It was mentioned above that the light from a salt-fed Bunsen flame is yellow. When this is passed through a prism, it is seen as a single, very narrow line. (A high-powered spectroscope shows it as two fine lines very close together.) If asbestos is dipped in a solution of lithium chloride and held in a Bunsen flame, the flame is colored red. Its light appears in the spectroscope as two rather widely separated lines. Gases at low pressure are made luminous by an electrical discharge passed through them. They then show one or more such thin lines of color. Some gases show many such lines, of various colors. If an electric spark from an induction coil is passed between metal electrodes held close together and the light resolved into its colors, a large number of bright lines will usually appear. Iron electrodes give an especially large

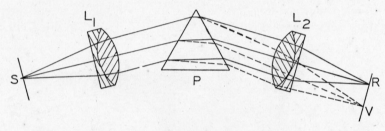

FIG. 118. Action of the spectrometer. (*S* is the slit; *R* and *V* the spectrum.)

number. Spectra such as these are called *bright-line spectra*. (See Frontispiece.)

## THE SPECTRUM OF SUNLIGHT

At a casual glance sunlight seems to give a continuous spectrum. Closer examination shows, however, that it is not quite continuous but is crossed by a great many fine, dark lines. A few of the most prominent are shown in the second spectrum of the Frontispiece. In honor of their discoverer they are called Fraunhofer lines. They are present because the light from the inner intensely-heated portion of the sun (the photosphere) in passing through the less highly-heated gaseous envelope (the reversing layer, directly above the photosphere), loses by absorption much of the light originally present in the colors corresponding to these dark lines. A spectrum like that of the sun is called an *absorption spectrum*. Absorption spectra and bright-line spectra are both discontinuous.

## IDENTIFYING CHEMICAL ELEMENTS BY THEIR SPECTRA

Since the line spectrum of each element is different from that of every other, it is possible by an examination of a spectrum to know by what element it was produced.   If two or more elements are present, as, for example, in the rarefied gas of a discharge tube, the spectra of both elements appear, and both may be identified.   This method of chemical analysis is simple, unfailingly accurate, and very convenient, especially for elements whose spectra, like those of sodium and lithium, are produced in the flame of a Bunsen burner.

The thin dark lines in the solar spectrum tell an interesting story which we may learn in part by referring to Fig. 119.

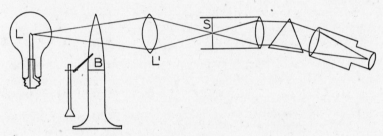

Fɪɢ. 119. ᐧ Absorption of light by a colored flame.

Here $L$ represents a brilliant lamp giving a continuous spectrum. $B$ is a Bunsen flame in which a piece of asbestos dipped in salt water is held.   $L'$ is a lens which concentrates the light from $L$ or $B$ upon the slit, $S$, of a spectrometer.   If the light from $L$ and from $B$ are passed in succession through the spectrometer, each will give its characteristic spectrum.   That from $L$, of course, gives a continuous band of color from red to violet, that from $B$ a narrow yellow line.   If both are focussed upon the slit together, the light from $L$ passing through $B$, they do not give a continuous band with an accentuated yellow line as might be expected, but a band with a dark line in the exact position of the yellow line of sodium.   The sodium flame has absorbed from the continuous spectrum of the lamp the wave of the length that it itself emits.

The dark lines in the solar spectrum are found to fall in the exact positions of the bright lines given by various elements. This shows unmistakably that these elements are present as gases in the solar atmosphere.

Many of the elements known on the earth have thus been found in the sun. One that has come to be of importance commercially as well as scientifically was discovered by its dark lines in the solar spectrum before it had been found on the earth. Because it was not then known to exist anywhere else, it was called *helium* (*Helios*, the sun).

An examination of the light of stars reveals their composition also. Many of them have spectra very similar to that of the sun. Each such star contains the elements which emit lines corresponding to the dark lines of the star.

## MOVEMENTS OF THE STARS

The spectra of the stars reveal to the astronomer not only the composition of those bodies, but also their motions, whether toward the earth or away from it, and at what speed. In considering the Doppler effect in connection with sound it was found that a sounding object, if approaching, gives a note of higher than normal pitch—that is, the wave is shortened. If the object is receding, the pitch is lowered—the wave lengthened. In a similar way an approaching star is seen as by light of a slightly shortened wave, a receding one as by a lengthened wave. The amount of change in apparent wave length is directly proportional to the radial speed of the star. This change is measured by comparing the positions of the dark lines of any element in the spectrum of the star with the positions of the bright lines of the same element as given by a flame, or an electric arc or spark. If a dark line in the spectrum of a a star is shifted toward the red as compared with the bright line of the same element obtained from a Bunsen flame, the star is receding. If the stellar line is shifted toward the violet, the star is approaching.

Stars at very great distances are nearly all moving from us at very high speeds—in some instances at hundreds of miles per second. The majority of those at small and moderate distances are receding also, but at much smaller speeds—ten to one hundred miles per second. It is this general outward movement of the stars at speeds roughly proportional to their distance that has given rise to the idea that our universe is now expanding.

## WHY ROSES ARE RED

A ribbon, scarf, or suit that looks very attractive in the usual light of a dry goods or clothing store may lose some of its appeal when seen in the daylight. Or, perhaps, it may seem even more attractive. It will rarely look the same unless in the store it has been seen in the light of a special "daylight lamp." A piece of colored paper, cloth, or yarn may look red or yellow in light of one color, but almost black in another color. Why is this? The color of an object is judged by the light it reflects to the eye. If it reflects only red light and absorbs all others, then when placed in red light or daylight (which contains red), it appears red. If placed in a light which does not contain red, it absorbs all that falls upon it, and appears black. Similarly an object may absorb everything except green. When placed in any light containing green, it looks green, but in any other light it also looks black.

Few objects have such sharply limited reflecting power as that assumed above. Reflection is usually strongest for one color, but considerable for some or all others. White reflects all colors almost equally well. Black reflects little of any color. The light of the usual incandescent lamp emits a smaller proportion of the shorter rays—blue and violet—than is present in sunlight. In the light from such a lamp the object, therefore, reflects a smaller proportion of these colors than it does in daylight. Its appearance changes accordingly, green, blue, and violet appearing unduly dark.

## GOLD IS SOMETIMES GREEN

Some objects, such as colored glass, are transparent to some rays but opaque to others. A piece of red glass interposed in the beam of a projection lantern transmits the longer light waves but absorbs the shorter ones, and shows the whole picture in red.   In the same way a plate of blue glass absorbs the longer rays and transmits the shorter ones, showing the picture in blue.   If both are held in the path of the beam, all colors are absorbed and the picture is completely blotted out.   Some substances which are opaque in thick sheets are slightly transparent in thin ones.   Gold is such a substance.   A very thin leaf transmits a small amount of light of a greenish color.   The light it reflects is yellow.

## DO YELLOW AND BLUE MAKE GREEN OR WHITE?

Adding blue and yellow lights is one thing, mixing blue and yellow pigments is quite another.   Blue light stimulates most strongly the nerve endings that give the impressions of blue, but it also affects faintly those that give the sensations of violet and green.   In the same way yellow light stimulates the yellow most strongly, and to a much smaller degree the colors on either side of it, the red, orange, and green.   If blue and yellow light fall upon the retina at the same time, all the nerve endings are stimulated and the sensation is that of white.   When blue and yellow pigments are mixed, however, the former absorbs nearly all the rays of greater wave length, the latter nearly all of those of shorter wave length.   It is only a narrow range in the middle that escapes extinction.   These are reflected to the eye and are seen as green.

# CHAPTER 18

# ELECTROSTATICS AND MAGNETISM

A rubber comb drawn a few times through the hair in dry, cold weather may make a crackling sound and cause the hair to stand on end. A spark may flash between the hand and a door knob just before they touch or between the hands of two persons if one has walked across a woolen rug. It is sometimes possible to light a gas jet by such a spark between the finger and a burner

These phenomena are due to what Benjamin Franklin called the electrical fluid. Franklin studied electricity by means of a kite. A great deal can be learned about it with the help of very simple equipment.

## ELECTRIC CHARGES

Stroke an ebonite rod briskly a few times with a piece of fur. The rod will then attract small bits of paper, lint, or a pith ball hung by a light silk thread. The attraction is of short duration. The object that at first was drawn to the rod is presently kicked off, and thereafter strongly repelled. Stroke a glass rod with silk in the same way. It will also attract paper and lint, and a second pith ball. Like the rubber rod, it will soon repel objects it at first attracted. If the glass rod is brought near the first pith ball, a strong and persistent attraction between the two is shown provided they are not allowed to touch. There is also an attraction between the ebonite rod and the second pith ball.

Each electrified ball is attracted by one of the rods and repelled by the other. It is therefore evident that the two rods

249

carry different kinds of charges. Each rod attracts one of the balls and repels the other. This shows that the charges of the two balls are also unlike. A rod covered with tar will leave some of the same kind of tar upon any object which it touches. Likewise, an electrically charged rod will convey some of its own kind of electricity to any uncharged object with which it comes in contact. The results of such observations may be summarized as follows:

1. There are two kinds of electrical charges.

2. Like charges repel each other; unlike charges attract each other.

## POSITIVE AND NEGATIVE CHARGES

Franklin considered electricity to be a tenuous, invisible fluid which may pass from one object to another. If an object has its normal amount of this fluid, it is electrically neutral—shows no electrical effects. If it has more than the normal amount, it has one kind of charge; if less than the normal amount, it has the other kind. The kind of charge carried by the glass rod he believed to be due to an excess of the fluid. He therefore called this positive. The kind carried by the ebonite he believed to be due to a deficiency. He called this negative. These names are still used to designate those charges.

## POSITIVE AND NEGATIVE CHARGES APPEAR SIMUL-
TANEOUSLY

It can be shown that when an ebonite rod is negatively electrified, as described above, a positive charge of exactly the same magnitude appears upon the fur. Likewise, when the glass rod is positively electrified, a negative charge of the same magnitude appears upon the silk.

## ELECTRONS

Scientists now universally accept the view that there are two kinds of electricity, positive and negative, and that both kinds exist as discrete units, or particles. The best known negative unit is the *negative electron*, discovered by the English physicist

J. J. Thomson in 1897.  It was soon found to be a constituent of every kind of atom, and to have a mass equal to about $\frac{1}{1840}$ part of that of the atom of hydrogen.  For many years it was called simply the *electron*.  No other negative particle was known to exist, and despite the most careful and diligent search no positive particle less massive than the proton (see Chap. 7) had been found.  Then in 1932 while studying the properties of cosmic rays (see Chap. 21), Carl D. Anderson discovered a positive particle whose mass and charge were just equal to those of the negative electron.  This was immediately named the *positive electron*, or *positron*.  The negative electron is also called the *negatron*.

Of the two, the negative electron is by far the more interesting. The positron manifests itself only rarely and under very special conditions.  The negatron, on the other hand, is busy everywhere, driving electric motors, operating electric lamps of every description, producing $X$ rays, carrying telegraphic and telephonic messages, actuating the radio, displaying motion pictures, and doing practically all of the multitude of other duties that in these electric days have been assigned to electricity to do.

As explained in Chap. 7, a neutral atom is now believed to consist of a heavy positive nucleus, and one or more negative electrons around it.  The nucleus contains all but a minute fraction of the mass of the atom.  It has an amount of positive electricity just equal to the negative with which it is surrounded. In solids the nuclei remain in relatively fixed positions, partaking only of the heat motions of the atoms.  It is somewhat different with the electrons.  In metals and other conducting solids, at least some of the electrons seem to move about more or less freely, like the molecules of a gas.  These mobile particles thus constitute a kind of unbound negative charge, though the object as a whole is electrically neutral.

## ELECTRICALLY CHARGED OBJECTS

According to this view of electricity, an object which is negatively charged has acquired an excess of negative electrons from some other object. An object which has lost some of its negatives has an excess of positive, and is positively charged. This theory accounts for the simultaneous appearance of equal and opposite electric charges. When the ebonite rod is stroked with fur, it takes some of the negative electrons normally present in the latter and becomes negatively charged. The fur then carries an equal positive charge. As the glass rod is stroked with silk, it gives up some of its negative electrons to the silk, and becomes positively charged. The silk has an equal negative charge.

When a negatively charged rubber rod touches a pith ball, it gives a small part of its excess negative electrons to the ball. Both are then negative and repel each other. When a positively charged glass rod touches a pith ball, it takes negative electrons from the ball, but not enough to neutralize its own positive charge. Both are then positive and repel each other.

## FORCES EXERTED BETWEEN ELECTRIC CHARGES

The magnitudes of the forces exerted by electric charges upon each other were carefully studied by Coulomb, a French scientist and engineer, about the year 1777. Coulomb found, as was to be expected, that the force exerted between two charges varies directly as the magnitude of either charge, and therefore directly as the product of their magnitudes. He also found that the force varies inversely as the square of the distance between the charges. If $q$ represents the number of electrostatic units of electricity in one of the charges, $q'$ the number of units in the other, and $d$ the number of centimeters between them, the number of dynes of force exerted by the charges upon each other in air is given by the equation

$$F = \frac{qq'}{d^2}.$$

To illustrate this relationship numerically, let us assume that a charge of 20 units is 5 cm. distant in air from a charge of 30 units. The force each charge exerts upon the other may be computed by means of the formula given above.

$$\text{Force} = \frac{20 \times 30}{(5)^2} = 24 \text{ dynes.}$$

If in the above formula $q = q'$; $d = 1$ cm., and $F = 1$ dyne,

$$q = q' = 1.$$

The formula constitutes a definition of the electrostatic unit of charge, which may be stated in words as follows:

The unit charge is one which will exert a force of 1 dyne upon an equal charge when the two are 1 cm. apart in air.

## EFFECT OF ELECTRIC CHARGES ON UNCHARGED OBJECTS

In Fig. 120, $M$ represents a metallic object mounted on an insulating stand.  A negatively charged ebonite rod, $E$, brought

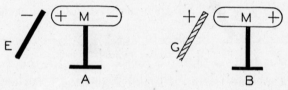

FIG. 120.   Effect of an electrical charge upon an insulated conductor.

near it as in $A$, repels the negative electrons of $M$, driving many of them to the farther end.   This leaves the nearer end with a deficiency of negatives.  A positively charged glass rod, $G$, brought near $M$ as in $B$, attracts negative electrons, drawing many to the nearer end of $M$ and creating a deficiency of negatives in the farther end.   If $M$ is grounded while $E$ is near it, the negatives which are driven to the farther end of $M$ can move still farther from $E$.   They then leave $M$, and go to the ground. If the ground connection is broken and $E$ then removed, $M$ is left with a positive charge.   This method of charging an object is called *induction*.   In a similar way, by means of the positive charge on $G$, $M$ may be negatively charged by induction.

Two conductors may be simultaneously charged by induction, one positively and the other negatively.   Let $M$ and $N$ of Fig. 121 represent two metal balls suspended in contact with each

other by silk threads.    A charged object, *E*, when brought near
one of the balls, causes electrons to flow from one ball to the

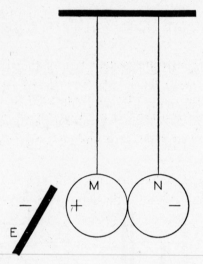

FIG. 121.    Charging an insulated ball.

other.    One then carries a negative and the other a positive
charge.    The balls retain the charges thus acquired if separated
while *E* is still near.

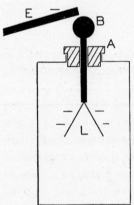

FIG. 122.    Gold leaf electroscope.

One of the most convenient instruments for studying electric charges is
the *gold leaf electroscope*, Fig. 122.    This
consists of a metal rod with a pair of
gold leaves, *L*, attached at its lower
end, and usually a metal ball, *B*, at
its upper end.    The rod passes through
a plug, *A*, of amber or ebonite, fitted
into the top of a metal case.    If a negatively charged rod, *E*, is brought near
the ball, it drives electrons into the
leaves.    These then separate because of
the repulsion of their similar (negative)
charges.    If a positively charged object
is brought near *B*, it attracts electrons, causing a deficiency of

negatives in the leaves, *L*.  Again the leaves separate, now because of the repulsion of their positive charges.

## THE LEYDEN JAR AND OTHER ELECTRICAL CONDENSERS

Objects such as *M* of Fig. 120 carry only a relatively small electric charge, even when intensely electrified.  They have little of what is called *capacitance*.  Objects such as those represented in Fig. 123 have a much greater capacitance.  Fig. 123A represents a glass jar with a large part of its surface covered with

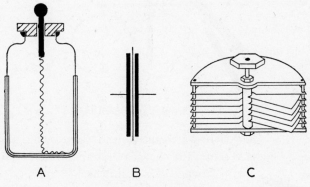

A               B               C

FIG. 123.    Condensers.

tin foil inside and out.  A light chain hangs from a metal rod extending through the wooden cover, and touches the inner tin foil coating.  This device is called a *Leyden jar*.  Fig. 123B represents a pair of metal plates, or sheets of tin foil, separated by a nonconductor, such as paraffined paper or mica.  It is a parallel-plate condenser.  Fig. 123C represents a multiple-plate variable condenser.  This consists of two groups of plates of sheet metal overlapping as shown, with air between.  One of the groups is held in a fixed position, while the other may be rotated to vary the amount of overlapping surface.  This varies the capacitance of the condenser.  It is by turning the dial of a condenser of this type that a radio receiver is tuned to one station or another.

## CHARGING A CONDENSER

If a charged object such as an ebonite rod is brought near the ball of a Leyden jar which has its outer coating connected by a wire to the ground, the jar will take an electrical charge, as represented in Fig. 124. The inner coating receives electrons driven from the ball by the repulsion of the negatively charged rod. Electrons are also driven from the outer coating by the repulsion of those of the inner coating. The outer thus becomes positive and remains so if the ground connection is broken.

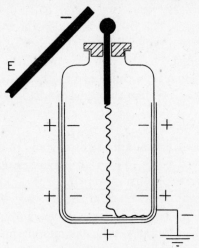

FIG. 124.    Charging a Leyden jar.

Because of the positive charge on the outer coating, the inner coating retains its negative charge even after the charged rod is removed.

The larger the metal coatings of the jar and the closer they are together, the greater will be the capacitance. The same is true of the other kinds of condenser represented in Fig. 123.

Condensers of the type represented in Fig. 124 may be strongly charged by bringing the ball into contact with one terminal of an electrostatic machine while the outer coating of the jar is connected by a wire to the other terminal. When charged in this way, the jar possesses a large amount of energy which it may discharge as a miniature stroke of lightning. This electric spark will puncture paper or cardboard, will ignite gas, and is accompanied by thunder (a snapping sound). Indeed it has in miniature all of the characteristics of the large-scale phenomenon in nature.

By means of huge condensers and impulse generators of special design, engineers of the General Electric Company have succeeded in producing tremendous discharges of this kind. In demonstrations in Steinmetz Hall at the New York World's Fair of 1939, flashes many feet in length were made to crash across the space between two metal balls mounted on high insulating towers. The voltage at which these discharges took place was about ten million volts. This is 90,000 times greater than that at which electric power is ordinarily used in homes and factories. The time consumed in the passage of one such flash was about one-millionth of a second.

## FRANKLIN AND HIS KITE

Before the days of Franklin, lightning and thunder were quite generally believed to be due to an exploding gas. Before his famous electrical experiments were made, Franklin believed this to be "the inflammable breath of the Pyrites, which is a subtle sulphur, and takes fire of itself." This was in 1737. Twelve years later he had found so many points of similarity between lightning and the sparks he obtained from his Leyden jars that he proposed to find out by experiment, if possible, whether or not lightning and the "electrical fluid" are the same. He had observed that sharply pointed wires draw off electricity from charged objects. His first idea was therefore to extend such a wire upward from a high tower to find whether the point would draw off an electric charge from a low cloud. No building or hill high enough for his purpose was available, so he decided to attach such a point to a kite made of a silk handkerchief and send it up into a rain cloud. When the rain moistened the kite string, to his great delight he was able to draw a spark from the string to his knuckle and to lead a charge from the string into a Leyden jar. He had proved that lightning is an electrical discharge and not the combustion of a gas.

## THE LIGHTNING ROD

Franklin not only showed that lightning is an electrical effect, but also discovered a way of warding off the damage which a lightning stroke may bring. The best way, Franklin knew, was to prevent the stroke. He therefore proposed that a heavy metal rod or cable be placed upon the building to be protected. One end of the rod was to be buried deep in the ground where it would always be in contact with moist earth. Above the building and mounted upon the rod were to rise several sharp metal points a few feet long. The points were to carry the electrical charge of the cloud quietly off to earth, and thus prevent the sudden discharge.

## MAGNETISM

In many parts of the world a mineral called *magnetite* is found. This is a hard, dark substance consisting chiefly of one of the oxides of iron. Some specimens of this mineral have the property of picking up small pieces of iron, such as tacks or filings. In this they exhibit a property which they are able to communicate to pieces of iron. Rocks having this peculiar property are called *lodestones*. The pieces of iron to which the property has been communicated, particularly if of hardened steel, so that they retain it, are called *magnets*. Lodestones are often called natural magnets. If a long, narrow lodestone is floated on a cork or is suspended by an untwisted thread it will take a position with its long axis in an approximately north and south line. This property enabled the Mediterranean navigators of the middle ages to keep their direction in cloudy weather when it was impossible to see the sun or stars. These stones were their guides. It was on this account that they were called lodestones or leading stones.

## POLES OF A MAGNET

If a magnet is dipped in iron filings, these will be found to cling to it chiefly at certain points. A bar magnet, for example, will usually hold the filings in quantity only in a small region near each end. These active regions are called the *poles* of the magnet. The pole which turns toward the north if the magnet is mounted in such a way as to permit it to turn freely about a vertical line is called the *north-seeking;* the other, the *south-seeking* pole. The magnetic compass consists of such a magnet pointed at the ends and pivoted in such a way as to swing freely in a horizontal plane.

## MAGNETIC PROPERTIES OF DIFFERENT METALS

Not all substances can be strongly magnetized. Iron possesses magnetic properties to a very marked degree. Nickel and cobalt can also be magnetized, but only slightly as compared with iron. These metals are attracted by a magnet. Many elements, such as bismuth, antimony, copper, aluminum, lead, zinc, gold, silver, and mercury show a reverse effect —that is, they are slightly repelled by a magnet. The first class are called *magnetic* or *paramagnetic substances*, the second *diamagnetic*.

Magnetic properties of materials are of great importance in the construction of telephone, telegraph, and radio equipment. Until recently iron and steel were the only materials used in the construction of any device whose magnetic properties are essential to its performance. In the last few years however, permalloy, an alloy of nickel and iron, and perminvar, an alloy of nickel, iron, and cobalt, have displaced iron and steel for many uses because of their more desirable magnetic characteristics.

## FORCES BETWEEN MAGNETIC POLES

If the north-seeking pole of a magnet is brought near the north-seeking pole of a compass, the latter pole moves away. The force is one of repulsion. The same action occurs if two south-seeking poles are brought near each other. If north-seeking is brought near south-seeking, however, there is an attraction. This fact is stated in the first law of force between magnetic poles, as follows:

*Like magnetic poles repel each other.*

*Unlike poles attract each other.*

The repulsion or attraction between two magnetic poles varies directly as the strength of either pole, and therefore as the product of their strengths. The force also falls off rapidly with increasing distance between poles. Experiment shows that it varies inversely as the square of the distance. These two relations may be expressed in a single algebraic statement, as was done in the case of electrostatic charges.

$$F = \frac{mm'}{d^2} \text{ dynes.}$$

Let us illustrate this law by a numerical example. Two poles of strength 50 and 70 units respectively are 10 cm. apart in air. What force does each exert upon the other?

$$\text{Solution: } F = \frac{mm'}{d^2} = \frac{50 \times 70}{(10)^2} = 35 \text{ dynes.}$$

In the equation expressing the laws of force between magnetic poles if $m = m' = 1$ unit pole, and $d = 1$ cm. then

$$F = \frac{1 \times 1}{1^2} = 1 \text{ dyne.}$$

The unit pole is defined as one which will exert a force of 1 dyne upon an equal pole when the two poles are 1 cm. apart in air.

## MAGNETIC FIELDS

A compass needle brought into the region of a strong magnet is usually deflected from its normal, approximately north-and-south direction. The stronger the magnet the greater the distance at which its influence may be detected. The region in which such magnetic forces are exerted is called a *magnetic field*.

The field of a magnet may be studied by means of a compass needle or iron filings. A small pocket compass placed in different positions as indicated by the circles of Fig. 125A will point as shown. The north-seeking pole of the needle is represented by the head of the arrow and the south-seeking pole by the feather. A north-seeking pole in any one of these positions tends to move in the direction of the arrow, and a south-seeking pole in the opposite direction. Any line in a magnetic field along which a north-seeking pole would travel if free to move is called a magnetic *line of force*.

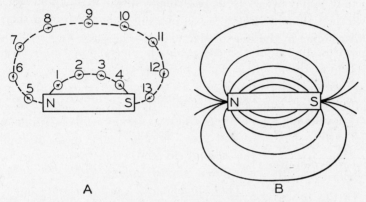

FIG. 125.    Field of a bar magnet.

If iron filings are sprinkled upon a pane of glass lying upon a bar magnet, the filings arrange themselves as shown in Fig. 125B.  By their directions they mark out the lines of force.

## STRENGTH OF A MAGNETIC FIELD

The force exerted by the magnet upon a pole of the compass needle at point 1 of Fig. 125 is much greater than at more distant points, such as 8 or 9.   The strength of the field is greater at 1.   The field strength at any point is defined as the number of dynes the field would exert upon a unit magnetic pole placed at that point.   If in a certain magnetic field a unit pole is magnetically subjected to a force of 10 dynes, the strength of the field is 10 dynes per unit pole.

## WHAT HAPPENS WHEN A PIECE OF METAL IS MAGNETIZED

Consider the following phenomena:

1. In magnetizing a piece of steel it is found that as the magnetizing force is increased, the intensity of magnetization

increases gradually to a maximum beyond which it cannot be carried.

2. If a magnet is heated to redness, it loses its magnetism. It may be magnetized again, however, as strongly as before.

3. Magnets lose some of their magnetism when hammered.

4. If a thin bar magnet, such as can be made from a short piece of clock spring, is dipped in iron filings, these will be found to cling in large tufts about the ends. Few, if any, will be held at the middle. This portion of the magnet apparently has no magnetic properties. If the magnet is cut into two approximately equal pieces, each part becomes a complete magnet, developing a pole where there was none before. If one of the parts is again divided, two complete magnets result from this second division. The process can be continued almost indefinitely.

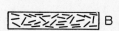 A

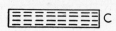 B

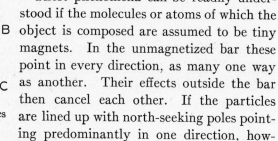 C

FIG. 126. Molecules in a magnet.

These phenomena can be readily understood if the molecules or atoms of which the object is composed are assumed to be tiny magnets. In the unmagnetized bar these point in every direction, as many one way as another. Their effects outside the bar then cancel each other. If the particles are lined up with north-seeking poles pointing predominantly in one direction, however, and south-seeking poles in the other, the cancellation is not complete, and the bar acts as a magnet. If still more of the particles are lined up, the magnet is stronger. When all are in line, no further strengthening of the magnet is possible. These various states are represented in Fig. 126.

If the bar is strongly heated, the violence of the motion of the particles throws them out of line, and the bar is demagnetized. Hammering does the same thing, but to a smaller degree. The particles can, of course, be lined up again, as before.

If the magnet is cut at the middle, the layer of atoms in one of the new surfaces will expose their north-seeking ends, while those in the other will expose their south-seeking ends. The newly formed ends therefore become north-seeking and south-seeking poles respectively.   These portions of the original bar did not manifest magnetic action because north- and south-seeking ends of particles were so close together that they cancelled each other's magnetic effects.

Unless the particles of which a substance is composed are tiny magnets, the substance cannot be magnetized.   The particles of iron are strong magnets.   Those of nickel and cobalt are weaker ones.   Those of most other substances are only very faintly magnetic, if at all.

## THE EARTH IS A MAGNET

Why does one end of the compass needle point toward the north?   Many answers have been given to this question. Bessard believed that the needle turned because it was somehow attracted to the pole of the zodiac.   Cortesius thought it was due to an attracting magnetic point far away beyond the heavens.   Cardan said it was caused by the attraction of the star in the tail of Ursa Major.   The true answer was not given until the year 1600 when Sir William Gilbert, physician to Queen Elizabeth, published his great book on magnetism (*De Magnete*).   In this he contended that compass needles point as they do because the earth itself is a magnet.   To establish the truth of this view he used a lodestone formed into the shape of a globe.   He placed a little compass needle at various points on all sides of this "terrella" or little earth, and found that in these various positions the needle was acted upon by the "terrella" in the same way that pivoted, magnetized steel needles are affected at corresponding points on the earth.   The only differences between the magnetic field of the earth and that of its little counterpart were those of size and intensity.

Gilbert's view is now universally accepted.   The earth acts as a huge magnet.   Its field is much like that of a bar magnet about four thousand miles long buried in the center of the earth in a direction which makes a small angle with the earth's axis. The magnetic poles of the earth are displaced several degrees from the geographic poles, and on that account the compass in most parts of the earth does not point exactly to the north or south.  In Fig. 127 $N$ and $S$ represent the north and south geographic poles of the earth; the two $P$'s, the magnetic poles. One $P$ represents a point on the Boothia Peninsula in northern Canada; the other, one in the Antarctic.  The curved lines, some of which pass through the two $P$'s, represent magnetic lines of force.  It is seen that these meet the earth's surface at various

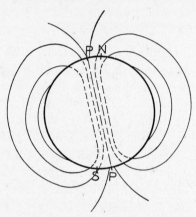

Fig. 127.  The earth as a magnet.

angles which increase from 0° at a middle line, called the magnetic equator, to 90° at the magnetic poles.

## THE USES OF MAGNETS

The mariner's compass, with its pivoted magnetic needle and direction circle, has for centuries enabled seamen to tell their directions at sea.  It is still used for this purpose, although the gyroscopic compass, which is not dependent upon the magnetic field of the earth for its operation, is superseding it for use on the larger ships.  Magnets of one kind or another are very extensively used in the construction of many kinds of devices. Instruments for measuring electric current, voltage, and electrical power and energy all make use of magnets.  So also do electric motors and dynamos, the telephone, telegraph, radio, and many others.  Some of these will be studied in the next two chapters.

# CHAPTER 19

# ELECTRIC CURRENTS

Electrical machines perform a giant's share of the work done in America today, and this share is steadily increasing. The earlier types of these machines were dynamos and motors. A dynamo produces electrical energy from other forms, such as that of a waterfall or of steam. A motor uses the electrical energy supplied to it by a dynamo to run street cars and to operate printing presses, lathes, and many other machines. Other types of electrical devices extract and purify valuable metals, provide light for homes and public places, carry messages with lightning speed, and do a multitude of other things that would be impossible by any other means. The major part of all such work is done by electric currents.

## WHAT IS AN ELECTRIC CURRENT?

If the ball of a positively charged electroscope is touched by the hand, electrons will flow along the hand and arm to the electroscope and neutralize the charge. If the electroscope is negatively charged, electrons will flow from it to the body until the excess of negative has been carried away. When a wire is brought into contact with both of the coatings of a charged Leyden jar, electrons will move along the wire from the negative coating to the positive until the jar is completely discharged. The stream of electrons in each case constitutes an electric current. In the cases mentioned, the charge is very quickly neutralized and then the current ceases. If a long, fine wire is connected to both terminals of a dry cell or a storage battery, there is also a movement of electrons along the wire. This current continues until the cell or battery is run down.

Electric currents in metals are always of this nature—a movement of electrons. They are analogous in many ways to the flow of water in a pipe. Electric currents in solutions such as are used in storage batteries or in electroplating cells consist of streams of particles of atomic size or greater, some of which carry positive, others negative charges. In this case the positive particles travel in one direction and the negative ones in the other.

## ELECTRIC CURRENTS PRODUCE HEAT

This fact is familiar to everyone. Many of the electrical appliances of the home are useful because they transform electrical energy into heat. The electric toaster, flatiron, waffle iron, cooking range, heating pad, and water heater all act in this way. The filament of an electric lamp glows because of its heat. The many devices which convert electrical energy into heat are also an indispensable adjunct to industry. Electric welding, for example, enables the automobile body manufacturer to construct the entire car body in a single piece. It greatly simplifies the process in making steel barrels, tanks, and containers of many other forms. It enables the manufacturer of household refrigerators to seal the refrigerating unit so effectively that not a trace of the refrigerant is lost in many years of service. Electric welding has made a greatly improved construction possible in the modern airplane, and enabled the builders of the German pocket battleships to provide heavier armament with less total weight. The rails of many city railway lines are electrically welded into two continuous bands. Without electric welding, the construction of the recently developed all-metal radio tube would be impossible. Electric heating is useful to the chemist also. In the high temperatures attainable in the electric arc furnace, for example, (3500° C.), he is able to manufacture some very important products. Among these is carborundum, an extremely hard substance used almost everywhere in grinding wheels, and in finely granulated or powdered form as an abrasive.

# ELECTRIC CURRENTS HAVE A MAGNETIC EFFECT

The great discovery from which the entire science of electro-magnetism originated was made by the Danish physicist Oersted in 1819. By holding a wire through which a current was flowing parallel to a compass needle, he observed that the needle was deflected, tending to take a position at right angles to the wire. When the direction of the current was reversed, the direction in which the needle pointed was also reversed. Arago, a French astronomer and physicist, observed in the following year that a wire through which a current is flowing attracts and holds

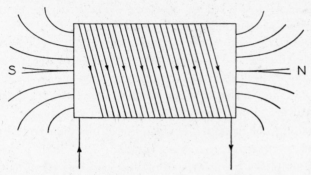

Fig. 128.   A solenoid carrying an electric current.

iron filings. Sir Humphry Davy showed that the magnetic field about a wire which is carrying a current is circular, and that the wire is at the center of the lines of force. Ampere, a French physicist, found that if a wire is wound in the form of a solenoid as represented in Fig. 128, the solenoid when carrying a current acts like a magnet. One end is a north-seeking; the other, a south-seeking pole. A core of soft iron becomes strongly magnetized if inserted in the solenoid while the current is flowing.

Electric currents may thus be used to produce very strong magnets. These are very useful both in scientific work and in industry. A lifting magnet for handling pig iron, scrap iron, or steel is represented in Fig. 129. The magnet is lowered by the crane upon the pile of scrap material. When the switch is closed, a great quantity of the iron clings to the magnet and is moved.

The electric motor, which performs a multitude of services, operates by reason of the magnetic effect of a current. The principle of operation of a simple direct-current motor is represented in Fig. 130. The main body of the motor, called the

*Marion Steam Shovel Co.*

FIG. 129. Lifting Magnet Handling Scrap Iron. Current for energizing the magnet is supplied by a 5 kw., 230 volt generator run by the gas engine which supplies power to operate the crane.

*yoke,* is made of soft iron. This is wound with insulated copper wire, called the *field winding.* Yoke and field winding together form a strong electromagnet with poles at *N* and *S.* In the space between the poles of this magnet another mass of soft iron usually cylindrical, is mounted upon an axis about which it may rotate. This is called the *armature*. The armature is also wound with wire, and constitutes a second electromagnet. When a current flows in the windings in the direction indicated by the arrows, the two electromagnets develop polarity as shown. Since like poles repel and unlike poles attract each other, the armature turns in a clockwise direction. When it has rotated through an angle of ninety degrees from the position shown, the commutator, *C*, which rotates with the armature,

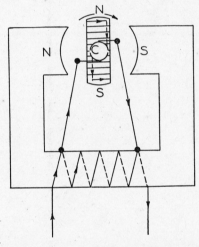

FIG. 130.    Principle of the direct-current motor.

reverses the direction of the current in the armature winding. This reverses the armature polarity. The direction of the current through the field winding and the polarity of the field magnet remain unchanged. Thus the armature still carries a current in such a direction as to make the upper pole north-seeking and the lower pole south-seeking. The armature current is reversed in this way at each half turn.

## INSTRUMENTS FOR MEASURING ELECTRIC CURRENTS

The strength of the magnetic field around a coil of wire is directly proportional to the magnitude of the current in the coil.

This property of currents is applied in the *galvanometer*, an instrument for measuring the strength of small electric currents. In the portable type of galvanometer, a coil to which a pointer is attached is delicately mounted on pivots between the poles of a permanent horseshoe magnet (Fig. 131). In the absence of current, the coil is held in its zero position by a weak coiled spring. When a current flows the coil is rotated, and the pointer

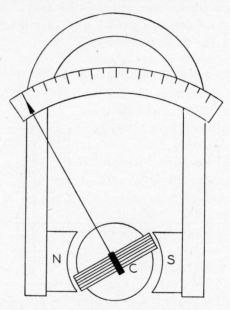

FIG. 131. Principle of the galvanometer.

moved. The strength of the current, which is proportional to the angle of deflection, is indicated by the position of the pointer on a suitably graduated scale.

Instruments for measuring larger currents than galvanometers will carry are called *ammeters* or *milliammeters*. Such an instrument consists of a galvanometer, with a metal strip or wire to serve as a by-pass for the larger part of the current. The scale is graduated to indicate the total current, not merely that flowing through the coil.

## ELECTRIC CURRENTS MAY PRODUCE CHEMICAL EFFECTS

Many substances when dissolved in water undergo a change called *ionization*. (See also Chap. 24.) In this process some of the molecules of the substance are assumed to separate into two parts. In so doing, one of the parts carries with it one or more electrons from the other. The former then has an excess of negative electricity; the latter, a deficiency. The former is a *negative ion;* the latter, a *positive ion.* The magnitude of the charge of the ion depends upon the number of negative electrons transferred. For example, when common salt (NaCl) is dissolved, the chlorine atom of each ionized molecule takes one negative electron from the sodium atom. The molecule then yields a singly-charged negative chlorine ion and a singly-charged positive sodium ion. When sulfuric acid ($H_2SO_4$) is dissolved, the $SO_4$ group of each ionized molecule takes one negative electron from each of the two hydrogen atoms. Each such molecule then yields one doubly-charged negative $SO_4$ ion and two singly-charged posi-tive hydrogen ions. When the salt

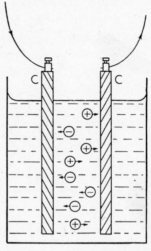

Fig. 132. Chemical effect of an electric current.

cupric chloride ($CuCl_2$) is dissolved, each chlorine atom takes an electron from the copper atom. Each molecule then yields two singly-charged negative chlorine ions and one doubly-charged positive copper ion. A solution containing ions is called an *electrolyte.*

Let Fig. 132 represent a tumbler containing a solution of copper sulfate ($CuSO_4$) into which two carbon rods are inserted to serve as electrodes. In the solution there will be many doubly-charged positive copper ions and an equal number of doubly-charged negative $SO_4$ ions. If the carbon rods are now connected to a source of electric power, a dynamo for example, the positive ions will be repelled by the positive electrode, which is called the *anode*, and attracted by the negative, which is called the *cathode*. The negative ions, on their part, will be repelled by the cathode and attracted by the anode. Copper ions will travel to the cathode, which will quickly become covered with a layer of copper. $SO_4$ ions will travel to the anode. There each such ion breaks up one molecule of water, combining with the hydrogen to form a new molecule of sulfuric acid ($H_2SO_4$) and setting the oxygen atom of the water molecule free. The oxygen collects on the anode, and rises in bubbles to the surface.

If the anode is made of copper instead of carbon, each negative ion reaching it combines with one atom of copper to form a new molecule of copper sulfate, which goes into the solution. In that case the strength of the solution remains unaltered. In the course of time the anode will all be carried across and deposited upon the cathode.

A solution of sulfuric acid gives a somewhat different result. In this solution there are a certain number of doubly-charged negative $SO_4$ ions, and twice as many singly-charged positive hydrogen ions. The $SO_4$ ions travel to the anode, where they liberate oxygen, as described above. The hydrogen ions travel to the cathode, where they are liberated as gaseous hydrogen. In this case oxygen rises from the anode, and hydrogen from the cathode. Twice as many atoms of hydrogen are liberated as of oxygen. The volume of hydrogen is likewise twice as great. A chemical change produced by an electric current in an electrolyte is called *electrolysis*.

Electrolysis is employed in the purification of some metals, such as copper. A thin strip of the pure metal is taken as the cathode and the copper to be purified as the anode. When a current is passed through the electrolytic cell thus formed, pure copper is carried to the cathode, while the impurities go to the bottom of the cell.

Steel gates and fences are covered with a protective coating of zinc in the same way. The object to be coated is made the cathode and a block of zinc the anode. The electrolyte (liquid) is a solution of a salt of zinc. Metal automobile trim is plated with chromium, tableware with silver, and watch cases and other objects with nickel or gold in the same way. The electrolyte in each case contains positive ions of the metal to be deposited. The anode is a block of the same metal.

## ELECTRIC CELLS

Electric currents may be produced in several different ways, but in every case the process depends upon the transformation of some other form of energy.

Perhaps the simplest process involves the transformation of chemical energy (Fig. 133). A strip of zinc, $Z$, and one of cop-

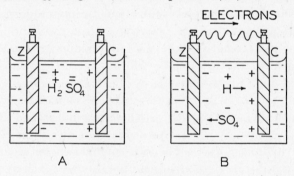

FIG. 133. A simple cell.

per or carbon, $C$, are placed together in a jar of dilute acid, usually hydrochloric or sulfuric. The acid slowly reacts with the zinc, carrying it into solution. Each zinc atom removed from the strip leaves two of its electrons behind. The electrons thus left quickly build up a negative charge upon $Z$. As the zinc atom leaves the zinc strip, two hydrogen ions, each carrying a single positive charge, are driven to $C$. Each hydrogen ion takes an electron from $C$, and thus becomes a neutral hydrogen atom. The removal of electrons from $C$ leaves this electrode with a positive charge. Thus the zinc strip becomes the negative electrode of the cell, and the copper or carbon strip the positive.

If the electrodes are connected by a wire outside the cell, electrons will move along the wire from $Z$ to $C$, tending to neutralize the charges of both electrodes. When this movement begins, the charging of the electrodes also immediately begins again, and a continuous flow of electrons in the outside circuit is maintained. Fig. 133A represents an idle cell, and Fig. 133B represents one supplying power to an outside circuit.

This system is a *primary cell*. Its action ceases when the zinc has been completely dissolved or the acid all used. It can be restored only by inserting a new strip of zinc or supplying more acid.

The best-known and most widely used of all primary cells is the dry cell. This is used for supplying current to flashlight bulbs, for ringing door bells, and for many other purposes. Its cylindrical container, which is of zinc, forms the negative electrode. A centrally located carbon rod forms the positive. A paste whose active constituent is ammonium chloride, a salt quite similar in some respects to table salt, takes the place of the acid.

Certain other types of cells are called *storage cells* or *accumulators*. The chemical action that takes place when they supply current can be reversed by passing current through them in the opposite direction. In the recharging process, the electrical energy supplied to the cell is converted into chemical energy.

The most widely used type of storage cell has lead dioxide for its positive plate and spongy lead for its negative. The electrolyte is a 20 per cent solution of sulfuric acid. This is the type used in automobiles and in home electric plants. Three such cells are connected together to form the usual automobile battery. Sixteen are commonly used in the home electric plant to supply current for lights, and to run milking machines, cream separators, grinders, and various other equipment. Batteries composed of great numbers of large storage cells are installed in connection with some city street railway and subway systems to supply auxiliary power during rush hours.

## THE DYNAMO

Mechanical energy is transformed directly into electrical by means of dynamos. It is in this way that the major part of the electrical energy used in the world is produced.  Wherever feasible, dynamos are operated by water power.  It is largely for this purpose that dams are built across the Mississippi, Tennessee, Columbia, and many other rivers in all parts of the country.  The electrical power generated in such plants may be transmitted for use over wide areas.

*Allis-Chalmers Mfg. Co.*

FIG. 134.  Huge Dynamo (center) of the San Joaquin Power and Light Co., King's River, Calif.  Driven by a double-impulse water turbine (one wheel at each end similar to that shown in Fig. 17).  The water is delivered at a head of 2243 ft., and drives the dynamo at a speed of 360 r.p.m.  Capacity of installation, 40,000 H.P.

Where adequate water power is not available, dynamos are driven by engines.  Steam engines or Diesels are commonly used in the large electric power plants of towns, cities, and public service corporations.  Gas engines are used in the small units designed for the individual home.  Every modern automobile carries a dynamo to supply current for lamps, for the ignition system, and for charging the battery.

The principle upon which the dynamo operates was discovered in 1831 by two men working independently.  One of these was the great English chemist and physicist, Michael Faraday.

The other was the American physicist, Joseph Henry. This principle may be understood from Figs. 135 and 136.

In Fig. 135, $S$ represents a solenoid, with the ends of the wire attached to binding posts, $A$ and $B$. The solenoid is connected

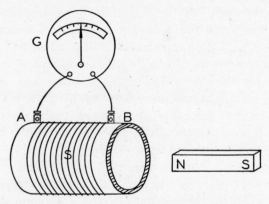

FIG. 135.　Current induced by moving magnet.

to a galvanometer, $G$. Any current flowing through the galvanometer is indicated by a movement of the pointer. If the magnet, $NS$, is gradually moved to a position inside the sole-

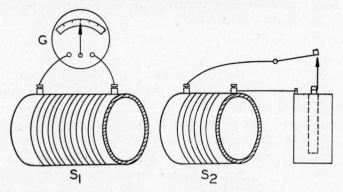

FIG. 136.　Current induced by changing current.

noid, the galvanometer shows a current during the time that the magnet is in motion. When the magnet stops, the current ceases. If the magnet is now withdrawn from the solenoid, the pointer of the galvanometer, $G$, moves in the opposite direction, indicating that the current is also reversed. Again the current exists only while the magnet is in motion. In Fig. 136, $S_1$ and $S_2$ represent two solenoids. $S_1$ is connected to a galvanometer. $S_2$ is connected through a key to a dry cell or storage cell. If the key is now closed so that current flows through $S_2$, there is a sudden movement of the galvanometer pointer with a prompt return to its undeflected position. This change indicates a momentary current through $S_1$, existing only while the current in $S_2$ was rising from zero to its final value. If the key is now opened so that the current in $S_2$ falls to zero, a current flows through $S_1$ in the reverse direction. A core of soft iron extending through the two solenoids greatly increases the strength of the current in $S_1$.

In the movement of the magnet of Fig. 135, the number of magnetic lines of force threading through the solenoid was increased when the magnet was inserted, and diminished when it was removed. The one operation induced a current in one direction; the other induced one in the reverse direction. By closing the key of Fig. 136, a current was made to flow in $S_2$. This produced a magnetic field, some of whose lines extended through $S_1$. When the key was opened, these lines disappeared. The two experiments have one thing in common. The movement of the magnet in the first, and the closing or opening of the key in the second, changed the number of magnetic lines of force threading the solenoid which was connected with the galvanometer. This change in the number of lines set up a current which was in one direction when the number of lines was increasing and in the reverse direction when the number was diminishing.

The dynamo is a machine for generating an electric current by magnetic action in a manner differing only in detail from that described above. The construction of the direct-current dynamo is similar to the motor, Fig. 130. The armature is rotated by mechanical power in the strong magnetic field between $N$ and $S$. As the armature rotates, the magnetic lines pass through it, first in one direction and then in the other, the entire number of lines being inserted and removed during each half rotation. This variation in the number and direction of the magnetic lines of force which pass through the armature sets up a current in any circuit with which the armature winding is connected.

The current in the armature alternates, flowing first in one direction, then in the other. If, as the armature rotates, each end of the armature winding continued to connect with the same wire of the outside circuit, the current in that circuit would also alternate. The machine would then act as an alternating-current dynamo. In the direct-current dynamo, that is, one whose current flows continuously in one direction in the outside circuit, a commutator is used for interchanging contacts at each reversal of current in the armature.

## THE THERMOCOUPLE AND THE PHOTOELECTRIC CELL

Two other means of producing small electric currents are widely used for special purposes. One of these is the *thermo-*

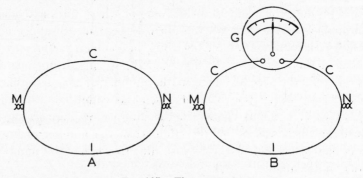

Fig. 137. Thermocouple.

*couple* or *thermopile*. The other is the *photoelectric cell*, sometimes called the *electric eye*.

The action of a thermocouple may be understood by referring to Fig. 137. At any point of contact between unlike metals, as at $M$ or $N$, a current tends to flow from one metal to the other. The measure of this tendency is called a *potential difference* (abbreviated P. D.).  The P. D. depends upon the nature of the metals, and upon the temperature at the point of contact.  If *M* and *N* are at the same temperature, there will be no current in the circuit because the P. D.'s at the two junctions are equal and opposite.  However, if one of the junctions is heated, the P. D.'s at the two junctions are no longer equal and a current flows.  If a galvanometer is inserted in the circuit as shown in Fig. 137B, the current may be accurately measured. Since its magnitude depends upon the difference in the temperatures of *M* and *N*, the temperature difference between the two junctions may be found by measuring the P. D.'s.  For measuring temperature it is desirable to provide the galvanometer with a temperature scale instead of a scale of electric current.  The instrument is then a direct-reading electrical thermometer.  Such a thermometer may be used for measuring high temperatures, such as those of furnaces; or very moderate ones, such as those of muscles or other organs of the body.  In using a thermometer of this type, one of the junctions is placed at the point whose temperature is to be measured, inside the furnace, for example, while the other is kept at some known temperature,

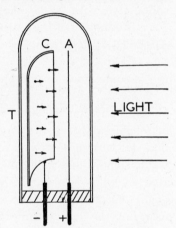

FIG. 138.   Photoelectric cell.

such as the freezing point of water.  The galvanometer pointer then indicates the unknown temperature.

A number of thermocouples are sometimes connected in series.  Such a combination, called a *thermopile*, is more sensitive than a single thermocouple.  It is often used in measuring faint radiation such as that of a star.

The photoelectric cell yields a small electric current in response to the action of light.  In one type of photocell the light ejects electrons from a photosensitive surface upon which it is allowed to fall.  This type is represented in Fig. 138.  *C* is the photosensitive electrode, usually consisting of a thin layer of cesium or a cesium compound on a surface of silver. *A* is a metal rod or loop which, when the cell is in use, is connected to the positive terminal of a battery. It is the collector of electrons, or anode. *C* is the cathode. *A* and *C* are connected to short light metal rods which extend through the base of the tube to form the supporting prongs.

Electrons moving across from *C* to *A* constitute a small electric current whose magnitude is directly proportional to the amount of light falling upon *C*.

Photocells perform a great variety of very important services. Perhaps the best known use is that to which they are put in connection with sound motion pictures. There they aid in the reproduction of the sound. (See Chap. 20.) They are also employed in television, where they perform an indispensable function in the transmission (Chap. 20). They are also essential in some types of photometer, one of which, called an exposure meter, is a very important item in the equipment of a photographer, as we have seen in Chap. 15. They are used in schools and factories to give automatic control of illumination, by turning lamps on or off as required. Burglar alarms, traffic signals, and many other types of safety devices are operated by photo currents. So also are devices for testing the quality of paints and other merchandise, and for counting and recording the daily output of factories.

## THE STRENGTH OF AN ELECTRIC CURRENT

It was mentioned above that electric currents are analogous in many ways to streams of water. A river, for example, may carry one million cubic feet per second; a water main or a fire hose may carry one hundred barrels per minute. The flow in either case is designated by the amount of water carried in a unit of time. The same idea is involved in specifying the strength of an electric current. If a wire transports ten *coulombs* of electricity per second, the current has a strength of ten *coulombs per second*. The unit of current strength, however, instead of being called one coulomb per second, is called the *ampere.* A current that carries ten coulombs per second is a ten ampere current.

The coulomb is defined as the amount of electricity which, in passing through a silver plating cell, will deposit .001118 gm. of silver on the cathode. A 1 ampere current is defined as a current of such strength as will carry silver to the cathode at the rate of .001118 gm. per second.

## ELECTRIC CIRCUITS. RESISTANCE

A river does not circle back upon itself. It has a source and a mouth, and the water that it empties does not go back to the source and flow through the same channel again. In this respect an electric current differs from the stream. The electric current can flow continuously only in a closed circuit. If this is broken at any point (that is, if there is not an uninterrupted path of conducting material), there will be no current.

Copper and silver are the best conductors of electricity. Aluminum is also a good conductor. Copper is used in the construction of electrical machinery, in house wiring, and in most transmission lines. Glass, porcelain, rubber, and bakelite are *insulators;* that is, they are nonconductors of electricity.

Every electric circuit offers at least some opposition to the flow of an electric current. This opposition is called *resistance.* The longer a wire, the greater its resistance. The thicker the wire, the more freely it will carry current, and the less its resistance. Resistance is measured in units called *ohms.*

The ohm is defined by act of Congress as a resistance equal to that at 0° C. of a uniform thread of mercury 106.3 cm. long and weighing 14.4521 gm. It is approximately equal to that of a copper wire 1 mm. in diameter and half a block long.

## ELECTROMOTIVE FORCE

Water will not flow in a pipe or a stream unless there is a difference in pressure or water level. Similarly, an electric current will not flow in a circuit unless there is a difference in what may be called electrical pressure, or level. We have seen that this may be supplied by dry cells, storage cells, dynamos, and other means. In our discussion of the thermocouple we called it a potential difference. The total P. D. created by any source is called its electromotive force, abbreviated E. M. F. P. D.'s and E. M. F.'s are measured in units called *volts*. The volt is defined as the E. M. F. which will produce a current of 1 ampere in a circuit whose resistance is 1 ohm.

The E. M. F.'s of various sources of electric energy vary widely. That of a new dry cell is about 1.5 volts. That of a well-charged lead storage cell is a little more than 2 volts. Current is supplied to domestic users at 110 to 115 volts. It is carried by long transmission lines at voltages as high as 250,000. In some devices for studying the structure of atoms several million volts have been used, and many times this amount is often manifest in lightning. The thermocouple gives a very small E. M. F.—a few millionths, or for some pairs of metals, less than one-millionth of a volt for each centigrade degree difference of temperature between the junctions.

## LAW OF THE ELECTRIC CIRCUIT

The current in a circuit varies directly as the E. M. F., and inversely as the resistance. These relationships are expressed in the law of the electric circuit which states that

$$\text{Current} = \frac{\text{E. M. F.}}{\text{Resistance}}.$$

This is Ohm's law, one of the most important in electrical science.

In symbols this law may be written

$$I = \frac{E}{R}.$$

In terms of the units defined above

$$\text{Amperes} = \frac{\text{Volts}}{\text{Ohms}}.$$

## QUESTIONS INVOLVING OHM'S LAW

1. What current flows through a 20 ohm toaster when connected to a 110 volt line?

Solution: $I = \dfrac{E}{R} = \dfrac{110}{20} = 5.5$ amperes.

2. What E. M. F. will be required to furnish a current of 10 amperes to an 11.5 ohm cooker?

Solution: $I = \dfrac{E}{R}$; $E = RI = 11.5 \times 10 = 115$ volts.

3. What is the resistance of a lamp which takes 1.6 amperes from a 32 volt home lighting plant?

Solution: $I = \dfrac{E}{R}$; $R = \dfrac{E}{I} = \dfrac{32}{1.6} = 20$ ohms.

## ELECTRIC POWER

In electrical devices as well as in mechanical ones, the rate at which work is done or energy used is an important consideration. To handle a large amount of electrical power by a single machine requires that it be a large one. For a small amount of power a small machine is more economical.

The amount of power supplied by a battery or direct-current dynamo depends upon two factors, the current and the voltage, and is directly proportional to each.

Power = Current × E. M. F.
Watts = Amperes × Volts.
In symbols, $P = IE$.
One kilowatt, (kw) = 1000 watts.

Dynamos delivering 1000 kw. or more are in use in moderate-sized power plants in almost every part of the country. Single units delivering 12,000 to 15,000 kilowatts are not at all uncommon. A few, in the larger installations, carry many times this amount.

## QUESTIONS ON ELECTRICAL POWER

1. How many kilowatts are supplied by a dynamo which delivers 50 amperes at 2200 volts?

Solution: Power = 50 × 2200 = 110,000 watts = 110 kw.

2. What current is supplied to a lamp which takes 75 watts from a 110 volt line?

Solution: $P = EI; I = \dfrac{P}{E} = \dfrac{75}{110} = .68$ ampere.

3. What is the resistance of a toaster which takes 575 watts from a 115 volt line?

Solution: $P = EI; I = \dfrac{P}{E} = \dfrac{575}{115} = 5$ amp.

$$R = \dfrac{E}{I} = \dfrac{115}{5} = 23 \text{ ohms.}$$

## ELECTRIC ENERGY—THE MONTHLY ELECTRIC BILL

Consumers of "electricity" do not pay for the amount of current their devices take, though this is a factor in determining the bill. The charge is for the energy used. This is equal to the power (that is, the energy used per second), multiplied by the number of seconds during which this power is taken.

Energy = power × time.
Watt-seconds = watts × seconds
Watt-hours = watts × hours.
Kw. hr. = kilowatts × hours.

## QUESTIONS ON ELECTRICAL ENERGY

1. How many kilowatt-hours are used in 30 days by a 75 watt lamp which is in use 4 hours per day?

Solution: Energy in kw. hr. = kilowatts × hours.
Energy = $^{75}/_{1000}$ × 4 × 30 = 9 kw. hr.

2. At 5 cents per kilowatt-hour what is the cost of running a refrigerator motor for 30 days if the motor takes 200 watts and runs 10 hours each day?

Solution: Energy = kw. × hr.
= $^{200}/_{1000}$ × 10 × 30 = 60 kw. hr.
Cost = 60 × $.05 = $3.00

# CHAPTER 20

# ELECTRICAL
# COMMUNICATION

Man has long entertained the inspiring dream of freeing himself from the restrictions of space. Although it is not to be expected that this dream will ever be completely realized, great progress has already been made toward its partial achievement. Our pioneer forefathers made their way through the colonial wilderness on foot or on horseback, or lumbered across the prairie in covered wagons at speeds that would now be intolerable. For his first inauguration as President, George Washington traveled from Mount Vernon to New York in seven days. A century later the completion of the main line of the Union Pacific established the first transcontinental railroad. It was then possible to travel from ocean to ocean in less time than it took our first President to travel the short distance from his home to the capital. Improved roadbeds, new types of motive power, and streamlined trains have considerably reduced the earlier transcontinental time by rail, while in point of speed the airplane has now far outstripped all other means of transport. The transcontinental journey, Los Angeles to Newark, was made by Howard Hughes in 1937 in less than seven and a half hours. At that speed, 332 miles per hour, the trip from Mount Vernon, Va., to New York would require about forty minutes. In 1938 the same daring airman made a world-circling flight from Floyd Bennett Field over Europe, Siberia, Alaska, and return, in about three days and nineteen hours. On this trip his average speed while in the air was 208.1 miles per hour. Space has been greatly reduced, and the indications are clear that the shrinking process will continue.

The story of communication is still more thrilling. Little more than a century ago a message could be carried no faster than the swiftest courier could travel on horseback. In 1815 Andrew Jackson fought an unnecessary battle at New Orleans three weeks after peace had been declared, because the news of the treaty had not yet reached him. Today messages are flashed with the speed of light—186,000 miles per second. The members of a radio audience scattered over an entire continent may hear the speech or music even before it reaches the last rows in the auditorium in which the program originates. This illustrates the remarkable degree to which means of communication have now been perfected. Let us sketch some of the more important steps in this development.

## THE TELEGRAPH

When it had been found that a wire carrying an electric current is surrounded by a magnetic field, that a solenoid with an iron core becomes a strong magnet even when the current through the coil is small, and that currents can be carried to considerable distances, men began to ponder the possibility of communication by electrical means. Joseph Henry, an American, in 1831 constructed a circuit in which he used an electromagnet to produce an audible signal at his home when he operated a key in his laboratory at the Albany Academy several blocks away. Gauss and Weber (Germany, 1833) operated a crude telegraphic line over a distance of nearly two miles. Morse, an American, devised a telegraph in 1837 in which the attraction of an armature produced dots and dashes on a moving tape. But it was not until 1844 that he publicly demonstrated the practicability of his device by sending a message from Washington to Baltimore.

The principle of the telegraph as used by Morse is shown in Fig. 139. $K$ represents a key and $B$ a battery at the sending station. $R$ indicates the receiving instrument in which $M$ is an electromagnet which is energized by current from $B$ when $K$

is closed. $P$ is a pen whose iron stem is pivoted at $O$. The pen is held back by a weak spring, $S$, when $K$ is open, but is attracted by $M$ when $K$ is closed. The pen then makes contact with a moving tape which is carried over a roller or bar at $T$. Just as now, messages were sent by means of code, in which the letters of the alphabet, the digits, and certain other symbols were represented by dots, dashes, and combinations of the two. Whether a dot or a dash was made depended upon how long $K$ was held closed. The operator at the sending station spelled out the message by making in order the combinations of dots and dashes which represented the various characters of the message. At the receiving station these were written as a permanent record on the tape.

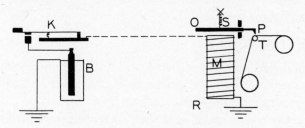

FIG. 139. The telegraph.

It was soon found that an operator at the receiving station could interpret the message from the sounds of the instrument. The tape was then unnecessary, and was soon eliminated. An iron bar was substituted for the pen. The receiving instrument thus made is called a *sounder*.

The simple telegraph described above will carry only one message at a time. Improvements were soon made whereby two messages could be sent simultaneously. In the multiplex telegraphy of the present day several may be sent at the same time in each direction.

## THE TELEPHONE

The telegraph greatly increased the speed of communication. But men were hopeful that a still more rapid method might be devised.  Might it not be possible to transmit speech itself instead of symbols representing the letters of the alphabet?  The earliest plan for accomplishing this is attributed to Charles Bourseul, a French telegrapher (1854).  Bourseul, however, did not develop an actual working instrument.  The next to suggest a practical telephone was Philip Reis, of Germany (1861).  His instrument was said to transmit musical sounds very well, but to be uncertain and erratic in transmitting speech.  Fifteen years later Alexander Graham Bell exhibited his telephone at the Centennial Exposition in Philadelphia (1876).  The trans-

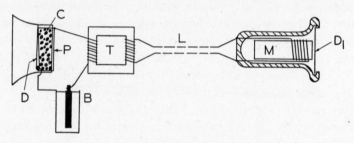

Fig. 140.   The telephone.

mitter and receiver of this telephone were alike, and similar in principle to the receiver used in the telephone of the present day.

The telephone transmitter now used consists of a quantity of carbon granules, $C$ (Fig. 140), contained in a shallow chamber having a rigid metal or carbon bottom, $P$.  The chamber is closed in front by a flexible diaphragm, $D$.  $P$ and $D$ are connected in a circuit with a battery, $B$, and the primary coil of a step-up transformer, $T$.  The electrical resistance at the points of contact of the carbon granules varies with pressure.  If the diaphragm moves inward upon them, their resistance is diminished and the current is increased.  If the diaphragm moves outward, the resistance is increased and the current diminished.

It was shown in Chap. 14 that sound waves consist of recurring condensations and rarefactions in the air.  When a sound is made in the transmitter, the waves cause the diaphragm, $D$, to vibrate, subjecting the carbon granules to alternately increased and diminished pressure.  The current in the circuit is thus made to vary.   At every instant it has a value which is determined by the pressure then existing upon the granules.

The variations of the current through the primary winding of the transformer, $T$, set up an alternating current of higher voltage in the secondary.   (An alternating current is one which flows alternately first in one direction, then in the other.) This current is carried over the line to the receiver.

The receiver consists of a permanent magnet, $M$, very close to which in a rigid mounting is held a thin steel diaphragm, $D_1$. One end of the magnet is surrounded by a spool of fine wire which is connected in series with the telephone line, $L$.   The line current not only alternates but also varies in strength according to the frequency and intensity of the sound made at the transmitter.   The strength of the magnetic field at $D_1$ and the force with which this diaphragm is attracted to the magnet, $M$, vary correspondingly.   By this means $D_1$ is made to duplicate the movements of $D$.   Thus the diaphragm $D_1$ produces sounds at the receiver which are very similar to those made at the transmitter.

## THE TELEPHONE CENTRAL STATION

In order to carry a message, the telephone circuit must be continuous between the transmitter and the receiver.   That the circuit may be established, all wires (except in some rural lines) lead to central stations.   Here they terminate in jacks or other parts which are so constructed that any two of the pairs of wires entering the station can be conveniently connected in a circuit which includes a battery.   In many central stations, circuits are thus completed by operators on duty for that purpose.   Operators also close the ringing circuit to signal the called subscriber. This method of establishing communication is called *manual switching*.

In a more modern development, switching is accomplished by electrical means.   To establish the desired circuit, the subscriber merely turns a dial.   One set of movements of the dial calls one telephone; a different set calls another.   Each group of movements results in sending current through a particular set of electromagnets at the central station. These then produce the movements necessary to connect the telephone of the

*Bell Telephone Laboratories.*

FIG. 141.  Combined hand telephone set.

calling with that of the called subscriber. A modern telephone set designed for dialing is represented in Fig. 141.

## THE RADIOTELEGRAPH

In 1888 Heinrich Hertz, a German physicist, performed experiments in which electromagnetic waves generated by a Leyden jar discharge produced effects through the air at a distance from their origin. About ten years later the Italian inventor, Marconi, succeeded in transmitting signals by means of such waves. He realized that if these could be made to carry messages, two great advantages would be gained. It would not only be possible to dispense with wires for transmission, but the message would be carried in every direction, and could be received by any operator with appropriate equipment anywhere within the range of the waves. Marconi rapidly extended the distance over which his equipment would operate. In 1899 he communicated by electromagnetic wave telegraphy between France and England, and in 1901 he succeeded in transmitting signals in one direction across the

Atlantic Ocean. The success of wireless telegraphy was then assured.

The principle of the damped-wave radiotelegraph transmitter may be understood from Fig. 142. $D$ represents an alternating current dynamo. $K$ is a key, manipulated by the operator in sending the message. $C$ is a condenser. $SP$ is a gap across which a spark passes when the voltage wave of the generator reaches a certain height. $P$ is the primary and $S$ the secondary of a transformer. $A$ is the antenna. When a spark occurs at $SP$ an oscillating current of high frequency but rapidly diminishing strength flows in the circuit including $C$, $SP$, and $P$. This sets up a corresponding current in $S$ and $A$, and sends out a

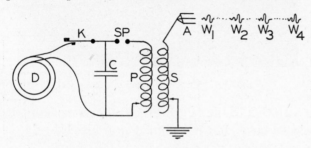

FIG. 142. Principle of the radiotelegraph transmitter.

group of electromagnetic waves, several of which are represented by $W_1$, $W_2$, and so forth. One such group is sent out in each half-cycle of the current in $D$. If the dynamo develops a voltage wave whose frequency is 500 cycles per second, 1000 groups of waves such as $W_1$, $W_2$, will be sent out by the antenna per second. If in making a dot the key $K$ is held closed for one-tenth of a second, 100 such groups of waves will be launched. If a dash requires one-fifth of a second, it is made by 200 such groups. While the key is open, the voltage of the dynamo is not impressed upon $C$, and no waves are sent out.

The essential features of one type of simple receiver are represented in Fig. 143. $L$ is a coil of 30 to 100 turns of wire connected at one end to the antenna, and at the other to the ground. $C$ is a condenser whose capacitance may be varied by turning a knob. This is the tuning condenser. $T$ is a vacuum tube with three electrodes, $F$, $GD$, and $P$. $PH$ is a telephone receiver; $B$ and $B'$ are batteries or their equivalent.

$F$ is a tungsten *filament* which is highly heated by current from the battery, $B$. $F$ then discharges electrons just as a moist surface discharges water molecules by evaporation. $P$ is a *plate* connected to the positive terminal of the battery, $B'$. Electrons then move from $F$, which constitutes the cathode of the tube, to $P$, which constitutes the anode. $GD$ is a wire *grid* whose function is to influence the movement of electrons in the tube.

When no waves are reaching the antenna, a steady stream of electrons flows from the heated filament, $F$, to $P$, and thence

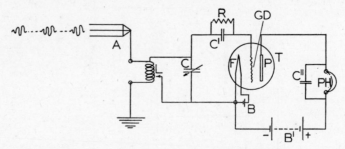

FIG. 143.   Principle of the radiotelegraph receiver.

through $PH$ and $B'$ back to $F$. This constitutes a small electric current. It does not give rise to sound, however, because it is a direct current of constant strength.

When the key at the transmitting station is closed, groups of waves strike the antenna of the receiver, each of which produces a momentary oscillating current in $L$. With the arrival of each group, the grid, $GD$, collects a certain number of the electrons that are evaporated from $F$. The small negative charge thus acquired by $GD$ tends to prevent other electrons from passing across from $F$ to $P$. This diminishes the current through the telephone receiver, $PH$, and causes a movement of its diaphragm. The result is a click. The charge on $GD$ quickly flows off through a high resistance, $R$, and the current through $PH$ is of normal strength again. With the arrival of the next group, the process is repeated. This continues as long as the key, $K$, at the transmitter (Fig. 142) remains closed.    If 1000 wave groups per second are received, the diaphragm makes 1000 vibrations per second, and the sound is heard as a musical note of that frequency.    Messages are sent in code by dots and dashes, just as in wire telegraphy.

## THE RADIOTELEPHONE

The type of transmitter described above for the radiotele-graph cannot be used for the radio telephone, since the intervals

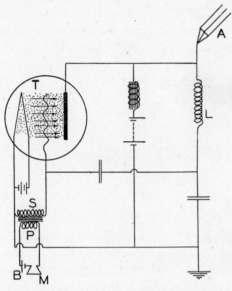

FIG. 144.    Vacuum-tube oscillator.

of inaction between the groups of emitted waves would destroy the characteristics of the sound to be transmitted.    For radio-telephony the transmitter must generate a continuous train of electromagnetic waves.    This is usually done by means of a very high-frequency alternating-current dynamo, or a vacuum-tube oscillator.    The latter is more commonly used.    For purposes of radiotelephony the oscillator may generate from about 35,000 to many millions of waves per second.    The fre-quencies used in radio broadcasting in the United States include the range from 550,000 to 1,500,000 per second.

Before leaving the transmitter, the wave train must be modulated, that is, it must be given characteristics corresponding to those of the sounds it is desired to reproduce at the receiver. A general plan by which modulation may be accomplished is represented in Fig. 144. *T* represents a three-electrode vacuum tube arranged to supply a continuous high-frequency electric current to the coil, *L*. *P* is the primary and *S* the secondary of a telephone transformer. *M* is a microphone in circuit with *P* and a battery, *B*.

When the tube is in operation but no sound is made in the microphone, continuous electromagnetic waves are sent out from the antenna as represented in Fig. 145A. When a sound

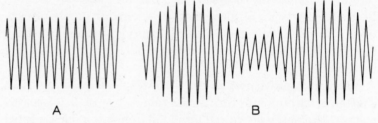

FIG. 145.   Radio Waves.   A. Unmodulated.   B. Modulated.

wave strikes the microphone, this varies the current in the circuit, *MPB*, and gives it characteristics corresponding to those of the sound. Through the secondary, *S*, of the transformer these characteristics are passed on to the current in *L*, and to the waves sent out from the antenna. A modulated wave is represented in Fig. 145B.

The same receiver may be used in radiotelephony as in radiotelegraphy. Instead of emitting a succession of longer or shorter sounds of an unvarying pitch which represent the dots and dashes of the telegraphic message, a sound is heard which may be a remarkably accurate reproduction of that made in the microphone, *M*.

## THE VACUUM TUBE

The type of vacuum tube briefly described above is the one upon which radiotelephony in its early days exclusively depended. It was invented by the American radio engineer De Forest about the year 1906. Though the invention consisted only of the insertion of a third electrode, the grid, between the filament and plate of the already well-known Fleming valve, it was this simple change that gave the tube the power and the versatility that has resulted, like magic, in the entire vast development of radio of the present day.

But De Forest's audion, as it was called, was destined to be improved upon in several different ways. The first of the changes was made in the filament. For the simple tungsten of the earlier tubes was substituted either tungsten with a small admixture of thorium, or a nickel alloy coated with certain metallic oxides (calcium, barium, and strontium). Both of these types of filament gave a copious supply of electrons at a much lower temperature than tungsten alone. They therefore entailed a much smaller drain upon the heating battery.

A second improvement in the tube was made by using as an emitter of electrons a very small thin sleeve of oxide-coated metal. Inside the sleeve and insulated from it is a fine tungsten filament by which the sleeve is heated. This is the construction of the so-called heater type of tube, which has the great advantage of eliminating the hum that was often troublesome when tubes of the filament type were operated from an alternating-current lighting circuit.

A third improvement was made by inserting additional electrodes in the tube. The first to be added was the *screen*. This is mounted between the plate and the grid, and acts as an electrostatic shield between them. On this account the screen grid tube gives high amplification and stable operation. It is widely used in both broadcast and short-wave receivers. The screen grid tube, because it has four electrodes, is often called a *tetrode*. The beam power tube is of this class.

In other types of tube a third grid, called a *suppressor grid*, is inserted between the screen and the plate. This grid is used to give either high amplification or a large output of power. Tubes of this type are called *pentodes*.

Still greater numbers of electrodes are often included in the same tube. In this case the tube is usually adapted to perform the functions of two or more tubes of simpler type.

A fourth improvement, and one of the latest, is the use of metal instead of glass for the envelope. The envelope itself then acts as a shield against outside electrical disturbances. Metal tubes are much smaller than glass tubes of equal numbers

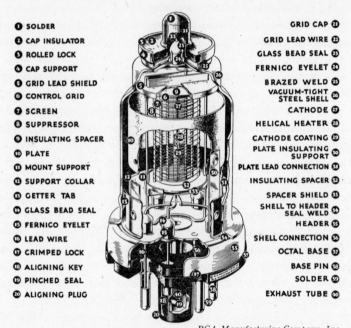

❶ SOLDER
❷ CAP INSULATOR
❸ ROLLED LOCK
❹ CAP SUPPORT
❺ GRID LEAD SHIELD
❻ CONTROL GRID
❼ SCREEN
❽ SUPPRESSOR
❾ INSULATING SPACER
❿ PLATE
⓫ MOUNT SUPPORT
⓬ SUPPORT COLLAR
⓭ GETTER TAB
⓮ GLASS BEAD SEAL
⓯ FERNICO EYELET
⓰ LEAD WIRE
⓱ CRIMPED LOCK
⓲ ALIGNING KEY
⓳ PINCHED SEAL
⓴ ALIGNING PLUG

GRID CAP ㉑
GRID LEAD WIRE ㉒
GLASS BEAD SEAL ㉓
FERNICO EYELET ㉔
BRAZED WELD ㉕
VACUUM-TIGHT STEEL SHELL ㉖
CATHODE ㉗
HELICAL HEATER ㉘
CATHODE COATING ㉙
PLATE INSULATING SUPPORT ㉚
PLATE LEAD CONNECTION ㉛
INSULATING SPACER ㉜
SPACER SHIELD ㉝
SHELL TO HEADER SEAL WELD ㉞
HEADER ㉟
SHELL CONNECTION ㊱
OCTAL BASE ㊲
BASE PIN ㊳
SOLDER ㊴
EXHAUST TUBE ㊵

*RCA Manufacturing Company, Inc.*
FIG. 146. Structure of a metal-type receiving tube.

of electrodes and equal power. They are especially useful where compactness is an important factor, as in car and portable receivers. The structure of an all-metal tube is shown in Fig. 146.

The three-electrode vacuum tube is rightly considered one of the most important inventions of modern times. It was this tube that opened the way for our first efficient and reliable long distance telephone transmission, our first effective radio receivers, and our present-day radio transmitters. It was this tube also that first made possible the amplification of sound in public address systems, thus enabling each member of an audience to hear a speaker or musician clearly no matter how large the audience, whether in an auditorium or out of doors. In conjunction with the photoelectric cell it supplied us with sound motion pictures and all the other benefits of the photo-cell mentioned in the preceding chapter. In addition, it has provided the scientist with a most powerful means of research, and has thus been instrumental in helping in a marked degree to accelerate the unparalleled scientific progress of the last half century.

The vacuum tube accomplishes its miracles by reason of its ability to perform in any or all of three different ways. In the first of these it may take radio impulses whose frequencies are hundreds of times greater than that of the shrillest sound the ear can hear, and convert them into electrical currents which, in the earphone or loud speaker, deliver intelligible audible messages. In the second mode of action it may take an electric current so faint as to produce almost no discernable response whatever in the earphone, and amplify it, if need be, into one that in a loud speaker will give a deafening roar. In the third mode of operation the tube acts as a generator of high-frequency alternating current. In so doing, it not only generates the carrier waves of our transmitting stations, but is an essential factor also in the operation of our most sensitive receivers.

## THE TELETYPEWRITER

This device is a means of communication used widely by newspapers, manufacturers, government bureaus, police depart-ments, and business houses. Messages are carried over tele-graph lines. Connections may be permanent, as in private-line telegraph service, or they may be temporary and made sepa-rately for each call, as in the usual telephone service.

The teletypewriter consists of a transmitter having a key-board very similar in appearance to that of an ordinary type-writer, and a receiver with a system of type bars corresponding to those of a typewriter. It might be called a modified telegraph in which the transmitter is a typewriter keyboard with added electrical and mechanical parts. The receiver is the rest of the typewriter plus the necessary electrical and mechanical means of operating the type bars.

The operation may be sketched as follows: The sending operator, at the home office in New York, for example, strikes (presses) a key of one of the letters of the alphabet, say $A$. This closes an electric circuit which initiates a set of quickly completed operations in his own machine corresponding to the letter $A$. To make these movements the machine is run by an electric motor. If the operator had pressed the key marked $B$, this again would have closed a circuit initiating a definite set of operations, this set corresponding to $B$. These operations consist of opening and closing electric circuits, and sending spurts of current over the telegraph line to the receiving station and through the receiving instrument installed there. The spurts occur in one way for $A$, in a different way for $B$, and so on for all the other characters used. These momentary currents energize electromagnets of the receiving instrument which, in turn, operate the type bars. When key $A$ is pressed at the transmitter, the letter $A$ is made at the receiver. Thus the message is carried and typed. The speed is about 60 words per minute.

This system is similar to the telephone in that it permits two-way transmission. It also permits group communication. An official in the home office may simultaneously call all of the branch managers in other cities. Though in widely separated places, these persons may then carry on a "conversation" somewhat as if they were sitting about a table, though more slowly. Any one of the group, through his own transmitter, may participate at any time.

## SOUND MOTION PICTURES

Two methods of reproducing sound in motion pictures have been devised. In one of these the sound record is made upon a disc as in the phonograph. When the picture is run, the disc is rotated and the sound reproduced by means of an electrical "pick up" and amplifier, just as in many other phonographs. In order to keep the sound in synchronism with the picture, the film is run and the disc rotated by the same motor. In the second method, which is more widely used than the first, the sound record is made upon the edge of the film that carries the picture. The sound is reproduced by means of a photoelectric cell, as mentioned in the preceding chapter.

In order to record the sound upon the film, the intensity of the light by means of which the record is produced must at every instant be made to vary with the intensity of the sound. This is accomplished by means of a device called a light valve. The principle of one type of valve is represented in Fig. 147.

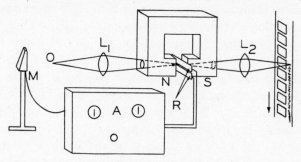

Fig. 147.   Light valve.

Two very light metal ribbons, $R$, which are electrically connected at their farther ends, are mounted under tension, about .001 inch apart, between the poles of a strong magnet. Light from a small but brilliant lamp, $O$, is directed by a condensing lens, $L_1$, upon the narrow space between the ribbons, and then focused by a second lens, $L_2$, upon one edge of the film. A microphone, $M$, generates a minute electric current in response to the sounds to be recorded. The current is greatly magnified by an amplifier, $A$, and passed through the ribbons. Since the current flows in opposite directions in the two strips it deflects one upward from its neutral position, and the other downward. A current in one direction in the circuit widens the gap between the ribbons, while a current in the reverse direction reduces it. Thus the width of the gap, and the amount of light allowed to pass are at every instant determined by the intensity of the sound at the microphone.

In running the film, the picture portion is strongly illuminated and passed in front of a lens which throws a greatly enlarged image on the screen. The sound trace is at the same time illuminated by an intense spot of light from a second lamp, *O*, Fig. 148. The light that passes through the sound trace enters a photocell, *C*. A current is thereby established in the electric circuit of the photocell which varies according to the amount of light entering the cell. The photo current is great where the original sound was intense, and small where the sound was weak, At every instant it has the frequency of the sound by which the light valve was controlled. The photo current is amplified

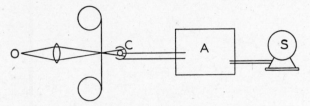

FIG. 148.   Reproduction of sound in motion pictures.

and led into a loud speaker. By this means the sounds by which the original trace was made are reproduced.

## TELEVISION

The latest development in the science of electrical communication, and one just now passing from the experimental into the practical stage, is television. Its aim is to enable the public not merely to hear of events as they occur as is now done in radio when we listen to a play-by-play report of a world series baseball game or a great football classic; not merely to see the performers in action days or weeks after the event as we now do on the motion picture screen. The ultimate aim of television is to bring to the people the rapidly changing panorama of important events as they happen: a view of the game from the 50 yard line as well as the cheering and the music; the visual presence of statesmen, actors, musicians, and other important public figures, as well as the sounds of their voices; a view of the milling crowds as they throng the shopping district, or of strikers as they are assembled to enforce their demands, or of a national political convention in the process of nominating its candidate for President. It is a complicated art, and one whose methods we can here sketch only very lightly.

In telephony the process is that of reproducing at a distance, by means of the electric current, sounds that are similar to those made at the transmitter. In radio the purpose is the

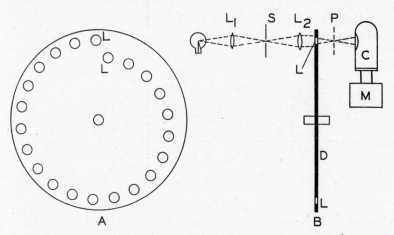

FIG. 149.   Scanning disc, with illuminator, lens system, and photoelectric cell.

same as in telephony, but because transmission is through space instead of over wires the means employed are different. In television the problem is the far more difficult one of reproducing immediately and at a distance a continuous view of a scene which may be ever changing. To accomplish this it is necessary to flash not less than twenty complete pictures every second. Each of these requires that the light and shade of each of many thousands of spots taken in order in the scene shall produce its electrical effect in the transmitting apparatus, and that each of these various effects shall reproduce its corresponding light or shadow in its correct time and space relation at the receiver.

The process by which the scene is made to produce the necessary electrical effects is called *scanning*. Various methods of scanning have been employed, one of which will be understood by reference to Fig. 149. For this description the scene is represented by a photograph, or photographic negative, $P$. A fine, intense, movable point of light from a brilliant lamp is thrown upon the picture by the lenses $L_1$, $L_2$, and $L$. $S$ is an opaque screen with a fine aperture. $C$ is a photoelectric cell which receives the light from the picture, $P$, and sends to $M$ an electric current whose strength is proportional to the amount of light received. $M$ is the modulator, that is, the means by which the light impresses its effect upon the waves of the trans-

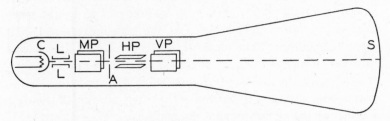

FIG. 150.   Principle of cathode-ray television receiving tube.

mitter. $D$ is a large disc with a row of holes arranged in a spiral as shown in Fig. 149A. In each hole is mounted a lens, $L$. In scanning the picture the disc is rotated. In one rotation each of the lenses, $L$, passes a fine pencil of light across the picture, the path of each beam lying just below and very close to the one preceding. Thus the entire scene is scanned once at each rotation. The disc is rotated at a speed of twenty or more rotations per second, in order that there shall be this number of complete pictures, and the view be made to seem continuous.

At the receiver the variations produced in the electric current or the radio wave by the variations in light entering $C$ must be used in such a way as to build up a true picture of the scene transmitted. This may also be accomplished in various ways, one of which is by means of a special cathode-ray oscillograph. The principle may be understood from Fig. 150.

The diagram represents a highly evacuated tube in which a heated cathode, $C$, supplies electrons. These are driven at high speed toward the farther end of the tube. By means of a suitable electrode, $LL$, called an electron lens, and a screen $A$ with a fine aperture, they are confined in a very narrow beam. On arriving at $S$, by their impact they cause a fluorescent material with which this end of the tube is internally coated to glow.

Three pairs of plates, $MP$, $HP$, and $VP$, provide the means for deflecting the electronic beam in such a way as to build up a luminous picture in $S$. The first pair, $MP$, is connected by a suitable amplifier with the receiving antenna. This pair controls the number of electrons passing through the aperture in $A$. It thus controls the brightness of the spot in $S$, bright when much light enters the photocell at the transmitter, and faint when little enters. The plates $HP$ by their electric field deflect the beam in a vertical line. This field is varied in exact synchronization with the rotation of the scanning disc, and the electron beam swept from top to bottom of $S$ at each rotation of the disc. $VP$ deflect the electron beam horizontally. Their electric field is so controlled as to sweep the beam across $S$ horizontally at each passage of one of the lenses, $L$, of the scanning disc. Thus each spot of $S$ glows strongly or faintly or not at all according to the amount of light entering the photocell at the transmitter from the corresponding spot of the scene or picture.

A special cathode-ray television receiving tube is shown in Fig. 151.

Television transmission requires a very broad band of frequencies, much broader than the entire band allotted to radio broadcasting. This is available only in the range of very high frequencies. Such waves have but a short dependable transmission range. If television programs are to become generally available, as radio programs are now, it seems likely that transmitters of such programs must become quite numerous. Cables such as those now used for carrying radio programs from a studio to distant transmitters would not be suitable for carrying a television program. Recent tests made by the Bell Telephone Laboratories on the *coaxial conductor* installed between New York and Philadelphia have shown that this type of cable

*Bell Telephone Laboratories.*
FIG. 151.   Cathode-ray receiving tube for television.

carries a television band extremely well.   This cable consists of a wire mounted coaxially in a copper tube by means of regularly spaced insulating discs. Perhaps in the not too distant future television networks may be established by which such programs may become available to a large part of our population.

## OTHER USES OF RADIO WAVES

Radio waves may be made to perform many other tasks more or less closely related to that of carrying messages. Chief among these is that of guiding the airplane pilot exactly in his airlane. The radio beams sent out from various landing fields along the way control a sensitive instrument mounted on his instrument board to warn him with one visual signal if he drifts too far to the right, and with another if too far to the left. Radio waves are also used by the pilot at night and in fog or storm to keep him continuously informed of his altitude above ground. A transmitter in one wing sends a beam downward which is reflected from the ground and caught up by a receiver in the other wing. The length of time required for the beam to make the round trip is registered on another instrument in terms of altitude. The movements of airplanes, motor cars, motor boats, and torpedoes may be controlled by means of radio beams sent out from fixed positions on the ground. Some modern radio receivers are adapted to be tuned from positions remote from the receiver itself. The control box is essentially a radio transmitter which sends out carrier waves whose frequency is different for each of the different push buttons. The wave controls a small electric motor in the receiver which responds by adjusting the tuning to the desired station.

# CHAPTER 21

# X RAYS AND
# RADIOACTIVITY

The term *ray* is commonly used to designate any wave phenomenon such as that of light. We think of a ray as a narrow beam traveling in one direction. A source of light sends out many rays in all directions. The waves emitted by a radio transmitter might also be called rays. They are of the same nature as light, and differ from it only in wave length. The word ray is also used to designate a stream of electrically charged particles traveling at high speed. Rays of both types will be described below.

## X RAYS

*A* and *C* (Fig. 152) represent two electrodes a few inches apart in a glass tube, *T*, and connected to a battery of ten

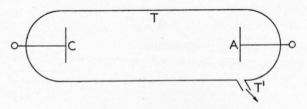

Fig. 152. Simple discharge tube.

thousand volts or more. *T'* is a small tube connected to an exhaust pump. Before pumping has begun, there is no sign of activity in the tube. The voltage is insufficient to carry a discharge from one electrode to the other. With the pump in operation, when about 95 per cent of the air has been removed,

306

an occasional faint, thin flash of light passes between the electrodes. When all but about one-tenth of 1 per cent has been removed, the tube is filled with a splendid pink glow. As the evacuation proceeds, the light grows fainter and finally disappears. Ultimately another glow is seen. This is of a different color and appears on the surface of the glass. In 1895 Roentgen, a German, found that when this condition had been reached, a photographic plate anywhere in the neighborhood of the tube was fogged, even when wrapped in dark paper. He also found that certain materials glow with a pale phosphorescence when near the tube. These effects seemed to be due to a new kind of radiation, similar to light in many ways. These rays could penetrate not only glass and other transparent substances but also paper, wood, aluminum, and many other opaque materials. Roentgen did not know whether this radiation consisted of waves or of streams of particles. Hence he called them $X$ rays.

## USES OF X RAYS

The news of Roentgen's discovery was quickly carried throughout the world. Physicists everywhere began to experi-

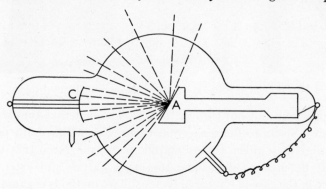

Fig. 153. *X-ray tube.*

ment with this new type of radiation. They soon found that the electrical discharge in gases at low pressure is carried by streams of electrically charged particles, that under the action of high voltages these may travel at speeds of many thousands of miles per second, and that when, moving at such speeds, they plunge into solid objects, particularly metals, the impact results in the generation of this new type of ray. The swifter the electrons, the more penetrating the resulting $X$ rays were found to be.

Physicians also began to wonder whether $X$ rays could not be put to use in medicine or surgery. By means of tubes of the form represented in Fig. 153, the rays were found to pass readily

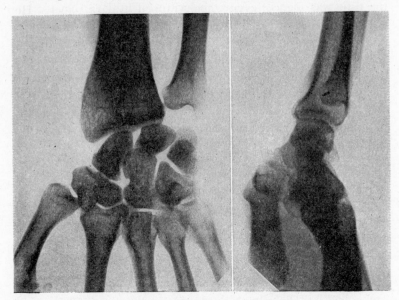

Fig. 154. *X*-ray shadowgraphs. Left—wrist. Right—elbow.

through flesh but not through bone. The fact that they cause certain objects to fluoresce, that is, to glow with a faint light, and that they affect a photographic plate, suggested that they might be used to determine the exact nature and extent of injury in the case of fractured bones. Two methods of examination were soon developed. In one of these a fluorescent screen was placed on one side of the injured member and the $X$-ray tube on the other. The screen then glowed everywhere except in the shadow cast by the bone. Any fracture was thus made visible. In the other method a photographic plate was used instead of the screen. A shadowgraph was obtained as before, but in permanent form. Photographs taken in this way are shown in Fig. 154.

The same general methods are extensively used for non-skeletal diagnosis, and their application has been greatly extended. It has become possible to photograph almost any part of the body. $X$ rays are commonly employed to examine teeth suspected of infection, to locate bullets or other foreign metallic objects in the body, to determine the condition of the internal organs, and make other tests. They are also widely used in the treatment of various diseases, such as cancer and tuberculosis. The rays from tubes of newer types, operating at 1,000,000 volts or more, have been found very effective, particularly in the treatment of deep-seated cancer.

Veterinarians as well as surgeons and physicians make extensive use of $X$ rays. Army horses, circus elephants, prize dogs, and many other animals have been examined for bone and other disorders.

In the Coolidge tube, invented by Dr. W. D. Coolidge of the General Electric Company, the electrons are supplied by a tungsten spiral heated to a high temperature by an electric current. The number of electrons emitted, and hence the abundance of the $X$ rays, increases rapidly with rise in temperature of the spiral. The amount of $X$ radiation produced is controlled by regulating the value of the heating current. The penetrating power of the $X$ rays is determined by the voltage supplied to the tube. By using high voltages, very energetic $X$ rays are produced which will penetrate many inches of steel or concrete. Because $X$ rays make it possible to peer into the interiors of objects which are opaque to light, they are of inestimable value to the manufacturer who wishes to inspect his product without the necessity of taking it apart, or of destroying a portion of it. Golf balls are $X$-rayed to find whether the heavy core is spherical and well centered. Articles made of wood are subjected to the rays to find any internal imperfections they may have, such as knots, worm holes, resin pockets, and defective fitting or gluing.   Carborundum grinding wheels are tested for incipient cracks which might render them unsafe for use at their high speeds.   Metal castings and forgings of many kinds are examined for hidden defects such as cracks, blowholes and corrosion.   Thus the propellers of airplanes and the pistons, cylinder heads, and crankcases of engines may be internally inspected.   By the use of very penetrating rays, even the huge steel propeller shafts of ocean liners may be made to reveal any internal faults.   Chocolate candy, diamonds real or pretended, ammunition, rubber tires, linen and other fabrics, greases and lubricating oils, and electric insulating materials are among the articles often subjected to the $X$-ray test.   Even the art connoisseur may call the $X$ ray to his aid in determining whether a reputed "Old Master" is genuine and unaltered by a later artist.   The test in this case is based upon the fact that the pigments used in more recent times are more penetrable and the sizing less penetrable to the rays than were those used by the painters of the fifteenth and sixteenth centuries.

## THE NATURE OF X RAYS

The term $X$ ray is still used to designate these radiations though the $X$ no longer stands for an unknown quantity. Following Roentgen's discovery, the rays were thoroughly investigated to determine whether they were waves, or particles.   Both theories had ardent supporters.   In 1912 Laue of Germany passed a narrow beam of $X$ rays through a crystal upon a photographic plate.   The photograph indicated that $X$ rays are of the first-named kind.   W. H. Bragg, an English physicist, who was the leading champion of the corpuscular idea, made many experiments later which supported the wave idea.   By means of crystals he also succeeded in measuring the lengths of the waves.   He found them to range from one thousandth to one ten-thousandth part of the wave length of light.   Many other scientists have since confirmed all of these results.

## RAYS FROM RADIUM

After Roentgen had shown that $X$ rays produce phosphorescence in many different materials, the question arose as to whether the converse might not also be true; that is, whether phosphorescent materials might not produce $X$ rays. Within a year after Roentgen's discovery, the French physicist Becquerel found that this is not usually the case. In the course of his study of this question, Becquerel made one of the most important discoveries in modern physics. In one of his experiments he wrapped a photographic plate in heavy black paper, laid a coin upon it, and suspended a small quantity of a sulfate of uranium a little distance above the coin. A few days later he found the plate to be fogged as if by $X$ rays—darkened everywhere except beneath the coin. In another experiment some of the sulfate was placed near an electrically charged object. It caused the charge to leak away. Many other compounds of uranium were tested and found to act in exactly the same way. So also did the uncombined metal. These effects were clearly due to the element uranium, and could be understood only on the assumption that the atoms of the element spontaneously emit rays that can penetrate paper, darken a photographic plate, and ionize the air through which they pass. This was the first instance ever observed of the property now called *radioactivity*.

Uranium did not especially appeal to the popular imagination. But two years later Pierre and Marie Curie separated from several tons of rock pitchblende about one one-hundredth of an ounce of a substance which was a million times as active as uranium. Then the whole world was interested. Because of its remarkable activity the new element was called radium.

The rays which caused the fogging of Becquerel's photographic plates proved to be of the same nature as $X$ rays—electromagnetic waves of very short wave length. E. Rutherford, then a professor of physics in McGill University, in Canada, soon found that rays of other kinds were also emitted by both uranium and radium. His method of testing these radiations is represented in Fig. 155. A little of the material to be tested is inserted in a small hole in a block of lead which is then placed in a magnetic field.   Rays are emitted as shown. A positive electrical charge when moving across a magnetic field is deflected in one direction, and a negative charge in the reverse direction.   Waves and uncharged particles are not deflected.   The particles represented in Fig. 155 as deflected to the left are positively charged.   They were later found to have the same mass as helium atoms, and to have a charge equal in magnitude to that of two electrons.   They move with speeds up to about 20,000 miles per second. These are called *alpha rays*.   The beam deflected to the right consists of negative electrons, much faster than the alphas.   These are called *beta rays*.   Beta particles from some of the radioactive elements move almost with the speed of light.   The undeflected rays, as has been said, are of the nature of $X$ rays, but have a shorter wave length.   They are called *gamma rays*.   It is chiefly because of the gamma rays it emits that radium is so valuable in the treatment of disease.

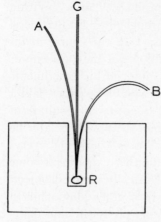

FIG. 155.   Rays from radium.

## TRANSFORMATIONS OF RADIOACTIVE ELEMENTS

What is the effect on the atom of emitting one of these rays? Let us first consider the alpha ray.   So large a mass, four times as great as that of the hydrogen atom, must of itself be of great importance, and when cast off, it must leave the parent atom greatly altered.   The alpha ray soon picks up two negative electrons from its surroundings and becomes a neutral helium atom.   It is evident that its emission has reduced the weight of the parent atom by four units, and has reduced its positive charge by two units.   The heavy parent atom now acts like one of a quite different kind.   It has become an atom of an entirely different element.   Thus we see that in an alpha-ray transformation the parent atom disappears as such, and in doing so gives rise to two new atoms, one of which is helium.

When a beta ray is emitted, the mass of the parent atom is left practically unchanged. Its charge, however, is reduced by one negative unit. This has the effect of changing the nature of the parent atom. It also becomes an atom of a different element.

In emitting a gamma ray the atom loses neither mass nor electrical charge. There is simply a rearrangement of its parts without any alteration of its character. It remains an atom of the same original element.

Through several centuries the alchemists tried vainly to transform elements one into another. Their great hope was to be able to transform the baser metals into gold. Meanwhile, all unknown to them, nature was spontaneously transforming many of the elements, but not into gold. In each alpha- or beta-ray change an atom is transformed into one of another element as described above. All radioactive atoms continue to undergo such changes until what remains has the mass and chemical properties of the atom of lead.

In the course of his study of radioactivity Rutherford discovered that an atom is not a solid spherical particle as it was once thought to be, but consists of a group of particles arranged as a sort of solar system. Each has a nucleus which is electrically positive and possesses nearly all the mass. Outside of this and at relatively very great distances from it are the planets, a number of negative electrons just sufficient to neutralize the nucleus. The chemical element to which an atom belongs is determined entirely by the magnitude of its positive nuclear charge.

## ARTIFICIAL TRANSMUTATION OF ATOMS

In every case of radioactivity the transformation of the element takes place at a definite rate. A certain fraction of the atoms undergo the change every second or year or century. This rate is very different for different substances. No one has been able to alter this rate in the slightest degree by the most intense heat, the most violent electrical discharges, or by any other means. Nor for 20 years was anyone able artificially to break up any kind of atom. The heaviest atoms, like those of uranium, thorium, and radium, were transforming spontaneously. The lighter ones, like nitrogen, oxygen, iron, and copper, remained unchanged. In 1916 Rutherford made experiments in which he allowed the swiftest of alpha rays to bombard atoms of some of the lighter elements. He found that these high-speed atomic projectiles, because of their tremendous energy, would break up atoms of nitrogen and several other elements. These were the first instances in which the disintegration of atoms was accomplished artificially.

In the last decade the Lawrence cyclotron, the Van de Graaff electrostatic generator, and other powerful devices have been constructed for imparting very high speeds to protons and deuterons (the nuclei of hydrogen of atomic weight two) and for producing high-speed neutrons. By means of these very energetic particles, atoms of many of the elements have been disintegrated, and other atoms formed in the process.

The "smashing" of atoms has already led to very important results. One of these has been a great extension of our knowledge of the structure of nonradioactive atoms. In particular it has shown that not only the atom as a whole, but also its nucleus is a complex structure composed of simpler units, such as protons and neutrons. Another result has been to place in the hands of scientists a means of producing at will many new kinds of radioactive atoms. One of the newly made elements, radio-sodium, possesses properties which will doubtless lead to its extensive use in the treatment of disease in place of the rare and expensive element, radium. Radio-sodium may be made by bombarding common table salt with high-speed deuterons.

By his new atom-smashing methods the scientist has been able to achieve at least a part of the great dream of the alchemists. He has succeeded in transmuting another element into gold. But this change will not yield the fabulous riches that thrilled the imaginations of the alchemists, for the element thus transmuted was not one of the baser metals, but platinum, a metal more valuable than gold itself.

## COSMIC RAYS

Physicists have never been able completely to eliminate the leakage of an electrical charge from a condenser or electroscope. It was long believed that this was due to a very slight conductivity of the materials of which the insulators were made, or to the nature of the surfaces of those insulators, which slowly carried off the charge. Later, when every precaution had been taken to eliminate these possibilities and the charge still gradually disappeared, the suspicion arose that the discharge resulted from an action of radium emanation or some other such material which entered the atmosphere from the earth. Between the years 1900 and 1914 several investigators tested the conducting properties of their electroscopes at widely varying elevations. The leakage was found to be more rapid at the higher altitudes than near the earth. Hence it was concluded that the cause of the discharge is not to be found in material passing from the earth into the atmosphere but in some type of radiation entering the atmosphere from outside. The evidence indicated that it came from beyond the solar system, probably even from beyond the milky way. This radiation is called *cosmic rays*.

These rays were at first thought to be of the same nature as light and *X* rays, but thousands of times more energetic than either. They are now believed to consist chiefly of electrical charges, some positive, some negative, entering the earth's atmosphere with tremendous energies. These rays exist in every part of the earth yet investigated. They are somewhat less numerous near the equator than in latitudes beyond 20° north or south. Whether they are entirely of a corpuscular nature or whether partly of this and partly of a wave nature is still uncertain. Whatever their nature, it is certain that they represent one of the most important stores of energy in the universe.

# CHAPTER 22

# SOME FUNDAMENTAL CHEMICAL PROCESSES

## THE CAUSE OF FIRE

The ancestors of the modern chemists were not experimental scientists—they were arm-chair philosophers. Long and loudly they might argue about some phenomenon of nature, but seldom did they endeavor to prove their contentions by experimental evidence.

One of the earliest phenomena observed by man was fire. First he was content that it should warm his body, cook his food, and please his eye. Later he sought to explain it. When a chunk of coal is burning, flames shoot out as though something were being expelled from the burning material, and the ashes that remain weigh less than the unburned chunk. Late in the seventeenth century the so-called Phlogiston Theory was propounded to account for all cases of burning or combustion. It assumed that every combustible material contained an intangible something, called *phlogiston*, and that its liberation was accompanied by heat and light. Hence, a burning substance was really being *dephlogisticated*. A century elapsed before this plausible, but false, theory was disproved.

## DISCOVERY OF OXYGEN

In the late seventeen hundreds the chemical balance and accurate weight measurements were introduced into chemistry (Fig. 156). They revealed that a burning material becomes heavier, rather than lighter, providing that all the gases from it are collected and weighed. In burning, then, a material does

not lose phlogiston, but it gains something.   This "something"
was discovered about 1773 independently by Scheele in Sweden
and Priestley in England and it was given the name "oxygen"
("acid former") by the Frenchman, Lavoisier.   The true
explanation of the burning process is the uniting of a substance

*Chicago Apparatus Company.*

FIG. 156.   Analytical Balance.   An indispensable tool of the chemist, and of
workers in many other branches of science.   The ordinary analytical balance
will detect a variation in weight of one ten-thousandth part of a gram.

with oxygen.   In the popular (but narrow) sense, any process
of union with oxygen is called "oxidation."   Such a process
always liberates heat, and for this reason is said to be "exothermic."   An oxidation action is designated as a *combustion* if the
heat is liberated so rapidly as to be perceived by the senses as
heat and light.   It should be noted, though, that in any given

case of oxidation the total amount of heat liberated is the same whether the process is completed in ten seconds or in ten years.

## KINDS OF ENERGY CHANGES

A chunk of wood liberates considerable heat during combustion. It does not create this heat on the spot because we learn from the law of the Conservation of Energy that "energy cannot, by ordinary means, be destroyed or created." The energy was acquired from the sun during the growth of the tree and incorporated into its cells as *chemical energy* or *internal energy*. The tree may be cut into boards or reduced to sawdust, but the chemical energy remains in the wood cells and the chemical identity of the wood still persists, that is, it retains its distinctive *properties* such as color, odor, taste, solubility, cell structure, and combustibility. We say that the cutting or powdering has produced only a *physical change*.

Now when wood is heated to a certain temperature, called its *kindling point*, it will burst into flame. That is, the oxygen of the air begins to combine with it, gaseous products are given off, and ashes are left. But the total chemical energy in the gaseous products and the ashes is much less than that in the original wood and the oxygen that combined with it. What has become of the extra chemical energy of the original materials? The answer is obvious. It was transformed from chemical energy into heat and light energy, hence the flame. It would not be far wrong to state that, in the presence of a coal fire, we are looking at the prehistoric sunshine which was imprisoned by the growing trees of an ancient geologic coal-forming era.

If union with oxygen—oxidation—liberates heat, the reverse of the process should consume heat. That is, the *liberation* of oxygen should convert heat energy into chemical energy. When lead dioxide is heated, it will decompose to form oxygen gas and lead monoxide. The action proceeds only while heat is being applied, hence heat is being absorbed by the process, or, better stated, heat is being transformed into chemical energy. A chemical process of this nature is said to be *endothermic*, and the removal of oxygen from a compound is named *reduction*, although the latter term may have a wider meaning.  We also state that, whereas wood is a combustible substance, the surrounding oxygen of the air is a *supporter of combustion.*

Interesting cases of combustion are the fires that originate from *spontaneous combustion.*  When varnishes, paints, and oils *dry*, the process does not involve the removal of water but the union with oxygen—or oxidation.  Imagine that a lot of rags, which have been used with turpentine or linseed oil, are thrown in a big pile and left for several days.  The oil begins to dry, that is, to oxidize exothermally.  Within the pile the heat is not conducted away and the material becomes warm.  The heat favors more rapid oxidation, which in turn generates more heat.  Finally the kindling point is reached, and the mass bursts into flame.  A similar process may occur in uncured hay or in piles of grass clippings.  In these cases oxidation is probably preceded by fermentation.

In the cutting of the wood, we stated that its identity was retained, hence it had undergone a physical change.  But combustion of the wood changed its characteristics—its properties —so completely that entirely new substances—gases and ashes —were formed.  It is said to have undergone a *chemical change.* A chemical change is one in which the identity of the original material is lost, and one or more entirely different chemical individuals are formed.

Chemical changes, as we have seen, are accompanied by energy changes.  The chemical energy within the material is either increased or decreased in amount.  The commonest energy manifestation is heat; others include light energy, electrical energy, and mechanical energy.  Light energy is liberated while the paraffin of a candle is burning and it is absorbed when a film is exposed in a camera.  Electrical energy is generated from chemical energy in a dry cell when a flashlight is snapped on; it is converted into chemical energy during the charging of a storage battery.  In the explosion of a gun cartridge we find that the mechanical energy which propels the bullet has its source in the chemical energy in the powder and, on the other hand, the chemical energy of a storage battery attached to a wind charger arises from the mechanical energy of the wind.

Energy changes are invariably linked with all chemical changes. When we define chemistry as "that science which treats of the composition of matter and changes in its composition," we assume that energy relationships are also involved. A brief survey of chemistry, such as this is, must stress ideas of matter rather than of energy.

## THE ROLE OF OXYGEN

The star role played by oxygen on the chemical stage should arouse our curiosity over its private and public life. Where does it come from? How does it behave? What is it good for? Like death and taxes, it is everywhere. Twenty-one per cent of the volume of the air is free, uncombined oxygen. In its compounds it makes up about one-half of the earth's crust; about nine-tenths of the weight of water; and a large part of all animal and vegetable matter. We speak learnedly of the foodstuffs—carbohydrates, fats, and proteins. The two former always contain oxygen in combination with carbon and hydrogen, and the latter contain in addition nitrogen and various other elements.

## THE NEED FOR OXYGEN

To supply the most important and universal demands for oxygen does not cost a cent—not even a sales tax or a luxury tax. It is as free as the air because it comes from the air. If it must be bottled or canned for industry, it is obtained from air or water and there is a processing charge. Respiration of animals and plants consumes tremendous quantities of atmospheric oxygen. When we inhale a lungful of air, with its 21 per cent of oxygen, some of this gas diffuses into the blood. The blood, in turn, gives up carbon dioxide and moisture. But only a part of the oxygen passes into the blood, because exhaled air always contains over 16 per cent oxygen. In such air a candle will scarcely burn. Hence we must be careful, in the cause of scientific accuracy, not to state that "all of the oxygen" is used up in respiration or in burning.  Its proportion in the air is merely reduced (Fig. 157).

It is hard to realize that countless tons of oxygen are utilized for combustion purposes.  Kerosene lamps, bonfires, factory furnaces, forest fires—all are dependent upon oxygen.  Portable fire extinguishers depend, for their action, upon forcing a layer of an inert gas between the burning substance and the surrounding oxygen of the air.

We state that sewage-contaminated rivers "purify themselves" as they flow.  This and other cases of decay are oxida-

*McKesson Appliance Company.*
FIG. 157.   Oxygen tent.

tion processes.  The oxygen of the air unites with the offensive material and converts it into harmless products.  Respiration, combustion, decay—these processes are the greatest consumers of atmospheric oxygen.

## HOW OXYGEN IS OBTAINED

What of the oxygen blowtorch of the welder, the oxygen tent of the physician, the oxygen helmet of the aviator?  Diluted oxygen will not serve in these cases.  The "pure stuff" is demanded.  The greater part of the pure oxygen of commerce is obtained from liquid air.  This product, once a curiosity, is now made cheaply by the cooling-compression-expansion cycle of changes such as are now in use in iceless refrigeration. The resulting liquid air is a mixture of two liquids—nitrogen and oxygen, of different boiling points. These are separated,

*The Puritan Compressed Gas Corporation.*
FIG. 158.    Cylinder of compressed oxygen.

giving a compressed oxygen product of about 95 per cent purity. It is confined in strong steel cylinders and shipped the country over (Fig. 158).

In a school laboratory, the commercial methods of producing oxygen would be too expensive and cumbersome. Small quantities of the gas are usually prepared by heating certain oxygen compounds (Fig. 159), and sometimes by dropping water upon peroxides.

## THE PROPERTIES OF OXYGEN

When potassium chlorate or sodium nitrate or lead dioxide is heated in a test tube, it is decomposed and oxygen is liberated. The gas may be identified as oxygen by applying certain "tests." These tests make use of the properties—both physical and chemical—of the gas. The pure gas has no color, odor, or taste. It is slightly heavier than air and will dissolve spar-

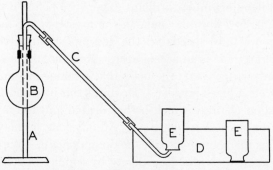

Fig. 159. Oxygen Generator Assembly. The oxygen compound is heated in flask *B*, which is supported by the standard *A*. The evolved gas passes through the delivery tube *C* and is collected in the bottles *E E*, which are inverted over water in the tank *D*.

ingly in water. This latter property is essential to all aquatic life. The special breathing mechanism of fish enables them to withdraw dissolved oxygen from the water; water plants likewise utilize such oxygen. Referring to its chief chemical property, oxygen will *support combustion*. This is demonstrated by inserting into some rather pure oxygen a glowing spark on the tip of a wood splinter. The spark will glow more brightly or even burst into flame.

Such substances as sulfur and phosphorus burn brightly in pure oxygen. They form oxides—*sulfur dioxide* and *phosphorus pentoxide*. If these oxides are united with water, acids are formed. This action gave Lavoisier the idea for naming the gas, because the word *oxygen* literally means *acid former*.

## CATALYSIS

A mysterious, almost uncanny phenomenon is associated with the production of oxygen when potassium chlorate is heated. Let us watch the chemist. He places a little of the white powder in a test tube and heats it gently. It crackles, melts, and boils. A gas is coming from the liquid. He introduces a spark on a splint and it glows a little more brightly. Very simple. The potassium chlorate is decomposing and liberating a little oxygen. Now, watch! He removes the flame and adds a tiny pinch of a black compound—manganese dioxide. Instantly gas boils forth from the mixture. He pushes a spark toward the tube and it bursts into a brilliant flame even before it enters the tube. This is "Episode One" in the mystery; the manganese dioxide powerfully speeds up the decomposition of the potassium chlorate. It is an accelerator. Now for "Episode Two." The experimenter treats the mass that remains in the test tube and recovers a black powder. He drops this into another batch of potassium chlorate which he has heated and the mysterious acceleration process is repeated. All day long he may recover and use his manganese dioxide, again and again. We conclude that the manganese dioxide, merely by coming in contact with the slowly decomposing potassium chlorate, greatly speeds up its decomposition rate; but the manganese dioxide, itself, is not permanently changed. A substance which functions in this way is called a *catalyst* and the process is termed *catalysis*. It is a universal process. Every chemical action, it is claimed, can be accelerated by the proper catalyst. In our bodies organic catalysts, called enzymes, bring about the digestion of food and other important vital processes.

## ELEMENTS AND COMPOUNDS

Repeatedly we hear the words "element" and "compound" used in conversation. "Elements" cause the weathering of rocks and erosion of soil. The "elements" of a good sermon or speech may be prescribed. The term is not used here in a scientific sense. What is its exact significance? Consider a small chunk of sulfur. We may divide it into two pieces, subdivide these by any ordinary means and continue the dividing process until we have the tiniest particle of matter that can exist.  It is still sulfur.  Sulfur, cannot, by ordinary means, be separated into two or more other substances.  For this reason, it is called an "element."  Examination of the matter that composes the earth and the atmosphere will reveal that it is made up of not more than 92 elements, some of which exist only in traces.  Ninety of the elements have been definitely discovered, and there is evidence that the other two have been detected. Our belief that only 92 elements exist will be made clear in Chap. 26.  (See Tables 3 and 4.)

TABLE 3

COMPOSITION OF THE EARTH

| | | | |
|---|---|---|---|
| Oxygen | 49.2% | Potassium | 2.4% |
| Silicon | 25.7 | Magnesium | 1.9 |
| Aluminum | 7.4 | Hydrogen | 0.9 |
| Iron | 4.7 | Titanium | 0.6 |
| Calcium | 3.4 | Chlorine | 0.2 |
| Sodium | 2.6 | Phosphorus | 0.1 |

The table shows that, according to an estimate of the abundance of the elements in the earth's crust, its water surface and atmosphere, eight elements constitute over ninty-eight per cent of these great masses.

TABLE 4

AVERAGE COMPOSITION OF THE HUMAN BODY

| | | | |
|---|---|---|---|
| Oxygen | 65.00% | Sodium | 0.15% |
| Carbon | 18.00 | Chlorine | 0.15 |
| Hydrogen | 10.00 | Magnesium | 0.05 |
| Nitrogen | 3.00 | Iron | 0.004 |
| Calcium | 1.50 | Iodine | 0.00004 |
| Phosphorus | 1.00 | Fluorine | very minute |
| Potassium | 0.35 | Silicon | amounts |
| Sulfur | 0.25 | and other elements | |

The human body contains traces of many elements, but only six are present to an extent of one per cent or more.

The vast majority of the natural and manufactured substances about us are not elemental in nature.  They are composed of two or more elements chemically united and are designated as *compounds*.  It is often possible to build (synthesize) a compound directly from its elements or to separate (analyze) a compound into its elements.  More commonly, however, the processes of synthesis and analysis are more circuitous and complex.  Mercuric oxide can be separated, simply by heating, into the elements mercury and oxygen. Iron oxide, on the other hand, must be heated to a high temperature with carbon in order to liberate the iron. Even then the oxygen is not freed but unites with the carbon to form carbon dioxide. Compounds known to science number approximately three hundred thousand.

A very striking effect appears when compounds are formed from their elements. Copper is a lustrous, bronze-colored, rather soft metal. It is a fine conductor of electricity; it can be melted; and it can be drawn into wires. Oxygen is a colorless, odorless, tasteless gas. Now heat copper and oxygen together and note the transformation. The two substances disappear as such and in their place appears a black, powdery solid—copper oxide—which in no respect resembles the copper or the oxygen. In forming the compound the elements have entirely lost their individual properties. Go one step farther. Copper oxide is black. Not so the compound of copper and oxygen with the colorless gas, nitrogen. This substance, called copper nitrate, forms beautiful, clear blue crystals. Strange that the product of the union of bronze-colored copper with colorless oxygen and nitrogen gases should differ so greatly from the constituent elements. The ultimate reason, as in many scientific phenomena, is not known. The theories of atomic structure, as presented in Chap. 7, afford some light on the problem.

## AN IMPORTANT LAW

We have stated that when copper and oxygen are heated together, they form a black compound—copper oxide. Now arises the question: will the composition of the copper oxide depend upon the relative amounts of copper and oxygen used? And will the percentages of copper and nitrogen and oxygen in copper nitrate vary, depending on how and where and by whom it is made? The answer is, No. *Every sample of any pure substance always contains the same elements in the same proportion by weight.* This fundamental fact is called the *Law of Definite Composition.* It is invaluable in chemistry.

## HYDROGEN IN THE WORLD'S WORK

Without heat to warm our homes, cook our food, and operate our machines, we should be little better off than prehistoric man. Coal, wood, gas, and gasoline contain the elements which, through exothermic processes of combustion, furnish the heat that does the work of the world. Chief among these heat-producing elements are hydrogen and carbon. We shall study carbon in Chap. 29. Hydrogen may well enter here for our inspection.

## HYDROGEN USEFUL IN PEACE AND WAR

Hydrogen moves through our lives incognito. We cannot see it, smell it, or taste it. We do not find it in the air or on the earth in the free state, to any extent. And yet the free gas is indispensable; it is a necessity in modern life. City gas, unless obtained from natural gas wells, is very rich in hydrogen. A municipal gas plant is an interesting place to inspect. Carbon and water, in the form of red-hot coke and steam, are brought together in "water gas" generators. The coke reduces the water to form carbon monoxide and hydrogen. The process is described in Chap. 29. When the city gas is burned in the kitchen gas range, much of the cooking heat is derived from the combustion of the hydrogen.

Cottonseed oil was at one time of little industrial value. It was useless for paints or lubrication. No cook would think of using it for shortening; she preferred lard. Then the chemist came to the rescue and showed that the essential difference between solid lard and liquid cottonseed oil was really a shortage of hydrogen atoms in the oil molecules. If hydrogen gas could be induced to unite with cottonseed oil molecules, the oil would change to a lard-like solid. This was accomplished, as described in Chap. 30. Large quantities of hydrogen are now employed in the "hydrogenation" process to produce vegetable cooking fats.

Another hydrogenation process is of interest. England, Germany, Japan, and some other nations have practically no petroleum fields. Hence, they must depend upon other countries for their petroleum products, including gasoline. In a search for national self-sufficiency in this field, a German chemist, Friedrich Bergius, succeeded in hydrogenating ccal and converting it into an oily fluid resembling petroleum. Extensive Bergius process plants have been built in the above-mentioned countries and are now converting low-grade coals into liquid fuels to be used for power and transportation.

Since hydrogen is the lightest of gases, it has long been used in lighter-than-air craft. There are three disadvantages. Light gases diffuse readily through porous objects and hence hydrogen escapes through the cell walls of dirigibles. When a dirigible must be recharged, the previous charge of hydrogen cannot be readily purified and is discarded. Most serious of all, the gas is highly combustible. Even a spark will ignite it. The mighty dirigible, *Hindenburg*, was so destroyed May 6, 1937, at a United States air base. Helium, where available, is replacing hydrogen for filling dirigibles. It shows none of the disadvantages of hydrogen and has 92 per cent of its lifting power.

Peace-time pursuits—and those of war—call for tremendous quantities of explosives. Once dependent upon Chilean nitrate fields, nations now synthesize their own explosives from materials at their very doors (see Chap. 25). One of the processes of manufacture—the Haber—employs gaseous hydrogen and consumes immense quantities of the element. Another important demand for hydrogen arises from the synthetic methyl (wood) alcohol industry. Once obtained only by distillation of wood, this valuable commercial solvent is now produced by the catalytic combination of hydrogen and carbon monoxide. The new process is a vigorous competitor of the older one.

## PRODUCTION OF HYDROGEN

It is evident from the foregoing illustrations that this colorless, odorless, tasteless, combustible, lightest-of-all-gases, hydrogen, is an important personality among the elements. Its identity was not even known until observed in 1766 by Sir Henry Cavendish, an English chemist. We find it united with other elements in petroleum; in all acids; in animal and vegetable matter; and in water. The student in the laboratory most conveniently prepares it from an acid, displacing it with an active metal (Fig. 160). Industry obtains its major supply from water, employing a modification of the water-gas process previously described. The two steps in the process may be briefly stated. Coke (carbon) reacts with steam to produce hydrogen and carbon monoxide. The carbon monoxide then reacts with more steam to produce more hydrogen and carbon dioxide.

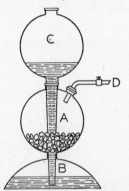

Fig. 160. Kipp Gas Generator. The metal, usually zinc, is placed in *A*. When not in operation, the acid is contained in the bowl *B* and reservoir *C*. If the stopcock *D* is opened, the pressure in *A* is released, acid flows into it, and hydrogen is generated and flows out through *D*.

## METRIC MEASUREMENTS

A discussion of fundamental chemical processes would not be complete without reference to methods of measuring in chemistry and the units employed. Chemistry passed from a speculative to an exact science at about the time that Lavoisier introduced exact methods of weighing. He has even been called "the father of modern chemistry." He employed a balance, which is a weighing device requiring weights equal in mass to the mass of the object being weighed. In contradistinction, a "scale" employs levers of unequal arms. Balances vary in sensitiveness. A "horn pan" balance, as used by beginners, is sensitive to one one-hundredth of a gram—a centigram. Ordinary analytical balances are accurate to one ten-thousandth of a gram—a tenth of a milligram (Fig. 156).

Metric units are employed in science in preference to the English system of weights and measures. Metric units are also used in business and industry on the European continent. Since they progress by tens, they are much simpler than the English units. Typical units of weight are milligrams (10 mg.

equal 1 cg.), centigrams (10 cg. equal 1 dg.), decigrams (10 dg. equal 1 gm.), grams and kilograms (1000 gm. equal 1 kg.). In approximate figures, there are 30 grams to the ounce, 480 grams to the pound and two pounds to the kilogram. For more accurate values, the reader should consult a metric conversion table.

*Abbott Laboratories.*

Fig. 161. A Modern Research Laboratory. Accuracy, system, and cleanliness are absolute requirements in an industrial chemical laboratory. A perfectly equipped and arranged research laboratory is pictured above.

The most frequently used units of length are the millimeter (mm.), centimeter (cm.), meter (m.), and kilometer (km.). An inch represents about 25 millimeters or two and one-half centimeters; a yard is about equal to a meter; and a mile is one and six-tenths kilometers.

Metric volumes are expressed in the small unit of cubic centimeter (cc.) or milliliter (ml.) and the larger unit, the liter (l.). A fluid ounce represents about 30 cc. or ml. and a quart is about equal to a liter.

The discussion in this chapter has introduced us to two common elements; to fundamental reactions which they typify; to several examples of chemical terminology; to certain laws and theories; and to measurements in science.   Next we shall study that common but unique substance which is built from oxygen and hydrogen.

# CHAPTER 23

# THE STORY OF
# WATER

## WATER A NECESSITY

The early pioneers penetrated frontiers of forest and plain and mountain in their search for a home. They chose a diversity of climate and soil. Differing in tastes and in every other particular, they unitedly agreed upon one necessity— water. Their homes were built where well water was obtainable; their towns were founded along rivers and lakes. From every viewpoint, water is the most common, the most useful, and the most indispensable chemical. How fortunate it is, then, that water can be found almost universally upon our earth.

## WATER, WATER EVERYWHERE

It covers the earth's surface to an average depth of over two miles. It permeates the rocks and soil of the earth's crust to considerable depths. Its vapor is always present in the atmosphere, and on a humid day in summer it may amount to fifty thousand tons over a square mile of land. Tremendous quantities are chained as ice in the polar regions. Meats and vegetables have a water content ranging from 60 to 95 per cent by weight. The human body is about 70 per cent water. Every object that we touch carries a film of water on its surface.

Common as water is, the average person without a scientific background knows very little about it. Its usefulness in the scientific world is fully as great and diverse as in domestic and industrial fields. In the following paragraphs, we shall explore the accomplishments of this versatile substance.

## WATER FOR DOMESTIC AND INDUSTRIAL NEEDS

Drinking water is a prime necessity for plants and animals. The human animal is of special interest.  As we have said, his body is 70 per cent water.  Daily he loses much of this through the kidneys, the intestines, the lungs, and the skin.  To supply

*Wallace and Tiernan Co., Inc.*

FIG. 162.  Water Chlorinating Equipment.  Two cylinders of compressed chlorine are shown in the center, standing upon scales.  The small, coiled tubes conduct the gas from the cylinders to the chlorinators on each side, from which it is injected into the water system.

the loss he eats and drinks much water, and usually should drink more.  His own well or city water system supplies it to him.  So important is pure water that most states require that the public water supply shall be frequently analyzed.  Even private well water should be tested if it is under the least suspicion.

The commoner water-borne diseases are typhoid fever, dysentery, and cholera.  Bacteria of these diseases need not actually be present to render water impure and dangerous. These bacteria are apt to come from the intestinal tract, and they thrive on organic matter. When, therefore, the water analyst finds any signs of human waste in the water or even an excess of organic matter, he condemns the sample as unsafe. The most common chemical indications of human pollution are urinary salt and nitrogenous material from protein of the diet.

Many cities obtain their water supply from open lakes, subject to contamination. Occasionally flood conditions will

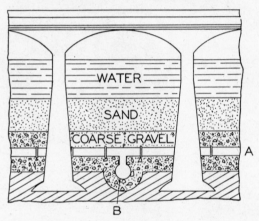

Fig. 163. Slow Sand Filter. An underground filter. Water trickles through the sand and gravel, penetrates through the walls of the porous pipes, *A*, and enters a main shown at *B*.

pollute even deep wells. In such cases a city must continue to supply safe drinking water to its citizens. The treatment consists of killing any harmful bacteria in the water by the chlorination process—essentially an oxidation effect. Compressed chlorine gas, contained in strong steel cylinders, is forced through an automatic device which introduces chlorine into the water mains at a definite rate (Fig. 162). The gas "oxidizes the bacteria to death" and, if properly operating, should give little or no taste to the water.

A water supply obtained from open lakes or rivers must usually pass through a three-stage purification process. First it is run into large tanks or basins where it is allowed to stand quietly while solid matter settles out, a process which is called *sedimentation*. The action is sometimes hastened by adding to the water a chemical which will form a fine, jelly-like solid all

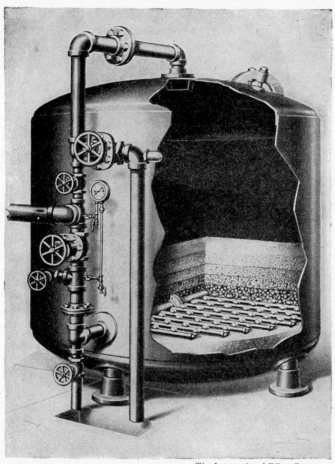

*The International Filter Company.*

Fig. 164. Pressure Filter. Water enters the top of the filter and is forced under pressure through the layers of sand and gravel. From there it passes into the perforated pipes at the base, and thence into the water mains.

through the water. As the solid settles, it carries down with it any floating matter which is in the water. It is a *flocculation* process.

Next comes the *filtration* process (Fig. 163). The water is forced through deep beds of gravel and sand in the bottom of which are perforated pipes of the city water system. As the water filters through the sand bed, the last of the suspended solid matter and many of the bacteria are removed (Fig. 164).

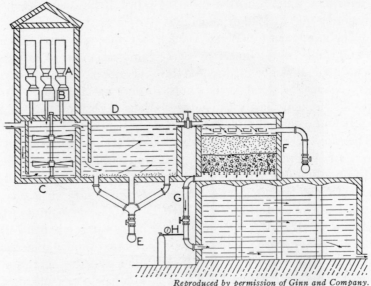

FIG. 165. Diagram Showing the Essential Parts of a Plant for Softening and Purifying the Water Supply of a City. The impure, raw water enters the mixing tank *C*, where it is thoroughly mixed with the purifying and softening reagents entering at the top of the tank. The mixture then flows into the settling basin *D*, where the solids formed by the action of the purifying reagents upon the water settle to the bottom and are drawn off through *E* from time to time. The water next flows through the rapid sand filter *F*, then through the pipe *G* (where the necessary chlorine is added at *H*) into the filtered water reservoir, and from here into the city mains. The rapid sand filters are cleaned by occasionally forcing a stream of water through them in the reverse direction. The water carrying the impurities flows out through the "wash water troughs" into the drain.

From here it passes to the third treatment, the chlorinators. In lieu of municipal purification, a suspected sample of water may be sterilized by treatment with bleaching powder (a chlorine compound) or by sufficient boiling (Fig. 165).

## HOW WATER BECOMES HARD

Not all of the water which passes through the meter or the pump spout is consumed internally. Even the small boy must wash his face; there must be water for the bath, for the laundry, and for generating steam. And here the demand is for "soft" water—water which is free from the mineral matter which would make it "hard." On a small scale rain water may be utilized—but not on an industrial scale. In order to understand how water is softened, let us watch it "growing hard," accumulating its load of minerals.

The commonest mineral, though not the only one, which water takes up is limestone or calcium carbonate ($CaCO_3$). This mineral will be used to illustrate the process. Rain water, as it leaves the cloud, is the purest form of natural water. As it falls through the air it dissolves various impurities, including carbon dioxide, ($CO_2$)—the gas of carbonic acid ($H_2CO_3$). The rain strikes the earth, soaks through the soil, and encounters a bed of limestone. Now, pure water will not appreciably dissolve limestone; but the carbon dioxide, or carbonic acid, attacks the limestone and changes it into a new substance, called calcium bicarbonate—$Ca(HCO_3)_2$. This new substance is *soluble*. It is the chief mineral in hard water and hence is largely responsible for its "hardness." Other common minerals in hard water are magnesium bicarbonate, and the sulfates of calcium and magnesium. This paragraph has briefly answered the question: "How does water become hard?"

## HOW HARD WATER BEHAVES

What is the result of heating hard water? Everybody has seen the "scale" (so-called "lime") in a teakettle. The hot water coil in the furnace has to be replaced occasionally because it clogs with "lime." Steam boilers must often be "blown out" if hard water is used in them. All of these cases are of common experience. Where does the "lime" come from? Hard water, as stated above, contains calcium bicarbonate— $Ca(HCO_3)_2$. At ordinary temperatures this is quite stable and permanent. But when water is heated almost to boiling, the compound becomes unstable and decomposes in reverse order to its formation. That is, it separates into the insoluble calcium carbonate (or limestone) and carbon dioxide. The calcium carbonate coats the teakettle and clogs the hot water pipes and chokes the steam boiler.

This same substance appears in a different form under special conditions. Many caves have been formed by underground streams of water dissolving out limestone deposits, as described above. Now, when water trickles through cracks in the ceiling of a cave, the calcium bicarbonate decomposes by loss of carbon dioxide, and the insoluble calcium carbonate is left clinging to the ceiling. As the process continues through decades and centuries, the pendant limestone deposits grow into great spines and rods. These are called *stalactites*. Some of the water, dripping to the floor of the cave deposits its limestone, to build a rod upward—a *stalagmite*. Finally, stalactites and stalagmites may meet to form columns and pillars. Many caves are rendered both beautiful and weird by these formations.

## HARD WATER AND THE SOAP BILL

Have you ever remarked, "Soap will not dissolve in hard water"? Don't say it again, because it is not true. Soap dissolves as well in hard water as in soft. Then why the curd, and the absence of suds? Soap is a mixture of several compounds of which we will consider only one—sodium stearate. When soap is added to hard water, the sodium stearate dissolves and then attacks the calcium compounds to form a slimy, insoluble substance—calcium stearate. Added slowly to water, the soap combines with more and more of the calcium compounds until they have all been changed into an insoluble "calcium soap." Not until then will addition of more soap produce "sudsing" and foam. Not only is this an expensive way to soften water, but the slimy, curdy substance formed is objectionable for the face, the hair, or the laundry.

## WATER SOFTENING

The softening of water consists of removing much or all of its mineral contents. Different processes and chemicals are available. On a large scale, the water must be analyzed and a suitable formula worked out.   There are, however, two major chemical processes for industrial and domestic purposes.

The best-known process employs soda ash (sal-soda, washing soda, sodium carbonate, $Na_2CO_3$).   The addition of a solution of washing soda to hard water converts the mineral contents into insoluble calcium and magnesium carbonates.   They

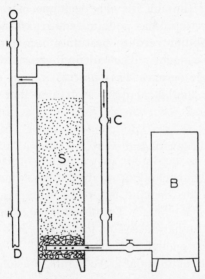

Fig. 166.   Zeolite Water Softener.   Water flows through the inlet pipe $I$ past the control valve $C$ and penetrates the zeolite softening material $S$.   As it flows into the home water system at the outlet $O$, it has been completely softened.   To regenerate the softener, valves are properly adjusted, brine flows from $B$ into the zeolite, and the unused brine and calcium chloride by-product are flushed into the sewer through $D$.

settle out and leave the water soft.   This treatment is used in the wash-day clothes boiler, and in big steam-generating plants.

A very modern method is the zeolite process.   The mineral here employed may be either mined or manufactured.   It is prepared in granular form, enclosed in a tank, and the water to be softened is forced through it.   To understand the action which occurs, we will designate this mineral as a sodium zeolite. While the water with its calcium and magnesium compounds flows through the softener, the compounds are decomposed to form *insoluble* calcium and magnesium zeolites.   The water which leaves the softener has, therefore, been freed from compounds of these two elements (Fig. 166).

After the softener has been operating for some time, it becomes inefficient because too much sodium zeolite has been replaced by the calcium and magnesium compounds. The softener must then be regenerated. Sodium chloride (salt) brine is forced through it. The sodium chloride acts on the calcium zeolite to produce sodium zeolite and calcium chloride. The original sodium zeolite has thus been recovered and is ready to work again. The calcium chloride by-product is flushed into the sewer. This process is now widely used in private homes and in a number of municipal and industrial softening plants.

## MAKING SEWAGE RESPECTABLE

The public is becoming increasingly conscious of stream pollution. It is demanding sanitation for swimming, boating, and fishing. This demand is forcing widespread construction of sewage disposal plants. The object is not to bury the sewage, but to render it harmless and inoffensive. It is true that if sewage flows far enough in a stream, it will be purified by the combined forces of dilution, green plants, sunshine, and oxygen. Sewage disposal, however, aims at purifying it before it reaches the river or lake.

In one process the sewage is first screened to remove gravel and coarse material. It then flows into large vats, called sedimentation tanks, where it remains while the main bulk of solid matter settles to the bottom. The liquid portion, the "effluent," is drawn off upon the surface of filter beds. These are large beds of crushed rock several feet thick with an underdrain to a river or other outlet. The rock surfaces are coated with slime, which contains bacteria. The effect is to purify the effluent as it trickles through and make it fit to discharge into surface waters. The settlings of the sedimentation tanks are transferred to other tanks called *digesters*. During its stay in them the sediment is subjected to bacterial action and to heat. It ferments, gives off a combustible gas, and partly liquefies. The fluid portion passes to the filter beds and the sludge is discharged upon drying beds. Here its water content is greatly reduced and the residue may be used for fertilizer. A part of the combustible gas from the fermentation is used to heat the digesters.

The "activated sludge" process differs somewhat from the one just described. It is cheaper to install and more rapid in its operation, but requires more careful control. The raw sewage is run into tanks and mixed with a sludge which is highly charged (activated) with suitable bacteria. Here it is churned and aerated to bring about rapid disintegration and oxidation. A portion of its sludge is then used for the next batch of raw sewage. Its main bulk is filtered or digested as in the other process.

Bacterial purification of sewage is also accomplished in home septic tanks. They are usually in two compartments. Almost all of the mass is finally liquefied and is fairly pure as it trickles from the overflow pipe.

## WATER AS A STANDARD FOR PHYSICAL UNITS

The versatility of water is amazing. The "man on the street" values water for drinking, for washing, for boating, for power, and for its industrial uses. But, like "hidden taxes," its less obvious contributions to his welfare are numerous. Water serves as a measuring stick in science. It is a standard of reference for specific gravities, heat units, specific heats, and boiling and freezing points. Its heats of fusion and vaporization are very large. Its vapor tension and vapor pressure, its relation to acids and bases, and its solvent power play an important role in science. We cannot study these multiple uses of water without being thankful that it is so cheap and available.

## BUNDLES OF HEAT

A thermometer measures heat *intensity*. It tells us "how hot," but not "how much heat." The *quantity* of heat is determined with a *calorimeter* (Fig. 167). In this instrument a piece of coal or a portion of food may be burned in pure oxygen, and the heat absorbed by water and measured. The heating power of the substance can be expressed in three units —all referred to water as a standard. These units, the small

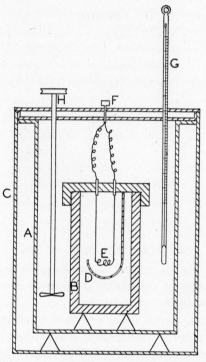

FIG. 167.    Bomb Type of Calorimeter.    A weighed portion of the food whose heat units are to be measured is placed in the cup *D*, contained in the steel bomb *B*, which also contains pure oxygen under pressure.    The food is ignited by electrically heating the wire coil *E*.    The heat from the burning food is transmitted to water which fills the insulated tank *A*, the water being constantly agitated by the stirrer *H*.    The change in the temperature of the water is registered by the thermometer *G*.    The entire assembly is enclosed within the casing *C*.

calorie (cal.), the large or kilogram or food calorie (Cal.), and the British thermal unit (B.t.u.), have been explained in Chap. 8.    It should be noted that, upon oxidation in the body, a gram of carbohydrates liberates four food calories, a gram of protein four, and a gram of fat nine food calories.    The heating power of coal is expressed in B.t.u.'s per pound and of gas in B.t.u.'s per cubic foot.

TABLE 5
SPECIFIC HEATS

| Substance | Temp. °C. | Specific Heat |
|---|---|---|
| Gold.................... | 20 | 0.031 |
| Silver................. | 20 | 0.056 |
| Copper............... | 20 | 0.092 |
| Aluminum............. | 20 | 0.214 |
| Sodium Chloride........ | 0 | 0.204 |
| Water................. | 15 | 1.000 |
| Ice.................... | 0 | 0.492 |
| Acetic acid............ | 0 | 0.468 |
| Olive Oil............. | 6 | 0.471 |
| Ether................. | 0 | 0.529 |
| Ethyl Alcohol.......... | 0 | 0.535 |
| Glycerine............. | 0 | 0.540 |

## A COMPARISON OF HEAT CAPACITIES

Fortunately, water ranks high in its ability to absorb and emit heat. Most substances exhibit a lower capacity. Comparative values are expressed as *specific heats* (Table 5), a topic which was introduced in Chap. 8. If a substance requires only one-half as much heat as water to warm a gram mass through one degree, it has a specific heat of one-half. On cooling, it is evident that only one-half as much heat would be emitted. The high specific heat of water—it is unity, or one —renders it very valuable wherever heating or cooling is done with water. Such cases include the hot water bottle, house heating, the automobile radiator and heater, and the moderation of climate near large bodies of water.

## KEEPING THINGS COOL

A gram of water, in cooling from one degree C. to zero, loses one calorie. At zero, water can be either a liquid or a solid. Suppose we desire to change this gram of water to ice without changing its temperature. Must it lose another calorie? In reality, it must rid itself of 80 calories. What a loss of heat just to orient the molecules into the crystalline structure of solid ice! It is obvious that, when a gram of ice changes back to water *at zero*, it must absorb 80 calories. This value is the *heat of fusion*, a term first discussed in Chap. 8. Here, again, water tops the list for high heats of fusion. How fortunate that it combines cheapness, availability, and high efficiency for our refrigerators.

## STEAM HEATING

Follow this gram of water, next, to the other end of the thermometer. As it warms from 99 degrees to 100, it takes up a calorie. What heat demand will it make to change into steam, *without change of temperature?* The price seems exorbitant, because it requires 540 calories just to break the molecules apart and form the gas. The condensing process, in turn, liberates 540 calories. This quantity of energy is its "*heat of vaporization*" (p. 101), and water again heads the list. It is small wonder that steam is in a class by itself as a heating agent.

## THE MARKS ON THE THERMOMETER

Before turning from the field of heat it should be noted that the centigrade temperature scale gets its goal posts from water. The freezing point of water is zero and its boiling point is 100 on the centigrade thermometer. Hence there are 100 degrees between these limits. The corresponding positions on the Fahrenheit scale are 32 and 212, respectively. The degree range here is 180. Hence the ratio is 100 to 180, or five to nine. Note, further, that the freezing point of water on the Fahrenheit scale is 32 degrees above its zero. From these relationships grow two temperature conversion equations: $F. = \frac{9}{5}C. + 32$ and $C. = \frac{5}{9}(F. - 32)$.

## SINK OR FLOAT

Turning to the field of weight, water is again the measuring stick. The weight of one cubic centimeter of water is called the *gram*. This relationship is also referred to as the *density* of water, because density is defined as the weight of a unit volume of a substance. A cubic centimeter of mercury weighs 13.6 grams. This is its density.

It is a common practice to accept the density of water as a standard and to compare the densities of other substances with it. These relative terms are the same *whether densities are expressed in the English or the metric system.* They are called *specific gravities.* Any definite volume of gold weighs 19.3 times as much as the *same volume* of water. Hence it has a specific gravity of 19.3. Expressed in the metric system, 19.3 would also be its density.

Two observations should be made here, to avoid any misconceptions. The density of water changes *very slightly* with changes in temperature. Unlike most liquids, it does not have its maximum density at its freezing point, but at four degrees C. Also, water is the standard of specific gravities for *solids* and *liquids*. The standard for gases is *air*, or sometimes *hydrogen*.

## MEASURING THE RAIN OF MOLECULES

Liquids evaporate. By this we mean that they pass from the liquid to the vapor state. At the surface of water its molecules are constantly hopping into the air. If we could measure this rain of upward-flying molecules, we would find that they exert a pressure. Expressed as the pressure over a *unit area*, let us say one square centimeter, it is called the *vapor tension* of water. Raising the temperature of water increases the evaporation rate; that is, its vapor tension is increased. "Ether has a higher vapor tension than water" is the technical way of saying that it evaporates faster.

The boiling point of water is the temperature at which its vapor tension just equals the atmospheric pressure. At sea level this balance is attained when the water is at 100° C. The atmospheric pressure is less at higher altitudes and hence the boiling point of water would be correspondingly lower. In general, there is a decrease of about five degrees in the boiling point of water for every mile above sea level. This would mean that on the summit of Mt. Everest, the highest mountain in the world, with an elevation of 29,002 feet, water would boil at about 72° C.  Cooking by means of boiling water is a real problem at high elevations because it is *temperature* which determines rate of cooking.  The difficulty may be overcome by the use of a pressure cooker (Fig. 168).

When a dish is partly filled with water and tightly covered, the water continues to evaporate at the same rate, for the vapor tension of water is fixed and definite at any given temperature.  But, after a time, the air space becomes saturated with water molecules and they return to the water at the same rate as that at which they leave.  The pressure effect of these returning molecules is called *vapor pressure*. Under such conditions the vapor tension and the vapor pressure are equal, that is, they are in *equilibrium*.

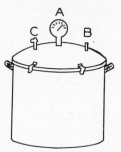

FIG. 168.  Pressure Cooker.  The boiling point of water varies with the pressure above it.  Water and the food to be cooked are placed in the cooker, the cover clamped on airtight, and the water heated.  The steam generated increases the pressure, raises the boiling temperature, and decreases the time required for the cooking process.  The gauge *A* registers the pressure, the blow-off valve *B* prevents development of excessive pressures, and the release valve *C* permits release of the steam.

Everyone is familiar with an interesting application of these terms.  Municipalities often "settle the dust" on some of their streets by sprinkling with powdered calcium chloride.  For some time after—or until several rains wash the material away—the road surface is damp and no longer offends neat housekeepers.  To explain the effect, consider a single particle of the calcium chloride.  Remember that there is always some moisture in the air.  A little moisture settles on the calcium chloride particle and forms a surface film of strong calcium chloride solution.  Now, a strong solution of this substance has a *very low* vapor tension.  In fact, its vapor tension is nearly always less than the vapor pressure in the air.  This is another way of stating that more water molecules condense on

the calcium chloride than leave it.   There can be only one
result—the water accumulates on the calcium chloride and keeps
it and the dust moist.   This spontaneous taking up of water from
the air, as here described, is
termed *deliquescence*.

The physical properties of
water have been taken up in
some detail because they are
a matter of such common
experience and are better
appreciated if understood.
There remains to add only
that water is colorless in thin
layers but is a blue or green
when observed through
greater depths; that its palat-
able taste is due to dissolved
air and minerals, a "flat"
taste resulting if they are
removed.   Next we shall investigate its chemical behavior.

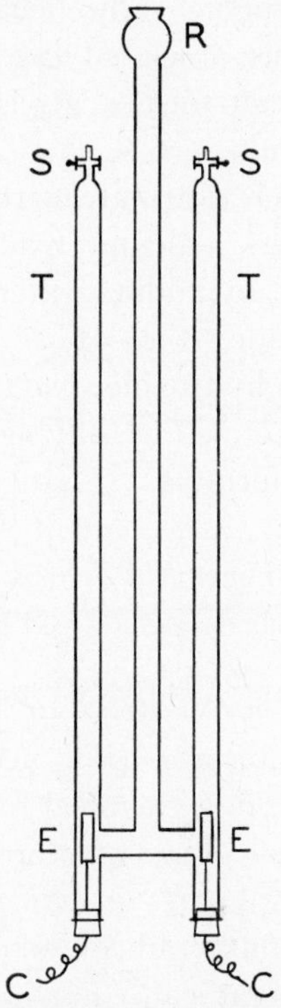

## CHEMICAL RELATIONS OF WATER

The well-known elements,
sulfur and phosphorus, burn
readily and form oxides.
When water is added to these
oxides, it combines with them
to form liquids which turn
litmus paper red.   They are
acids, sulfurous ($H_2SO_3$) and
phosphoric ($HPO_3$) by name.
Water unites with a large
number of oxides to produce acids.   These oxides are classified
as *acidic oxides*.

Fig. 169.   Apparatus for the Electrolysis of Water.   Upon decomposition,
water yields two volumes of hydrogen to
one volume of oxygen.   This may be
demonstrated by filling the apparatus
with acidified water and attaching the
electrodes $E$ $E$ through the wires $C$ $C$
to a source of direct current.   Gases
rise in the tubes $T$ $T$, and the gas from
the cathode (hydrogen) occupies twice
the volume of that from the anode
(oxygen).   The gases force the excess
liquid into the reservoir $R$.   By opening
stopcocks $S$ $S$, the gases may be collected and identified.

The formula for an inorganic acid can always be identified because it has one or more hydrogen symbols standing first in the formula. More technically, the *positive radical of every acid is hydrogen.* This behavior of water with acidic oxides offers a means of classifying many elements. Any element whose oxide can form acids is classed as a *nonmetallic element* or a *nonmetal.*

Water will unite with certain other oxides to form bases or alkalies. Calcium oxide or quicklime is slaked, in making mortar, by adding water. The product, slaked lime, is calcium hydroxide—$Ca(OH)_2$. Sodium oxide, united with water, forms sodium hydroxide ($NaOH$), commonly called lye. All bases are characterized by having one or more OH groups standing last in the formula. That is, the hydroxide group is their *negative radical.* Any element whose oxide can form a base is called a *metal* or *metallic element.* These reactions are the true criteria in the classification of elements as metals and nonmetals.

## CHEMICAL RADICALS

The term *radical* needs further explanation. Most compounds, in a chemical reaction, tend to separate into two parts or units. The two words used in naming a compound refer to these two parts or *radicals.* Furthermore, the first-written and first-named radical is called the *positive* and the other, the *negative* radical. For example, $H_2SO_4$ is hydrogen sulfate, HCl is hydrogen chloride, NaCl is sodium chloride, $Na_2SO_4$ is sodium sulfate, and NaOH is sodium hydroxide. The hydrogen and sodium are positive radicals; the sulfate, chloride, and hydroxide are negative radicals. A radical composed of one element is a *simple radical;* one made up of two or more elements is a *compound radical.* The exceptions to this terminology will not be considered here.

## COMPOUNDS CLASSIFIED

To understand another behavior of water, we shall examine what happens when an acid and a base are brought together. They can no more remain indifferent to each other when placed in the same beaker than can a small boy and a piece of pie when left alone in the same room.  When mixed, an acid and a base swap radicals and form two new compounds.  Expressed in words, in the case of two such pairs, these are the reactions. Sodium hydroxide reacts with hydrogen chloride to produce sodium chloride and hydrogen hydroxide (water).  Hydrogen sulfate reacts with calcium hydroxide to produce calcium sulfate and hydrogen hydroxide (water).  Several facts grow from these illustrations.  First, there is an exchange of radicals—a "swapping" of partners.  This general type of reaction is classified as *double decomposition* or *metathesis*.  Second, one of the products in each case is water.  Third, the other product is made of the positive radical of the base and the negative radical of the acid.  It is always classed as a *salt*.  Fourth, the acid and the base have given up their properties to produce two neutral substances.  Hence such a reaction is called *neutralization*.  Neutralization is a special case of double decomposition involving an acid and a base.  Fifth, the positive radical of a salt is a metal, and the negative is made up of one or more nonmetals. Sixth, a neutralization action brings into play *all three classes of inorganic compounds—acids, bases,* and *salts*.  Water is in a class by itself.

## WATER-SALT PARTNERS

Certain salts behave in a peculiar way toward water.  Consider three cases.  Copper sulfate ($CuSO_4$) is a white substance. When it is dissolved in water and the solid is recovered by evaporation, it has changed into a blue substance of composition, $CuSO_4 5H_2O$.  The salt has combined with five molecules of water.  Cobalt chloride is a blue salt of formula, $CoCl_2$.  When dissolved in water and recovered by evaporation, it has become wine-colored and has combined with six molecules of water— $CoCl_2 6H_2O$.  Washing soda can exist in two forms, both white: $Na_2CO_3$ and $Na_2CO_3 10H_2O$.  Salts in combination with water are called *hydrates* and the water, *water of hydration*.  Application of heat will drive off water of hydration.  This chemical process is one of *dehydration*.  Hydrated washing soda—

$Na_2CO_310H_2O$—and some other hydrates become dehydrated merely by standing in the air. This spontaneous action is one of *efflorescence*.

Washing soda is on the market both as the dehydrated salt ($Na_2CO_3$, Mol. Wt. 106) and the hydrated salt ($Na_2CO_310H_2O$, Mol. Wt. 286). Assuming high purity, there is as much of this water-softening salt in 37 cents' worth of the dehydrated salt as in a dollar's worth of the hydrated salt, because the latter contains such a large quantity of water of hydration.

## HYDROGEN PEROXIDE

A less well-known cousin of water is hydrogen peroxide. They are related only because both are compounds of hydrogen and oxygen. Hydrogen peroxide has annexed an extra atom of oxygen, as shown by its formula, $H_2O_2$. The drugstore sample is 3 per cent hydrogen peroxide and about 97 per cent water. It decomposes readily, especially in the presence of some catalysts, and yields water and oxygen. The oxygen, on the instant of liberation, is in an especially active condition, called the *nascent* state. In this state it readily oxidizes such substances as dyes and bacteria. To oxidize a dye is to fade it, and to oxidize a bacterium is to kill it. Hence hydrogen peroxide is a bleaching and mild sterilizing agent. It will bleach hair, whence the term, "peroxide blonde." Poured on a fresh wound, it is always seen to froth and foam as a result of the escaping gas. A catalyst in the blood—an enzyme called *catalase*—causes the hydrogen peroxide to decompose and liberate oxygen. Being insoluble, this gas sweeps up through the liquid, producing foaming. The bubbling, frothing effect noticed when an insoluble gas makes its way, in fine bubbles, through a liquid is called *effervescence*. The process was also encountered in the study of Henry's law in Chap. 9.

## CHEMICAL SHORTHAND

In the preceding pages, numerous examples of chemical changes have been encountered. The employment of formulas to represent molecules was explained on page 80. With this background we are now in a position to familiarize ourselves with equations.  To the uninitiated a chemical equation is mysterious and meaningless.  But a student of chemistry finds it a most convenient tool.  It is made up of formulas and signs ($+$ and $\rightarrow$) and expresses a chemical reaction.  A few actual cases will assist in writing and interpreting equations.  In the study of hydrogen it was observed that it combines with oxygen to produce water.  Write the *formulas* for hydrogen and oxygen, separated by a plus sign, thus: $H_2 + O_2$.  These are called the *reactants* and constitute the *left-hand member* of the equation.  Next write an arrow, thus: $H_2 + O_2 \rightarrow$.  The arrow, interpreted, means "produces" or "forms."  After the arrow write the formula for water, thus: $H_2 + O_2 \rightarrow H_2O$.  $H_2O$ is called the *product* and constitutes the *right-hand member*.  So far we have written a *skeleton* equation.  That is, we have indicated just one molecule of each substance involved.  It merely states that hydrogen unites with oxygen to form water.  It expresses no *quantitative* relationship.  In fact, it seems to refute the law referring to the conservation of mass, which states that matter cannot be destroyed or created.  Examine the skeleton equation closely.  It indicates that one molecule of hydrogen containing two hydrogen atoms unites with one molecule of oxygen having two oxygen atoms to produce one molecule of water containing two hydrogen atoms and one oxygen atom.  Manifestly this is impossible because two atoms of oxygen cannot become one atom.  To correct this error, we must *balance the equation*.  That is, we must indicate such a *number of molecules* of each substance that the *total quantity of matter* in the left-hand member and the right-hand member will be equal.  This is done, always in the same way, by placing figures called *coefficients* before the proper formulas.

Consider the equation again.  The one molecule of oxygen contains two oxygen atoms but the molecule of water has only one oxygen atom.  We never use fractions as coefficients, hence we cannot indicate less than one molecule of oxygen.  This furnishes enough oxygen atoms for two molecules of water.  Hence we write: $H_2 + O_2 \rightarrow 2H_2O$.  But two molecules of water require four hydrogen atoms for their formation. The molecule of hydrogen in the left-hand member can furnish only two hydrogen atoms. It will, therefore, require two molecules of hydrogen, and we write: $2H_2 + O_2 \rightarrow 2H_2O$. The equation is now balanced. Prove it thus: two molecules of hydrogen with four hydrogen atoms will unite with one molecule of oxygen containing two oxygen atoms to produce two molecules of water having four hydrogen atoms and two oxygen atoms. A more completely quantitative relationship will be developed under reaction weight problems. Suffice it here to present equations in the simplest possible form.

Examine next the reaction studied under "Oxygen" in which potassium chlorate ($KClO_3$) decomposed to produce oxygen ($O_2$) and potassium chloride ($KCl$). $KClO_3$ is the reactant and makes up the left-hand member. $O_2$ and $KCl$ are the products and appear in the right-hand member. The skeleton equation then reads: $KClO_3 \rightarrow KCl + O_2$. Evidently the oxygen is not balanced. How many molecules of $KClO_3$ and of $O_2$ will equalize the oxygen? Since $KClO_3$ furnishes oxygen in trios and $O_2$ shows it in pairs, we shall need $2KClO_3$ and $3O_2$, and we write: $2KClO_3 \rightarrow KCl + 3O_2$. Now, $2KClO_3$ must produce $2KCl$; so the balanced equation is: $2KClO_3 \rightarrow 2KCl + 3O_2$. It should be noted that, in balancing a skeleton equation, it is not rewritten as has been necessary here.

One more illustration will be helpful—the neutralization equation between $Fe(OH)_3$ and $HCl$. The skeleton equation is: $Fe(OH)_3 + HCl \rightarrow FeCl_3 + H_2O$. This illlustrates one general rule and one exception to the rule. Evidently the O, H, and Cl are all unbalanced. With which shall we start? The general rule is: "Start with the highest subscript." But O, H, and Cl each have 3 for a subscript. May we, then, take our choice? The exception to the rule is: "If a highest subscript refers to an element which appears in two or more substances *in the same member of the equation*, start with a different element." In this equation, H appears both in $Fe(OH)_3$ and $HCl$ in the left-hand member. That leaves 3O or 3Cl as the starting point, and there is no choice. Suppose we begin with 3O. Since one molecule of $Fe(OH)_3$ furnishes 3O atoms and they produce $H_2O$, it will require that $3H_2O$ be formed. Hence, $Fe(OH)_3 + HCl \rightarrow FeCl_3 + 3H_2O$. But $3H_2O$ requires 6H, of which the molecule of $Fe(OH)_3$ furnishes three. It will require 3HCl to furnish the other three and we write: $Fe(OH)_3 + 3HCl \rightarrow FeCl_3 + 3H_2O$. Checking on the remaining element, Fe, we find that there is one atom in each member and the equation is now balanced.

## REACTION TYPES

An inspection of inorganic reactions shows that, in general, they can be classified under four different types. All of these types have now been illustrated in the preceding pages. Below, each type is named, defined, illustrated, and an equation and reference is given.

1. Combination: A process in which two or more substances unite to form one substance. Hydrogen unites with oxygen to form water (page 327). $2H_2 + O_2 \rightarrow 2H_2O$.

2. Decomposition: A process in which one substance separates into two or more substances. Potassium chlorate decomposes to produce oxygen and potassium chloride (page 323). $2KClO_3 \rightarrow 2KCl + 3O_2$.

3. Displacement: A process in which a free element and a compound react to produce a free element and a compound. Displacing hydrogen from an acid with a metal (page 329). $2HCl + Zn \rightarrow H_2 + ZnCl_2$.

4. Double decomposition or Metathesis: A process in which two compounds react by exchange of radicals to produce two different compounds. Interaction of sodium hydroxide and hydrogen chloride (page 349). $NaOH + HCl \rightarrow NaCl + HOH$ (or $H_2O$).

## REACTION WEIGHTS

It is often necessary to determine what weight of some substance is required or produced in a given reaction. A knowledge of molecular weights and of equations makes such a computation a simple matter. With reference to the decomposition action just mentioned, consider this problem. What weight of oxygen is produced by the complete decomposition of 30 gm. of potassium chlorate? An equation expresses not only the number of molecules involved but the number of molecular weights. Hence the equation, $2KClO_3 \rightarrow 2KCl + 3O_2$, states that two molecular weights of $KClO_3$ will produce two molecular weights of KCl and three of $O_2$. These are always the weight ratios involved in this particular action. Only the $KClO_3$ and the $O_2$ are desired in the problem. These are in the ratio of $2KClO_3$ to $3O_2$ or $2 \times (39.1 + 35.457 + 48)$ to $6 \times 16$—a ratio of 245.114 to 96. The atomic weight values used here may be obtained from the table on p. 82. The 30 gm. of $KClO_3$ will be in the same proportion to the unknown $(X)$ gm. of oxygen as 245.114 is to 96. Hence we can write: $245.114 : 96 = 30$ gm. $: X$ gm. The answer is 11.7 gm. The method may be summarized thus: Step 1. Write the equation. Step 2. Compute the total molecular weight of the substance whose weight is given and of the one whose weight is desired. Step 3. Use these two molecular weights together with the given weight and the unknown term, $X$, in a proportion and solve for $X$.

The solution here described assumes ideal conditions. These seldom exist. Where the problem asks for the yield if only 70 per cent of the oxygen is actually recovered, one more step is necessary. The actual yield will be 70 per cent of 11.7 gm. $11.7 \times .70 = 8.19$ gm.

Percentage composition and reaction weights are the only types of chemical problems which will be considered in this book.

# CHAPTER 24

# IONIZATION AND
# EQUILIBRIUM

## WATCHING MOLECULAR WHEELS GO AROUND

What a riot of movement the mention of a chemical reaction conjures up in our imagination! The process might be likened to that of a peasant village dance with the participants joining in couples, separating, trading partners, grouping in threes and fours and fives. Do molecules meet and separate and trade and lose partners? In many cases this analogy will account for a chemical change. However, there are many reactions which must be explained differently. For them the Theory of Ionization is the explanation. This theory will show us still another side of the versatile substance, water, which was studied in the last chapter. It is an important and highly technical theory of which only the barest, simplest essentials will be considered.

## THEORY OF IONIZATION

Dry tartaric acid (from grapes) and dry baking soda ($NaHCO_3$) can be mixed and nothing happens. Dry litmus paper is not affected by contact with dry citric acid (from lemons). Dry oxalic acid (from rhubarb) gives no taste on a dry tongue. Dry acetic acid (from vinegar) will not conduct an electric current. But dissolve these substances in water and what a change occurs! The tartaric-soda mixture effervesces vigorously and liberates carbon dioxide. The litmus paper turns pink. The oxalic acid tastes sour. And a current will flow through the acetic acid circuit.

355

Water, itself, possesses none of these properties.   Neither has it acted as a catalyst, in the true sense.   For an explanation of the action of water we are indebted to a Swedish chemist, Svante Arrhenius.   His theory, advanced in 1887, may be called the *Theory of Ionization*.   It has since been modified in some particulars, especially by the proposals of Debye and Huckel.   The essentials of the theory can be briefly and non-technically presented.

When acids, bases, and salts are dissolved in water, it separates some, if not all, of the molecules into their radicals. These radicals carry electric charges, positive and negative, whence the name "positive" and "negative" radicals.   The charged radicals are named *ions*.   Ions carrying positive charges are called *cations* and those of negative charge, *anions*. Consider a pinch of salt.   In the dry state its atoms are quite closely packed in the molecular structure and rigidly fixed. The electrons and protons exhibit the same general relationship as was described for sodium fluoride and magnesium fluoride in Chap. 7.

When salt is dissolved in water, it acts upon some of the molecules to separate the sodium and chloride radicals.   In separating, as described for sodium fluoride on page 88, the sodium radical loses an electron to the chlorine.   This loss leaves the sodium with one excess positive charge and the chlorine with one excess negative charge—whence their ionic charges.   In a similar way, all acids form hydrogen ions and all bases, hydroxide ions.   It is actually the hydrogen ions of acids which cause them to taste sour and to turn litmus paper pink. It is the hydroxide ions of bases which turn litmus paper blue. In fact, *all reactions of acids, bases, and salts in water occur between ions, rather than between molecules.*

A few factual statements may now be made, for reference purposes, but they will not be elaborated upon.

Water is the only ionizing liquid with which a beginning student is familiar.

Not all of the molecules are necessarily separated into ions (ionized).   The per cent of molecules ionized is called the *degree of ionization* or *degree of dissociation*.

Most salts show a high degree of ionization. They are *highly ionized*.

Some acids and bases, such as hydrochloric acid, nitric acid, and sodium hydroxide, are highly ionized (perhaps completely ionized). They are called *strong acids and bases*.

Other acids and bases, such as acetic acid, carbonic acid, and ammonium hydroxide, are slightly ionized. They are called *weak acids and bases*.

Water does not appreciably ionize.

Solutions which contain ions are called *electrolytes*. The mechanics of flow of a current through an electrolyte and through a copper wire is different. In the latter case, swarms of electrons stream along the wire; in the former, electricity is transferred by the ions. These move through the solution toward the electrode opposite in charge to the charge on the ion.

When the ions strike the electrode, they lose their charge. This loss accounts for the current flow in the outer circuit.

The ion, after it is neutralized, is called the *primary product* of electrolysis and behaves like the ordinary molecular substances. Thus, in a copper sulfate solution, the blue color is due to copper ions. Upon discharge at the cathode, they become ordinary copper and plate the electrode as a bronze-colored layer. This deposited copper is a primary product.

If the primary products can react with the surrounding medium to form other substances, the latter are called *secondary products*. Upon electrolysis of sodium chloride, the sodium ions are discharged at the cathode to become neutral sodium atoms—a primary product. Immediately the sodium attacks the water to form hydrogen and sodium hydroxide. The latter are secondary products.

## CHEMICAL EQUILIBRIUM

The term *equilibrium* implies two opposing forces in a state of balance. Within a closed jar of water, as described on page 346, there is an equilibrium between vapor tension and vapor pressure. That is, vaporization and condensation proceed at an equal rate, and the volume of the water remains constant.

The principle is the same where equilibrium among ions is involved. Examine solutions of sodium chloride and potassium nitrate. These salts are highly ionized. The former solution contains countless sodium ions and chloride ions; the latter, potassium ions and nitrate ions. Now mix the two solutions. Considered from the molecular standpoint, double decomposition would occur, and sodium nitrate and potassium chloride would be formed. $NaCl + KNO_3 \rightarrow NaNO_3 + KCl$. *But all four of the salts are dissolved, highly ionized, and the reaction really occurs between the ions.* Expressing the ionic state with plus and minus signs, we could write: $Na^+, Cl^- + K^+, NO_3^- \rightarrow Na^+, NO_3^- + K^+, Cl^-$. The left-hand member contains four kinds of ions, and the right-hand member contains *the same four kinds of ions.* From the kinetic viewpoint, there is nothing to hinder the ions of the products from forming the reactants. In other words, the action can and does proceed forward and backward constantly. The reactants and products are in *equilibrium.* The equilibrium equation would show double arrows, thus: $Na^+, Cl^- + K^+, NO_3^- \leftrightarrows Na^+, NO_3^- + K^+, Cl^-$. When NaCl and $KNO_3$ solutions are mixed, then, there is no visible action because an equilibrium exists.

Turn, next, to a neutralization action, as referred to on page 349. It was expressed: $NaOH + HCl \rightarrow NaCl + H_2O$. NaOH, a strong base, forms sodium ions ($Na^+$) and hydroxide ions ($OH^-$). HCl, a strong acid, yields hydrogen ions ($H^+$) and chloride ions ($Cl^-$). NaCl, a salt, yields sodium ions ($Na^+$) and chloride ions ($Cl^-$). Water is not ionized. The ionic equation would read: $Na^+, OH^- + H^+, Cl^- \rightarrow Na^+, Cl^- + H_2O$. Sodium ions and chloride ions are common to both sides of the equation. To form the reactants, the $Na^+$ and $Cl^-$ of the products would need to react with $H^+$ and $OH^-$. But the product, water, being unionized, does not return these ions to the solution. The action, then, cannot produce an equilibrium (cannot be reversible); as a result the NaOH and HCl are finally used up and the reaction *goes to completion* (is irreversible). Reactions in solution do not reach an equilibrium if one of the products uses up the ions, either

because it is un-ionized or because it is an insoluble solid
or gas.

## UPSETTING AN EQUILIBRIUM

An interesting and not too technical illustration of "shifting
an equilibrium" is met in very dilute acetic acid. Such a
solution is very weakly ionized, say one-tenth of one per cent.
The molecules are in equilibrium, however, with the small
quantity of ions. The equilibrium equation is

$$HC_2H_3O_2 \leftrightarrows H^+ + C_2H_3O_2^-.$$

Acetic acid   Hydrogen      acetate ions
99.9 %      ions   .1 %

Even the relatively small quantity of hydrogen ions present
turns litmus paper red.

Now, dissolve in the solution considerable solid sodium
acetate. This will ionize highly, being a salt, and furnish a
host of sodium ions and acetate ions. These acetate ions
greatly reinforce the acetate ions from the acetic, and together
they act upon the thinly scattered hydrogen ions and force
them into combination as acetic acid. Expressed technically,
the equilibrium is displaced toward the left, toward the reactants. If tested with litmus paper, the solution now reacts
neutral, because the $H^+$ has become $HC_2H_3O_2$. This equilibrium displacement is an illustration of the *Law of Mass Action;*
explanation of the law will be found in more detail in chemistry
texts.

We are now on speaking terms with oxygen, hydrogen, and
water, as chemical substances. The theories just described
apply most commonly to water solutions. It will be of interest
next to explore that familiar material, the atmosphere, which
was discussed in Chap. 11, to discover how the chemist has
harnessed its ingredients in the service of mankind.

# CHAPTER 25

# NITROGEN AND ITS
# COMPOUNDS:
# OTHER GASES OF THE
# ATMOSPHERE

## THE NITROGEN OF THE AIR

Our earth, as it travels through space, is always enveloped in a great blanket of gas many miles deep. This atmosphere, as described in earlier chapters, is essential for sound conduction, for transportation, and for weather conditions. Respiration, combustion, and decay are dependent upon its 21 per cent oxygen content. Yet these processes are equally dependent upon not having too much oxygen. The consequences would be disastrous if the proportion of oxygen were suddenly to be increased. Fires would burn with almost uncontrollable vigor and all other oxidative actions would be greatly accelerated.

The oxygen must be diluted with some substance which will play little, if any, part in the usual oxidation processes—a substance which is chemically inactive. Such a lazy substance is the gas nitrogen. Its negative qualities are highly important in our air. It is a colorless, odorless, tasteless, diatomic element of atomic weight 14.008. It is slightly soluble in water and has a density a little less than air. Although it is valued for its negative quality of inertness, it can be induced to unite with other elements. The compounds so produced rank among the most useful in modern life (Fig. 170).

360

## NITROGEN AND BACTERIA

Outside of the small amount of nitrogen compounds formed during a lightning discharge, the greatest natural factor in producing nitrogen compounds is the family of legumes. The members of this family—clover, alfalfa, soybeans, and others—carry small swellings (nodules) on their roots, which are the homes of "nitrogen fixing" bacteria (Fig. 171). These tiny

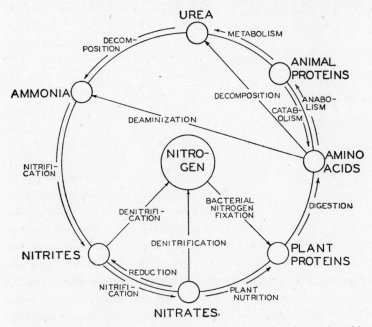

FIG. 170. Cycle of Nitrogen. The diagram shows the various forms of combination into which nitrogen may enter as the result of natural processes.

organisms have the power of taking nitrogen from the air and building it into compounds which serve as plant food. Every person raised on a farm knows that a good farmer frequently uses a legume crop to build up the soil. Nitrogenous materials in barnyard manure help to make it a valuable fertilizer.

## COMMERCIAL NITROGEN FIXATION

To supplement Nature's slow and limited *nitrogen fixation* processes, man has applied his chemical and general technical knowledge to large-scale production of nitrogen compounds from the air and other sources.  Not only are the offspring of nitrogen used in fertilizers; they are necessary for explosives, for synthetic silk, and for a wide variety of the conveniences of modern life.  Hence cheap methods of producing nitrogen compounds by *fixation* have been developed on a tremendous scale.

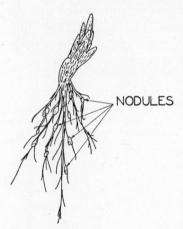

NODULES

FIG. 171.  Root system of a legume.

What shall be the starting point and what is the first generation of the nitrogen progeny? One answer is *ammonia*.  This irritating, stifling gas has the formula $NH_3$.  Its manufacture appears simple—merely unite nitrogen and hydrogen.  The development of the actual process, however, offered tremendous difficulties.  It was finally accomplished by a German chemist, Fritz Haber.  His process employs a direct union of the two gases under a suitable temperature, pressure, and catalyst (Fig. 172).  Since air and water, the sources of the nitrogen and hydrogen, are available within any country, the Haber process makes a country self-contained for its supply of ammonia.

A roundabout, but efficient, process for obtaining ammonia by nitrogen fixation is called the cyanamid process.  For raw materials it requires limestone, coal, nitrogen, and water—also cheap electric power for its high-temperature furnaces.  It is this ammonia process which the United States selected for its war-time plant.  Electric power was obtained by damming the swift Tennessee River at Muscle Shoals, Alabama (Fig. 173).  In brief, the steps in the process are: limestone ($CaCO_3$) is heated to produce quick lime ($CaO$); this is combined with coke to give calcium carbide ($CaC_2$); nitrogen reacts with $CaC_2$ to form calcium cyanamid ($CaCN_2$); alkaline steam ($H_2O$) changes $CaCN_2$ to ammonia.  Calcium cyanamid, called "nitro lime," is also used as a fertilizer.

Another nitrogen fixation process first produces nitric oxide, instead of ammonia. It is the Birkeland-Eyde method, named after its inventors. Air is drawn through a high-temperature, flaming electric arc. Under this intense heat the oxygen and

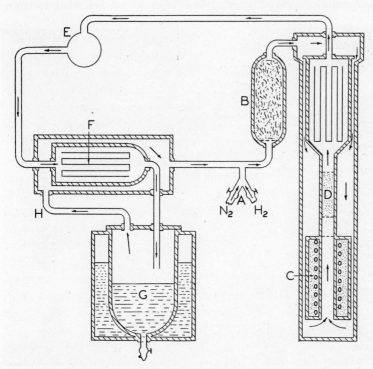

FIG. 172. Haber Process of Nitrogen Fixation. Nitrogen and hydrogen gases are introduced at $A$, purified in $B$, and then enter the catalyst chamber. They are heated to the proper temperature at $C$, and as they pass through the catalyst $D$, they unite to produce ammonia. Through the action of the compressor $E$ and the cooling coils $F$, the gaseous ammonia is liquefied and flows into the tank $G$. The very cold ammonia gas which evaporates from $G$ passes through $H$, assists in cooling the incoming gas in $F$, and goes through the cycle again.

nitrogen of the air unite to form nitric oxide (NO), which can then be converted into other useful compounds.

## AMMONIA FROM COAL

The greater part of the ammonium salts on the market are made from ammonia derived from by-product coke. The steel industry requires large quantities of coke in the metallurgy of its iron ores.   Coal is heated in large retorts to liberate gases and leave a residue of coke.  The gases are separated into their valuable ingredients, among which is ammonia.   Capture of the ammonia is effected by running it through sulfuric acid, forming

*Official photograph, Ordnance Department, U. S. Army.*

FIG. 173.   Liquid Air Columns of Liquid Air Building, Muscle Shoals, Ala. The nitrogen for the cyanamid process is obtained by liquefying air in the battery of machines shown in the picture.     •

ammonium sulfate.   From ammonium sulfate other commercial ammonium compounds are made.

## AMMONIA WATER

Ammonia is highly soluble in water.   At its freezing point, water can dissolve thirteen hundred times its own volume of ammonia.   Some of the gas actually combines with water to produce the weak base, ammonium hydroxide ($NH_4OH$).   At all times an equilibrium exists between the dissolved gas and the compound as expressed in the equilibrium equation: $NH_3 + H_2O \leftrightarrows NH_4OH$. Household ammonia and the ammonium hydroxide of the laboratory are solutions whose composition can be expressed by the above equation. Because of the base present, the material is useful for softening water, for washing windows, and for similar purposes.

If ammonium hydroxide is neutralized by acids, valuable salts result. Sulfuric acid produces ammonium sulfate, a valuable fertilizer; hydrochloric acid yields ammonium chloride, an ingredient of dry cells; nitric acid forms ammonium nitrate, an explosive.

## MANUFACTURE OF NITRIC ACID

The nitrogen fixation processes which convert atmospheric nitrogen into ammonia or nitric oxide represent only the first step. The ultimate product desired is nitric acid ($HNO_3$). We can prepare this acid by three routes. First, ammonia, from whatever source, can be oxidized, as expressed by the equation:  $12NH_3 + 21O_2 \rightarrow 8HNO_3 + 4NO + 14H_2O$.  It is accomplished by bringing a mixture of air and ammonia into contact with red-hot platinum as a catalyst. Second, the nitric oxide of the Birkeland-Eyde process can be treated with oxygen and steam to give nitric acid, essentially as follows: $4NO + 3O_2 + 2H_2O \rightarrow 4HNO_3$. The third and oldest process depends upon the interaction of saltpeter ($NaNO_3$) and sulfuric acid ($H_2SO_4$). The mixture is heated and nitric acid distills over: $2NaNO_3 + H_2SO_4 \rightarrow 2HNO_3 + Na_2SO_4$.

## THRICE A KING

Nitric acid, made by whatever process, is one of the most valuable of chemicals (Fig. 174). Its earlier name—*aqua fortis*—which means "strong water," was well applied. It is thrice a king among chemicals because it is a powerful acid, a powerful oxidizing agent, and a powerful nitrating agent.

It is a powerful acid because it is one of the most highly ionized of all acids.

A spark on a splint can be plunged into the cold acid and the spark glows brilliantly. Powdered sulfur is vigorously oxidized by the concentrated acid, to produce sulfuric acid. These cases illustrate the strong oxidizing power of nitric acid.

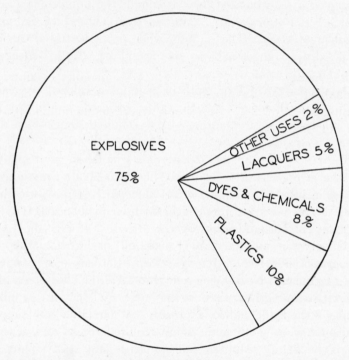

EXPLOSIVES

75%

OTHER USES 2%

LACQUERS 5%

DYES & CHEMICALS 8%

PLASTICS 10%

Fig. 174.   Uses of Nitric Acid.   The distribution of the annual production of nitric acid among the various nitrating industries is shown by the segmented circle.

The nitrating power of nitric acid holds the greatest popular interest of any of its properties. Consider first the nitration of cellulose, the skeletal framework of plants.

## NITRIC FOR POLISH, PAINT, AND PICTURES

When cotton or wood fiber is treated with nitric acid in the presence of sulfuric acid, some hydroxy (OH) groups of the cellulose are replaced by nitrate groups ($NO_3$). In a mild nitration action the product is largely a trinitrate of cellulose, called *pyroxylin*. A more vigorous nitration forms a hexanitrate—a high explosive. These products are worthy of examination here.

Pyroxylin is dissolved in an alcohol-ether mixture to produce *collodion*. Painted over a wound, the liquids evaporate and leave a transparent "skin" of pyroxylin which protects against infection. The solution when properly tinted can be brushed upon finger nails to give the glossy, colored effect so popular at present.

Mixed with camphor, with or without a colored pigment, pyroxylin will form a plastic called *celluloid*, which can be moulded into desired forms. New celluloid articles usually retain the camphor odor.

Canvas or similar tough materials can be so impregnated with a colored solution of pyroxylin as to give an attractive, glossy, resistant surface. Such products include patent leather and the artificial leathers which are used for handbags, automobile cushions, and book covers.

Dissolved in amyl acetate (banana oil) or a great variety of other organic solvents, pyroxylin forms the base of our widely used lacquers. Nearly everyone associates the odor of banana oil with some lacquer used in the home, and they are familiar under such trade names as Duco. At one time the proper finishing of an automobile body required weeks and several coats of paint. Modern body finishes are really films of pyroxylin applied with a spray gun, requiring a minimum of time and labor.

Another pyroxylin product of the nature of celluloid is universally known. It is photographic film, both still and motion picture. Like other cellulose nitrates it is combustible and must be kept away from fire. To reduce the danger, films for home projectors are usually made of the more expensive, but incombustible, cellulose acetate. Thin sheets of cellulose acetate or of a newly developed vinyl acetate plastic are pressed between two sheets of plate glass to form safety glass. When such glass is shattered by a blow, the glass sticks to the binding material instead of breaking out in sharp, jagged pieces.

Synthetic silk, or rayon, is made by several methods. In one process pyroxylin solution is forced through fine openings and the emerging threads are "denitrated" in a chemical bath. They have a more brilliant luster than natural silk; they will dye readily; and the denitrification greatly reduces their combustibility. The other types of rayon will be considered in Chap. 30.

## THE OUTLAW PROGENY OF NITROGEN

The hexanitrate of cellulose is used under the name of gun cotton. In the open it burns actively but harmlessly. Set off by a detonating cap, it explodes violently. When gun cotton is treated with acetone and vaseline and allowed to dry, the product is smokeless powder. The guns of modern warfare are fired with this explosive.

Not all of the nitro-explosives are derived from cellulose. That sweet, thick liquid from the soap industry—*glycerine*—which is such a valuable auto radiator anti-freeze can also form valuable explosives. Nitric acid converts glycerine—$C_3H_5$-$(OH)_3$—into glycerine trinitrate, $C_3H_5(NO_3)_3$, commonly called nitroglycerine. This yellowish oil is a powerful explosive and dangerous to handle. Through an accident, its power has been harnessed.

In 1862 a young Swedish chemist, Alfred Nobel, was manufacturing this temperamental explosive. One day he noted that some of the liquid had run from a leaky can into the porous packing. The pasty mass proved to have explosive properties but was much safer to handle. Thereafter Nobel soaked up his nitroglycerine in sawdust mixed with saltpeter and molded it into sticks. The product he named *dynamite* (Fig. 175). In this form it may safely be handled by a trained person; it can even be thawed out by heat. Nobel amassed a large fortune from his explosive business and directed that, upon his death, his wealth should be used for the welfare of mankind. The Nobel Prizes, amounting to about forty thousand dollars each, are awarded annually by the Nobel Foundation to the person (or persons) who have contributed most notably to human advancement in the six fields: chemistry, physics, medicine, physiology, literature, and peace.

*E. I. du Pont de Nemours & Co., Inc.*

FIG. 175. Mixing House in a Dynamite Plant. Extreme precautions must be taken to insure cleanliness and absence of heat developed from friction or sparks in this room.

T.N.T. is almost a synonym for a smashing, shattering destruction. It stands for tri-nitro-toluene—an explosive produced by the nitration of toluene, a coal tar product.  It was a major explosive of the World War.

Phenol is commonly called carbolic acid.  It can be nitrated with nitric acid to produce tri-nitro-phenol, commonly called picric acid.  This brilliant yellow explosive found use in the World War, and the large stocks on hand after the war closed have been employed in blowing up stumps in the process of clearing land.

## MAN-MADE TORNADOES

After this study of explosives, the question might reasonably be asked: "Why do explosives have such powerful effects?" The answer is a very striking example of the force of moving molecules.  An explosive is a solid or a liquid.  In this state it occupies a small volume.  When the explosive is set off, it is converted into gases whose volume is hundreds and thousands of times as great as that of the original explosive.  These gases are formed suddenly and the surrounding materials, whatever they may be, must get out of the way and give them room.  If the explosion is in the air, the air is driven away forcefully and with tremendous velocity.  It is a small, but terribly forceful, tornado.  When the explosion occurs in a rock or stump or mass of earth, the solid material is shattered and driven out ahead of the expanding gas.  It is little wonder that explosives set things in motion—tremendously rapid motion.

## THE RARE ELEMENTS OF THE AIR

Before we close this discussion of the lazy element, nitrogen, we might well give some attention to its much lazier companions of the atmosphere: helium, neon, and argon.  These are the most inert, inactive elements known.  They will not even unite with another of their own kind to form a two-atom molecule, as do hydrogen, oxygen, nitrogen, and most gaseous elements. This indifference is due largely to the fact that they are the "bathing beauties" of the elements; they have a perfectly symmetrical shape or structure (p. 85).  For example, helium has two planetary electrons—just enough to complete its K shell. Neon contains ten planetary electrons—just enough to complete its K and L shells. And argon, with its eighteen planetary electrons, has its K, L, and M shells just complete.

Helium was first found in the sun (*helios*) and hence named helium. It is next to the lightest gas known and has 92 per cent of the lifting power of hydrogen, the lightest gas. The main world source is from the natural gas wells of western United States. Because of its lightness and its incombustibility, it is the ideal gas for filling dirigibles. Our ill-fated *Akron* and *Macon* were filled with it. If the mighty *Hindenberg* had carried helium instead of hydrogen, its explosion and burning would have been averted. Since helium would be a great asset in case of war, this country wisely refuses to sell large quantities of the gas abroad.

A helium-oxygen mixture is finding wide use for filling chambers in which workers must be submitted to high pressure. Air, as we have previously learned, consists of 21 per cent oxygen and 78 per cent nitrogen. A synthetic air, in which the nitrogen is replaced by helium, is fed at high pressure to deep sea divers. It greatly increases their efficiency and comfort and permits working at greater depths than is possible with ordinary air. A similar gas mixture is also utilized for high-altitude flying and in "decompression chambers." These chambers are compartments of progressively lower air pressures through which depth-pressure workers, such as those employed in underwater tunnel construction, must pass on their way to the surface. By the use of helium the time required to pass through the chambers is lowered and danger from the painful "bends" is eliminated.

A very recent development substitutes an oxygen-helium mixture for the oxygen tent in cases of severe respiratory trouble, such as acute asthma. The patient is first given a mixture of 20 per cent oxygen and 80 per cent helium through a special mask. The per cent of oxygen can then be gradually increased even up to 100 per cent—a proportion far greater than is possible in the oxygen tent.

Neon, obtained from liquid air, is best known to the public because of its brilliant red glow when subjected to an electric discharge. In practice, glass tubes are bent to form any desired lettering. The air is then pumped from them and replaced by neon under low pressure. When a small electric current is sent through the gas, it glows brightly. The various colors of neon signs are produced in different ways. Admixture of argon and neon changes the color. The color also depends upon the kind of glass used. Of late, the inside of the tube is charged with certain fluorescent powders such as salts of zinc, lead, cadmium, and tungsten, which affect the color.

Argon is used for filling electric light bulbs. A filament is more permanent if the bulb is filled with an inert gas than if it is evacuated. Nitrogen gas is often used, but argon, since it is more inert than nitrogen, is very satisfactory for gas-filled electric bulbs.

In marked contrast to the laziness and indifference of nitrogen and the rare gases of the air is the unusual activity of a group of elements called the halogens. These elements form a number of compounds which resemble those of nitrogen in the multitude of their uses for peace- and war-time purposes. The next chapter reveals to us the private life of the halogen family.

# CHAPTER 26

# THE HALOGENS.
# THE CLASSIFICATION OF
# THE ELEMENTS

## A CHEMICAL FAMILY

When a new baby is announced to the world, interested relatives and friends always ask the same two questions: "Is it a boy or a girl?" and "Whom does it look like?"  To the casual observer, it looks like every squinting, red-faced mite of humanity.  But in its eyes, ears, mouth, or nose some ultra-discerning friend sees a resemblance to parent or other close relative.

Among our chemical elements there are also striking resemblances.  Several groups of elements can be selected which show family relationships.  Very closely related, in the similarities of their properties, is a group of four elements called the *halogen family*.  They are *fluorine, chlorine, bromine,* and *iodine*.  They will all unite with the same element, say sodium, to form typical salts: sodium fluoride, sodium chloride, sodium bromide, and sodium iodide.  Hence they are called *halogens* or "salt formers."

## CHLORINE, THE BLEACHER AND STERILIZER

Best known of the family is chlorine, although, as a free element, it is seldom observed in daily life.  One of our most active elements, its restless, sociable disposition is utilized for the good of humanity in many ways.  Chlorine is especially partial to water, and when the two join they produce a very valuable substance called *hypochlorous* acid ($HClO$).  The

373

equation might be written: $H_2O + Cl_2 \rightarrow HCl + HClO$.   The hypochlorous acid takes the oxygen from the water, but does not retain it.   The oxygen on the instant of release is in an especially active condition, called the *nascent* state.   In this form, oxygen is an especially powerful oxidizing agent.   If a nascent oxygen atom, after it has been formed, meets a bacterium such as the typhoid bacillus, it oxidizes and kills the bacillus.   Nascent oxygen coming in contact with a dye oxidizes its molecules to new compounds which are colorless or of a paler color.   Chlorine, then, by indirectly freeing the oxygen from water can function as a bactericide and a bleacher.   As mentioned in Chap. 23, chlorine is pumped into public water supplies and into swimming pools to purify them.

Aside from its use as a free gas, it is usually handled in safe, convenient compounds.   When united with lye, it forms sodium hypochlorite ($NaClO$).   Under the name of Javelle water a solution of this substance is commonly used in the home for bleaching and sterilizing.   An especially pure, carefully prepared form of sodium hypochlorite was a godsend in the late war.   Many of the casualties of war result from blood poisoning which sets in from deep, jagged wounds which cannot be completely sterilized.   In an attempt to reduce such fatalities, Dakin, an English scientist, perfected a special formula for sodium hypochlorite and Dr. Alexis Carrel, of the Rockefeller Institute, adapted it to deep irrigation methods within wounds. As a result of the Dakin-Carrel method, ugly wounds responded to treatment, literally thousands of lives were saved, and untold suffering was alleviated.

Calcium hypochlorite ($CaClOCl$) is commonly called bleaching powder.   It results from the action of chlorine upon slaked lime.   In the presence of an acid it liberates chlorine and hypochlorous acid.   As a result it is widely used for bleaching purposes and to some extent for sterilizing water.

## USEFUL CHLORATES

The chlorine compounds second in interest only to the hypochlorites are the *chlorates*.   Whereas hypochlorites are formed by the interaction of chlorine and cold bases, chlorine and bases reacting at a high temperature produce chlorates. If chlorine is bubbled through a hot solution of sodium hydroxide, sodium chlorate forms and crystallizes out. This compound is a valuable weed killer, especially effective against the Canadian thistle. Potassium chlorate is used in medicine, but more extensively as an ingredient in match heads and fireworks. At high temperatures it decomposes to liberate quantities of oxygen, accelerating the burning process.

## CHLORINE FROM SALT

The chlorine of industry, as well as the products made from it, is obtained from the immense, widely scattered deposits of "common salt," sodium chloride (NaCl), which is one of the earliest known chemicals. Biblical allusions to it are frequent, ranging from Lot's unfortunate wife to the "salt that has lost its savor." Salt deposits were mostly the beds of ancient lakes and oceans. Rivers carried the salt from the land to the sea, and when the sea water evaporated, the dissolved solids were left behind. An excellent example of a salt bed in process of formation is Great Salt Lake in Utah. That steadily disappearing body of water carries over 20 per cent of salt. Its briny water is so dense that the bather cannot sink, but will float like a cork on its surface. Many deposits of salt have been covered with rock and earthy material; as a result deep mining processes must be employed. In some places, as in Germany, the salt is mined much like coal. The rooms and corridors so formed, with their glistening walls of salt crystals, have been used as meeting places, especially for political groups. Russian convicts have long been subjected to banishment to the dreaded salt mines of Siberia. Mining of the extensive salt deposits of New York and Michigan is accomplished by driving wells and pumping up brine. The derricks that dot the landscape suggest petroleum regions.

## CAPTURING CHLORINE

The recovery of chlorine from salt on a commercial scale is an electrolytic process. Row upon row of electrolytic cells are charged with brine (Fig. 176). They are so constructed that the products released at the electrodes do not mix, and the chlorine which appears at the anodes can be piped away to be compressed into strong steel cylinders. The by-products of the process are also valuable. Perhaps the best-known chlorine plant is at the government Edgewood Arsenal. This entire set

*Diamond Alkali Company.*

Fig. 176. Brine Cells. A view of part of the cell room of the Diamond Alkali Company in Painesville, Ohio. The cells are charged with brine and, upon electrolysis, yield chlorine and alkali. The former is conducted away in the pipes which are shown between each double row of cells.

of buildings was constructed in a phenomenally short time when the United States was frantically preparing for its part in the World War. For toxic gases and other "sinews of war" the country required chlorine, and this the Edgewood Arsenal was able to supply.

## FIGHTING WITH CHLORINE

Pure chlorine was actually the first toxic gas to be used in the World War. Because of its high density—two and one-half times as heavy as air—it could be swept along close to the ground by a gentle wind.  The effect of inhaling chlorine is to sear terribly and to inflame the delicate membranes of the lungs.  But, as a toxic war gas it is not entirely suitable, and it gave way to other toxic gases—some of them chlorine compounds.  Mustard gas, which lurks long and unseen where it falls and frightfully burns the skin, is dichlor diethyl sulfide, $(C_2H_4Cl_2)_2S$.  It is the outstanding member of the *vesicants* or skin irritators.  Chloracetophenone and bromacetone are *lachrimators*—toxic gases which cause severe weeping and eye pains.  Among the chlorine compounds which produce violent sneezing and coughing—*sternutators*—is diphenyl-chlorarsine.  Lung injurers include carbonyl chloride or phosgene and chloropicrin.

## CHLORINE JOINS MARSH GAS

An interesting series of chlorine compounds may be considered as derivatives of methane or marsh gas—that important organic compound described in Chap. 30.  Methane has the formula $CH_4$.  If we substitute one chlorine atom in the formula, the resulting substance is $CH_3Cl$ or methyl chloride.  This chemical is used in some of the mechanical refrigerators.  The substitution of three chlorine atoms gives $CHCl_3$, or chloroform—the well-known anesthetic.  Complete substitution of chlorine for hydrogen yields liquid $CCl_4$, called *carbon tetrachloride*.  A solvent of fats, it is used as a dry cleaner to remove greasy stains from clothing.  It is also widely used as a fire extinguisher; when sprayed on a fire, it forms a heavy gas that blankets the fire and keeps the air from it.  These three compounds are formed indirectly and not by the actual action of the chlorine upon methane.

## ANOTHER IRREPRESSIBLE—BROMINE

A second member of this irrepressible halogen family is even more dangerous to handle, though actually less active, than chlorine.  It is the highly corrosive, reddish-brown liquid, bromine (Br).  Sodium, potassium, and magnesium bromides are found mixed with sodium chloride in salt deposits, and are also present in sea water.   Thousands of tons of this element are annually recovered from sea water, and a considerable quantity is obtained from the brine out of which salt has been taken. Three methods are available for liberating bromine.   They are electrolysis, displacement, and oxidation.   Since these methods are typical, they will be presented here, at least for reference.

*Electrolysis:* The solution containing the bromides is placed in electrolytic cells.   When a current is passed through the solution, bromine is released at the anodes and can be collected.   At the cathodes a hydroxide and hydrogen, both useful by-products, are formed.

*Displacement:* When a bromide solution is sprayed into the top of tanks, it comes in contact with chlorine gas injected at the bottom.   The chlorine is more active than the bromine and displaces the latter, according to this typical action: $2KBr + Cl_2 \rightarrow 2KCl + Br_2$.   The freed bromine is then recovered.

*Oxidation:* Since the oxidation process for the small-scale laboratory preparation of the halogens is most commonly encountered in the preparation of chlorine, we shall again refer to this element briefly.   For the substance to be oxidized we select hydrochloric acid (HCl), one of the best-known acids of commerce.   In the impure form it is called *muriatic acid* and is shipped in very large, enclosed glass bottles called *carboys*. These carboys are familiar sights in plants which are concerned with galvanizing, making dyes and drugs, corn sugar products, glues, textiles, and so forth.   Of the many oxidizing agents used for the liberation of the chlorine, manganese dioxide ($MnO_2$) is most frequently employed.   The reaction proceeds as follows: $MnO_2 + 4HCl \rightarrow Cl_2 + MnCl_2 + 2H_2O$.

The oxidation process of producing bromine (and also iodine) is identical with this, with one exception.   It would seem that we might oxidize hydrobromic acid directly.   The difficulty is that hydrobromic acid is so unstable that it cannot be kept as a laboratory chemical.   It decomposes.   Hence it is necessary to mix the oxidizing agent ($MnO_2$) not with hydrobromic acid itself, but with a pair of chemicals which can produce hydrobromic acid.   Such a convenient pair is potassium bromide (KBr) and sulfuric acid ($H_2SO_4$).   The oxidation process for preparing bromine consists, therefore, of mixing together in the right proportions manganese dioxide, sulfuric acid, and a bromide.   Upon heating, bromine is liberated.   An equation is given, for reference:  $MnO_2 + 3H_2SO_4 + 2KBr \rightarrow Br_2 + 2KHSO_4 + MnSO_4 + 2H_2O$.

If, in such a reaction, sodium chloride or sodium iodide were to be substituted for the potassium bromide, the main products would be chlorine and iodine, respectively.

## BROMINE BECOMES RESPECTABLE

As a free element bromine finds little use except in manufacturing dyes.   Some of its compounds are useful.   "Ethyl fluid" is added to ordinary gasoline to reduce the knock in high-compression automobile engines.   The "ethyl" part of this preparation is "tetra ethyl lead"—$Pb(C_2H_5)_4$.   When the spark plug explodes the gasoline-air mixture, the lead molecules are freed and, for some reason not thoroughly understood, modify the explosion to reduce the slap on the bottom of the pistons.   In order that the liberated lead shall not remain in the cylinders and cause trouble, *ethylene bromide* is added to the "ethyl fluid," and it probably forms lead bromide which is swept out through the exhaust.

The doctor's medical kit contains sodium bromide tablets. If a patient is jittery and excitable, the physician prescribes these tablets, which act as a sedative—a quieter.   Easy-going, unexcitable people are described as being of a "bromidic" temperament.

## TAKING PICTURES

Silver bromide is an important part of photographic films, plates, and paper.   It is mixed with the gelatine emulsion which is spread upon celluloid or glass.   When a film or plate is exposed to the light entering through the lens, the silver bromide is changed wherever the light strikes it.   The effect upon the film is not visible.   It is called a *latent image*.   Suppose that a white cross on a black card is being photographed. The film receives much light reflected from the white cross, but very little from the dark card. The latent image on the film is, of course, not visible, but that part of the silver bromide which was in line with the white light has really been reduced to a sub-bromide. Then the film is placed in a reducing solution called a "developer." Wherever a sub-bromide was formed (corresponding to the white cross), the developer reduces this to black, metallic silver. The amount of silver formed is proportional to the amount of light which struck it. Hence the dark parts of

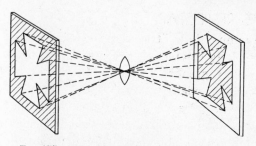

FIG. 177.    Photographic Negative and Positive.    The object—a white cross on a dark card—is represented at the left, with the rays of light from its surface being focused by the lens upon a photographic plate, to produce the negative when developed.    At the right is the positive print.

the film correspond to the light parts of the object and the light, unchanged silver bromide on the film corresponds to the dark part of the object (the card, in this case). For this reason, the developed film is called a *negative*. Finally the unchanged silver bromide is dissolved from the negative with sodium thiosulfate—also called sodium hyposulfite or "hypo" or "fixing bath."

In making a print, the light-sensitive paper, carrying silver bromide, is pressed tightly against the negative and exposed to light. The dark part of the negative, which corresponded to the light part of the object, will not allow light to strike the paper. Those parts of the print, therefore, appear light. Likewise, the light transparent parts of the negative, corresponding to the black card, allow light to shine through and strike the paper. Hence those portions of the paper appear dark.  Considered in order, then, the card was "positive," the film a "negative," and the print is a "positive," corresponding in shades to the original object (Fig. 177).  There are, of

*D. Appleton-Century Company.*

Fig. 178.   The First Human Portrait.   Artotype copy of the earliest sunlight picture of a human face.   It was taken in 1840 of Miss Dorothy Catherine Draper by her brother, Professor John William Draper of the University of the City of New York (now New York University).

course, many modifications in photographic technique, but the essential processes are as described.  If the reader will draw simple sketches to illustrate the steps here depicted, this apparently complicated process will appear quite simple.

## THE CONSERVATIVE MEMBER

"Like a violet" is the attractive, literal meaning of the name of the third of the halogen sisters—iodine. Formed of dense, flat, steel-gray crystals at ordinary temperatures, this halogen actually does become a gorgeous violet-colored gas at higher temperatures. Dissolved in alcohol, it is the well-known tincture of iodine. Athletes appreciate the value of the tinc-

*American Potash Institute, Inc.*

Fig. 179. Loaded Kelp Harvester. During the World War the United States was forced to obtain part of its iodine supply from the giant kelp beds off the California coast. The elevator shown in the foreground, equipped with an endless apron and with knives at its lower end, was lowered and forced through the beds. This particular harvester was christened the *Joseph Priestley* by Dr. J. W. Turrentine, then in charge of the Government's Demonstrational Kelp Products Plant at Summerland, California.

ture as a counterirritant to reduce swellings. It is also the very best antiseptic for cuts and open wounds and should be in every home medicine kit.

A loyal member of the family, iodine is found with chlorine and bromine. A giant seaweed, called kelp, has a great fondness for the sodium iodide of sea water. If these great weeds are cut, dried, and incinerated, iodine can be extracted from the ashes (Fig. 179). Much of the world's supply in peace time is obtained from saltpeter or sodium nitrate ($NaNO_3$), which contains as an impurity sodium iodate ($NaIO_3$). The free element is recovered by methods similar to those for bromine.

A few compounds of iodine are of general interest. Silver iodide, a light-sensitive substance, is usually present with silver bromide on the photographic film. Iodoform ($CHI_3$) is an antiseptic and possesses a very typical odor. Sodium iodide and certain organic compounds of the element are used as a cure and preventive of the ordinary endemic or adolescent goiter. The thyroid gland secretes an essential, iodine-containing hormone, called *thyroxin*. In certain regions of the United States the soil, and hence the water and the crops, are deficient in iodine. Deprived of its iodine supply, the thyroid gland develops into a goiter, often visible as an enlargement. Since the gland is intimately related to sex functioning, a goiter is most apt to develop at the adolescent period and is more prevalent among girls. Iodine compounds, *prescribed by a doctor*, usually cure such goiters if taken in time. Administration of iodine compounds under a doctor's prescription just before and during the adolescent period will prevent goiter. A better prophylactic treatment arises from the fact that if the expectant mother receives plenty of iodine in her diet, her child will not develop a goiter. It should be noted that other types of goiter, such as toxic goiter, are caused by over-secretion of the hormone. To such types iodine is like gasoline on a smoldering fire. For hypothyroidism, then, iodine is the treatment; for hyperthyroidism the surgeon's knife is the usual solution.

## NOTORIOUS FLUORINE

The least-known halogen is fluorine—a pale-yellow gas. It is the most active member. Like the proverbial "universal solvent," almost nothing will hold it. When placed in any ordinary container, even glass, it attacks and combines with it. Three of its compounds will be referred to. Calcium fluoride, called *fluorspar*, is a beautiful green crystalline substance of common occurrence, which is used as a flux in the iron industry. Its formula is $CaF_2$. Hydrofluoric acid ($H_2F_2$), derived from fluorspar, acts upon glass. If a smooth piece of glass is held in the gas or is painted with the acid, it is roughened or etched according to the following typical equation: $CaSiO_3 + 3H_2F_2 \rightarrow$

$CaF_2 + SiF_4 + 3H_2O$. Thermometers can be marked by coating them with a wax which is not affected by hydrofluoric acid, then scratching through the wax to expose the glass for each mark, and finally covering with the acid. Wherever the glass was exposed, an etched mark will appear.

Certain localities in the United States have reported cases of "mottled teeth" in some of its young people. The dental enamel has formed imperfectly and appears spotted. The difficulty has been traced to excessive amounts of fluorides in the drinking water. If this water is used during the growth of the teeth, mottling may result, but if used by adults, no harm follows. Certain localities have been obliged to install expensive processes for treating the water to remove or reduce its fluoride content.

## THE CLASSIFICATION OF THE ELEMENTS

The existence of several families of elements, in which the members of any given family have similar properties, raises an important problem. Are there any similarities running through *all* of the elements? Is it possible to interrelate the elements, to classify them, to construct a sort of family tree?

An examination of the atomic structure of the elements (Chap. 7) suggests a relationship. They are all composed of the same ultimate "building stones." All have a nucleus surrounded by planetary electrons. The atom of each element, as we ascend in atomic weights, has one more planetary electron than its next lighter neighbor. These and other facts, derived from recent researches, point definitely toward a family tree for all of the elements.

The history of this problem of similarities among the elements began long before scientists had any true conception of atomic structure. It really started with the observation that there are small family groups within the list of elements.

## THE EARLY TRIADS

Over a century ago, Doebereiner made an interesting observation, referred to now as Doebereiner's Triads. Among the elements are several families of three in which the "middle" element has an atomic weight which is approximately the average of the heaviest and lightest elements.  For example:

|  | Chlorine | Iodine | Bromine |
|---|---|---|---|
| Actual Atomic Wt. | 35.457 | 126.92 | 79.916 |
| Computed Atomic Wt. | | $(35.457 + 126.92) \div 2 = 81.188$ | |

|  | Lithium | Potassium | Sodium |
|---|---|---|---|
| Actual Atomic Wt. | 6.94 | 39.096 | 22.997 |
| Computed Atomic Wt. | | $(6.94 + 39.096) \div 2 = 23.018$ | |

Since several sets of triads displayed this striking result, it could hardly be a random coincidence.

## "NEWLANDS' FOLLY"

About 1864 an English scientist, Newlands, arranged the elements in a long row in the regular order of increasing atomic weights, starting with lithium (hydrogen would not fit in). The rare gases of the atmosphere,—helium, neon, and so forth— were unknown, and so were not included.  With the elements so arranged, he noted that many of them were similar to the eighth element preceding and following, and to multiples of the eighth.  Let us examine the first 21 elements in such a series.

Starting with number 8, sodium, and counting back eight, we reach the number 1, lithium; or counting forward eight, we stop at 15, potassium. Now lithium, sodium, and potassium are actually a closely related family of elements. Again, starting with number 7, the halogen, fluorine, and counting forward eight, we encounter number 14 or chlorine—also a halogen.  The next count of eight would bring us to number 21, manganese.

| Number | Element | Approximate Atomic Wt. |
|---|---|---|
| 1 | Li | 7 |
| 2 | Be | 9 |
| 3 | B | 11 |
| 4 | C | 12 |
| 5 | N | 14 |
| 6 | O | 16 |
| 7 | F | 19 |
| 8 | Na | 23 |
| 9 | Mg | 24 |
| 10 | Al | 27 |
| 11 | Si | 28 |
| 12 | P | 31 |
| 13 | S | 32 |
| 14 | Cl | 35 |
| 15 | K | 39 |
| 16 | Ca | 40 |
| 17 | Sc | 45 |
| 18 | Ti | 48 |
| 19 | V | 51 |
| 20 | Cr | 52 |
| 21 | Mn | 55 |

This element only slightly

# Table 6
## PERIODIC TABLE OF THE ELEMENTS

| Group / Series | 0 | I | II | III | IV | V | VI | VII | VIII |
|---|---|---|---|---|---|---|---|---|---|
| 1 | He (2) 4.003 | H (1) 1.008 | | | | | | | |
| 2 | Ne (10) 20.18 | Li (3) 6.94 | Be (4) 9.02 | B (5) 10.82 | C (6) 12 | N (7) 14 | O (8) 16 | F (9) 19 | |
| 3 | A (18) 39.94 | Na (11) 23 | Mg (12) 24.32 | Al (13) 26.97 | Si (14) 28.06 | P (15) 31.02 | S (16) 32.06 | Cl (17) 35.46 | |
| 4 A | | K (19) 39.10 | Ca (20) 40.08 | Sc (21) 45.10 | Ti (22) 47.90 | V (23) 50.95 | Cr (24) 52.01 | Mn (25) 54.93 | Fe (26) 55.84, Co (27) 58.94, Ni (28) 58.69 |
| 4 B | Kr (36) 83.7 | Cu (29) 63.57 | Zn (30) 65.38 | Ga (31) 69.72 | Ge (32) 72.6 | As (33) 74.93 | Se (34) 79.2 | Br (35) 79.92 | |
| 5 A | | Rb (37) 85.44 | Sr (38) 87.63 | Y (39) 88.92 | Zr (40) 91.22 | Cb (41) 93.3 | Mo (42) 96.0 | Ma (43) ? | Ru (44) 101.7, Rh (45) 102.91, Pd (46) 106.7 |
| 5 B | Xe (54) 131.3 | Ag (47) 107.88 | Cd (48) 112.41 | In (49) 114.8 | Sn (50) 118.7 | Sb (51) 121.76 | Te (52) 127.5 | I (53) 126.9 | |
| 6 A | | Cs (55) 132.8 | Ba (56) 137.36 | Rare Earths 57–71 | Hf (72) 178.6 | Ta (73) 181.4 | W (74) 184 | Re (75) 186.3 | Os (76) 190.8, Ir (77) 193.1, Pt (78) 195.23 |
| 6 B | Rn (86) 222 | Au (79) 197.2 | Hg (80) 200.6 | Tl (81) 204.4 | Pb (82) 207.22 | Bi (83) 209.00 | Po (84) 210 | (85) ? Ala-bamine | |
| 7 | | (87) ? Virginium | Ra (88) 226 | Ac (89) 226 | Th (90) 232.15 | Pa (91) 234 | U (92) 238.17 | | |

Rare Earths:

| | | | | | | | |
|---|---|---|---|---|---|---|---|
| La (57) 138.9 | Ce (58) 140.1 | Pr (59) 140.9 | Nd (60) 144.27 | Il (61) ? | Sm (62) 150.43 | Eu (63) 152 | |
| Gd (64) 157.26 | Tb (65) 159.2 | Dy (66) 162.52 | Ho (67) 163.4 | Er (68) 167.7 | Tm (69) 169.4 | Yb (70) 173.6 | Lu (71) 175 |

resembles the halogens, but there are some similarities. Newlands' idea, now referred to as the Law of Octaves, was ridiculed
by many of his fellow scientists, one suggesting that he might
discover other valuable facts if he would arrange the elements
alphabetically.

## A CORNERSTONE OF SCIENCE

Newlands' proposal received more serious attention in certain
quarters, especially from Lothar Meyer in Germany and D. I.
Mendeleeff in Russia. To the latter we are indebted for a
tabulation and an interpretation which have been called one of
the greatest formulations of science—namely, the Periodic
Classification of the Elements. So fundamental is this in
science, that it was selected as the central piece in the main
room of the key building of the Chicago Century of Progress—
that great exposition dedicated to Science.

In Newlands' list, if the row of elements 8 to 14 were placed
directly beside the row 1 to 7 and if the row 15 to 21 were likewise placed beside the other two rows, we would have similar
elements grouped on the same line. For example, lithium,
sodium, and potassium would be on the first line. Fluorine,
chlorine, and manganese would be on the seventh line.
Starting with the lightest element, hydrogen, and ending with
the heaviest element, uranium, Mendeleeff proceeded to arrange
all of the known elements in such a tabular form. This periodic classification is shown in Table 6. The elements discovered since Mendeleeff's time are indicated in lighter type.

So satisfactory is this classification of the elements that its
author was able to make certain predictions and formulate
generalizations which have been exactly verified by subsequent research. He summarized his ideas in the Periodic law,
which states that *the properties of the elements are periodic
functions of their atomic weights.*

## FACTS ABOUT THE TABLE

The ramifications of this table are too numerous and technical
to warrant inclusion in this book. Suffice it to point out a few
of the most obvious facts:

1. The members of any given family of elements are found in the same column or "group."

2. The elements in each horizontal row or "series" increase, from left to right, in atomic weights, with few exceptions.

3. In preparing the table, element 20, calcium, belonged in group II and automatically fell into that position. Titanium, now numbered 22, was next in atomic weight to calcium. That would place titanium in group III, next to calcium. But titanium resembled the elements of group IV. Hence Mendeleeff placed titanium in group IV and left a blank space between calcium and titanium. Following the same principle, blank spaces were left at several other places in the table. Mendeleeff next assumed that the blank spaces represented elements which had not yet been discovered and that they would possess properties which would be characteristic of the positions of the blanks. Hence he predicted that certain unknown elements must exist and he assigned them typical sets of properties. Subsequently those elements were discovered and their properties were found to coincide closely with the predicted properties. These discoveries were a great triumph for Mendeleeff's theoretical formulation and went far to establish its validity.

4. The rare elements of the air, later discovered, fitted into the table nicely by the addition of a zero group.

5. All of the table is filled now, with the possible exception of numbers 85 and 87, and claims have been made, yet to be substantiated, for their discovery.

6. We believe that only 92 elements naturally exist, because that number just completes the table.

7. Careful analysis of the table shows a progressive change, along the series or within the groups, in such properties as valence, activity, metallic and nonmetallic nature, density, atomic volume, spectra, and many others.

8. Group VIII consists of three triads which show close resemblance within the triad group but do not fit into successive groups.

9. The *rare earth* elements—numbers 57 to 71—likewise are interrelated but do not fit into the main table.

10. Three pairs of elements are inverted as to atomic weights. They are 18 and 19, 27 and 28, and 52 and 53.

11. Hydrogen must be placed by itself in series 1, group I.

12. The relationship can be shown by such devices as graphs and spirals as well as by the table.

13. The atomic structures show a definite periodicity throughout the table. Elements in any given group have closely related atomic structures.

14. The Periodic Table is the best classification device for the elements. It is one of the most fundamental conceptions in science and has greatly extended scientific frontiers.

An application of the periodic table is seen in the relationship of this chapter to the one which follows. The halogen family is found in group VII. Hence they exhibit similarities in properties. But they also show a progressive relationship to their neighbors, the elements of group VI. In comparison with group VI elements, they have a lower negative valence; are more active, more nonmetallic; and yield strong acids. The best-known elements of group VI are oxygen and sulfur. Having studied oxygen in Chap. 22, we now turn to sulfur in the next pages.

# CHAPTER 27

# SULFUR

## OLDER THAN HISTORY

The knowledge of sulfur antedates recorded history. It has been a curse and a blessing. According to early theology it formed the fiery lakes of Hell and, in more modern times, it was mixed with molasses and fed to protesting youth each spring by well-intentioned mothers. Of late, sulfur and its compounds have contributed notably to modern life, its necessities and its luxuries.

## OFFSPRING OF VOLCANOES

Man's search for sulfur and his ingenuity in wresting it from nature really parallel the development of his mechanical genius. In earliest times the crude material was probably utilized in the same form in which it was dug from the ground. Among the first countries which attempted to export the yellow substance was Sicily. Its sulfur, as well as that of certain other countries, was formed in its volcanoes. These phenomena of nature often generate immense quantities of the gases, hydrogen sulfide ($H_2S$) and sulfur dioxide ($SO_2$). It is probable that, within certain volcanoes over a long period of time, the hydrogen sulfide was reducing the sulfur dioxide, as follows: $2H_2S + SO_2 \rightarrow 3S + 2H_2O$. Gradually the sulfur built up huge deposits in the rocky interior of the volcano.

## THE RECOVERY OF SULFUR

In Sicily the sulfur and rock mixture was mined and thrown into huge piles. An opening was left at the base and this "fireplace" was ignited. The heat from the burning sulfur slowly melted the rest of the mass, and as the molten sulfur flowed away from its rocky impurities, it was collected and allowed to harden. The modern method is similar in principle but more refined in its details.

The United States has large supplies of sulfur underlying certain sections of Louisiana and Texas, derived possibly from gypsum (CaSO$_4$). It has been almost inaccessible, however, because it is overlaid with deep layers of quicksand, making ordinary mining operations impossible. A courageous, ingenious engineer, at about the turn of the century, overcame tremendous handicaps and braved the ridicule of his fellows to succeed finally in tapping these sulfur beds. Herman Frasch already had an enviable record in engineering when he undertook the expensive, discouraging, possibly unsuccessful job. Explained in brief, Frasch drilled down through overlying layers to the sulfur beds. Down through the drill hole he

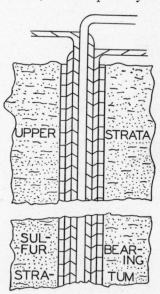

FIG. 180. Sulfur Well. The outermost pipe is a protective casing. Next is the superheated water pipe, inside of this the pipe through which the sulfur rises; the innermost pipe carries the compressed air.

forced four concentric pipes (Fig. 180), the largest serving merely as a casing to hold back the sand. Highly superheated steam was forced down the outer pipe until sufficient sulfur was melted. Next hot air was forced down the inner pipe and made the melted sulfur frothy and light. Air pressure could then force the liquid sulfur up through the center pipe. Perhaps no more significant and triumphant words have been spoken in modern engineering than the exclamation which burst forth when, after many discouragements, delays, and expensive trials, the engines and pump finally reached down for the prize and the pipe suddenly disgorged its golden stream. "She's pumping!" shouted the engineer at the top of his voice.

The molten material is pumped into temporary wooden bins, whose sides are built higher and higher as the sulfur level rises. When several hundred thousand tons have been collected, the wooden framework is removed from the immense block, and it

*Texas Gulf Sulphur Company.*

FIG. 181. Landscape in a Sulfur Field. Drilling for sulfur, as for petroleum, requires the construction of tall derricks to handle the drills. At a distance this view might easily be mistaken for an oil field.

is blasted out and loaded into railroad cars, as needed (Figs. 181 and 182). The Louisiana beds have become partially exhausted, and Texas now supplies the sulfur for home consumption and export.

## SULFUR REFINING

For greater purity, sulfur is boiled in a retort and the vapors forced into a large, bare room (Fig. 183). The vapor condenses on the walls to form tiny, flower-like tufts. The fine material is scraped off to become "flowers of sulfur." This form of sulfur finds uses where a powder is required, such as in insecticides.

*Texas Gulf Sulphur Company.*

FIG. 182.   Base of a Sulfur Derrick.   Note the pipes, with their connections, which penetrate the sulfur-bearing strata.

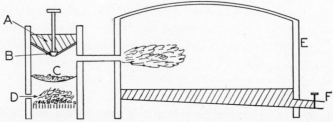

FIG. 183.   Sulfur Still.   Heat from the fire pot *D* boils the crude sulfur *C*. The vapors pass into the chamber *E*, condense on the walls, finally melt and collect as liquid sulfur on the floor.   This is drawn off at *F* and runs into molds. The process is made continuous by adding more crude sulfur, *A*, through an opening at *B*.

As the sulfur room heats, the vapors from the retort condense into a liquid.   Molten sulfur is then conducted into cylindrical-shaped forms, where it is allowed to cool and harden.   This product, called "roll" sulfur, finds wide use.   The finest and purest form is obtained by precipitating sulfur from solutions of its compounds.   It gives the liquid a milky appearance before it is filtered off.   Hence it is called "milk of sulfur" or "sulfur lac."   This fine, pure form is prescribed by physicians.

## ALLOTROPIC FORMS

Not only has sulfur three *manufactured* forms—roll, flowers, and milk, but it exhibits at least three "natural" forms.   At

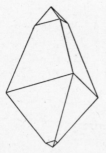

FIG. 184A.   A crystal of rhombic sulfur.

FIG. 184B.   Crystals of mono-clinic sulfur.

temperatures below 96° F. its crystals assume the *rhombic* shape; above 96° C. they become *monoclinic* (Fig. 184).   At high temperatures and when boiling sulfur is suddenly chilled, it shows a viscous, noncrystalline form and is called *amorphous* (without form) sulfur.   Any element which can exhibit different natural forms, as does sulfur, is said to show *allotropy* or to possess *allotropic forms.*

Of the sulfur consumed annually in the United States, running well over a million tons, about 70 per cent is used in the manufacture of sulfuric acid, about 18 per cent in the paper industry, and the other 12 per cent goes into the manufacture of rubber, explosives, insecticides, bleaches, and so forth.

# NOTORIOUS HYDROGEN SULFIDE

When the two odorless elements, sulfur and hydrogen, form a partnership, the product is one of the foulest-smelling gases, hydrogen sulfide ($H_2S$). This gas is largely responsible for the odor of rotten eggs and of some rotten vegetables. It is present in traces in the air and slowly acts upon unused silverware to produce a superficial coating of black silver sulfide, or silver tarnish. Sulfur compounds in an egg have the same effect upon silver table service.

# SULFUR DIOXIDE

The older methods of fumigation involved burning sulfur to produce the bactericide, sulfur dioxide: $S + O_2 \rightarrow SO_2$. This gas is formed during the burning of cheap coal. It irritates the nose and throat of a bystander when a coal-burning railroad engine passes by. It finds use as a mild bleach for straw, in the production of paper pulp, in certain mechanical refrigeration, and in the bleaching and preserving of food.

# INDISPENSABLE SULFURIC

"The barometer of business and civilization" is the appellation applied to a very important sulfur compound—sulfuric acid or "oil of vitriol" ($H_2SO_4$). This designation is literally true. Sulfuric acid enters into the manufacture, at some stage, of more of the comforts and conveniences of our modern civilization than does any other chemical. When this country was passing through its late depression, the production figures for the acid showed a very marked decline.

Two major methods are employed in the manufacture of sulfuric acid. The older is the "chamber" process. It consists, in effect, of forcing four substances—oxygen (as air), sulfur dioxide, steam, and a catalytic gas of formula $N_2O_3$—into immense chambers. The reaction may be expressed as: $O_2 + 2SO_2 + 2H_2O \rightarrow 2H_2SO_4$. The dilute "chamber" acid may be used as such or it may be concentrated by evaporating some of its water content. The newer "contact" process is similar except that it passes sulfur dioxide and oxygen (air) through large tanks which contain a hot catalyst, such as finely divided platinum (Fig. 186). The two unite to produce sulfur trioxide: $2SO_2 + O_2 \rightarrow 2SO_3$. The latter is then combined

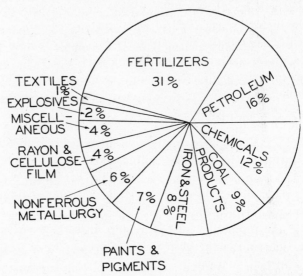

FERTILIZERS
31%

TEXTILES 1%
EXPLOSIVES 2%
MISCELL-ANEOUS 4%
RAYON & CELLULOSE FILM 4%
NONFERROUS METALLURGY 6%
PAINTS & PIGMENTS 7%
IRON & STEEL 8%
COAL PRODUCTS 9%
CHEMICALS 12%
PETROLEUM 16%

Fig. 185. Uses of Sulfuric Acid. The consumption of sulfuric acid by the various industries is shown by the segmented circle.

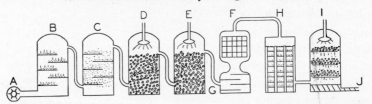

Fig. 186. Contact Sulfuric Plant. Sulfur is burned, or pyrite is roasted, in the sulfur burner $B$. The resulting sulfur dioxide, along with air, is forced by the blower $A$ through the dust chamber $C$ and the scrubber $D$ into the dry-ing chamber $E$, where it is sprayed with concentrated sulfuric acid. The gases then flow through the arsenic remover $G$ and the heater $F$ into the contact chamber $H$. Here the hot sulfur dioxide and oxygen gases unite under the influence of the catalyst to produce sulfur trioxide. In the absorption tower $I$ the sulfur trioxide meets a stray of concentrated sulfuric and combines with the water present in this acid spray to form sulfuric acid, which is drawn off at $J$.

with water to form sulfuric acid. The total consumption in the United States in 1938 amounted to about 6,760,000 tons.

The common concentrated acid is an almost colorless, oily liquid, nearly twice as heavy as water, containing about four per cent of water.   It is a strong acid, a good oxidizing, and a powerful dehydrating agent.   The latter term means that it has a great attraction for water.   When properly brought in contact with a moist gas, it will almost completely dry the gas. Dropped upon cellulose ($C_6H_{10}O_5$), such as wood, paper, or cotton, it will actually abstract the $H_2O$ and leave only black carbon behind.   This is the acid which makes holes in chemistry students' clothing, because it rapidly dehydrates the fabric and leaves only carbon (soot) along with some nitrogen gases if the fabric is wool or silk.

## SULFURIC AT WORK

But sulfuric acid is not designed for destructive uses. It has constructive work to do in a work-a-day world.   Let us follow it through a day's work.

(1) Petroleum furnishes us with clean, attractive-appearing products which supply our automobile fuels, lubricants, dry cleaners, oil-burner fuels, and the air-tight coating on glasses of jellies and jams.   But the crude petroleum contains dark, smeary, tarry substances which would ruin our engines or fabrics or jellies.   These are removed from the petroleum by agitating it with sulfuric acid and subsequently drawing off the layer of "acid sludge."   (2) Overcropped farm land finally issues the ultimatum; "Give me phosphorus, or I won't give you crops!"   The solution is phosphate fertilizer.   Now, calcium phosphate rock is abundant in certain states, but it is insoluble and the plant rootlets cannot absorb it.   If phosphate rock is treated with sulfuric acid, it changes into the soluble calcium acid phosphate—the fertilizer called "superphosphate," $Ca_3(PO_4)_2 + 2H_2SO_4 \rightarrow 2CaSO_4 + CaH_4(PO_4)_2$.   (3) As mentioned in Chap. 25, sulfuric acid is used to absorb the ammonia in the by-product coke process, producing ammonium sulfate. The resulting sulfate is used as a fertilizer and as a source of other ammonium compounds.   (4) The various explosives and pyroxylin products described in Chap. 25 require the presence of sulfuric acid in their manufacturing processes.   For example, the production of nitroglycerine may be expressed: $C_3H_5(OH)_3$

$+ 3HNO_3 \rightarrow C_3H_5(NO_3)_3 + 3H_2O$.   If the water formed in the reaction were allowed to accumulate, it would slow up and finally stop the action.   Sulfuric acid is added to the mixture and, because of its great attraction for water, unites with the water, removing it as an interfering factor.   The same principle applies to the other "nitro" products.   (5) The galvanized wash boiler, the enameled bath tub, and all other articles of iron or steel which are given a protective or beautifying coating need sulfuric acid. The iron base is first given a bath in sulfuric acid (is "pickled") to remove rust or other films.   If this were not done, the coating applied later would not stick but would crack, peel, and chip. (6) Many useful chemicals are made with sulfuric acid.   The ether of the operating room is made from the acid and grain alcohol.   Blue vitriol, alum, and other sulfates are derived from the acid.   (7) The "battery fluid" of the automobile is sulfuric acid, and the Babcock acid used in the butterfat test of all creameries is sulfuric acid of specific gravity 1.823.

The list of uses of sulfuric acid might be extended indefinitely.   Enough cases have been described to justify the statement that we meet the products of sulfuric acid at every turn. Deprivation of this acid would almost return us to the days of the sod house, the wooden plow, and the stone-age tools.

## THE HUMBLE MATCH

If this book had been written a few generations ago, it would have included a discussion of the use of free sulfur in the manufacture of matches.   The head of the earlier type of matches contained sulfur as the combustible substance.   Such matches often ignited with considerable violence and sprayed burning particles on surrounding objects.   Since a sulfur compound is now employed, it might still be relevant to discuss matches under the subject of "sulfur."

Many chemical principles enter into the manufacture of matches (Fig. 187).   Blocks of straight-grained wood are selected from which the match sticks are cut.   Each stick is mechanically inserted into a hole on an endless belt which will carry thousands of sticks.   An examination of the end of a match stick will usually show a one-eighth-inch circular impression where it was forced into the hole. The stick is dipped in a solution of ammonium phosphate—an antiglow. This solution insures that the spark will die immediately after the flame is extinguished. The striking end is next dipped in paraffin for a half inch or more. In lighting the match, the burning head ignites the paraffin which in turn ignites the wood. A careful inspection of a match stick next to the head, immediately after it is lighted, will show a film of melted paraffin.

From this point the treatment differs, because two types of matches are manufactured: the double-tipped, "strike any-

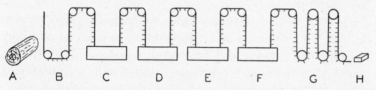

A    B    C    D    E    F    G    H

Fig. 187. Match Manufacture. This sketch illustrates diagrammatically the steps in the manufacture of double dip matches. A block of wood $A$ is cut into match sticks, which are then inserted, row upon row, into an endless traveling belt $B$. The sticks are treated with an antiglow in $C$, dipped in paraffin at $D$, tipped with the bulb in $E$, given the friction tip in $F$ and dried at $G$. Automatic packing in boxes is suggested at $H$.

where," and the safety match. The formulas for the match heads represent a tremendous amount of research. Problems arise as to oxidizing agents, combustible substances, binders, fillers, rate of burning, smoothness of ignition, resistance to moisture, response to friction, rate of drying, and flame temperature—just to mention a few.

The "strike anywhere" match has a double head. The main head or "bulb" must have a fairly high kindling point and the tip a lower kindling point. The match stick is first dipped into a paste which hardens to form the "bulb." This contains combustible materials such as rosin and sulfur, a supporter of combustion such as potassium chlorate, a filler and mild abrasive such as ground glass, and a combustible binder such as glue. This head has a high kindling point, as can be shown by carefully removing the striking tip of a double-tipped match and endeavoring to ignite the remaining head by friction. The main bulb is next dipped lightly into a paste which forms its striking tip. It differs in composition from the bulb by containing a large proportion of phosphorus sesquisulfide ($P_4S_3$), which has a low kindling point and is ignited by the heat of friction when the match is struck.

Some years ago white phosphorus was used in the bulb of the "strike anywhere" match. Constant contact with the fumes from the phosphorus produced a distressing and fatal jawbone disease among many of the factory workers. In 1912, Congress passed a law barring the manufacture and sale of white phosphorus matches. The phosphorus sesquisulfide has since been used.

The bulb of the safety match has too high a kindling point to be ignited by mere friction. In addition to a binder and filler, it contains a considerable amount of oxidizing agent and the combustible antimony trisulfide ($Sb_2S_3$), but no phosphorus compound. The striking surface of the box is coated with a mixture of the combustible red phosphorus, an abrasive of powdered glass, and glue. Upon scratching the head over this surface, a little of the phosphorus is ignited and communicates its heat to the bulb of the match, which then "lights."

From the burning glass, the flint, and the friction stick to the modern match and the automatic lighter is a long road marked with the most intensive research, with fortunes gained and lost, with disheartening discouragements, and finally with triumphant success. The history of firemakers typifies the evolution of science.

The chemical elements presented up to this point have been nonmetallic in character. They are found in the later groups of the periodic system. Of no less interest and importance are the metals—those elements located in groups I to IV and group VIII. To them we devote the next chapter.

# CHAPTER 28

# SOME COMMON METALS

## MAN AND HIS TOOLS

The historic ages of man are recorded in the tools which he fashions. A cave for protection, a club for defense, and raw food for diet satisfied primitive man. Later came the stone age, when man fashioned instruments of war and implements of agriculture from the rocks at hand. It is only since he has learned how to obtain and use metals and their alloys that man has been able to mold his environment to his needs and desires. The present age is, in very fact, the Age of Metals. It is only reasonable therefore that the well-informed person should have some acquaintance with these useful substances.

## WHAT IS A METAL?

If all of the known elements were on display and the task assigned of dividing them into metals and nonmetals, how should we proceed? Making use of their physical properties, we should segregate as metals those elements which possess certain typical characteristics. We shall examine a few typical metallic properties. (1) *Luster*. Most metals can be polished to a more or less bright surface, such as the yellow of gold, the bronze of copper, the white of silver, and the gray of lead. (2) *Malleability*. It is possible to roll or hammer metals, in varying degrees, into sheets. (3) *Ductility*. Just as a small boy's gum may stretch into a long thread, so metals exhibit the power to be drawn into wires. (4) *High density*. The unfamiliar metals, lithium, potassium, and sodium, will float on water.

The other metals, however, will sink in water because of their greater density. Magnesium and aluminum are approximately twice as heavy as water (see Table 7). They are called the "light" metals and are utilized in engineering where strength and lightness are a factor. Copper, iron, lead, gold, and nearly all other metals are several times as dense as water. (5) *Conductivity.* Metals exhibit marked, but varying, abilities to

*Carnegie-Illinois Steel Corporation.*

Fig. 187A.   An open-pit iron mine.

conduct heat and electricity. Aluminum and copper are especially noted for this property.

The physical criteria above listed will usually serve to identify a metal. In addition, an excellent chemical test was described in Chap. 23. The oxide of a metal will yield a base, whereas oxides of nonmetals form acids. Metals, then, are elements which yield hydroxides or bases. They appear in the early groups of the Periodic Table (see Chap. 26). They tend to lose electrons and become positively charged ions.

The metals are buried within the earth's crust.   Unless they have been exposed by weathering or other geological processes, they must be recovered by underground mining.   A few, such as gold, silver, and platinum, are recovered in the uncombined, or *native*, state.   But the larger group of metals occur in combination with nonmetallic elements.   The commonest compounds are the oxides, sulfides, and carbonates.   Sulfates, chlorides, and silicates are also quite abundant.

TABLE 7

DENSITIES OF SOME COMMON METALS

| Metal | Density gm/cc |
| --- | --- |
| Lithium | .53 |
| Potassium | 0.85 |
| Sodium | 0.95 |
| Magnesium | 1.7 |
| Aluminum | 2.7 |
| Iron | 7.8 |
| Copper | 8.8 |
| Silver | 10.4 |
| Lead | 11.3 |
| Mercury | 13.6 |
| Gold | 19.3 |
| Platinum | 21.3 |
| Osmium | 22.5 |

## METALLURGICAL PROCESSES

Metals which occur in the native state need only to be purified or *refined* to fit them for use.   Compounds of the metals, called *ores*, must first undergo treatments which will liberate the crude metal.   These processes, referred to as the *metallurgy* of the ore, will vary according to the nature of the ore.   If the ore is an oxide, it is subjected to *reduction*, in which case the metal is liberated and the reducing agent unites with the oxygen. By far the commonest reducing agent is carbon in the form of coal or coke.   Its application will be discussed under the smelting of iron.   Sulfide ores are usually subjected to a preliminary treatment called *roasting*.   The ore is heated intensely in contact with air, which brings about oxidation of the metal to the oxide and of the sulfur to sulfur dioxide.   The resulting oxide may then be reduced.   Reduction, roasting, and a third metallurgical process—electrolysis—are illustrated in the case of the zinc ore, sphalerite ($ZnS$).   A process long in use consists of first roasting the ore. $2ZnS + 3O_2 \rightarrow 2ZnO + 2SO_2$. Then it is reduced with coke. $ZnO + C \rightarrow Zn + CO$, and $ZnO + CO \rightarrow Zn + CO_2$.

By a newer process, the ore is converted into zinc sulfate with sulfuric acid and the zinc sulfate is electrolyzed, the zinc collecting upon the cathode.   Another important electrolytic process is employed in the recovery of aluminum from its fused ores.

Carbonate ores cannot be reduced until they have been converted into oxides by heating. For example, the zinc ore, smithsonite ($ZnCO_3$) is heated to form the oxide; then the latter is reduced. $ZnCO_3 \rightarrow ZnO + CO_2$. $2ZnO + C \rightarrow 2Zn + CO_2$.

Many other metallurgical processes are used, but the commonest are those described as roasting, heating, reduction, and electrolysis.

## METALS FOR CONSTRUCTION

*Iron.* Iron takes first place in the construction of buildings and machines. It is so interesting and useful a metal that we pause here and follow it from the mine to the kitchen stove and the razor blade. We start our trip in the Lake Superior region, where there are vast deposits of the oxide ore of iron, hematite. Here the ore is blasted and dug from the earth. From one open-pit mine enough ore has been dug to leave an immense

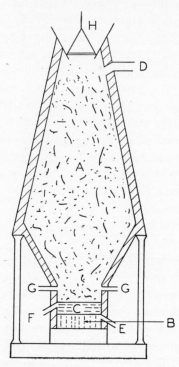

FIG. 188. Blast Furnace for Pig Iron. Ore, coke, and flux are charged in at *H* and the reduction process goes on in *A* as hot air is blown in at *G G*. The molten iron *B* is tapped off through *E* and the slag *C* is withdrawn at *F*. Gases escape through *D*.

pit over two miles long, nearly a mile wide, and 300 or 400 feet deep. The ore is shipped by rail to a lake port, say Duluth, and dumped directly into great ore boats, usually of 10,000 tons or more capacity. Hardly has the last car of ore been dumped than the boat noses out from the dock on its way to the great smelters, perhaps at Pittsburgh or Gary.   Arrived at its port, great power shovels make short work of unloading the cargo, which is soon to be "tried by fire" in the great blast furnaces.   These furnaces perform two major chemical processes—reduction of iron oxide to iron and removal of impurities. They are great steel structures, towering some 90 feet high, with a waist measure of 70 to 75 feet and each mothering a flock of four "stoves," for preheating air for the blast (Fig. 188). The charge, carried up elevators and dumped into the top of the furnace, is made up of ore, coke, and a flux, usually limestone.   Once started, the furnace is never stopped except for repairs.   The heat from the exothermic processes, augmented by a blast of hot air blown in from the bottom, brings about the chemical changes.   As the charge settles lower and lower, meeting higher and higher temperatures, the following typical reactions occur:

The ore may be reduced directly: (1) $Fe_2O_3 + 3C \rightarrow 2Fe + 3CO$.

The carbon monoxide from (1) reduces ore: (2) $Fe_2O_3 + 3CO \rightarrow 2Fe + 3CO_2$.

Coke may partially burn to form CO, which then functions as in (2), $2C + O_2 \rightarrow 2CO$.

The flux combines with impurities to form a liquid *slag*. Using sand and limestone to represent the impurity and flux, respectively, we may write: $SiO_2 + CaCO_3 \rightarrow CaSiO_3 + CO_2$.

The heavy, molten, impure iron settles to the bottom of the furnace.   Upon this floats the lighter, molten slag.   The iron is withdrawn from an outlet at the base; the slag is tapped off at a higher level; and the gases are withdrawn from the top of the furnace.   The latter are used to heat the "stoves."   The slag may be used in cement manufacture, for road construction, or it may be discarded.   The impure iron is called *pig iron* and contains undesirable impurities: silicon, carbon, phosphorus, sulfur, and manganese.   These must now be removed by transferring the pig iron to various types of furnaces where the impurities are burned out or are caused to combine with some added purifying agent.

Heated in a "cupola furnace" with scrap iron and coke, pig iron becomes *cast iron*. This form breaks readily and cannot be welded or forged, but it serves admirably for kitchen stoves, household radiators, and other purposes.

When cast iron mixed with the proper purifying agents is heated from above in a "puddling furnace," its impurities are

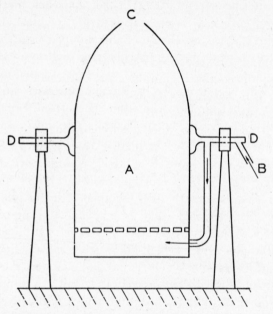

FIG. 189. Bessemer Converter. Molten pig iron, mixed with purifying agents, is charged into the converter $A$, which can be tipped on the trunions $D\ D$ in order to receive the charge and to discharge the steel. Hot air is blown in through $B$, and the exhaust gases escape at $C$.

burned out and a fairly pure form of iron called *wrought iron* is produced. Though not so strong as steel, it can be hammered into desired shapes and is suitable for chains, anchors, horse shoes, plows, and bolts.

Three important steel-making processes will be briefly described. Oldest of modern methods is the *Bessemer* process. A *Bessemer converter* is a great, pear-shaped furnace capable of holding about twenty tons of pig iron (Fig. 189). It is mounted on trunnions so that it can be tipped into a horizontal position to receive the molten charge. Hot air is blown upward through the mass, and, as the purification proceeds, flames of dazzling brilliance shoot toward the sky. After ten to twenty minutes the purification is complete. Necessary elements to give it the desired composition are then added and the product is *Bessemer steel*—of many uses.

In the open hearth process of steel manufacture, the charge is heated from above. A charge may be as much as 75 tons. Impurities are removed as gases and slag, and the result is an excellent grade of steel called *open hearth steel*. Bessemer steel can be produced more cheaply than open hearth steel, but the latter is of better quality and now represents about 80 per cent of the steel output.

Surgical instruments, tools, watch springs, and the like require a steel of such exact quality that a more easily controlled, small-scale process of steel manufacture must be employed. This is the crucible process. Small charges of Bessemer or open hearth steel together with purifying agents and necessary elements such as manganese, tungsten, chromium, and so forth are heated in smaller containers called *crucibles* to give a very high-grade steel called *crucible steel*.

The various uses to which the products of steel are now put impose upon it very exacting requirements. A surgical scalpel or a razor blade must take and hold a fine "edge." Tool

TABLE 8

COMPOSITION OF TYPICAL ALLOYS OF IRON

| Name | Composition |
|------|-------------|
| Allegheny Metal | Fe, Cr, Ni, Mn, Si |
| Duriron | Fe, Mn, Si, C |
| High Speed Steel | Fe, W, Cr, V |
| Magnet Steel | Fe, Co, W, Cr |
| Molybdenum Iron | Fe, Cu, Mo |
| Nickel Steel | Fe, Ni |
| Stainless Steel | Fe, Cr, Mn |
| Steel | Fe, C |
| Tungsten Steel | Fe, W |

steel must be very hard.   A steel kitchen article must not rust
or discolor.   An automobile drive shaft must withstand tremendous strains.   Armor plate must resist the terrific impact of
enemy shells.   Cigar and gas lighters must emit sparks under
friction.   Typical alloys of iron which meet these requirements
are listed in Table 8.

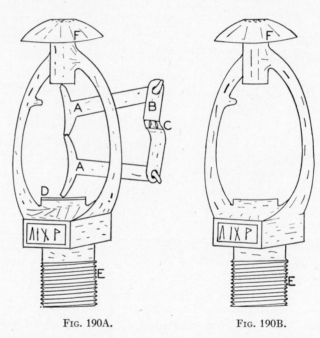

FIG. 190A.                    FIG. 190B.

FIG. 190.   A. An assembled sprinkler head.   The sprinkler head is screwed into
the water pipe at $E$.   When the heat from the fire warms the sprinkler to a pre-
determined temperature, the low-melting alloy $C$ melts, allowing the yoke $B$ to
separate.   The springs $A$ $A$ fly apart, and the water forces off the plug $D$.   The
stream of water strikes the cap $F$, throwing a circular spray downward upon the
fire.   B. Sprinkler head in operation.

Alloys, in general, are mixtures, or indefinite compounds of
two or more metals.   The ferrous alloys—alloys containing
iron—are very numerous and increasing in number yearly.
Of no small extent, also, is the field of "nonferrous" alloys,
some of which will be referred to in the discussion of copper and
aluminum.   A few will be mentioned here.

Automatic sprinkler systems consist of water pipes placed in or near the ceiling with sprinkler outlets at regular intervals (Fig. 190). The openings of these outlets are plugged with a low-melting-point alloy. Such an alloy is Wood's metal, composed of bismuth, lead, tin, and cadmium. If a fire starts in a room so equipped, the heated air rises and melts the alloy plug, permitting the water to spray upon the fire.

The alloy from which type is cast is composed of lead, antimony, and tin. Ordinary solder is an alloy of lead and tin. Lead shot is alloyed with about one per cent of arsenic.

Iron for structural purposes is not alloyed to produce certain properties, but is often coated with a metal to add permanence or beauty. Galvanized articles have an iron base coated with zinc. The zinc is resistant to oxidation and protects the iron against rusting. "Tin" dishes are really iron dishes carrying a thin layer of tin to prevent rusting. Certain parts of automobiles carry an electroplating of chromium. This metal takes a high, silver-like polish which does not tarnish or scratch easily.

*Aluminum.* Another metal widely used for structural purposes is aluminum. It occurs widely, but until recently its metallurgy was very difficult, and aluminum articles were expensive. In 1886, Charles M. Hall, a recent graduate of Oberlin College, working with crude equipment in his home, succeeded in liberating aluminum by electrolizing bauxite ($Al_2O_3$) dissolved in molten cryolite (sodium aluminum fluoride—$Na_3AlF_6$). Present production of aluminum runs as high as 100,000 tons a year. Several outstanding properties account for the popularity of the metal. (1) Although it is an active metal, aluminum acquires a very thin, impervious coat of the oxide and thereafter is unaffected by the air. (2) It has high tensile strength and hence stands up under hard usage. (3) One of the lightest of the strong metals, it can be used where "lightness" is an important factor. (4) Aluminum is an excellent conductor of electricity and heat. This property makes it useful in the electrical industry and for cooking dishes. (5) Its silvery color gives a pleasing appearance to dishes and to aluminum-painted articles.

The unalloyed metal is used in cooking utensils, as a wrapping for food products, in electrical conductors, and as the "body" of aluminum paint. At least two of its alloys find application in transportation. Magnalium (a magnesium-aluminum alloy) and duralumin (an aluminum alloy containing copper) are used in the framework of dirigibles, high-speed trains, and automobile parts.

*Copper.* The third metal which we shall consider under "metals for construction" is copper. Unlike iron and alumi-

TABLE 9

THE ACTIVITY SERIES OF METALS

| | | | |
|---|---|---|---|
| 1. Potassium | 5. Aluminum | 9. Tin | 13. Mercury |
| 2. Sodium | 6. Zinc | 10. Lead | 14. Silver |
| 3. Calcium | 7. Iron | 11. Hydrogen | 15. Platinum |
| 4. Magnesium | 8. Nickel | 12. Copper | 16. Gold |

num, it is an inactive metal and is found in the native state, as well as in combination (Table 9). Table 9 arranges the metals in the order of their decreasing activity. Any metal can displace from combination those standing after it. Those metals standing before hydrogen can displace it from an acid. The most important deposits of native copper are found in northern Michigan. Its sulfide ores are mined in the Rocky Mountain region. One stage in the metallurgy of the ores makes use of a modern process, called *flotation*—separating the valuable ore from the earthy material. The crushed mass is mixed with water containing about one per cent of a special oil, such as pine oil, and the whole is vigorously churned with air. A surface froth is formed which selectively adsorbs the heavy ore and allows the lighter impurities to settle to the bottom. The froth carrying the ore is mechanically skimmed off and its ore content recovered. This *concentration* process makes it possible to work many low-grade ores—not copper only—and still realize a profit.

Copper for electrical conductors must be very pure. In the electrolytic refining process, the blocks of impure copper are made the anode; the cathode is a thin sheet of pure copper; and the "bath" is sulfuric acid. During electrolysis, the pure copper separates from the anode and deposits upon the cathode (Fig. 191). The impurities settle beneath the anode as a "sludge."

Copper is a typical metal. It is placed in group I of the periodic Table. It has a red-brown color, is very malleable and ductile, an excellent conductor of electricity. Its alloys are

*Ontario Refining Company, Limited.*

FIG. 191. Tank House for Copper Refining. The illustration shows countless rows of alternating plates of impure and pure copper, supported vertically and dipping into the electrolyte bath. When the process is complete, the sheets are lifted out vertically, as shown in right foreground, for replacement.

numerous and important. Copper salts, when dissolved in water, yield blue cupric ions.

The chief use of the pure metal (over 99.9% pure) is to make the wires which carry the electricity for our lighting and heating, for our telephone and telegraph messages, and which constitute the coils for the armatures of dynamos and motors.

The manufacture of alloys consumes the largest share of our copper output. The five-cent piece, or nickel, is an alloy of 75% copper and 25% nickel, and silver coins are 90% silver and 10% copper.   Gold jewelry is an alloy of copper and gold, as will be described later, and silver jewelry is 80% silver and 20% copper.   The various bronzes are copper-containing alloys.   For example, medal bronze is composed of copper, tin, and zinc.   Red brass is 85% copper and 15% zinc.   An alloy of copper, zinc, and nickel is known as German silver.   The useful monel metal is copper, nickel, and iron.

Many compounds of copper are widely used.   Copper sulfate or blue vitriol ($CuSO_45H_2O$) is used in the preparation of *Bordeaux mixture* for spraying to combat certain fungi and insects.   Added to swimming pools, it kills the algae which often infest them.   A salt of copper with acetic and arsenous acids is known as Paris green.   This also is an insecticide. Copper salts are present in Fehling's solution and Benedict's solution, widely used in medicine to detect the urinary sugar characteristic of diabetes.

## METALS FOR ADORNMENT

*Gold.*   The metal of adornment, *par excellence*, is gold. Since it occurs almost universally in the native state and exhibits a shiny, yellow color, it has been known from the earliest times.   In its contribution to romance, to tragedy, to the covetousness and the passions of man it vies with the sparkling diamond.   The California gold rush of '49 grew out of the lure of gold.   The Alaskan Klondike was the scene of untold hard- ships and the source of many great fortunes; it gave the lie to "Seward's folly," as a result of which the United States had paid seven and a half million dollars for an apparently worthless Arctic waste.

The glittering grains and nuggets of *placer gold* (gold mixed with loose sand) can be recovered in the "pan" of the lone prospector or in the big sluices of hydraulic mining operations. In either case the gold-containing sands are treated with water which carries away the lighter particles of earth and sand and allows the heavy gold particles to settle to the bottom.   Gold has a specific gravity of 19.32.   The steadier stream of gold comes to the market from the great mining operations which recover it from solid veins of quartz. This quartz is dug by power machinery, pulverized in *stamp mills*, and the gold particles removed from the rock material in one of two ways. In the *amalgamation* process, the powdered material flows over copper plates carrying a surface alloy of the copper with mercury. The gold alloys with the mercury, and the rock material passes on. Next the gold amalgam is scraped from the plates and its gold content recovered. An alloy of any metal with mercury is an *amalgam*. The *cyanide* process of gold recovery makes use of the property of gold to combine with sodium cyanide and form a complex, soluble gold compound, from which the metal can be recovered. The process of analyzing a gold ore, or other precious metal ore, is called *assaying*.

Gold is the most malleable and ductile of all metals. A grain of the metal can be drawn into a wire many miles long; gold leaf can be rolled so thin as to require two and one-half million sheets, laid flat, to give a thickness of one inch. In this form it is used for the titles on book covers and to surface domes of public buildings. For many years its value was fixed by law at $20.67 per troy ounce and as such formed the basis of international credit. In January, 1934, the price was changed to $35 per troy ounce.

Because the pure metal is too soft for general use, it is hardened by alloying with copper. For such alloys the gold content is expressed in terms of the *carat*. Pure gold is twenty-four carats. American gold coins are 21.6 carats or 90% gold. About the highest gold content of jewelry is 18 carats, i.e., 18 parts gold and 6 parts copper. Fourteen carat gold is more commonly employed for jewelry. When the carat is only ten, the copper content is so high ($^{14}/_{24}$ copper) that such articles, when worn as a ring or necklace, are apt to form a green stain on the skin. The sodium chloride of perspiration produces green copper chloride. Gold-plated articles carry a layer of gold over a base metal. White gold is an alloy with nickel and zinc, and blue gold an alloy of gold with iron.

Because of its inertness gold is listed as a "noble metal." It will form a soluble compound with cyanides, as before mentioned, and it can be "dissolved" by a mixture of three parts hydrochloric acid and one part nitric acid. This acid mixture, which is a solvent of the "noble metals," gold and platinum, is fittingly called *aqua regia* or "royal water."

Other metals chosen for personal adornment because of their beauty and permanence are silver and platinum. The former occurs in the native state and must be refined before it is fabricated into jewelry or coins. For these purposes it is alloyed with copper. Sterling silver contains 90 per cent of the precious metal. Silver-plated articles are produced by electroplating silver on a base metal. Depending upon the thickness of the silver layer, such articles are designated as double, triple, or quadruple plate. The reflecting surface of many mirrors is silver.

Platinum is found as the native metal in Russia, Colombia, and South Africa. It is a white, inert metal of high specific gravity (21.45) and high melting point (1755° C.). In the spongy form it adsorbs gases strongly and is an excellent catalyst. It finds wide use for electrical contacts, for X-ray tubes, and in jewelry. Platinum apparatus is almost indispensable in the chemical laboratory.

Many other metals are known to the general public, at least by name. Radium, because of its peculiar property of spontaneous decomposition, is valuable in medicine where it is used to treat unhealthy tissue. Tungsten, vanadium, molybdenum, cobalt, nickel, manganese, and other metals produce valuable alloys. Mercury is employed in thermometers and in "make-and-break" electrical apparatus. Metals which, when first isolated, were merely scientific curiosities are gradually finding important fields of usefulness. In truth, we are just entering upon the "era of alloys."

# CHAPTER 29

# CARBON AND ITS COMPOUNDS

Every well-informed person should be conversant with the "life and work" of carbon and its compounds. They are often alluded to in business, in the club, and in the schoolroom; they are of vital interest to capital, to labor, and to the buying public. Wars have been fought for the lowly coal mine, and royal heads have been sacrificed for the priceless diamond.

Coal and diamonds, both, are carbon. The element, its oxides, carbonates, and related compounds will be discussed in this chapter. Its organic compounds will be considered in the next.

## "SPARKLERS"

Carbon, like sulfur, exhibits allotropy. It exists in the amorphous form and in two crystalline forms—graphite and diamond. Human emotions have long been linked with the diamond. It seals the love pact between a man and a maid. It becomes the heirloom from grandmother to mother to daughter. It is coveted, alike, by the thief, the socialite, and the monarch. Several factors contribute to its great value. (1) The hardest natural substance known, it will scratch and mar other substances but cannot be marred by them. The "scale of hardness" is a series of numbers from one to ten designating increasing hardness. Number one, the softest, is typified by talc, which can be easily scratched. Number ten is the diamond. (2) It is inert and is not affected by anything with which it comes in contact. (3) It has a high index of refraction.

When properly cut, it refracts light to give the brilliant sparkle and play of spectral colors which make it so beautiful. (4) It is relatively rare. Diamonds are placed on the market at such a rate that the law of supply and demand will maintain their price at a fairly uniform level, year after year.

Diamonds were formed by very slow crystallization of pure carbon at a high temperature and under tremendous pressure (Fig. 192). They are mainly found in the "pipes" of extinct volcanoes. Investigators, using the greatest forces known to science, have succeeded in producing only imperfect microscopic diamonds. For use as gems, the stone must be flawless, crystal

FIG. 192. The Cullinan Diamond. This diamond was found in the Premiere mine of South Africa in 1905. It was given to the King of England and later sent to Brussels for cutting. From it were obtained ninety-six small cut diamonds and nine large ones, the largest being set in the English scepter.

FIG. 193. A Cut Diamond. Diamonds are so cut that their faces will reflect and refract the maximum amount of light. The sketch illustrates one form of a cut diamond.

white, and "cut" with the greatest skill (Fig. 193). None but an expert can evaluate the gem. The unit of weight—and of value—of a diamond is the *carat*, which is two-tenths of a gram. The largest diamond ever discovered was the Cullinan. In the rough it weighed 3,032 carats, or 1.37 pounds. Impure, black diamonds, called *carbonados*, are useful for tipping drills employed in cutting very hard materials.

## GRAPHITE

The humble sister of the flashy diamond is graphite—a soft, black, shiny, oily-feeling material which is made up of tiny scales or plates. Although found in several natural deposits, it is also manufactured. In the Acheson process, hard coal is heated without air in electric furnaces and changed to a gas—a sublimation process.   Upon cooling, the gas crystallizes to form graphite.   It is more useful, though less expensive, than diamonds.   Mixed with very fine clay, it is the "lead" of our lead pencils.   In fact, the word "graphite" comes from the Greek word which means "to write."   The higher the proportion of graphite, the "softer" the lead and the blacker its mark. Cheap pencils usually contain more of the less-expensive clay and sometimes "scratch" because of its coarse, sand-like particles.   Because of its scaly, slippery nature, graphite is an excellent lubricant.   It is used where a fluid lubricating oil would be unsatisfactory, such as on bearings that are porous, that are subjected to high temperatures or are exposed to dust and sand.   Graphite is a conductor of electricity.   For this reason it is used to coat wax molds.   Then a metal is electro-deposited on the graphite; the graphite is removed from the metal surface; and a "positive" model of the mold results.   The plates in the electrotyping process of printing are so prepared. Graphite is also used for stove polish, for crucibles which are to be subjected to high temperatures, and for certain parts of electrical equipment.

## IMPRISONED POWER

Amorphous carbon, in its various guises, greets us frequently every day.   Shall we get acquainted with its several "aliases"?

Coal contains a high proportion of carbon compounds, but it is partly free carbon.   It is, as geology teaches, the buried residue of prehistoric plant life (Fig. 194).   Generally speaking, the better the grade of coal, the higher the per cent of free carbon. Coal ranges in quality upward from lignite and brown coal through subbituminous, bituminous (soft coal), and semi-anthracite to anthracite (hard coal).   Coal is purchased wholesale upon the findings of its analysis, which is expressed in terms of $a$. moisture, $b$. ash, $c$. volatile combustible matter—the smoke-producing ingredients, $d$. fixed carbon—the combustible mass that remains after the gases have burned off, $e$. sulfur—actually present as pyrite, $FeS_2$, and $f$. heat units.   The cheaper coals usually run high in *a*, *b*, *c*, and *e*.   Analyses of typical coals, expressed as percentages, are shown in Table 10.

### TABLE 10
#### COMPOSITION OF COALS

| | Mois-ture | Volatile Matter (Smoke Producer) | Fixed Carbon | Ash | Sulfur | Heat Units B.t.u. |
|---|---|---|---|---|---|---|
| Subbituminous | 13.03 | 36.29 | 40.06 | 10.62 | 1.53 | 9,616 |
| Bituminous | 6.69 | 33.55 | 47.94 | 5.25 | .96 | 12,110 |
| Semianthracite | 3.00 | 28.00 | 65.18 | 3.82 | .61 | 14,423 |
| Anthracite | 3.4 | 16.3 | 74.7 | 5.6 | .55 | 14,320 |

Heat units by analysis are hardly comparable to the heat units obtained in ordinary furnace firing.   The analysis measures maximum heat units, but in firing, much of the heat is lost

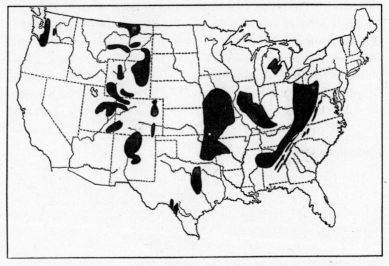

Fig. 194.   Locations of the coal deposits of the United States are shown by the shaded portions of the map.

up the chimney as smoke and partially burned gases.   In general, the cheap coals are not the most economical unless special furnace-stoking devices are employed.

## CHARCOAL

Several forms of charcoal are on the market.   They are made by heating wood (for wood charcoal) or nut shells and pits (for nut charcoal) or bones (for animal charcoal) out of contact with the air—a process called *destructive distillation*. Valuable by-products from the destructive distillation of wood include acetone, acetic acid, and wood (methyl) alcohol. Wood charcoal is employed in metallurgical processes, in black gunpowder, and as a clarifying and decolorizing agent for syrups and other fluids. Animal charcoal is especially effective as a decolorizing agent. Any highly porous substance, such as animal charcoal, has a tremendous internal surface. When a colored syrup filters through it, the myriads of tiny, colored particles cling to the surfaces of the pores and the liquid passes on devoid of color. This process in which particles or molecules cling to *surfaces* is called *adsorption* and was discussed in Chap. 9.

The phenomenon of adsorption is very strikingly exhibited in the application of nut and similar charcoals to gas masks. The canister of a gas mask is charged with various chemicals to remove toxic gases from inhaled air. One section of the canister contains "activated" charcoal. Polluted air drawn through this is partially purified because the molecules of the toxic gas are strongly *adsorbed* by the charcoal.

## SOOT

Natural gas and "sooty" oils are burned and their "smoke" collected to give us *lamp black* or *carbon black*. It is widely used in automobile tires to impart several desirable properties. It is the pigment of India ink, printers' ink, certain paints and polishes, and often of typewriter carbon paper and ribbons.

## THE CARBON ATOM

Carbon has an atomic weight of twelve and an atomic number of six. Its $L$ shell carries four electrons; hence it exhibits valences of both plus and minus four. It occurs in group IV, series 2 of the Periodic Table; hence it is more nonmetallic than metallic in nature. Although oxygen is the most commonly occurring element, carbon forms the largest number of compounds of any element—running well up into six figures.

## CARBON MONOXIDE

The two elements, carbon and oxygen, pair off in two different ways, to form the compounds, carbon monoxide and carbon dioxide.

*Carbon monoxide* results whenever carbon or its compounds burn but cannot obtain all the oxygen they need for a complete job. In the presence of sufficient oxygen (or air), *carbon dioxide* is formed. Typical equations would be *a.* $2C + O_2 \rightarrow 2CO$; *b.* $C + O_2 \rightarrow CO_2$.

It will be noted that the amount of oxygen in proportion to carbon is twice as great in equation *b* as in *a*. Carbon monoxide is formed in the automobile engine and ejected through the exhaust. Selecting octane, a gas of formula $C_8H_{18}$, as a typical ingredient of gasoline, we may write for its incomplete combustion: $2C_8H_{18} + 17O_2 \rightarrow 16CO + 18H_2O$. The gas is a valuable component of city gas (water gas), which is made by the action of steam upon hot coal: $H_2O + C \rightarrow H_2 + CO$.

Carbon monoxide is utilized mainly as a fuel and as a reducing agent. In the metallurgy of ores, it reduces oxide ores to free the metal. Iron ore is a case in point: $Fe_2O_3 + 3CO \rightarrow 2Fe + 3CO_2$. Useful as carbon monoxide may be in its proper sphere, it is fatal when it invades the human body. It passes from the lungs into the blood stream and unites with the hemoglobin, the colored molecules in the blood which transport oxygen. Destruction of the hemoglobin, if too extensive, produces death through lack of oxygen—a process called *asphyxiation*. Many preventable deaths are caused annually because the victims remain in a closed space where an automobile engine is running or where a defective coal stove or a gas stove is discharging carbon monoxide into the air.

## CARBON DIOXIDE

*Carbon dioxide*, the other oxide of carbon, has some properties in common with nitrogen. It is colorless and odorless, very inactive, will not burn or support combustion, and is removed from the air by plants. Since it is the normal result of the oxidation of carbon, it is produced in the respiration of plants

and animals, in combustion and decay.   It is also formed in
the alcoholic fermentation of sugar.   On the other hand, certain
natural processes are continually removing carbon dioxide from
the air.   Rain and surface waters dissolve it.   It is consumed in
weathering processes whereby rocks, such as the feldspars, are
changed into soil.   Immense quantities of carbon dioxide are
utilized in *photosynthesis*—the process whereby green vegeta-

Fig. 195.   Dry Ice as a Refrigerant.   Note the difference in the relative compactness and weight of dry ice and water ice for refrigeration.   Both containers
hold the same amount of ice cream.

tion, under the influence of light and the green chlorophyl, unites
(synthesizes) carbon dioxide and water to produce carbohydrates
(cellulose and starch).

A large proportion of the carbon dioxide used industrially is
obtained from the fermentation industries.   The most convenient small-scale laboratory method involves the interaction
of an acid with a carbonate.   For example, if some pieces of
limestone ($CaCO_3$) are covered with hydrochloric acid, carbon

dioxide is liberated, producing a frothing or bubbling (effervescence) as it escapes through the liquid: $CaCO_3 + 2HCl \rightarrow CO_2 + H_2O + CaCl_2$.

Certain subterranean processes have produced carbon dioxide which has been trapped in earth pockets. Almost pure gas has been obtained from such deposits.

A few of the properties of carbon dioxide render it very useful. (1) Its specific power to react with water, under proper conditions, to produce carbohydrates makes possible the formation of cellulose, starch, and sugar in plants. (2) Under sufficient pressure at low temperatures, the gas becomes a white mass of solid carbon dioxide, called "dry ice," whose temperature is 112° F. below zero. This solid passes into the gaseous state again without melting and in so doing absorbs a large amount of heat (Fig. 195). Hence "dry ice" is an effective cooling agent which produces no "mussy" liquid. It should not be handled directly with the hands *nor be placed in the mouth* because a severe freeze may be as harmful as a severe burn. (3) Since carbon dioxide will not support combustion and is quite heavy (one and one-half times as heavy as air) it serves as an excellent fire extinguisher. It rests like a blanket over the burning substance and so separates the supporter of combustion (air) from the combustible substance. The type of hand fire extinguisher which must be inverted utilizes this principle (Fig. 196). It contains a concentrated solution of a carbonate—baking soda, $NaHCO_3$—and an acid—sulfuric, the two being in separate compartments. Inversion of the extinguisher mixes the two; they react to liberate carbon dioxide; and the pressure developed forces the gas and liquid through the outlet hose upon the fire. The piston type of fire extinguisher sprays the fire

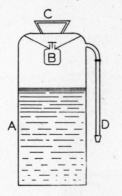

FIG. 196. Fire Extinguisher. The carbonate solution is shown at $A$, the bottle of acid at $B$, the carrying handle at $C$, and the hose outlet at $D$.

with liquid carbon tetrachloride, which vaporizes and blankets the burning material. (4) The pleasing taste and sensation of carbon dioxide is experienced in carbonated drinks and fermented liquors. Soda water contains carbon dioxide under pressure. The gas escapes with effervescence when the pressure is reduced at the spigot of the soda fountain or when the bottle cap is removed. (5) The cook and her hungry family are deeply indebted to carbon dioxide. Without it, the bill of fare would contain "unleavened" bread and pastry. Bread "rises" because enzymes in the yeast cause fermentation of the sugar in the dough, to produce carbon dioxide. Baking powders contain baking soda (sodium bicarbonate) and a dry acid (alum, or calcium acid phosphate, or cream of tartar). When water is added, the acid and carbonate release carbon dioxide. This gas, by whichever method formed, penetrates the dough, causing it to expand (rise), and fills it with tiny holes which remain when the mass is "set" by the oven heat. Technically, a "light" bread or pastry is one that has a low density because so much of its bulk is occupied with tiny air pockets. (6) We need only refer here to the role of dissolved carbon dioxide in underground waters by virtue of which the water brings minerals into solution and becomes "hard" (see Chap. 23).

## CARBONATES

The salts of carbon dioxide (or carbonic acid, $H_2CO_3$) are the carbonates and bicarbonates. Baking soda ($NaHCO_3$), also called sodium bicarbonate or saleratus, has been previously mentioned. It and table sugar are probably the purest chemicals on the kitchen shelves. Baking soda as a leavening agent is mixed with sour milk (containing lactic acid) or with cream of tartar, in the process of food preparation. Baking powder, the ready-mixed product, is more commonly employed. In either case, the addition of water causes the acid and carbonate to dissolve and ionize. Then the hydrogen ions from the acid and the bicarbonate ions from the soda unite to form carbonic acid. The latter decomposes immediately to liberate carbon dioxide:

$$H^+ + HCO_3^- \rightarrow H_2CO_3 \rightarrow CO_2 + H_2O.$$

Baking powders contain, in addition to soda and a dry acid, powdered starch to give bulk (a filler) and to absorb moisture (dryer). Many brands of baking powder contain a mixture of calcium acid phosphate and alum as the acids. At least one widely advertised brand uses cream of tartar and tartaric acid for the dry acids. The main consideration in the choice of a baking powder is personal preference and experience.

Other well-known carbonates include sodium carbonate, whose use in softening water was explained in Chap. 23, and calcium carbonate, which exists in such forms as limestone, Iceland spar, marble, shells (such as egg and clam), natural chalk, stalactites, pearls, and coral.

## GAS FOR THE HOME

Closely related to carbon and its oxides is the topic of domestic fuels. They will receive brief treatment at this point.

Homes are heated and meals are cooked with wood, coal, petroleum products, natural gas, or manufactured gas. The subject of coal has been discussed earlier in this chapter. At least five different fuels are obtained from petroleum. Liquid petroleum and natural gas are mixtures of hydrocarbons (compounds of hydrogen and carbon—see Chap. 30). Those of low molecular weight, chiefly methane, constitute the first of the five petroleum fuels—*natural gas*. It is purified and pumped for great distances through interstate pipe lines to consumer cities. Pentane ($C_5H_{12}$), another gaseous hydrocarbon, is compressed into steel cylinders and sold as a "canned gas." Its use is growing rapidly in homes and communities which are not supplied with piped-in gas. The other three fuels come from liquid petroleum and are recovered by fractional distillation. They are gasoline, kerosene, and fuel oil. Of these, gasoline has the lowest kindling point (and boiling point) and fuel oil has the highest.

Our cities and towns, in the main, supply their citizens with manufactured *water gas*. After studying the method here described, the reader will find a visit to the local plant a most interesting experience (Fig. 197). Tall steel cylinders, called *generators*, are charged with coal or coke. This fuel is kindled to a glowing temperature and thereafter not allowed to cool. To produce the water gas, hot air is forced through the mass to raise its temperature to about 1800° F. The air is then shut off and steam is injected into the hot carbon. The water is reduced to hydrogen and carbon monoxide: $C + H_2O \rightarrow CO + H_2$.

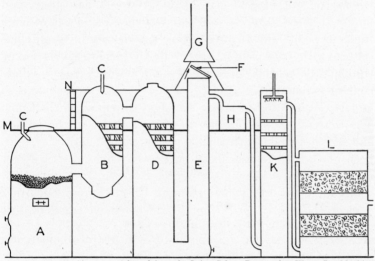

*Adapted from the Semet-Solvay Reverse-flow Water Gas Machine.*

FIG. 197. A Water Gas Plant. The gas is produced in the generator *A*; treated with oil, from *C C*, in the carburetor *B*; intimately mixed in the super-heater *D*; conducted through the stack *E*, the wash box *H*, the scrubber *K*, the sulfur purifier *L*, and then into the city gas mains. During the "blowing" interval, the waste gases escape through the valve *F* and the chimney *G*. *M* is an operating floor and *N* a "cat-walk." The reverse-flow mechanism is not shown.

After this "generating" process has continued for a few minutes, the coal cools. Then the steam is shut off and the hot air blast introduced for a few minutes. The processes of blasting and generating must be alternated continually. The water gas from the generator is next passed into another high-temperature compartment, called the *carburetor*, where oil is sprayed in and "cracked"—that is, decomposed into smaller molecules. The oil admixture causes the gas to burn with a yellow flame, imparts an odor, and increases its heat units. It should be noted that both hydrogen and carbon monoxide are odorless and that the latter is a deadly respiratory poison. Hence, if water gas is not rendered odorous, one might inhale it without detecting its presence—until too late.

The carbureted water gas passes through a *superheater*, in which its components are thoroughly vaporized; then a *scrubber*, where water removes any tarry particles which might otherwise settle out in cold city mains or clog a gas stove; and finally through a *purifier*. The latter device consists of large tanks or boxes which contain broken corn cobs or wood chips coated with brown iron oxide $(Fe_2O_3)$. The gas is forced through the purifier beds and its offensive hydrogen sulfide content is removed. After continuous use the iron oxide is so largely changed to black iron sulfide as to reduce its efficiency. The contents of the purifier are then dumped on the ground and left in contact with the oxygen of the air until they have been re-oxidized to iron oxide, after which they are ready for use again. After leaving the purifiers, the gas is ready for consumption, although in some plants it is put through one other device—the electric *precipitators*, which remove traces of dust and vapors.

## ANOTHER HARD SUBSTANCE

Carbon joins with silicon to produce one of our best-known abrasives, silicon carbide (SiC), which goes under the trade name of *carborundum*. It is produced in long, electric furnaces from a charge of sand, coke, salt, and sawdust. When the furnace is torn down at the completion of a "run," its core contains beautiful, iridescent masses of carborundum crystals. It is said that when this product first appeared in the market, it sold to jewelers for several dollars a pound. The crystals are ground to varying degrees of fineness and pressed into the form of wheels and stones for grinding purposes. Carborundum rates nine in the scale of hardness.

## SILICON COMPOUNDS

The element silicon, which is united with carbon in carborundum, is in the same family (group IV) with carbon. Its best-known natural forms are silicon dioxide ($SiO_2$). Of these, the commonest is sand. Other manifestations of the dioxide are quartz, onyx, agate, opal, jasper, flint, and petrified wood (Fig. 198).

Silicon also appears in oxygen salts, called *silicates*. Sodium silicate, a rather complex material, but usually represented as $Na_2SiO_3$, is called "water glass" and is semi-soluble in water. It is usually sold as a thick, watery syrup. Owing to its adhesive properties, it is used for sticking together layers of coarse paper in the manufacture of shipping boxes. Mixed with

FIG. 198. Quartz crystals.

freshly boiled and cooled water in the ratio of one part water glass to ten or eleven parts of water, it is an excellent preservative. Fresh eggs when entirely covered with the solution will not spoil for many months. The sodium silicate closes the pores of the shell and checks the entrance of decay-producing bacteria.

The greater number of the silicates are insoluble in water. They find various uses, as suggested by their names: mica, garnet, asbestos, soapstone, and zeolites. The beautiful colors of some of the silicon compounds are caused by impurities, and their banded appearance is due to the fact that they were gradually built up, layer by layer, from siliceous sediment deposited by water.

## GLASS

Commercial mixtures of synthetic silicates are known to everyone. They are classed as *glass*. The common window and bottle glass is essentially a soda-lime glass. That is, it is a mixture of sodium silicate and calcium silicate. The technique of glassmaking and the composition of glasses vary widely. Only the simplest outline can be presented here. In the manufacture of soda-lime or "soft" glass, sand, sodium carbonate, and calcium carbonate are heated together in a furnace. The resulting clear, pasty mass gradually cools and hardens into the "super-cooled" liquid, glass. Substitution of potash for soda produces "hard" glass. The potash-lead glasses have a high index of refraction and are formed into lenses, gems, and

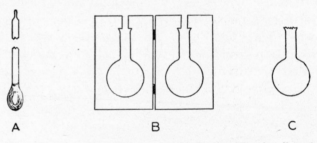

A                         B                         C

FIG. 199.    Blowing a Glass Object.    A gob of molten glass is collected on the end of a blow pipe *A* and inserted in a hinged form *B*, which is then closed and the bulb of glass blown out to fit the form.    The unused glass is broken away from the object *C*, and the neck is properly rounded and shaped.

cut-glass articles. "Pyrex" is a soda-lime-boron-aluminum glass of high silicon content. It has a very low coefficient of expansion, and for this reason it will withstand sudden heating and cooling without cracking. Pyrex is now used successfully for oven glassware and even for frying pans. A borosilicate glass similar to pyrex was cast into the great 200-inch astronomical mirror for the new telescope now being constructed on Mt. Palomar in California. In general, flat glass products are formed by passing semi-molten glass between properly spaced rolls. Articles such as bottles are made by blowing out a "gob" of glass within a suitably shaped mold (Fig. 199). Supplementary reading in this absorbing subject will richly repay the investigator for the time so spent.

## CERAMICS

Closely related to the glass industry is another "silica field," that of ceramics.   This term includes porcelain, pottery, stonewear, brick, tile, and other products from clay.   Pure clay, called *kaolin*, is white, and from it are made porcelain and china articles.   From impure clay, colored by compounds of iron and other elements, the other ceramic products are manufactured. After the raw materials have been molded into the proper shape, they are placed in a furnace or "kiln" and partially melted.   Upon cooling, they retain their shape and are resistant to breakage.   In order to close the surface pores and improve the appearance, articles such as stonewear and kitchen china have their surface so treated and heated that a smooth, shiny, impervious "glaze" is formed.   Glazing processes differ widely.

Enamel ware should not be confused with ceramic products. It is formed by covering an iron article with a tenaceous coating of glass, often colored for decorative effect.

# CHAPTER 30

# ORGANIC AND FOOD CHEMISTRY

## ORGANIC CHEMISTRY

The tiny cell is Nature's laboratory. Within it she fashions a multitude of complex substances—some of which man, with all his chemical knowledge, has been unable to duplicate. The building stones of these compounds are mainly carbon, hydrogen, oxygen, and nitrogen—but always carbon. Since these compounds are the products of living animal and vegetable matter, the realm of their chemistry is called *Organic Chemistry*. And because all organic compounds contain carbon, organic chemistry is defined as the *chemistry of the compounds of carbon*. A few compounds, such as the carbonates, are classified as *inorganic*, but the vast majority belong to the realm of organic chemistry.

## BREAKING THE BARRIER

It was believed until a century ago that organic compounds must originate in living material—never in a test tube. Then came an epoch-making "accident" in chemistry. In 1828 Friedrich Wöhler, a German chemist, was working with an inorganic substance, ammonium cyanate ($NH_4CNO$). Following an evaporation there appeared long, glistening, needle-like crystals not at all resembling his inorganic salt. Analysis showed them to be *urea*—$(NH_2)_2CO$—an *organic* compound produced in animal bodies. Within the test tube Wöhler had converted an inorganic compound into an organic one. He had broken the barrier between inorganic and organic chemistry.   He had shown that the synthesis of organic compounds can come by way of the living cell or from the lifeless contents of the test tube.

## THE SIMPLEST COMPOUNDS

Carbon, with its valence of four, is present in every organic compound.   The next most common element is the univalent hydrogen.   Hence, the very simplest organic compounds must be composed of these two elements.   There are two such compounds, and each represents the starting point of an extensive series.

One of the compounds is methane ($CH_4$).   In its molecule a tetravalent carbon atom is attached to four univalent hydrogen atoms.   If we use a straight line to represent each "valence

bond," we may write the "graphic formula" thus:

$$H - \underset{\displaystyle |}{\overset{\displaystyle H \atop |}{C}} - H.$$

It and several other members of this same series of compounds are obtained from petroleum (which may also furnish paraffin) and they are called the *paraffin series* of organic compounds. The term *aliphatic* (fat-like) *series* is also employed.

The other of the simplest hydrocarbons is benzene.   It is a *ring* compound, consisting of six carbon and hydrogen atoms, each, to the molecule.   Its simple formula is $C_6H_6$.   To account for the tetravalency of carbon, its graphic formula is written:

Benzene heads the list of a series of compounds which are found in coal tar. Many of these have an aroma. The series is therefore called the *coal-tar* or *aromatic* family of organic compounds.

## A FAMILY OF COMPOUNDS

We shall examine the aliphatic series in some detail. The first eight members of the hydrocarbons are:

1. methane—$CH_4$
2. ethane—$C_2H_6$
3. propane—$C_3H_8$
4. butane—$C_4H_{10}$

5. pentane—$C_5H_{12}$
6. hexane—$C_6H_{14}$
7. heptane—$C_7H_{16}$
8. octane—$C_8H_{18}$

Beginning with the fifth member, the name indicates the number of carbon atoms in the molecule. Examination will also show that each molecule is larger than the preceding by one atom of carbon and two of hydrogen—a $CH_2$. Any series of compounds—and there are many such series in organic chemistry—whose successive members differ by a common difference (usually $CH_2$) is called a *homologous* series.

It is very easy to account for this common difference— at least on paper. The following explanation would involve complicated reactions in the laboratory, but here we shall merely "juggle formulas." Consider methane. Its formula is

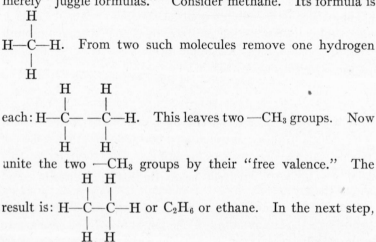

$H$—$C$—$H$. From two such molecules remove one hydrogen

each: $H$—$C$— —$C$—$H$. This leaves two —$CH_3$ groups. Now

unite the two —$CH_3$ groups by their "free valence." The

result is: $H$—$C$—$C$—$H$ or $C_2H_6$ or ethane. In the next step, remove one H from ethane, leaving the group, $-C_2H_5$ or

$$H-\underset{\underset{\displaystyle H}{|}}{\overset{\overset{\displaystyle H}{|}}{C}}-\underset{\underset{\displaystyle H}{|}}{\overset{\overset{\displaystyle H}{|}}{C}}-.$$ Attach a $-CH_3$ group at the free valence of

$-C_2H_5$ and there results: $$H-\underset{\underset{\displaystyle H}{|}}{\overset{\overset{\displaystyle H}{|}}{C}}-\underset{\underset{\displaystyle H}{|}}{\overset{\overset{\displaystyle H}{|}}{C}}-\underset{\underset{\displaystyle H}{|}}{\overset{\overset{\displaystyle H}{|}}{C}}-H$$ or $C_3H_8$ or pro-

pane. By the same procedure each member of the entire series of these aliphatic hydrocarbons may be produced from the preceding member.

## FORMULA VARIETIES

The question now arises: How are these types of formulas designated? We shall illustrate with ethane. Its simple molecular formula is $C_2H_6$, in which all of the atoms of each element are grouped together and their numbers designated by subscripts. This kind of formula—see the list of eight above—is called a *simple* formula. The ratio of C to H in ethane is 1 to 3 or $CH_3$. This formula would stand for *any* hydrocarbon in which the hydrogen atoms are three times as many as the carbon atoms. It is called an *empirical* formula, and simply represents the atomic ratio. In the formula for

ethane written: $$H-\underset{\underset{\displaystyle H}{|}}{\overset{\overset{\displaystyle H}{|}}{C}}-\underset{\underset{\displaystyle H}{|}}{\overset{\overset{\displaystyle H}{|}}{C}}-H$$ we indicate how *each* H is

attached to *each* C, every atom being indicated separately. This is a *graphic* formula. We indicated that ethane is the product of joining (on paper) two $-CH_3$ groups. It might be written $CH_3CH_3$. This may be called a *structural* formula. It merely shows the groups of which the molecule is composed. Finally, let us seek an expression which can represent the entire homologous series. Examination of the list above, from methane to octane, will reveal that in every molecule there are *two more than twice as many* hydrogen as carbon atoms. If we use the letter $n$ to represent the number of carbon atoms, then all of the formulas could be expressed as: $C_nH_{2n+2}$. Octane, for example, contains eight carbons. Two times eight plus two is eighteen —the number of hydrogens. We call these *type* formulas. In summary, organic formulas can be expressed as *empirical*, *simple*, *structural*, *graphic*, and *type*. *Empirical* formulas are seldom used. *Simple* formulas fill the needs of inorganic chemistry, but in the organic field a simple formula may stand for several substances. To differentiate between the different compounds having the same simple formula, we express their varied compositions in *structural* formulas. The complexity of many organic compounds makes it desirable to have a "picture" of all parts of the molecule and here the *graphic* formula functions. It simplifies learning if we can have one "master" formula which will stand for a whole series of compounds; consequently the *type* formula finds frequent use. A detailed study of kinds of formulas is justified in this book because they represent the only approach to a knowledge of organic compounds.

## FAMILY REPRESENTATIVES

Methane is commonly called *marsh gas*. It is formed by the decomposition of vegetable matter in the bottoms of ponds and sloughs and may be seen rising to the water surface in bubbles. The main component of natural gas is methane, and it constitutes about 30% of coal gas. The "bottled" gases which are sold in steel cylinders for domestic fuels are propane and butane. The dry-cleaning fluid from petroleum is a mixture of pentane, hexane, and heptane. Hexane to nonane ($C_9H_{20}$) make up a large proportion of natural gasoline. Octane, when exploded in a suitable motor, produces no "knock." The "antiknock" properties of gasolines are recorded as their *octane numbers*. The less the knock, the higher the octane numbers.

Although crude petroleums differ somewhat in composition and in distillation methods, we may state that, in general, the "fractions" which distill off as the temperature rises are, in order, petroleum ether, gasoline, kerosene, fuel oil, vaseline,

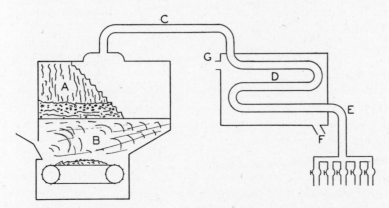

FIG. 200. Petroleum Still. Crude petroleum is charged into the still, *A*, and heated by the hot gases from *B*. The vapors are conducted through the outlet pipe, *C*, to the condenser, *D*, which is cooled by water entering at *F* and leaving at *G*. There are several outlets, *E*, from the still delivering into as many tanks. As the boiling point rises, the various fractions of distillate are discharged from one outlet after the other.

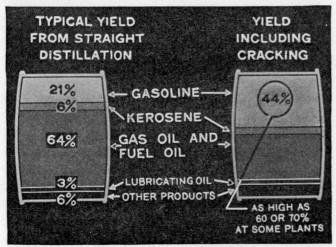

*Standard Oil Company (Indiana).*
FIG. 201. Products from petroleum.

paraffin, and tar. The residue in the still is coke (Figs. 200 and 201).

## ORGANIC RADICALS

In our juggling of formulas, we removed an H from methane to leave the grouping —$CH_3$, with its "free valence"; and an H from ethane to leave —$C_2H_5$ or $CH_3CH_2$—, with its "free valence." The same procedure might be followed with propane, butane, and the other members. These groupings appear in a great many compounds, and are called *radicals*. $CH_3$—, derived from methane, is called the *methyl radical;* $C_2H_5$—, from ethane, is the *ethyl radical*. Taken as a group, they have the type formula, $C_nH_{2n+1}$—, and are called *alkyl* radicals. There are many radicals besides the alkyl radicals, but these will serve to illustrate the principle.

## ALCOHOLS

A radical, it should be understood, does not exist alone. Some element or group is always attached through its "free valence." We shall now consider some of the *derivatives of the paraffin series of hydrocarbons;* that is, compounds which contain certain groups attached to alkyl radicals. First for consideration are the hydroxyl (OH) derivatives. We have learned that the inorganic hydroxides are bases. The organic hydroxides of the paraffin series, however, are *alcohols*. The hydroxide of the methyl radical is methyl hydroxide or *methyl alcohol*. Since it was once obtained entirely from wood, it is also called *wood alcohol*. It is now being synthesized commercially from carbon monoxide and hydrogen, with the aid of a catalyst:

$$CO + 2H_2 \rightarrow CH_3OH.$$

It is poisonous, and when grain alcohol which has been denatured with methyl alcohol is used as a beverage, blindness often results—even death. Varnishes and shellacs are dissolved in methyl alcohol. It is widely used in the preparation of drugs and other commercial chemicals.

Ethyl hydroxide ($C_2H_5OH$) is called *ethyl alcohol*, or grain alcohol. It is so named because it is formed by the fermentation of sugar made from the starch of grains. Large quantities are prepared by fermenting blackstrap molasses, a by-product of the sugar industry. The fermentation of sugar also produces large quantities of carbon dioxide; hence fermented liquors exhibit frothing and a slight explosion when their air-tight bottles are suddenly opened and the carbon dioxide escapes. Full strength ethyl alcohol, as produced under government supervision, is about 95% alcohol or 190 "proof" ($2 \times 95$). It could be made and sold for much less than one dollar a gallon, but the government tax raises the selling price to about six dollars a gallon. Even then, the law restricts its sale to non-beverage purposes. Ethyl alcohol has a host of legitimate uses. It is essential to the manufacture of extracts, drugs, medicinal preparations, anesthetic ether and chloroform, shellac and varnish, and toilet preparations. Owing to its very low freezing point and solubility in water, it is used extensively as a radiator anti-freeze. Before being placed on the market, it is "denatured" by a wide variety of formulas. This is accomplished by adding to it substances which render it unfit to drink. The other members of this hydrocarbon series have their corresponding alcohols. Several of them are commercially valuable, but are less familiar to the general public.

While we are considering the alcohols, we shall examine two which belong to another classification but which can be understood through reference to the aliphatic hydrocarbons. Ethane is $C_2H_6$ or $CH_3CH_3$. Ethyl alcohol is $C_2H_5OH$ or $CH_3CH_2OH$. Evidently, the formula for ethyl alcohol can be derived by substituting an OH for an H in $CH_3CH_3$. That is,

$$\begin{array}{ccc}
 & H & H \\
 & \diagup & \diagup \\
 & C\!-\!H & C\!-\!H \\
 & \diagdown & \diagdown \\
 & H & H \\
 & \rightarrow & \\
 & H & H \\
 & \diagup & \diagup \\
 & C\!-\!H & C\!-\!H \\
 & \diagdown & \diagdown \\
 & H & OH
\end{array}$$

Suppose, now, that we were to substitute an OH for one of the H's which is attached to *each* C.   The result would be $CH_2OH$

$CH_2OH$ or

$$
\begin{array}{c}
\quad\quad OH \\
\quad\quad / \\
C-H \\
\quad \backslash \\
\quad\quad H \\
\quad\quad H \\
\quad / \\
C-H \\
\quad \backslash \\
\quad\quad OH
\end{array}
$$
, a *dihydroxy* alcohol.

Chemically, this is called *ethylene glycol*.   Its trade name is Prestone.   It has all of the advantages of ethyl alcohol as a radiator anti-freeze.   In addition, it has a high boiling point and hence does not evaporate from the radiator, but can be used year after year.   Its manufacture is more complex and expensive than ethyl alcohol and its price ranges around three dollars per gallon.   Being unpalatable, it carries no high federal revenue tax.   Ethylene glycol has other less well-known uses.

In order to study the other alcohol, let us treat the formula for propane as we did that of ethane.   Propane is $CH_3CH_2CH_3$

$$
\begin{array}{c}
\quad\quad H \\
\quad\quad / \\
or\ C-H. \\
\quad \backslash \\
\quad\quad H \\
\quad\quad H \\
\quad / \\
C \\
\quad \backslash \\
\quad\quad H \\
\quad\quad H \\
\quad / \\
C-H \\
\quad \backslash \\
\quad\quad H
\end{array}
$$
  Replacing one H attached to each C with an OH, we

arrive at: $CH_2OH$ $CHOH$ $CH_2OH$ or

$$
\begin{array}{c}
OH \\
/ \\
C-H \\
\backslash \\
H \\
OH \\
/ \\
C \\
\backslash \\
H \\
H \\
/ \\
C-H \\
\backslash \\
OH
\end{array}
$$

or $C_3H_5(OH)_3$.

This is the *trihydroxy* alcohol called *glycerol* or *glycerine*. We recognize this at once as the third member of the great triumvirate of radiator anti-freeze fluids. Like ethylene glycol, it has a high boiling point (and low freezing point) and hence does not lose its efficiency by evaporation. Glycerine is a by-product of the soap industry. Under certain economic conditions, glycerine is almost unobtainable for anti-freeze purposes, because it has so many other valuable applications. As mentioned in Chap. 25, it can be nitrated to produce the valuable explosive, nitroglycerine, which is also the explosive ingredient in dynamite. Glycerine is the non-drying component of certain brands of cigarettes and smoking-tobacco. Its non-drying or its sweet property renders it popular in the formulas for skin lotions, medicines, and confections. The *glyptals*, one of the types of modern synthetic resins, require glycerine in their manufacture. With such a demand for this trihydroxy alcohol, it is little wonder that the motorist finds it difficult to obtain.

## PHENOLS

The aromatic hydrocarbons, as well as the aliphatic, have their hydroxy derivatives—or *phenols*, as they are usually called. The substitution of an OH for an H in the formula of benzene

($C_6H_6$) yields the formula, $C_6H_5OH$.   This substance is called *carbolic acid*.   It is a well-known poison and a valuable antiseptic.   Many of our dyes, explosives, and photographic developers have their origin in carbolic acid.   It is prepared from coal tar and also by synthetic processes.

## PLASTICS

Carbolic acid contributed to the early development of our noncellulose plastic industry and this interesting and important application of chemistry deserves a place here.

The Ellis Laboratories, Inc.

FIG. 202.   A 25,000-ton pile of synthetic urea.

Plastics are substances which can be molded, pressed, stamped, turned, blown, bent, or carved into various forms. Rubber and resins are plastics formed in nature, but synthetic plastics are of recent development.   Carbolic acid entered the picture in 1872, when Prof. Bayer discovered that carbolic acid and formaldehyde could be united to form a strong, hard, resinous material.   This was merely a curiosity until 1909, when Dr. Leo H. Baekeland developed a commercial process for producing this resin and fashioning it into various forms. His product is called Bakelite, after its inventor, or chemi-

cally, "polymerized oxybenzyl-methylene-glycol-anhydride."
Bakelite and closely related plastics are products of the union
of phenols and aldehydes.

The "synthetic house," together with all its furnishings,
which was exhibited at the Chicago Century of Progress and the
New York World's Fair was fabricated from another resin
plastic, Vinylite. This is a complex plastic produced from the
so-called "vinyl" chemical compounds. It is clear and colorless, but can be dyed to any shade, plain or mottled or streaked.

Perhaps the drinking cup in your bathroom is still another
plastic resin—a product of the chemical laboratory. Within
the last ten years urea-formaldehyde plastics have been produced in this country. Urea is now manufactured from
ammonia and carbon dioxide, but it is best known as the chief
nitrogenous compound in urine (Fig. 202). Urea plastics are
used as table dishes and all-white electrical fittings.

We are now told that the cow produces over three-fourths of
the world's fancy buttons, buckles, and dress ornaments. The
casein of milk can be united with the aldehydes to give plastics
which are widely used to manufacture buttons, buckles, beads,
automatic pencils and fountain pens, cigarette holders, and
many other products which resemble celluloid and ivory.

The DuPont Corporation is now constructing an eight-
million dollar plant for the manufacture of a new plastic called
Nylon. This is said to have a protein-like structure. Claims
are made that its fibers will produce a hosiery fabric "which
possesses extreme sheerness, great elasticity, high strength, and
improved resistance to runs." If it fulfills expectations, it may
become the most serious competitor of natural silk for hosiery.

All of these noncellulose plastics which were conceived and
nurtured in the chemical laboratory and were then transplanted
to the factory have added greatly to the comfort, utility, and
beauty of our surroundings. How keenly we should feel their
deprivation can be appreciated if we but name a score of their
uses:

Grips on the levers in an automobile.

Radio and clock bodies.

Handles of combs, brushes, and mirrors.
Vanity cases.
Door knobs.
Paneling for floors, walls, ceilings, fireplaces.
Pen and pencil barrels.
Umbrella handles.
Bracelets and beads.
Spectacle frames.
Phonograph records.
Telephone parts.
Buttons and buckles.
False teeth.
Electric light switches.
Vacuum cleaner parts.
Toothbrush handles.
Desk and table tops.
"Silent" gears.
Billiard balls.

The plastics from cellulose, which are fully as important as the synthetic resin plastics, will be considered later in this chapter.

## ALDEHYDES

We digressed in the study of the organic hydroxides (alcohols and phenols) to discuss plastics. Let us return now to the alcohols and examine the results of oxidizing them. When methyl alcohol is mildly oxidized, the oxygen does not react by joining the molecule. Rather, it unites and "elopes" with two atoms of hydrogen. Expressed in graphic formulas, the oxygen atom of the following equation combines with the two hydrogen atoms within the dotted lines and then the valence bonds "close up" to form HCHO, which is *formaldehyde*.

$$
\begin{array}{c}
H \\
| \\
C\!-\!H \\
\end{array}
\quad\rightarrow\quad
\begin{array}{c}
H \\
| \\
C\!-\!H + H_2O. \\
\| \\
O \\
\end{array}
$$

Applying the same technique to ethyl alcohol, we should write:

$$
\begin{array}{c}
\text{H} \\
\diagup \\
\text{C--H} \\
\diagdown \\
\quad\text{H} \\
\quad\text{H} \\
\diagup \\
\text{C--H} \\
\diagdown \\
\text{O} \; \text{H}
\end{array}
\quad + \; \text{O} \;\rightarrow\;
\begin{array}{c}
\text{H} \\
\diagup \\
\text{C--H} \\
\diagdown \\
\quad\text{H} \\
\quad\text{H} \\
\diagup \\
\text{C} \\
\diagdown\!\diagdown \\
\text{O}
\end{array}
\quad + \; \text{H}_2\text{O}.
$$

$CH_3CHO$ is acetaldehyde. The radical —CHO is present in all aldehydes. Most sugars contain this radical, and it is responsible for certain of their properties.

Formaldehyde, best known of the aldehydes, is an excellent disinfectant and preservative. As a 40% solution in water, it is on the market as *formalin*. Huge quantities are employed annually in the plastic industry.

## ACIDS

Suppose, now, that we carry the oxidation, as described above, one step further. When an aldehyde is oxidized, the oxygen atom actually enters the molecule, "squeezing in" between a C and an H, thus:

$$
\begin{array}{c}
\text{H} \\
\diagup \\
\text{C--H} \\
\diagdown\!\diagdown \\
\text{O}
\end{array}
\; + \; \text{O} \;\rightarrow\;
\begin{array}{c}
\text{H} \\
\diagup \\
\text{C--O--H} \\
\diagdown\!\diagdown \\
\text{O}
\end{array}
$$

Formaldehyde      Formic acid

$$
\begin{array}{c}
\text{H} \\
\diagup \\
\text{C--H} \\
\diagdown \\
\quad\text{H} \\
\quad\text{H} \\
\diagup \\
\text{C} \\
\diagdown\!\diagdown \\
\text{O}
\end{array}
\; + \; \text{O} \;\rightarrow\;
\begin{array}{c}
\text{H} \\
\diagup \\
\text{C--H} \\
\diagdown \\
\quad\text{H} \\
\quad\text{O--H} \\
\diagup \\
\text{C} \\
\diagdown\!\diagdown \\
\text{O}
\end{array}
$$

Acetaldehyde      Acetic acid

The product of the oxidation of an aldehyde is an aliphatic acid, such as formic and acetic acids. And just as the —CHO radical is typical of all aldehydes, so the group found in all organic acids is 

$$\begin{matrix} & O\text{—H} \\ | & / \\ C & \\ & \backslash \\ & O \end{matrix}$$

, more commonly written structur-

ally as —COOH and called the *carboxyl* radical. Any one who has been "bitten" by a red ant or "pricked" by a stinging nettle has received a hypodermic injection of this irritating formic acid. Acetic acid is the well-known, sour ingredient of vinegar, and makes up from four to six per cent of this food. In the formation of vinegar, sugar—as in apple cider—is fermented to ethyl alcohol, and this in turn, is oxidized to acetic acid.

Since the aliphatic acids are composed of an alkyl radical attached to a carboxyl radical, their type formula can be expressed as $C_nH_{2n+1}COOH$. The homologous acids ranging from $C_3H_7COOH$ (butyric) to $C_{17}H_{35}COOH$ (stearic) are called *fatty acids* because they occur in combination in fats and oils. Butyric acid develops in rancid butter, imparting to it an unpleasant odor and taste. It is also present in perspiration. Palmitic acid ($C_{15}H_{31}COOH$) and stearic acid form when lard and other solid fats become rancid.

## ETHERS

Brief reference should be made here to one of the *alkyl oxides*. The oxide of hydrogen is water, $H_2O$, and the corresponding oxides of the *alkyl radicals* are called *ethers*. For example, ethyl oxide, $(C_2H_5)_2O$, is ordinary ether. Produced from ethyl alcohol, it is an excellent fat solvent and our most important general anesthetic. In the days before anesthetics, a major operation—and even a minor one—caused excruciating pain. Ether brought relief from agony and a greatly increased efficiency in operations. Dr. C. W. Long, practicing far from a railroad in Jackson County, Georgia, first used ether in removing a tumor for one patient and in amputating two fingers for another. This was in 1842. In 1846 Dr. W. T. G. Morton first employed ether in a dental extraction and brought it to public attention. A dramatic scene was witnessed in Massachusetts General Hospital on the morning of October 16, 1846, when Dr. Morton anesthetized a tumor sufferer while Dr. J. C. Warren removed the growth in the presence of professional colleagues. The name "anesthesia" which signifies "insensibility" was first applied to the state of unconsciousness by the great Dr. Oliver Wendell Holmes.

## KETONES

The preparation of modern varnishes, of explosives, and of chloroform requires huge quantities of a liquid called *acetone*. Its molecule is composed of two methyl radicals united to the CO— radical, $(CH_3)_2CO$. It is one of a series of substances called *ketones*.

## ESTERS

The toilet-preparation counter is a powerful magnet for women shoppers—and for some men. It offers to the purchaser creams and perfumes, but to the chemist its stock is largely composed of *esters*. What is an ester? Let us revert to the common inorganic reaction of neutralization. In such a reaction an *acid* and a *base* interact to produce a *salt* and water. For example, hydrogen chloride (hydrochloric acid) will react with potassium hydroxide to yield potassium chloride and water. $HCl + KOH \rightarrow KCl + H_2O$. Recalling that the organic hydroxides are not bases but alcohols, we would expect that an *organic acid* would react with an *alcohol* in a similar way. Such is the case, but the resulting "salt" is called an *ester*. For example, hydrogen acetate (acetic acid) reacts with ethyl hydroxide (ethyl alcohol) to yield ethyl acetate (an ester) and water.

$$CH_3COOH + C_2H_5OH \rightarrow CH_3COOC_2H_5 + H_2O$$

Acetic       Ethyl       Ethyl
acid        alcohol     acetate

Ethyl acetate has a pleasant odor resembling that of apples.

Amyl acetate (from amyl alcohol, $C_5H_{11}OH$, and acetic acid) is banana oil. Its pleasant odor is encountered in enamels and fingernail polishes. It is used as a solvent in preparing gun-cotton products. Methyl butyrate is the pineapple odor.

Methyl salicylate (from salicylic acid and methyl alcohol) is oil of wintergreen. These are called *essential oils.* Other representatives furnish, in whole or in part, the odor or flavor of peppermint, lemons, oranges, roses, lavender, and many other fruits, flowers, and herbs.

Another important group of esters, derived from the fatty acids and glycerine, will be discussed under the fats.

## DYES

Dyes are complex organic substances related to the aromatic series. They are formed in limited quantities in the plant and animal world. "Royal purple" suggests that this color was once available to royalty alone because the dye could be extracted from natural sources only at great expense and labor. Until the chemical laboratory entered the picture, most dyes were expensive and of limited variety. It was William Henry Perkin who, in 1856, introduced synthetic dyes to the world. In an attempt to prepare quinine artificially, he accidentally obtained a beautiful violet dye which he named "mauve." It was derived by oxidation of aniline (a coal tar product), and marked the starting point of the great "coal tar" dye industry. Some dyes will attach themselves directly to the fabric (usually wool or silk) and are called *direct* dyes. Many others require a third substance, such as an aluminum or an iron salt, which can attach itself both to the dye and to the fabric. The salt is called a *mordant* and a dye which requires such a "go-between" is a *mordant dye.* Examination of dye molecules reveals that they must possess certain types of groupings in common. One set of such groupings is called *chromophore* or "color producing" groups. In the event of their absence, the substance has no distinct color. Another set is called the *auxochrome* (helper of the color) group. It is through them that the dye attaches itself to the fabric. Dyes have entered the field of medicine, not only as stains for microscopic specimens, but as anti-septics. Mercurochrome (bromhydroxymercurifluorescein) is an example. German-made dyes predominated previous to the World War, but the conflict made it necessary for our country to produce its own dyes. So complex an industry could not be developed in a day, and the first American products left much to be desired. But our domestic dyes are now of excellent quality and of great variety.

## THE FOOD WE EAT

Behind the dinner pail and the banquet table is the chemical laboratory. We are acutely conscious of the baker, butcher, and grocer because so much of the pay check goes to them, and of the cook because she converts the foodstuffs into such delicious menus. And yet, the production of our foods, their preparation for the table, and their utilization in our bodies are essentially chemical processes. The organic foodstuffs are classified as carbohydrates, fats, and proteins; the inorganic, as "mineral salts." Closely related to their metabolism in the body are the enzymes and hormones. These classes will receive brief attention at this point.

## CARBOHYDRATES

The carbohydrates, as the name implies, are literally compounds of carbon and water. Their type formula might be written: $C_m(H_2O)_n$. For convenience of study, we divide them into three classes: monosaccharides, disaccharides, and polysaccharides. These terms, being interpreted, mean "single sugars," "double sugars," and "multiple sugars." The first two classes actually are sugars, but not the third.

The monosaccharides may contain from three to seven carbon atoms to the molecule, but the most important representatives contain six carbons. Hence, they are called *hexoses* and have the formula $C_6H_{12}O_6$. This is an excellent example of one formula representing many compounds. To differentiate them we must employ structural or graphic formulas.

The most familiar monosaccharide is *glucose*, also called *dextrose, grape sugar, diabetic sugar*, or *corn sugar*. Its structural formula is $CH_2OH(CHOH)_4CHO$. There are sixteen sugars of this formula, but we shall consider only glucose. It accounts for the sweetness of many of our fruits and vegetables. The name "corn sugar" arises from the fact that it is manufactured from the starch of the corn kernel. Corn starch is "dissolved" in water, a little hydrochloric acid is added, and the mass heated. Through the *catalytic action* of the acid, the starch is *hydrolized* to produce glucose as the end product. The acid is finally neutralized and the sugar is crystallized from the solution. If crystallization is not effected, the sweet, syrupy liquid reaches the consumer under the trade name of Karo. The digestion of the starches in our food is a parallel case. The enzymes (organic catalysts) of the saliva and intestinal juice cause the starches to be hydrolized to form glucose. In this form, it enters the blood—never as starch. Under normal conditions, this sugar is completely metabolized, but in the disease *diabetes mellitus* some of it is excreted, unchanged, in the urine. Hence it is called *diabetic sugar*.

Not infrequently, the oxidation of glucose in the body to give the end-products, carbon dioxide and water, is expressed thus: $C_6H_{12}O_6 + 6O_2 \rightarrow 6CO_2 + 6H_2O$.

There are actually many intermediate, complex processes, some of which are incompletely understood. Probably the commonest medico-chemical test in use is the test for urinary glucose. In doctors' offices, hospitals, educational institutions, and wherever physical examinations are required, this routine test for "sugar" is applied. The chemical solution (reagent) required is Fehling's or Benedict's or Haines' solution. Each contains a complex copper compound which can oxidize the sugar. The reagent is, therefore, *reduced* in a test and produces a brick red precipitate, cuprous oxide ($Cu_2O$). You will recall that the aldehyde group, —CHO (p. 443), can be oxidized to the acid group, —COOH, and that glucose contains this aldehyde group. Hence glucose responds to these "reduction" tests. Certain sugars, such as cane sugar, do not contain an aldehyde group (nor a ketone group, which is also a reducing group). Cane sugar therefore does not respond to the test. The test is carried out by heating a few cubic centimeters of the reagent with a few drops of the suspected urine. In the presence of sugar there appears a yellow precipitate of cuprous hydroxide or a brick red precipitate of cuprous oxide. The number of drops of urine required to produce the precipitate gives a measure of the amount of sugar—the severity of the case. The technician or physician then rates the case as $+$, $++$, $+++$, or $++++$. Most of the body glucose is used to furnish energy (because the oxidation of glucose is an exothermic action), but some of it enters into the body structure.

The hexose, fructose or fruit sugar or levulose [$CH_2OH$ $(CHOH)_3COCH_2OH$], is formed during the digestion of cane sugar. It is present in fruit juices and especially in honey, and is the sweetest of sugars. While writing about "sweetness," mention might be made of saccharine which is 500 times as sweet as cane sugar. However, it is not a sugar or a food, but an aromatic, coal-tar product, and its use in commercial foods is forbidden by law.

All disaccharides have the simple formula, $C_{12}H_{22}O_{11}$. Their relation to the monosaccharides can be shown thus: $(C_6H_{12}O_6 + C_6H_{12}O_6) - H_2O \rightarrow C_{12}H_{22}O_{11}$. That is, they are compounds of two molecules of a hexose, less a molecule of water. The commonest disaccharide is sucrose, also called cane sugar or beet sugar. It is crystallized from the juice of the sugar cane or sugar beet by rather complicated processes. Its uses are too well known to require comment. An action occurs in the digestive tract which is the exact reverse of the equation shown above. The sugar is hydrolized, under the influence of an enzyme of the intestinal juice, to produce a molecule, each, of glucose and fructose. Sucrose is said to ferment, but this fermentation can occur only after it has been hydrolized to the fermentable monosaccharides.

Lactose, or sugar of milk, is also a disaccharide. It is the carbohydrate ingredient of milk and is especially adapted to infant diet because it is much less irritating to the stomach and less sweet than sucrose. It is also not subject to fermentation.

The polysaccharides may be considered as formed by the union of many molecules of a monosaccharide, each molecule of the monosaccharide having first lost a molecule of water: $nC_6H_{12}O_6 - nH_2O \rightarrow (C_6H_{10}O_5)_n$. $n$ is a large value—about 200 in one case—and it probably has a different value for each of the polysaccharides. The different members include the starches, the dextrins, the celluloses, and glycogen.

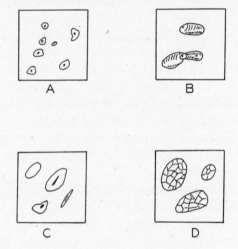

FIG. 203. Starch Granules. A. Corn starch. B. Potato starch. C. Wheat starch. D. Oat starch.

Starches are derived from the kernels of corn, oats, wheat, rice, and other grains, also from peas, potatoes, and so forth (Fig. 203). They are composed of tiny granules, whose shape and size vary with the source. A microscopic study of the granules of an "unknown" starch will usually determine its source. These granules are really little sacks of starch. When raw starch is heated in water, the sack swells and bursts, allowing the contents to flow out. The product has the typical properties of boiled starch and is a colloid. Starch unites weakly with iodine to give a dark blue substance, fairly stable at room temperature. Formation of the blue product with iodine constitutes an excellent test for starch. As mentioned on page 448, starches are hydrolized to glucose through the catalytic action of either enzymes or acids. It is interesting to note that, in the ripening of such fruits as the banana, starch changes to sugar. An overripe banana is almost sickeningly sweet. On the other hand, when fresh-picked peas and sweet corn are allowed to stand, they become less sweet. Their sugar content is being changed to starch.

The dextrins are interesting polysaccharides. They are formed in the early stages of the conversion of starches to glucose. For example, digestion of starches in the body yields dextrins first, as can be shown by a careful test with iodine. Iodine yields a blue product with starches, a pink with dextrins, and no color with sugars. A fresh starch-saliva mixture will give all of these color reactions if tested at intervals with iodine. Karo, as before described, contains large amounts of dextrins. The toasting of bread consists largely in dextrinizing it, and the stiff, glossy mass formed by the ironing of starched clothes is dextrin. A dextrin smear coats the back of postage stamps and envelope flaps.

The structural "framework" of plants is composed of celluloses (also polysaccharides). Surgical cotton is almost pure cellulose. The many uses to which we put wood and cotton suggest the importance of the celluloses. Man's digestive tract does not contain a cellulose-digesting enzyme. Their only use in our food is to furnish bulk or "roughage."

A very important and modern use for cellulose is found in the cellulose plastics industry. By treatment with the proper reagents, cellulose is converted into soluble compounds which can be fabricated in various ways. They can be formed into various objects such as a fountain pen set; they can be converted into sheets such as cellophane; they can be formed into threads from which fabrics are woven.

The various fabrics which are derived from cellulose are all designated as *rayon*, the threads of which are formed by forcing the synthetic fiber, while still fluid, through tiny holes or dies (Fig. 204).

Nitrocellulose products are produced by treating cellulose with nitric acid, in the presence of sulfuric acid as a dehydrating agent. As mentioned in Chap. 25, they are employed in the manufacture of celluloid, photographic films, artificial leather, lacquers, collodion, and synthetic silk. The threads for fabrics are "denitrated" in order to produce less combustible yarn.

Cellulose is converted into a "xanthate" by the use of carbon disulfide. This is the *viscose* process. Formed into threads it is woven into synthetic silk fabrics. Made into sheets, it is the well-known cellophane.

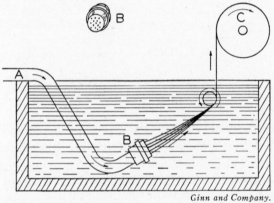

*Ginn and Company.*

Fig. 204. Making Rayon Thread. Filtered viscose enters at *A* and is forced through tiny apertures at *B* (also shown in detail above) into a hardening bath composed of sulfuric acid, sodium bisulfate, and water. The resulting thread is wound at *C*.

Cellulose acetate furnishes the synthetic silk called *celanese*. Although more expensive than cellulose nitrate, it is incombustible and is frequently used to produce the home motion picture films.

An ammonia-copper-sulfate solution will dissolve cellulose to give a fourth synthetic silk, called *Bemberg*.

Glycogen, the last polysaccharide to be discussed here, is sometimes called "animal starch." Just as starch is the reserve energy supply of grains, so glycogen is the form in which the animal stores its carbohydrate fuel. When the monosaccharides—products of the digestion of carbohydrates—enter the blood stream, a portion may be oxidized directly to furnish energy. The greater portion, however, is stored in the liver and muscles as glycogen. Between meals, as the body needs energy, the glycogen is converted into glucose, which then undergoes oxidation.

## FATS

The most concentrated forms of food energy are the fats. Technically expressed, they are the glyceryl esters of the fatty acids. That is, they are the esters which are produced when the fatty acids (butyric acid and its higher homologues) react with the alcohol, glycerine. This is the type of reaction described on page 445.

$$3C_3H_7COOH + C_3H_5(OH)_3 \rightarrow (C_3H_7COO)_3C_3H_5 + 3H_2O$$

Butyric acid      Glycerine      Butyrin (fat)

$$3C_{17}H_{35}COOH + C_3H_5(OH)_3 \rightarrow (C_{17}H_{35}COO)_3C_3H_5 + 3H_2O$$

Stearic acid      Glycerine      Stearin (fat)

Actions like these occur in the intestinal tract where fats are regenerated, just previous to entering the lymphatic system. The digestion of fats is the reverse of the process illustrated in the above equations; that is, they are hydrolized to produce fatty acids and glycerine. $(C_{17}H_{35}COO)_3C_3H_5 + 3H_2O \rightarrow 3C_{17}H_{35}COOH + C_3H_5(OH)_3$. Their oxidation in the body is an exothermic one yielding finally carbon dioxide and water, but with many complex intermediate products.

Fats and oils are in great demand for the manufacture of soap. If the hydrolysis illustrated by the preceding equation is carried on in the presence of a base—usually sodium hydroxide—the fatty acid is neutralized to form its salt. The process is called *saponification* and the salt so formed is a *soap* (Fig. 205). The details of soap manufacture vary widely, but in essence, the fats and fatty acids are heated in huge tanks with sodium hydroxide (soda lye). The soap which forms is separated from the liquid, purified, and pressed into cakes. Using stearin as the fat, the equation can be written:

$$(C_{17}H_{35}COO)_3C_3H_5 + 3NaOH \rightarrow 3C_{17}H_{35}COONa + C_3H_5(OH)_3$$

Stearin      Soap (sodium stearate)      Glycerine

Observe that glycerine is a by-product of the soap industry.

An interesting bit of information about fats has to do with our vegetable cooking fats. In order to understand these important foods, we must refer back to ethane and its homologues—a discussion which was deferred until we should be working with illustrative material. It was shown (p. 432) that if an H is removed from each of two methane molecules and the

*The Procter & Gamble Company.*

FIG. 205. A Soap Kettle. Looking downward three stories into an empty giant kettle. Steam from the perforated pipes heats the tons of soap stock and soda as they unite to form soap and glycerine.

two resulting methyl groups are joined *through the free valence* of each, the product is ethane. Suppose, now, that an H is removed from each carbon of ethane. The formula then would

appear as:
$$\begin{array}{c} \text{H} \quad \text{H} \\ | \quad | \\ \text{H—C—C—H} \\ | \quad | \end{array}$$
. These "free valences" then join to produce a *double valence bond* between the two carbon atoms, thus:

$$\begin{array}{c} \text{H} \quad \text{H} \\ | \quad | \\ \text{H—C}=\text{C—H} \end{array}$$
. This product is called *ethylene. Propy-*

*lene* is:

$$H-C=C-C-H$$

with H atoms attached above each of the three carbons and H below the third carbon. Such compounds are said to be "unsaturated."

Since it really requires only one valence bond to connect the two carbon atoms, this second valence is an extra attachment and will readily separate to unite with some "passing" element or radical. For example, it will unite with two OH groups to yield ethylene glycol (p. 438). *Any aliphatic compound, therefore, which contains at least one double bond between carbons is unstable; it also tends to be fluid.* And here is where the fats enter the story. Oils, such as cottonseed, corn, and peanut oils have essentially the same composition as solid fats, such as lard, except that they contain double bonds between carbons, because of fewer hydrogen atoms. By way of illustration, there are written below, in semistructural form, the formulas of *stearin* (a solid fat) and *olein* (a fluid oil).

$$[CH_3(CH_2)_7C-C(CH_2)_7COO]_3C_3H_5$$

Stearin

$$[CH_3(CH_2)_7C=C(CH_2)_7COO]_3C_3H_5$$

Olein

The double valence bond between carbons, by imparting instability, causes its oils to become rancid easily; it also renders its compound fluid. If, now, it were possible to add hydrogen to these unsaturated molecules of our liquid vegetable oils, they would change into edible, solid fats. By treating such oils—cottonseed mainly—with hydrogen gas at the proper temperature and pressure and in the presence of a catalyst—such as finely divided nickel—the double bond "breaks"; hydrogen enters the molecule; and the product is a *solid vegetable* cooking *fat* (such as Spry, Crisco, and so forth). The process is called hydrogenation (p. 327). The hydrogenated oils are used in the soap industry as well as for cooking purposes.

These hydrogenated products should not be confused with oleomargarine. The latter is prepared by churning together beef fat, oils, and milk to give the proper consistency. It may be colored with butter color by the purchaser. It is a wholesome food, but it is said to lack the vitamins of butter.

## PROTEINS

Of the three classes of foodstuffs, the proteins remain to be discussed. All contain carbon, hydrogen, oxygen, and nitrogen; most contain sulfur; and some contain phosphorus, iron, and other elements. The molecules are very large and complex —so complex and unstable that, in most cases, their formulas and molecular weights are unknown. Proteins, for convenience, are classified as *simple, conjugated,* and *derived.* The significance of these terms can be found in chemistry reference books. Plants synthesize their own protein matter from the elements of their food. Animals must obtain their proteins "ready made" from their animal and vegetable foods. Typical proteins of the diet include casein of milk, albumin of eggs, lean meat, beans, peas, and the cereals. Because of its nitrogen and sulfur content, spoiled protein is notorious for its foul odors, such as the stifling odor of ammonia and the rotten-egg odor of hydrogen sulfide.

The proteins are tissue builders. In their digestion they are finally hydrolized into amino acids. These acids are absorbed from the intestines into the blood stream and resynthesized into proteins for tissue building. The structure of an amino acid can be understood in the case of the simplest one, glycine. Acetic acid is $CH_3COOH$. Ammonia is $NH_3$. The removal of an H from acetic acid leaves:    H    The removal of

$$
\begin{array}{c}
\text{H} \\
\diagup \\
\text{C}\!-\!\text{H} \\
\big| \diagdown \\
\big| \quad \text{O} \\
\big| \quad \diagup\!\!\diagup \\
\text{C} \\
\diagdown \\
\text{O}\!-\!\text{H}
\end{array}
$$

an H from ammonia leaves:     H, called the *amino group*.

Now if these two residues are united through their free valences, the result is:     H     , also written $CH_2NH_2COOH$.    This

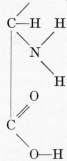

substance is *amino acetic acid* or *glycine*.   Proteins, upon hydrolysis, yield about 21 different amino acids.   Some of the proteins lack certain amino acids in their structure and hence are "incomplete" food proteins.   Gelatine is an incomplete protein.

A balanced diet must contain, in addition to the three classes of foodstuffs, *mineral salts*.   These include compounds of such metals as sodium, potassium, calcium, and magnesium.   They function to maintain the proper osmotic pressure, to build bone and teeth, to maintain the neutrality of body fluids, to govern the "irritability" of muscle, to assist in holding water in the tissues, and so forth.

## ENZYMES

In every portion of the body, in fact in every cell, are found complex substances called *enzymes*.   They are organic catalysts and play a part in nearly every physiological process.   The enzymes of the alimentary tract accomplish the digestion of food; enzymes in the cells effect various food transformations and oxidations.   Some enzymes are designated by their older names, such as the *ptyalin* of saliva, the *pepsin* and *rennin* of

gastric juice, and the *trypsin, steapsin,* and *amylopsin* of pan
creatic juice.

According to modern terminology, that upon which an
enzyme acts is called its *substrate*. The enzyme is named by
attaching the ending *ase* to the substrate. For example, a
protein-digesting enzyme is called a *protease;* a sucrose-digest-
ing enzyme, a *sucrase*. The protease enzyme of the pancreas
would be called a *pancreatic protease*. Enzymes are sometimes designated according to the type of reaction which they
bring about. *Oxidases* cause oxidation and *hydrolases* cause
hydrolysis.

## HORMONES

*Chemical messengers* or *hormones* are substances which are
secreted by certain types of cells and are carried by the blood
to other cells, causing the latter to function. One group is
concerned primarily with digestion. For example, when the
acid foodstuff or chyme is "squirted" from the stomach through
the pyloric valve into the intestine, a hormone called *secretin* is
generated in the intestinal walls. It rushes along with the
blood to the pancreas and causes that organ to send a supply
of pancreatic juice to the intestine. Another group of hormones
is secreted by the so-called *ductless* or *endocrine glands*. If
these hormones are deficient or too plentiful, they cause serious
disturbances. A few of the endocrine glands, the names of one
of their hormones, and a condition caused by their under- or
over-activity are listed below:

| Gland | Hormone | Condition |
|---|---|---|
| Pituitary | Pituitrin | Dwarfs and giants |
| Thyroid | Thyroxin | Goiters |
| Islands of Langerhans (in the pancreas) | Insulin | Diabetes |
| Adrenals | Adrenalin | Blood sugar control |
| Ovaries | Theelin | Secondary sex traits |

Remarkable results have been obtained by the proper administration of endocrine hormones. This phase of medicine is
still in its infancy.

# CHAPTER 31

# THE EARTH AND ITS ROCKS

## THE LITHOSPHERE

The word is derived from a Greek word *lithos* (stone) and means stone-sphere, or the solid part of the earth. The form of the earth is not a perfect sphere, but an oblate sphere; that is, flattened at the poles. The polar diameter is 7899.7 miles while the equatorial is 7926.5 miles. The total area of the earth is 197,000,000 square miles of which 143,000,000 square miles is water.

FIG. 206. Origin of continental plateau and continental shelf.

The surface of the land is irregular. The lowest point is Tuscarora Deep, near Japan, which is 35,433 feet below sea level, and the highest peak is Mt. Everest of the Himalaya Mountains, north of India, which is 29,141 feet. Unevenness of the land surface is known to geographers as *relief*. The sea bed, like the land surface, is also very uneven.

The irregularities or relief features may be grouped into three orders, those of the first, second, and third magnitudes.

*Relief Features of the First Magnitude* are continental plateaus and ocean basins. A continental plateau includes the land above water, *AB* (Fig. 206), together with the continental shelf bordering each plateau, *AC*, *BD* (Fig. 206). It should be

noted that a continental shelf is a part of the continent.   There
are six continental plateaus: North America, South America,
Africa, Australia, Antarctica, and Eurasia.   The land area of
the northern hemisphere is more than twice that of the southern.
The edge of each continental plateau is bordered by a continental shelf, $AC$, $BD$ (Fig. 206).   The water over the continental shelves is shallow, not exceeding 600 feet.

Ocean basins are the depressed portions of the lithosphere
which lie between the borders of the continental shelves.   Since
the quantity of ocean water is greater than the capacity of the

FIG. 207.   Glacial plain strewn with granite boulders.

ocean basins, the excess overflows into the continental shelves.
Those portions of the ocean covering the continental shelves
(an area of about 10,000,000 square miles) are known as the
*epicontinental seas*.

Continental plateaus and ocean basins were made by
vertical warping or faulting of the earth's crust (Fig. 245, Chap.
34).   Stresses set up by a slowly cooling, contracting earth
caused great segments to rise in some places and to settle in
others.

*Relief Features of the Second Magnitude*.   Continental plateaus and sea beds are further diversified by smaller relief
features.   One of the most important of these is a *plain*.   A
plain is a large, more or less level tract of land, lower on one
side, both sides, or on all sides than the surrounding lands.

Denver Tourist Bureau.

FIG. 208.   Long's Peak in Colorado.

It has, as a general rule, no great elevation above sea level (Fig. 207).

Plains may be formed in several different ways.  They may be designated as river plains, lake plains, glacial plains, marine plains, and erosional plains, depending upon the agents which produced them.

Plains are of great economic importance to man. They are comparatively level or gently rolling. For this reason, building of public highways, railroads, airports, and canals is easier than in plateau or mountainous areas. The soil is generally of greater depth, is more fertile, and is not subject to as rapid erosion. Rivers are more frequently navigable, and their shallow valleys tend to keep the ground water surface higher, thus rendering the farmer's crops less exposed to damage from severe droughts.

Another relief feature of the second magnitude is the plateau. Plateaus are large, more-or-less level tracts of land higher on one side, both sides, or on all sides than the surrounding regions. Usually they have considerable elevation above sea level, but unlike mountains, they possess large summit areas. Plateaus result from erosion, lava flows (Columbia Plateau), and warping or faulting of the earth's surface. The high lands are usually trenched with gorges or canyons, which make transportation difficult. They are generally more poorly watered than the plains, and for this reason, are not so well adapted to support dense populations.

*Relief Features of the Third Magnitude* are hills, ridges, valleys, and shallow basins. Mountains, high elevations of land with limited top areas which stand out conspicuously above the surrounding country, are made by volcanic action, by erosion, and by warping of the earth's surface (Fig. 208).

## MINERALS AND ROCKS OF THE LITHOSPHERE

To know and appreciate the changes taking place on the earth's surface, it is first essential that one should have some knowledge of the nature and the properties of the minerals that make up the solid part of the earth. Rocks are composed of minerals, and most minerals are a combination of elements. To understand minerals it is necessary to have some knowledge of chemistry.

An element is a substance that cannot be decomposed by any ordinary means. The chemist has discovered about 92 chemical elements in nature (see Chap. 26), but not all of them are found in our common rocks. Some of the most common are oxygen, silicon, aluminum, iron, calcium, sodium, potassium, magnesium, titanium, hydrogen, sulfur, chlorine, copper, and manganese. However, the first eight of these constitute about 98 per cent of the earth's crust.

A mineral is a natural, inorganic substance, having a definite chemical composition, and as a rule, a definite form and structure. Most minerals are a combination of elements rather than a single element.

Rocks are usually composed of two or more minerals; they are aggregates of minerals. But some minerals are rocks; for example, salt, gypsum, certain iron ores, and many of our limestones.

## THE COMMON ROCK-MAKING MINERALS

To explain the nature of rocks, we must first undertake to describe some of the common minerals of which they are composed.

Minerals possess certain physical properties which are used to identify them. Most minerals are crystalline, although some have no definite form; that is, they are amorphous. In the crystalline forms the molecules out of which they are built arrange themselves into definite geometrical figures; for example, galena or lead sulphide molecules are grouped in the form of a cube, quartz in a six-sided prism.

The manner in which minerals break when struck with a hammer is so characteristic as to be of great value in distinguishing them. If they break with smooth plane surfaces, they are said to possess cleavage. Good examples are calcite, lead, and halite or salt. If the mineral does not break with smooth planes, the nature of the broken surface is called "fracture."

One of the most conspicuous physical properties of minerals is *color*. Some minerals always run true to color; they always have the same color; for example, native gold, galena—lead-gray, sulfur—yellow, and magnetite—iron-black. A great many minerals may have various colors in different specimens; for example, quartz and calcite. The various colors of the same mineral are due to the presence of iron or some other pigment.

All minerals have *luster*. The luster of a mineral, its appearance in light, is due to the quality and intensity of light which it is able to reflect. Luster should not be confounded with color; they are not synonomous. Minerals have either a metallic-like luster as in magnetite, galena, and pyrite, or a non-metallic luster as in quartz, calcite, and halite.

Minerals vary greatly in hardness, a physical property which is very important in helping to identify them. A mineral's hardness may be determined by comparing it with those which have been selected to form a standard scale. The standard scale generally used is as follows: 1, talc; 2, gypsum; 3, calcite; 4, fluorite; 5, apatite; 6, orthoclase feldspar; 7, quartz; 8, topaz; 9, corundum, and 10, diamond. To determine the hardness of an object, find which of these minerals it will scratch and which it cannot scratch. Your fingernail is 2 in the scale; a copper penny is 3, and the steel in a pocketknife is 6.

Minerals are heavier than water; they are sometimes designated as being heavy or light. The weight of a mineral is expressed as a number that indicates how many times heavier a given volume of the mineral is than an equal volume of water. This is known as the specific gravity (p. 345) of the mineral. Magnetite, lead, and native gold have high specific gravities, while quartz, calcite, and the feldspars have low specific gravities.

One of the commonest minerals is *quartz* ($SiO_2$). Quartz has a glassy appearance and is so hard that a high-grade steel knife will not scratch it. When broken, it shows a rough, irregular surface. It may be colorless or exhibit a wide range of colors. Some of the common varieties of crystalline quartz are rock crystals, rose quartz, ferruginous (iron) quartz, and milky quartz (Fig. 209). A dense, translucent variety is known as *chalcedony*. In this form it is used as gems. Some of the more important are agate, onyx, sardonyx, carnelian, jasper, and opal.

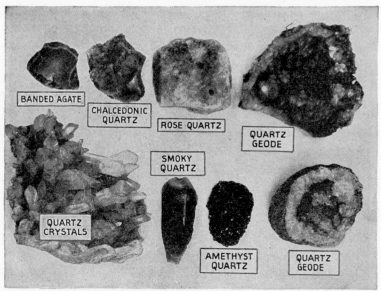

FIG..209. Varieties of quartz.

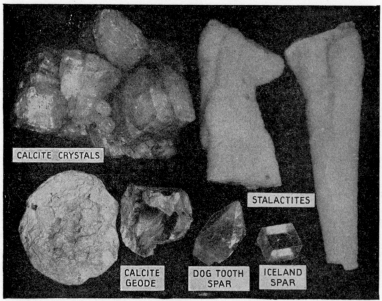

FIG. 210. Varieties of calcite.

*Calcite* ($CaCO_3$) is a common mineral. Unlike quartz, it is soft, is easily scratched with a knife, and is readily soluble in a dilute solution of hydrochloric acid. In a pure state it is colorless and shows distinct cleavage; it will break into rhomb-like pieces with smooth surfaces (Fig. 210).

*The Micas.* Muscovite or white mica, biotite or black mica, and phlogopite or yellow mica are the easiest of all minerals to detect. Very soft, they are composed of thin, elastic plates which separate easily. The micas are composed of the elements potassium, iron, aluminum silicon, and oxygen. They are frequently found in coarse-grained, igneous rocks, but differ from quartz in having distinct cleavage surfaces.

*The Feldspars*, of which there are many, constitute about 60 per cent of our igneous rocks. They are generally of a red, pink, gray, or green color. Like quartz, they are hard, glassy, and insoluble, but may be distinguished from quartz in that they have distinct cleavage surfaces. They are composed of the elements potassium, calcium, sodium, aluminum, silicon, and oxygen.

*Augite and Hornblende*, which occur in many of the dark-colored igneous rocks, exhibit a greenish-black color, distinct cleavage and marked hardness. They contain large amounts of iron with magnesium, silicon, and oxygen.

In addition to the common ones already described, many other minerals are present in our igneous rocks.

## THE ROCKS OF THE LITHOSPHERE

Three classes of rocks make up the solid part of the earth: *igneous, sedimentary*, and *metamorphic*. The igneous rocks (fire-rocks) are found widely distributed in the earth. In the earliest history of our planet the stony material was probably in a gaseous state. As the gases cooled, they passed into a liquid or molten state and later into a solid. It has been fairly well shown that the earth is solid throughout. The study of the nature of earthquake waves and the speed with which they travel vertically through the earth quite definitely proves that the earth's core, 4,000 miles in diameter, is very dense. It is now believed that it is composed of iron alloys and of iron and nickel (Fig. 211). Around this extremely dense core is a layer about 1,000 miles thick of less dense rocks in which the nickel and iron content is smaller than in the central core. The next layer, about 960 miles thick, is still less dense and is composed of iron, magnesium, and silicon. The outside or surface of the

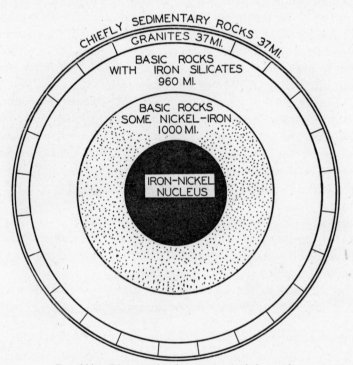

Fig. 211.   Diagram showing structure of the earth.

earth is about 37 miles thick and is composed chiefly of sedimentary rocks and their weathered products.

This onion-like structure is strong evidence that the earth, in its earlier history, must have been in a molten state to permit the various rock materials to arrange themselves according to their density.

When molten material solidifies, it usually forms crystals. If the rate of cooling is slow, the various ingredients crystallize to form coarsely crystalline rock; if rapid, the resulting rock is either very dense or glassy.

When molten rock from a fissure or volcano is poured out on the surface, it cools rapidly and will either be dense or glassy in texture. Of such a nature is Obsidian Cliff in Yellowstone National Park. If, on the other hand, lava is forced into the rock far beneath the surface, it cools very slowly, forming

FIG. 212.   Types of igneous rocks.

immense crystals. In some cases lava may cool slowly for a long time and then, for some unknown reason, the rate of cooling is greatly increased. As a result we have rock in which very large crystals are embedded in a background of smaller crystals. Such rocks are called *porphyries* (Fig. 212).

Igneous rocks may be quite easily distinguished because of their rather massive and uniform structure. Unlike sedimentary rock, there are no layers or stratification planes. On close examination crystals may be seen quite uniformly distributed. In some instances, if the rock is dense, the individual crystals are invisible to the naked eye.

Igneous rocks are very complex in their chemical composition. Two groups of minerals, the feldspathic and the ferro-(iron) magnesian, constitute the chief ingredients. The first group are largely the feldspars, quartz, and white mica. They are usually light in color and light weight. The second group are composed chiefly of pyroxene or hornblendes, and black mica. They are generally dark in color and heavy. These two groups of minerals sometimes resemble unfriendly clans. Where the light-colored minerals dominate, it often happens that the dark-colored minerals are scarce or missing completely. Sometimes both groups are friendly and intermingle, forming a rock mottled in light and dark colors.

TABLE 11.  FIELD KEY

I. CRYSTALLINE ROCKS, MINERALS VISIBLE TO UNAIDED EYE, INTRUSIVE

| (a) Feldspathic Groups of Minerals, usually Light Colored | | (b) Ferro-Magnesian Minerals, usually Dark Colored | |
|---|---|---|---|
| Rocks containing quartz, feldspar, and white mica, or quartz and feldspar, or quartz and white mica with or without a small amount of ferro-magnesian minerals. Example: Granite. | Rocks with the same minerals as granite except quartz. Example: Syenite. | Rocks containing the ferro-magnesian minerals equal in amount to or greater than the feldspathic group. Example: Dolerite. | Rocks containing chiefly the ferro-magnesian minerals. Example: Pyroxenite or Hornblendite. |

II. DENSE ROCKS, MINERALS INVISIBLE TO UNAIDED EYE, MAINLY INTRUSIVE

| (a) Feldspathic Group of Minerals, usually light colored. Example: Felsites. | (b) Ferro-Magnesian Minerals, usually dark colored. Example: Basalts. |
|---|---|

III. GLASSY ROCKS, MAINLY EXTRUSIVE

| Examples: Obsidian, | Perlite, | Pumice, | Pitchstone. |
|---|---|---|---|

Igneous rocks in the field may be distinguished by their texture, color, minerals present, and by their luster. The preceding field key will assist in identifying igneous rocks.

## SEDIMENTARY ROCKS

The term sedimentary is derived from a Latin word, *sedimentum* (sediment). Fragmental rock material such as peb-

FIG. 213.   Fossil limestones.

bles, sand, clay, limestone, and other weathered minerals are carried to the sea by running water and there deposited to form, in time, conglomerates, sandstone, shale, and limestone.

We have already stated that the original rocks of the earth are igneous, not sedimentary. As soon as the earth acquired its atmosphere, the chemical and mechanical breakdown of the igneous rocks began. The weathering of igneous rocks through chemical and mechanical action produces sand, limy material, and a product called clay, composed of aluminum and silica. The products of weathering, after they are deposited in the sea, are bound together by pressure and cement into solid rocks known as limestones, sandstones, shales, and conglomerates.

Limestone is composed chiefly of $CaCO_3$. Much of the limy material was carried to the sea by rivers and ground water. Limestone is usually formed in relatively shallow water where neighboring lands are too low to contribute much clastic sediment. It is formed from shells and hard parts of lime-secreting animals and plants (Fig. 213). Living bacteria also aid in causing precipitation of $CaCO_3$ in sea water. Under certain conditions limestone may result from chemical precipitation.

*Chalk* is also a special form of limestone, and is usually composed of foraminifera shells; shells of other organisms are often associated with it.

*Breccia* is a rock composed of angular fragments of other rocks which have been cemented together. The fragments have not been transported a great distance by water from their source region.

*Sandstone* consists of small grains of quartz which are firmly bound together by the same cements as are found in limestone. When the sand particles are bound together by iron, the color is brownish-yellow; when lime is the cement, they are of a whitish color. Sand particles cemented with silica, which is the hardest and most durable of the cements, form a rock called *quartzite*.

*Shales* are composed of muds. Mud is the insoluble product of soluble rocks. It is composed of aluminum and silica. Since the material has been weathered chemically, it is broken down into fine flour-like material. This, unlike the porous sandstone, is impervious to water.

*Conglomerate*, as the name suggests, is composed of pieces of fragmental rock of many kinds. Usually the fragments are rounded because, in the removal from their original position by running water, the edges have been worn off. The angular or rounded pieces are cemented by iron, lime, and silica.

## STRUCTURE OF SEDIMENTARY ROCKS

Sedimentary rocks differ greatly in structure from the igneous variety. They form beds of successive layers varying in thickness from a few inches to thousands of feet. This layered appearance causes them to be called *stratified* rocks. When a bed of limestone is first elevated above the sea, it appears as a solid, uniform mass. After exposure for some time to weathering agents, structural lines begin to appear, and the mass grad-

*A. C. Trowbridge.*
FIG. 214. Limestone quarry showing structure of sedimentary rocks.

ually separates into layers or strata (Fig. 214). Upon longer exposure the layers separate into still thinner divisions called *laminae* (leaf-like). Sedimentary rocks, when broken, part along the planes separating the layers and laminae. These parting planes are known as *bedding planes*. Cracks or fissures extending down in a vertical direction are called *joints* (Fig. 214).

## METAMORPHIC ROCKS

Metamorphic rocks are those rocks which have undergone a partial change from their original state by means of heat, action of gases, pressure, and water saturations. They were originally sedimentary or igneous rocks, but have become so altered that their original nature is not easily recognized.

Many of the minerals found in the igneous rocks are present in the metamorphic rocks, as for example, quartz, white and black mica, the feldspars, amphibole, and so forth.

Most metamorphic rocks show a foliated (Latin, *folium*—a leaf) structure, that is, the material is arranged in bands which permit cleavage along the planes of foliation.

Metamorphic rocks may be classified into the foliated and nonfoliated groups on the basis of their structure and texture. In the fine-grained foliated group are the schists, slates, and gneiss. *Schists* split into thin, flaky sheets or slabs. *Slate* is a homogeneous, fine-grained rock which separates into thin sheets with rather smooth surfaces. *Gneiss* is a banded coarse-textured rock with alternate layers of unlike mineral composition. The bands in gneiss are somewhat thicker than are those in the latter groups. The nonfoliated group is represented by quartzite, marble, and soapstone. *Quartzite* is a metamorphosed sandstone with a siliceous cement and may be multicolored. *Marble* is a recrystallized limestone. *Soapstone* is a rock composed chiefly of talc with some mica, quartz, and tremolite.

# CHAPTER 32

# THE GRADATIONAL
# AGENTS

## INTRODUCTION

The chief source of energy for the earth is the sun's heat. Other sources are combustion, chemical reactions, and heat from the interior of the earth, but they are almost negligible. Different parts of the earth receive unequal amounts of radiant energy during the year. This results in unequal pressure and in air movement or winds. Heat supplied to bodies of water causes evaporation. Winds transfer the invisible water vapor to the land where, upon condensation, it falls as rain or snow. Some of the moisture sinks into the ground and becomes ground water; some enters into chemical combination with the rocks; some is evaporated; and the remainder goes to the sea as runoff.

Not all of the sun's energy is used in changing water into the invisible state. Heat causes an expansion in rock material and, as a result of unequal heating, even the hardest and most resistant rocks will in time crumble and fall to pieces. The sun and the atmosphere are constantly at work on portions at or near the earth's surface causing tremendous quantities of rock waste to be broken up. This is then transported to the sea, effecting great changes upon the lands of the earth.

## GRADATION DEFINED

This process, a very complex one, is constantly at work on the exposed parts of the lithosphere. The constant movement of air and water, together with the extreme changes in temperature, give rise to a series of interactions among dynamic agents.

These agents are wind, running water, plant and animal life, glaciers, and ground water. *Weathering* is the breaking up of rocks and rock waste, while *erosion* is a wearing away of the solid part of the earth. Erosion consists of three more or less distinct processes. These are (1) weathering—loosening rock material, (2) picking up of the loosened material, and (3) its transportation by winds, water, and ice.

## THE WEATHERING AGENTS

Two great classes of weathering agents are constantly at work on the exposed rocks of the earth. They are designated as the *chemical* and *mechanical*.

To understand the work of the chemical agents, one needs to have some knowledge of chemistry. When a piece of iron or steel, such as a knife blade, is placed in moist air, it rusts. The oxygen and water of the air enter into a chemical combination with the iron and produce a yellowish-brown coating called *rust*. In time, the entire blade will crumble and fall to pieces. There are many rocks which contain iron, and which disintegrate after long exposure to the moist air. This process of rock-breaking is called *oxidation*.

If a piece of limestone is placed in a weak solution of hydrochloric acid, a violent effervescence takes place, and soon the limestone disappears. It has gone into solution in the acid, a process called solution or *carbonation*. Rain water with carbon dioxide dissolved in it enters the limestone bedrock and dissolves out the soluble portions of the rock.

There are certain rocks, the granites for example, that have a "liking" for water. When rain falls on them, some of it unites chemically with the rock material and becomes a part of the rock. This is known as *hydration*. When a rock unites with a considerable amount of water, it may increase in volume, and deep fractures often develop. It will be seen that the chemical agents of weathering are closely associated with moisture and rock composition.

The mechanical agents—those which break rock by force—are more numerous than the chemical. Some of the most important are heat and cold, frost, prying work of roots, waves, animal life, electricity, and gravity.

An important mechanical agent is heat and cold. Many rocks are poor conductors of heat. When they are exposed to the sun's rays, the rock particles expand, setting up a strain between the outer portions and those beneath. At night, when the surface particles cool, they contract upon those directly beneath. This expansion and contraction sets up strains in the rock which lead to fracture.

When the pores and cracks of a rock are filled with water, and freezing temperatures occur, rocks may be disrupted by the "wedge-work" of ice. When water freezes, it expands one-tenth of its volume and in so doing exerts a tremendous pressure. This agent works best in regions of high elevations where there are frequent changes in temperature and where there is sufficient rainfall. Tiny rootlets of plants penetrate the pores and crevices of the rocks, and as they grow, may break the rocks.

There are many forms of burrowing life, such as earthworms, squirrels, and ants, which aid in weathering. Some pass the soil through their bodies and, in so doing, break it into fine particles. Others make tunnels in the ground, admitting air and water which hasten weathering.

## RESULTS OF WEATHERING

Lightning often strikes rock ledges sending down tons of fractured rock waste. During its fall, it is further disintegrated and accumulates at the base of the cliff as *talus* material. Talus is an accumulation of weathered rock material transported to the base of a steep slope or cliff by running water or by gravity. The steeper the slope, the coarser the material.

Weathered rock material which covers solid bedrock is called *mantle-rock* (*ABC*, Fig. 215). It consists of clay, sand, gravel, and boulders. This layer ranges in thickness from a few inches to many hundreds of feet. Not all mantle-rock comes from weathering of the bedrock; it may have been transported by glaciers, running water, and winds.

The upper portion of the mantle-rock, *A* (Fig. 215), which is finely weathered and mixed with organic matter, is called *soil*. The portion of the mantle-rock below the soil. *BC*, is known as *subsoil*.

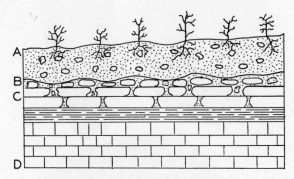

FIG. 215.   Mantle-rock.

## WORK OF THE WINDS

In the absence of tools, wind has little or no effect on bedrock; but arm it with sharp, hard tools, and it will act like a file or a sand blast.   The wearing away of the rocks by wind action is termed *abrasion*.   This agent is most active in arid or semi-arid regions where there is great irregularity in the surface, and where bedrock is exposed.   In time the rocks are carved and polished (Fig. 216) into fantastic forms.   Where exposed bedrock is absent, the wind often scoops out loose material, leaving depressions.

The wind is not everywhere using its tools to abrade the surface.   In some places, because of obstructions or overloading, the wind deposits its tools in the form of mounds or hills.   A hill of wind-blown sand is called a *dune* (Fig. 217).   It may be oval, longitudinal, or irregular in shape, and may vary in height from a few to several hundred feet.   Dunes usually have a gentle windward slope and a steeper leeward slope.

Dunes are found even in moist climates along shore lines where there is an abundance of sand, as for example, along the south and east shores of Lake Michigan and in many places along the Atlantic seaboard.   They are not stationary objects

FIG. 216.   Wind-polished boulders.

FIG. 217.   Sand dunes.

but are slowly moving; when they advance on rich, fertile lands, they cause considerable damage. The marching dunes not only make the soil barren but may even bury forests and buildings.

## WORK OF RUNNING WATER

Of all the agents of erosion, running water is the most universal. Streams are of common occurrence in most lands. It is only in areas covered with perpetual ice, like Greenland and Antarctica, or in deserts like the Sahara that there are no permanent streams.

The total annual amount of moisture that falls on the lands of the earth is chiefly in the form of rain and is estimated at 30,000 cubic miles. Of this amount about three-fifths sinks into the ground and becomes ground water, and one-fifth is carried back to the sea by rivers. The average altitude of the land above sea level is one-half mile, a height which will give some conception of the enormous amount of energy which is developed by runoff. This energy is used in wearing away the land and transporting the waste to the sea.

## SOURCES OF RIVER WATER

Some of the most significant sources are rainfall, melted snow and ice, ground water, lakes, and all moist surfaces.

As rain water flows over slopes on which it falls, it picks up particles of finely weathered soil and rock waste and transports them to streams and rivers. If the slopes are steep and unprotected by vegetation, the amount of waste carried by the runoff will be large, but if the slopes are steep and covered with vegetation, the amount of the load will be small. Gullies often develop in sloping plowed fields, but seldom on level grassland. The rapid removal of soil in rough, cultivated areas (Fig. 218) has resulted in widespread destruction of valuable farm land in many parts of the United States. This has led the Federal government to initiate a rigid plan of soil conservation.

The chief factors which affect rapid runoff are steep cultivated slopes, heavy rainfall, compact soil, and removal of forest from rough areas.

## STREAM LOAD AND ITS TRANSPORTATION

A stream secures its load by erosion along the banks and bottom of its channel, by weathering along valley walls, from glaciers, tributary streams, and runoff, and through chemical action of river water. The last is the source of the invisible load.

The visible load is carried in suspension throughout the water, while the coarser material is rolled along the stream's bed. The chemical or invisible load, while it may be large in some streams, has little effect as a cutting tool. The visible load is the effec-

Fig. 218.   Field showing soil erosion.

tive tool by which rivers cut their channels. Rivers without visible tools do little work, whereas swift streams with sand grains and boulders are very effective agents of erosion.

The wear effected by running water is known as *corrasion*. It should be emphasized that the chief gradational function of rain is to transport the land into the sea. Running water first makes a region rough and irregular. After its elevation has been greatly reduced, the water again levels it.

## VALLEY DEVELOPMENT

When water falls upon the surface, it does not generally flow off evenly, but tends to collect in the low places and flows off as rivulets. Even if the land is more or less level, inequalities in rainfall and hardness of rock will cause the water to concentrate and flow off as streams. The beginning stage of many valleys is the gulley. With each new rainfall, the depression lengthens, widens, and deepens until, in time, a valley is formed. Not all valleys are formed in this way. A large portion of North America was once covered with a great sheet of snow and ice. Rivers which had developed valleys ceased to flow while the ice covered them. Many of the valleys were partially or entirely filled with glacial debris. When the ice melted, water accumulated in the partially filled valleys and started to flow along the line of lowest descent. Thus, the stream began to excavate a valley from its source to its mouth. The ice, in many places, deposited its load unevenly which resulted in large depressions. Many of these depressions had no outlets. The water from the melting ice and the regional rainfall was sufficient to fill the depressions and cause many of them to overflow. The outgoing water from the lakes developed valleys.

Most valleys pass through a life history during which they present certain characteristics that enable us to distinguish their ages. The time required for valleys to pass through the stages of youth, maturity, and old age is called a *cycle of erosion*.

*Young Valleys.* Young valleys are usually easily recognized because they are narrow, steep sided, and V-shaped (Fig. 219). Young streams are usually swift and occupy the entire valley bottom. Since they are doing most of the cutting in their valley bottoms, they quickly encounter hard and soft rock and produce waterfalls and rapids. Tributary valleys are few in number and are poorly developed.

*Mature Valleys.* In maturity the gradient (slope) of the stream is not so steep as in youth. This lessens the stream's velocity with the result that it will begin to meander from one side of its valley to the other, cutting the walls of the valley more rapidly than the bottom. The valley widens out and becomes U-shaped. The river no longer occupies all of the valley bottom, and wide, flat areas appear along the stream. In time of flood, the river overflows its banks out upon the flats. This low land along the river which is inundated during floods is known as the *flood plain* (Fig. 220). Usually the river flat meets the valley wall sharply; the stream is meandering; and

Northern Pacific R. R.

FIG. 219. Young valley.

rapids are absent or of little consequence. The tributaries are numerous and well developed.

*Old Valleys.*   When a stream has reached old age, its gradient
is so gentle as to cause the current to become sluggish.   A
comparatively small obstacle will turn it out of its course and
cause it to meander widely over its flat.   Old valleys are wide,
shallow depressions with a broad flood plain.   It is difficult to
distinguish the line between valley wall and river flat.   Waterfalls and rapids are absent, and the tributary streams take on
the characteristics of the parent stream.

We have observed that young rivers deepen their valleys
rapidly, since most of the cutting is done on the valley bottom.

*United States Geological Survey.*
FIG. 220.   Mature valley.

In maturity they begin to cut more rapidly along their valley
walls than in their bottoms.   In old age the erosion is entirely
along the valley walls.   Thus in old age, the divides between the
valleys are lowered until the entire land mass is reduced to
the lowest level attainable from running water.   If the land
were to suffer no upheaval, running water would eventually
reduce it to a *peneplain* (*paene*—almost).   A cycle of erosion
is the time necessary for rivers to reduce a land mass to a
featureless plain.   No cycle has ever been completed, since the
land does not remain quiet for a sufficient length of time.

## STREAM AGGRADATION

It might appear as if streams everywhere are constantly
engaged in cutting down their channels.   While the chief effect

of running water is to wear away the land and transport the waste to the sea, rivers in many parts of their courses are depositing portions of their loads, and thus elevating their beds.

The principal causes of stream deposition are overloading, obstacles in the bed of the stream, decrease in the volume of water, changes in the shape of the river channel, and friction

*United States Geological Survey.*
Fig. 221. A fan.

resulting from the flowing of the stream into quiet bodies of water.

## FANS AND CONES

When a mountain stream heavily laden with rock waste emerges from a gully, canyon, or gorge, upon a more-or-less level lowland, its velocity is suddenly checked. The stream, instead of following in a definite course, divides into numerous distributaries spreading the load in the form of a *fan* (Fig. 221). If the deposit is steep, it is called a *cone* (Fig. 222). Fans and cones are usually found at the base of mountains.

*United States Geological Survey.*

FIG. 222.   A cone.

*United States Geological Survey.*

FIG. 223.   The river delta.

## THE DELTA

A large part of the stream's load eventually reaches its mouth. When any river flows into a body of water, its velocity is suddenly checked, and much of the load is deposited. Not all rivers are building deltas. If the load is sufficiently large, the waves and tides not too strong, and the bottom of the body of water into which the river flows remains quiet, deltas will result. The name delta has been given to this type of deposit because it has the triangular shape of the Greek letter delta ($\Delta$), (Fig. 223). Among the noted deltas are those of the Mississippi, 12,000, the Nile, 10,000, and the great Hwang-Ho of China, 100,000 square miles in area. Most deltas are of little use for producing crops, since they are too frequently subjected to floods.

## THE FLOOD PLAIN

We have learned that mature and old streams do most of their cutting along their valley walls. In this way the valley bottoms eventually become much broader than the streams. In flood time, when the rivers overflow, their waters spread over the flat land to deposit their loads and build flat areas called *flood plains* (Fig. 220). The Mississippi River has built up a large flood plain especially along the middle and lower stretches of its course.

## NATURAL LEVEE

When a stream overflows onto the flood plain, the first sudden check in velocity of the water occurs near the river banks. The coarsest portion of the load is dropped here. In time, a ridge is built which stands above the level of the surrounding flood plain (Fig. 224). This high land is called the *natural levee*. In the lower portion of the Mississippi River the natural levee reaches a height of 20 feet or more above the level of the adjacent land.

The soil of the levee is composed largely of silt and clays. Much of the material has come from the black-soil farm lands of the North Central States. The levees are frequently utilized for agricultural purposes, for the location of roads, and even for sites of towns and cities.

## THE WORK OF GLACIERS

Have you ever observed a heavy snowfall in winter? The deep white blanket, if it does not melt off too quickly, will gradually change into a coarse granular snow or even into ice. This change represents the method by which all glacial ice is formed. All glaciers start in snow fields. A "snow field" is a region of *perpetual snow*. Many of the higher mountains

*United States Geological Survey.*
FIG. 224.   Natural levee of the Mississippi.

in the western part of the United States have snow fields. The lower limit of the snow field is called the *snow line*. Its height varies depending upon the amount of snowfall, direction of slope, and latitude. At the equator it is at an altitude of 18,000 to 20,000 feet; in the northwestern part of the United States at an altitude of 8,000 to 10,000 feet; in Greenland at 2,000 feet; and in Antarctica at sea level.

Glaciers, as before stated, have their origin in snow fields. Fresh fallen snow, when exposed to the sun's rays, does not lie on the surface long before it undergoes a visible change. The light flakes are soon transformed into granules. This is accomplished by a partial melting of the snow crystals at their points. The water runs to the center of the crystal where it refreezes, changing the flaky snow into a granular state much like small pellets of hail, known as "névé" or "firn." Successive snowfalls are thus transformed into *névé* (granular snow), and finally into solid ice. All glaciers are huge masses of snow crystals in motion from higher elevations to lower. They have been given different names depending upon their size, form, and location.

## ICECAPS OR ICE SHEETS

Snow fields and ice fields in high latitudes may give rise to great masses of glacial ice. This process may take place on a

Fig. 225. Antarctica continental glacier.

plain or plateau. When the ice in such a region begins to spread, it moves from the center in all directions. Such glaciers are called *icecaps* or *ice sheets* (Fig. 225). Antarctica is now covered with a great ice sheet. When smaller masses of land such as Greenland are covered with ice, the name icecap is applied.

*Cliff Glaciers.* Small, crescent-like masses of ice and snow nestling against steep mountain cliffs are known as *cliff glaciers*

*Glacier National Park.*

FIG. 226. Cliff glacier.

(Fig. 226). This type of glacier is quite common in the Rocky Mountains.

FIG. 227. Alpine valley glaciers.

*Alpine Glaciers.* Alpine glaciers are masses of ice that form in the snow fields at heads of mountain valleys. This type of glacier, meaning "lofty," was first studied in the Alps, whence the name (Fig. 227).

*Piedmont Glacier*. Often several valley glaciers move down from adjacent mountain valleys *out* onto a more-or-less level surface. Here the lower end of the glaciers unite and spread out into one large glacier called a *piedmont* (foot of the mountain).

*Polar or High Latitude Glacier*. This type of glacier is common along the western coast of Greenland. The western margin of this plateau is trenched with numerous deep valleys. As the ice from the icecap, which is thousands of feet in thickness, moves out to the margin of the plateau, large tongues enter the heads of the valleys and move down to the sea. Such glaciers are known as high latitude glaciers.

## MOVEMENT OF GLACIERS

Glaciers, even as rivers, move, but much more slowly. The rate varies from a few inches to 50 or even 100 feet per day, depending upon several factors. Some of the more important are thickness of the ice, slope and topography of the surface, amount of water in the ice, temperature of the regions, and the slope of the upper surface of the ice.

Glaciers do not move with the flowing motion of a viscous liquid like pitch. Neither do they slide down slopes as a solid. The nature of their movement is complex. We learned that glacial ice is made up of snow granules. In the middle and lower portions of the glacier the granules are under great pressure. Pressure lowers the melting point and the result is a melting of the granules at points of contact. Since glacial ice is not compact and dense but has considerable pore space, the water formed in the melting process enters the pore spaces where it quickly passes into ice. Water expands about one-tenth of its volume on freezing. This expansion exerts a tremendous pressure upon the surfaces of the granules and results in a slipping, compacting, and rotating motion among the granules, in this way moving the glacial ice forward and down the slope.

Glaciers, like rivers, move faster in the middle than along their sides, and faster on top than along their bottoms. These unequal movements result because of friction along the sides and on the bed over which the glaciers move. Although ice

*Glacier National Park.*

FIG. 228. Glacier, showing crevasses.

will bend and twist without fracture, yet when great pressure is exerted, it will break like any solid subjected to strong tension.

## SURFACE FEATURES OF GLACIERS

The upper surfaces of glaciers are usually very rough and irregular which makes travel over them most treacherous.

Glacial ice is readily fractured, as the presence of numerous gaping crevasses show. The crevasses may extend transversely or obliquely across the glacier or longitudinally (lengthwise). Ice tends to crack when subjected to a sudden tension (pulling apart). Where there is an abrupt slope of the surface over which the ice moves, it is not able to mold itself quickly to the irregularity. The result is a fracture of the ice (Fig. 228). Melting of the edges of the fissures enlarges them. When the ice has suffered complex fissuring, and melting has taken place, the solid blocks may become sharp, irregular pinnacles called *seracs* (Fig. 229).

FIG. 229. Alaskan glacier, showing seracs.

Large, flat boulders which have fallen on the ice from the valley walls protect the ice underneath from melting and, in time, are left suspended on ice pedestals. Such features are known as *rock tables*.

Most glaciers have rocks and earthy material scattered unequally over their surfaces, but it is more often arranged in definite belts. When the debris accumulates along the sides of the glacier, it forms ridges called *lateral moraines*. Where belts of rock waste are located near the central portion of the ice, they are known as *medial moraines* (Fig. 227). The debris which accumulates near the lower end is called a *terminal moraine*.

Glaciers carry their rock loads throughout the entire mass of the ice as well as in the upper and basal portions. The load carried in the ice and underneath is frozen solidly into the ice and is not free to shift quickly.

## EROSIONAL WORK OF GLACIERS

Ice without tools can do little work, but armed with rocky debris it becomes a powerful agent of erosion. The rasping and grinding action of rock fragments frozen solidly in the ice produces a profound effect upon the surface. Bedrock surfaces

*Glacier National Park.*

Fig. 230.    U-shaped and hanging valley.

are polished, scratched, and grooved. Angular boulders are smoothed and faceted.

The topographic effects of glacial erosion are numerous. When a glacier passes through a young valley, it not only widens and deepens it, but may also polish and groove the valley walls. The form is changed from a V to a U shape (Fig. 230). Often when the main valley is lowered by glacial erosion to a greater depth than its tributary, the lower end of the tributary valley will be some distance above the floor of the main valley when the ice retreats. Such a valley is called a *hanging valley* (the valley on the left, Fig. 230).    Many such hanging valleys are found in our western mountains.

A mountain glacier often descends rapidly near its source, effecting rapid erosion in the valley head.    As a result the valley head is extended back into the mountain wall, producing a rounded-out valley with steep sides called a *cirque* (Fig. 231). Often these depressions fill with water and produce cirque lakes (Fig. 231).

*Glacier National Park.*

FIG. 231.    A mountain cirque.

When great ice sheets override mountains or "solid rock" hills, they polish and round them off into forms known as *drumloids* or *roches moutonnées* (sheep-back hills).

## DEPOSITIONAL WORK OF GLACIERS

Glaciers do not always erode the surface over which they move.    Often, because of obstructions, overloading, check in velocity, or melting, the ice deposits its load.    All material carried by the ice is known as glacial drift.    There are two types of deposit made by glaciers: the unassorted or ice-deposited, and the assorted or glacio-fluvial made by waters coming from the melting of the ice. The ice-made deposits are the terminal, lateral, and ground moraines, and drumlins.

*Glacier National Park.*

FIG. 232. A glacier forming a terminal moraine.

*A Terminal Moraine.* A terminal moraine is a thickened belt of glacial drift composed of a maze of small knob-like hills and irregularly distributed kettle-hole-like depressions (Figs. 232–233). Since the depressions have no outlet, they often fill

with water and form lakes.   A great terminal moraine is more
or less traceable across the United States.   It marks the southern extension of the great glaciers of the last Ice Age.

*Lateral Moraines.*   Linear belts of glacial drift are frequently
found in many of the valleys in our western mountains.   When

*United States Geological Survey.*

Fig. 233.   A terminal moraine.

the ice melted, ridges of debris formed along the ice walls leaving
ridges known as lateral moraines.

*Ground Moraine* is the term for rock waste that is deposited
beneath an ice sheet.   Moving ice produces rapid erosion which
often results in overloading.   When the ice melts rapidly or
passes from higher to lower slopes, a large part of the load is
dropped.   After the ice retreats, there is left a gently rolling
plain called a ground moraine.   It is characterized by long, low

swells with wide, gentle depressions (Fig. 234). The thickness of the ground moraine varies from a few feet to many hundreds of feet. The material is composed largely of clays, with some boulders, and furnishes one of the best types of glacial soils.

A. C. Trowbridge.

FIG. 234. A ground moraine plain with poor drainage.

*A Drumlin.* An elliptical hill of glacial drift formed beneath a continental glacier is known as a drumlin. It often rises to an altitude of 50 to 100 feet. One of the finest displays of drumlins may be seen in the region between Syracuse and Rochester, New

United States Geological Survey.

FIG. 235. Drumlins.

York. Their origin is not, as yet, definitely known, but there are two plausible explanations. They may have been formed near the margin of an ice sheet by the accumulation of drift under the ice and then later eroded and shaped, or they may have been deposited under it where obstructions were sufficiently large to cause lodgment of the debris.  Drumlins are always associated with the ground moraine (Fig. 235).

The water-made deposits are valley trains, outwash plains, eskers (serpent-like ridges), and kames.  Waters emerging from the melting ice are usually heavily laden with rock waste.  As the waters flow down the valley which slopes gently away from the

A. C. Trowbridge.

FIG. 236.   Kame hills.

end of the ice, most of the load will be deposited on the valley floor.  Valley trains often extend miles beyond the ice front.

*Outwash Plains.*  These deposits are associated with ice sheets.  When the front of the ice pauses for some time upon a rather level surface, the debris-laden waters emerging from the ice spread out, uniting laterally to form a network of streams. They deposit their loads more or less uniformly over the surface to form an outwash plain.

*Eskers.* Winding ridges of stratified sand and gravel are called *eskers*. As streams issue from tunnels along the lower margin of the ice where it is more or less stationary, they drop their excess loads to fill the tunnel. When the ice melts, there is left a winding ridge of water-worn debris. Such ridges frequently extend for miles and often reach a height of from 50 to 100 feet.

*Kames.* Rounded, knob-like hills of sand and gravel are called *kames*. Like eskers, they form along the ice margins. The streams, which issue from tunnels or from fissures in the ice, may be obstructed by a terminal moraine and deposit their loads in the form of hills (Fig. 236).

## ANCIENT ICE SHEETS

In the earth's long geological past there have been many climatic changes, some of which favored the formation of great ice sheets. Those huge ice sheets, in some cases, invaded great land areas. The last widespread invasion in North America is known as the *Glacial Period*. Enormous ice centers were formed, one to the east of Hudson Bay on the Labrador Plateau, known as the Labrador Center, one to the west of Hudson Bay in the province of Keewatin, known as the Keewatin Center, and one in the mountains of western Canada known as the Cordilleran.

The ice from the first two centers spread far southward into the United States. Five distinct times these invasions moved southward, and as many times retreated. The names of these ice sheets in their order are Nebraskan, Kansan, Illinoian, Iowan, and Wisconsin.

The southern limit of the ice in the United States extends somewhat as follows: central New Jersey, across northeastern Pennsylvania, northwestern Pennsylvania, southeastern Ohio, south central Indiana, and extreme southern Illinois to about the mouth of the Missouri River. From here it follows the Missouri River in its northward course across the country. In some places it extends from 50 to 100 miles west of the river (Fig. 257).

All of North America north of this line was glaciated with the exception of a small area in west central Wisconsin and possibly small areas in northwestern Illinois and southeastern Minnesota. This area of about 10,000 square miles is known as the "Drift-less Area." Just why this region was not covered by the various ice invasions is not positively known. The North American continental ice sheet moved outward from three centers of dispersion; the Cordilleran in western Canada, the Keewatin to the west of Hudson Bay, and the Labrador to the east of Hudson Bay. The Keewatin center inundated the central part of the continent west to the Rockies, while the Labrador center covered eastern Canada and the New England states.

Ice, like rivers, is influenced in its movements by the surface of the land. As the Keewatin ice sheet moved southward, the thinner ice margin was particularly guided by lowlands, basins, and troughs. The ice edge became lobate, the lobes extending furthest in the direction of the greatest depressions and low-lands. The largest depressions, now occupied by the Great Lakes, were, at the time of the ice invasions, inner lowlands of a highly dissected, ancient, belted coastal plain. Thus great tongues, or ice lobes, known as the Lake Superior, Green Bay, Lake Michigan, Saginaw, and Lake Erie occupied the depressions where these lakes now exist. The Lake Superior and Lake Michigan lobes were widely separated from each other as the ice moved southward. It is quite possible that the high land in northern Michigan and Wisconsin, where the ice edge was thin, prevented the ice lobes from uniting until they had moved around it, there to unite and move on into the Mississippi Basin. Over extensive areas in the upper part of the Mississippi basin the soils in most areas were made deeper and richer because of these ice invasions.

# CHAPTER 33

# GROUND WATER AND
# ITS WORK

## GROUND WATER

Not all the water that falls as rain or that results from the melting of ice and snow runs off. Much of it sinks into the soil and rocks and becomes ground water. The amount that is absorbed is largely determined by the rate of rainfall, porosity

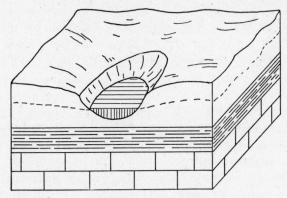

Fig. 237. Water table.

of the soil, slope of the surface, temperature and humidity of the atmosphere, and the nature of the cover on slopes.

Water will sink into the ground as far as there are pores and openings. It has been estimated that water may penetrate the lithosphere to a depth of six to twelve miles.

The ground water table, level, or plane of saturation, is the upper surface of the zone in the earth below which all the pores and cracks are filled with water (broken line in Fig. 237). It is

501

seldom level, but consists of an undulating surface. It tends to follow the topography of the surface of the land, and generally lies deeper below a hilltop than below the valley. The height of the water table is largely influenced by the amount of rainfall, porosity of the soil, and the slope of the land. It is higher during periods of heavy rainfall and lower during periods of drought.

## FORMS OF GROUND WATER

Most of the water that sinks into the ground returns to the surface later in the form of springs, wells, or geysers, or is evaporated from the soil and vegetation.

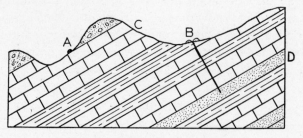

Fig. 238.   Hillside and fissure springs.

Springs are ground water issuing from the surface in sufficient quantity to produce a distinct current. Two types of springs are common: the gravity or hillside, and the hydrostatic (water pressure) or fissure spring. In the gravity or hillside spring, surface water descends through the porous material until it reaches a nonporous layer, *C* (Fig. 238). Then it flows along until it comes to the surface at a lower level, *A*.

## HYDROSTATIC SPRINGS

Hydrostatic springs are often called fissure springs. In a hydrostatic spring the water moves underground through a porous layer (dotted rock layer *D* of Fig. 238), which is situated between two nonporous rock layers. When it reaches a natural opening or fissure, *B*, it usually comes to the surface with considerable force.

## GEYSERS

Intermittent, eruptive hot springs are called *geysers*. They are found in Yellowstone National Park, Iceland, and New Zealand. Most geysers have a tube or tubes leading down to

FIG. 239.  Old Faithful.

hot rock, a basin or bowl about the opening, and a nearby supply of ground water to fill the tubes.

A geyser tube that is long and irregular interferes with the circulation (by convection) of its water content. The water in the lower portion of the tube reaches the boiling point first, and the steam pressure thus developed lifts the water above it.

A part of the water in the upper portion of the tube overflows into the geyser basin.   Under the reduced hydrostatic pressure, the water in the lower portion of the tube passes quickly into steam whose pressure suddenly forces all the water from the geyser tube.   This last phenomenon constitutes the geyser eruption (Fig. 239).   The geyser will then remain quiet until the tube refills and the water is again heated to the boiling point.

*Northern Pacific Railroad.*

FIG. 240.   Mammoth hot springs.

The material of the craters has come from the tube through solution by the hot water.   Hot water dissolves mineral matter more readily than cold.   When the hot water reaches the air, the temperature is lowered and much of the mineral load is suddenly deposited around the opening, building up the bowl. If the tube is a boiling hot spring, mineral matter is also deposited by cooling and evaporation around it (Fig. 240).

In ancient times, man secured his water supply from springs, rivers, and lakes.   The location of his dwelling was largely determined by the ease with which he could secure water.   With

the advance of civilization and the constant increase in the
density of population, large quantities of water were required in
regions where surface water was not available, or where it was
not suitable for drinking purposes.   Diggings and borings for
water were made long before the Christian era.   We find
records in India, China, and Babylonia of such attempts.

A well is an artificial boring or hole made in the earth for the
express purpose of obtaining water.   There are two kinds of
wells: the shallow or gravity well, and the deep or artesian type.

## GRAVITY WELL

A gravity well is a shallow opening made into the ground
some distance below the water table, $AB$ (Fig. 241).   Three-

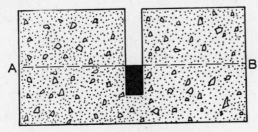

FIG. 241.   Gravity well.

fourths of the population of the United States depend upon
wells for their water supply.   It is very important that surface
wells be free from contamination (Chap. 23).

## HYDROSTATIC WELL

A deep-drilled well in which the water rises because of water
pressure is known as a hydrostatic well.   The term "artesian"
is derived from Artois, France, where a deep hole was made
and the water rose to overflow the surface.   A hydrostatic well
does not now mean that it is necessarily a flowing well, although
it may be.

Certain kinds of rock structure are necessary for this type of
well ($D$, Fig. 242).   The rocks must be in an inclined position
and composed of a layer of porous and nonporous material.
The porous rock, $A$, usually a sandstone, must outcrop so that

the surface water can enter and then flow between $B$ and $C$, nonporous rock.   When the well, $D$, is made at a lower level than the outcrop of the porous rock, the water, which is under pressure, will rise in the well and may even overflow at the surface.

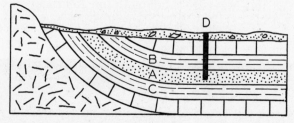

FIG. 242.   Rock structure necessary for artesian wells, east of the Rockies.

## WORK OF GROUND WATER

When rain water enters the ground, it begins to dissolve the soluble rocks and minerals when they are present.   If ground water, however, were chemically pure, little solution would take place, but as rain water falls through the atmosphere it absorbs

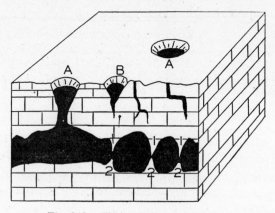

FIG. 243.   The work of ground water.

oxygen, carbon dioxide, and other gases.   As it enters the ground, the decaying organic matter near the surface supplies to the percolating ground water organic acids which greatly increase its solvent power.

The most soluble bedrock is limestone.   When exposed at or near the surface, water readily enters along the joints and bedding planes.   In time, enough of the limy material will be removed to produce large, underground passages or caverns (Fig. 243).   Some of the noted caves in the United States formed in this way are Mammoth in Kentucky, Carlsbad Cavern in New Mexico, Wyandotte in Indiana, and Luray in Virginia.

*United States Geological Survey.*

FIG. 244.   Cave showing stalactites and stalagmites.

Often caverns are enlarged to such an extent that their roofs fall in and sinkholes result (*A*, Fig. 243).   Not all sinkholes are formed in this way.   Often joints which permit a ready entrance of rain water are enlarged, forming surface depressions (*B*, Fig. 243).

Among the most common forms of deposits found in a cave are *stalactites* and *stalagmites*.   Water dripping from the roof of caves evaporates and forms around the margin of the drop a ring of lime.   Successive drops continue to make deposits on the lower edge of the ring until, in time, a long tube appears (at

1, Fig. 243, and Fig. 244). After this tube is formed, water may deposit lime in the center, completely closing it. A cross section of a stalactite shows a ring structure.

When water drips from the stalactite to the floor of the cavern, there is built up directly under the stalactite a blunt-shaped deposit, a stalagmite (at 2, Fig. 243). When the two formations unite, they constitute a *pillar* (Fig. 244).

Small cavities and fissures are frequently filled with mineral matter deposited by water. *Geodes* and *agates* are examples of cavity fillings (Fig. 209, 210, Chap. 31).

## WATER DOWSING

The divining-rod dates back to antiquity. The Romans used the *vigula divina* for discovering something hidden. It consisted of a forked stick of hazel or willow like that used in the early part of the sixteenth century for locating mineral deposits or water beneath the surface. The divining-rod or "dowser" is of more modern interest. It, too, dates back to its use by the Germans (Harz Mountains) in prospecting for mineral deposits. M. E. Chevruel, a French chemist, assigns its first mention to Basel Valentine, an alchemist of the late fifteenth century. Because of its supposed magical power, it might be taken as a historical analogue to such fairy wands as the medieval witch's broomstick, the caduceus of Mercury, or the golden arrow of Herodotus' Abaris the Hyperborean.

The existence of the modern water-finder or dowser makes the divining-rod a matter of more than mythological or superstitious interest. The chief investigator of the significance of the divining-rod, Professor W. F. Barrett, regards its use as originating prior to the Renaissance and based on the medieval doctrine of "sympathy," which claimed that the drooping of trees and the character of the vegetation could indicate mineral deposits beneath the surface by means of some sort of attraction.

By 1663, the use of the divining-rod or dowser for locating mineral deposits below the surface had almost entirely disappeared and was afterwards transferred to water-finding. It was also used in olden times to locate buried objects, and in the

seventeenth century, it was employed in tracking down crim-
inals and heretics.

In modern times the professional dowser, a "water-finder," is
one who claims that he can locate water beneath the surface.
There has been a good deal of investigation into the possibility
of a scientific explanation for such a procedure, but as yet
without positive results. The water dowser uses a forked hazel
twig, which, twisting in his hands, leads him by its directing
power to a place where a boring into the earth will find water.
Whether this can be justified or not, a widespread faith does
exist because of the frequent success of the dowser's method.
The question might be raised as to whether his success is due to
some inherent faculty or to the twig itself. Held rigidly in
equilibrium, the forked stick in the dowser's hand moves with
sudden and often violent motion, and the appearance of life in
the twig, though regarded by many as mere stage-play, is in the
popular mind associated with the dowser's success. Modern
science repudiates the idea that there is any direct connection
("sympathy" or electrical influence) between the forked twig
and the water or metal beneath the surface.

Could it be that the turning of the twig, without any intention
of voluntary deception on the part of the professional dowser,
results from a "motor automatism," a reflex action excited by
some stimulus upon his mind? Such a stimulus might be an
internal subconscious suggestion or an actual impression from
an external mind. Both sorts of stimuli are possible, so that the
dowser himself may make erroneous inferences (and fail) by
simply believing that the stimulus itself is an external one
(water or mineral deposits).

It might be reasonable to assume that the professional dowser
does actually possess a genuine supernatural perceptive faculty,
and that his mind, possessing the mental constitution or temperament of motor automatism, does become a blank or *tabula
rasa*, so that the stimulus (water) creates an involuntary or
automatic motion of the forked stick.

It should be emphasized here that all dowsers do not use the
same kind of rod. Some use a willow rod or withy; others use a

hazel twig (the traditional material), while still others may use a beech or holly twig or one from any other tree. The professional dowser may have some inherent attribute that enables him to engage in his trade successfully, but as yet modern science approaches the subject with the attitude that possibly it can be explained by some natural but, up to the present, obscure cause. It is certain that not everyone can wield the water-rod successfully.

# CHAPTER 34

# DIASTROPHISM AN EVER-WORKING PROCESS

We have learned that the gradational agents, wind, water, and ice, are constantly at work on the lithosphere eroding it and removing the waste to the sea. If the land were to remain quiet long enough, it would eventually be lowered to sea level. The fact that land masses remain above the sea is evidence that there must be other processes at work within the earth which force these masses upward. Movement in one part of the lithosphere with respect to another is called *diastrophism*.

FIG. 245. Origin of continental plateaus and ocean basins.

There are many evidences that the earth's surface is not stationary. Along many coast lines, we find wave-cut beaches that are now high above the water level. Ruins of ancient temples that have been submerged are again visible. Beds of marine shells of species now living in the sea are found along many shore lines at high elevations. These and many more evidences could be cited to prove that the earth's surface is changing.

The probable causes of diastrophism are shrinking of the earth's surface as a result of a cooling in the interior, volcanism, and earthquakes.

511

The earth is not a true sphere, but is oblate in form—that is, flattened at the poles, with the polar diameter 26 miles shorter than the equatorial. When the cooler outer portion adjusts itself to the cooling and contracting interior, there must be an upward wrinkling of the lithosphere in places and a downward wrinkling in others. The elevated earth segments form the continents, and the depressed portions, the ocean basins (Fig. 245).

In addition to the vertical movements, there are also horizontal movements which are the result of shrinkage. Mountainous regions supply evidence of such a horizontal pressure. When the bedrock in various parts of the earth is examined, it is found to be bent, twisted, or folded, yet it was originally laid down in the sea in a nearly horizontal position.

## ROCK STRUCTURES RESULTING FROM DIASTROPHISM

By rock structures we mean the relation of rocks to the surrounding rocks, nature of jointing, and their general attitude—

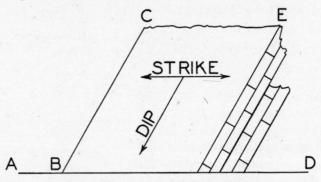

Fig. 246.   Dip and strike of tilted rock layers.

that is, the position of the beds with reference to a horizontal surface or plain.

Many terms are used to express the arrangement or structure of the rocks at the earth's surface. In many regions this is not always easy, as the bedrock in most areas is screened with a deep covering of rock mantle. It is where rivers have cut valleys down through the bedrock, or in mountainous regions

where the rocks have been greatly deformed, that their structural relations may be readily seen. Where the rocks are
deeply covered with drift, well logs obtained by drilling are
often used to determine the rock structure.

## DIP AND STRIKE OF ROCKS

In mountain regions, the bedrock is not only greatly inclined,
but the outcropping rocks take a certain trend or direction
across the surface. The
angle which the outcrop-
ping rocks make with the
horizontal plane, angle
*ABC* (Fig. 246), is called
the "dip," or the amount
of inclination. The dip is
always measured at right
angles to the strike. The
"strike," *CE*, is the direction that the outcropping
rocks take on the hori-
zontal plane.

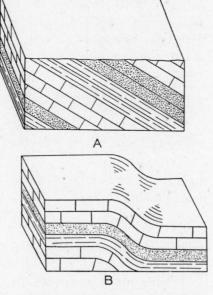

## HOMOCLINE

When the beds dip in
one direction only, *A* (Fig.
247), we have a homocline.
The word is derived from
the Greek (*homo*—one and

FIG. 247.   A. Homocline.   B. Monocline.

the same). If the flexure or fold *B* (Fig. 247) is found
between rocks which are essentially horizontal or which have
uniform low dips on both sides, it is called a monocline
(*mono*—simple).

## FOLDS

In many regions the sedimentary rocks, which were originally
in a horizontal position, are found to be greatly disturbed.
The original horizontal beds are found bent into more or less

symmetrical series of folds with alternating crests and troughs. A rock bend is called a *fold*. When the rock layers are arched up, *anticlines* or crests result, *A* (Fig. 248); when the layers are flexed downward, *synclines* or troughs are formed, *B* (Fig. 248). Synclines are inverted anticlines. The flanks of both the up folds and down folds are its limbs (Fig. 248), while the crest line or the trough line is called the axis. Anticlines and synclines may be symmetrical, that is, with equal dip on each side of the axis, and then again they may be very complex. The

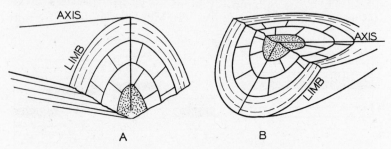

FIG. 248.    Anticline and syncline.

Appalachian Mountains are an excellent example of this complex type of folding.

## JOINTING OF ROCK

The surface rocks in most places on the earth are intersected by deep cracks called *joints*, which usually extend in two directions, horizontally and vertically. In regions where the rock has been little disturbed, the joints are, for the most part, in a vertical position; but where there has been marked diastrophism, they may intersect each other at all angles. In igneous rocks the jointing may be of such a nature as to give the impression of stratification. Jointing in rocks is produced either by tension (pulling apart) or by compression during the time when the rocks were disturbed.

## FAULTING

Rocks subjected to great stress and strain not only twist and bend, but actually break. When fracture occurs, and there is movement along the plane of fracture, it is called *faulting*.   In some instances the movement may be only a few inches, while in others it may amount to thousands of feet.   The movement is generally sudden and rapid.

The probable cause of faulting is horizontal pressure or tension.   These forces give rise to two types of faults, normal or gravity fault, and thrust or tension fault.   In the former, "2" (Fig. 249), the footwall, *E*, goes up and the overhanging, *D*, down.   In the tension fault, "3" (Fig. 249), the footwall goes down and the overhanging wall up.   The geologist uses certain terms in connection with faults.   In Fig. 249, "1" is horizontally

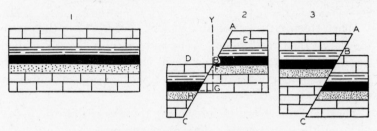

Fig. 249.   Normal and thrust faults.

bedded rock before faulting has occurred.   The fractured surface along which movement takes place is called the *fault plane, ABC*.   *D* is the overhanging wall, and *E* the footwall. When the overhanging wall drops vertically some distance, there appears on the surface a cliff, *AB*, called the *fault scarp*.   The vertical movement, *FG*, is known as the *throw*, and the horizontal displacement, *HG*, the *horizontal heave*.   Angle *HBG* or *ABY* is the *hade*, or the horizontal displacement of the rocks from the vertical (the broken line).   If the overhanging wall should rise and the footwall sink, a thrust fault would result, "3" (Fig. 249).

It is very important for the mining engineer to understand thoroughly the nature of faulting; it affects the position and depth of mineral deposits.

# CHAPTER 35

# EARTHQUAKES AND
# VOLCANISM

## EARTHQUAKES

When tremors of appreciable violence occur within the earth, they are called *earthquakes*. The moving of a heavily loaded truck over a concrete pavement will set up tremors in the earth that may be felt some distance, yet they are not of sufficient violence to be destructive.

There are many causes for violent tremors within the upper rocks of the lithosphere. The most common are faulting of rocks, volcanic explosions, falling in of the roofs of large underground caverns, and slumping of the fronts of steep submarine deltas.

Earthquakes are very frequent on the earth. There is probably never a time when the lithosphere is free from tremors, but only a few of them are sufficiently severe to produce destructive effects.

No part of the earth is immune from earthquakes. There are, however, certain regions where they are frequent: young mountain regions, along shore lines where deep oceans border high mountain lands, where great earth segments meet great ocean segments, and in areas of active volcanism.

The destructiveness of an earthquake is due to the suddenness and the strength of the vibrations of the rock matter, together with the freedom of movement of the earth matter. Solid rock transmits the tremors, or waves, with a small up-and-down movement of the particles, but loose material which is free to move will transmit vibrations to objects on the surface with considerable violence. A sharp tap of a hammer on a firm rock will cause a marble resting upon it to jump upward some distance. Buildings on solid bedrock are likely to be less disturbed than those on loose, uncemented material.

There are three types of waves accompanying an earthquake shock. Two of these tremor waves travel vertically through the earth. The first is a rapidly moving one, which is immediately followed by a second one of less velocity. The first tremor travels at a speed of six to seven miles per second. The third, which is the largest and most destructive, is a horizontal surface wave which travels out from the *epi-centrum* (above the center) in all directions like ripples in a quiet body of water when a stone is tossed into it. The horizontal wave travels more slowly than the vertical tremors, rarely exceeding two miles per second. The greater speed of the waves which pass vertically gives evidence that the earth's interior is much denser than the surface rocks, since waves travel more slowly in less dense substances.

Earthquakes are of short duration, rarely lasting more than two minutes and more frequently only a few seconds. Great destruction of property and life takes place in a relatively short time.

Where the horizontal wave meets a tall object such as a tree or high building, what really takes place? The base of the object moves forward with the wave, and at the same time the forward motion starts up the object, but at a much slower speed. The forward movement of the earth matter is quickly followed by a backward movement, or recoil of the objects. This reverses the forward movement of the objects and starts a backward movement up the building or tree. Since the tops of the objects have not traveled as far forward as their bases, a quick snapping effect results, which is extremely destructive.

## EFFECTS OF EARTHQUAKES

Earthquakes often interfere with underground drainage. Springs have ceased flowing and reappeared in new positions. Tops of caverns have fallen in and the depressions later filled with water, forming lakes. Reelsfoot Lake, in Tennessee, is a good example. Huge fissures sometimes open in the ground, such as those which appeared in the San Francisco earthquake in 1906.

When earthquakes occur on the ocean floor, great tidal waves are formed which travel over the land, often submerging cities and causing great destruction of life and property.

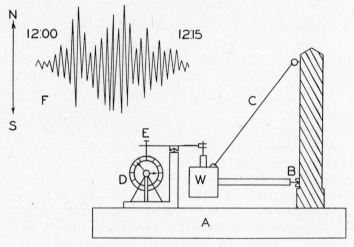

FIG. 250. Horizontal-pendulum Seismograph. *B* is a bearing carrying a beam to which a weight *W* is suspended to a vertical shaft by a wire *C*. *E* is a stylus activated by the weight *W*. *D* is the drum operated by a clock. The stylus records the earthquake wave on a paper attached to the drum.

Distant earthquakes may now be located by an instrument called a *seismograph* (Fig. 250). It is set on a concrete or solid rock foundation, *A* (Fig. 250). A heavy weight *W* is suspended to a vertical shaft by means of a wire *C*. The weight remains at rest, or nearly so, until an earthquake wave arrives; then it begins to move slowly, whereas the ground beneath oscillates rapidly. A stylus (pen) *E* attached to the suspended weight moves over a ribbon of paper fastened on the drum *D* which is kept slowly rotating by means of a clock. The seismograph *F* shows not only the amplitude of the wave but also the intervals of time during which the earthquake lasted.

Man has learned many things about the nature of earthquakes and their disturbing effects, and this knowledge is now rapidly being applied to the present construction of homes and public business structures. Wherever earthquakes of appreciable violence have occurred in the past, they are quite likely to occur again. People who live in an earthquake region should seek to build structures with due regard to the future. There are certain areas where buildings should never be placed. Locations near steep river bluffs, deep excavations, lines of important fracture, and regions of relatively loose soil foundations should be avoided. The construction of buildings is equally important. Dwelling houses should be one-story buildings. They should be built of light material. The rafters should extend from the ridge pole to the sills, and mortices and tenons should be replaced with iron straps. Such a house would move as a unit during an earthquake and not as separate parts. Heavy roofs and chimneys should be dispensed with. High structures of masonry are little suited to withstand severe quakes. High steel structures have the disadvantage of having their riveted fastenings sheered quickly by the vibrations. Large structures of reinforced concrete and steel are well adapted, since there is elasticity in both the steel and concrete to withstand heavy tremors without the direful effect of sheering as in riveted steel. All corners and floors should be well braced and tied together.

## VOLCANISM

Volcanism is a movement of deep-seated lava toward the surface of the earth. Not all lava that starts from deep in the earth reaches the surface. Molten rock material that starts surfaceward but cools and solidifies before it reaches the surface is known as *intrusive lava.*

An active volcano is a restricted vent in the earth from which issues hot lava and gases. The ejected material accumulates around the vent and, in time, builds up a cone or mountain. The tops of active volcanoes have a cup-like depression called the *crater*. Craters vary in size; some are a quarter of a mile to a mile in diameter.  The largest crater is Mauna Loa in Hawaii, which is three miles long and two to three miles wide.

Volcanoes are either of the explosive or quiescent type. Stromboli, north of Sicily in the Mediterranean Sea, Vesuvius in Italy, Krakatoa between Java and Sumatra, and Mt. Pelee on the Island of Martinique, are examples of the violent, explosive type, while the Hawaiian volcanoes represent the quiet type of eruption.  In the quiet type the lava instead of being hurled high in the air wells up to overflow the crater's rim and flows down the mountain side in great river-like masses.

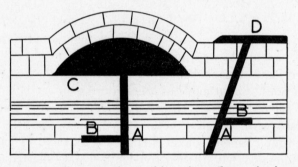

Fig. 251.   Diagram illustrating forms of intrusive and extrusive igneous rock.

Its lava cones have gentler slopes than do the cones of the explosive type.

In the violent, eruptive type, a vast amount of molten material is hurled into the air to great heights, where it suddenly cools and falls back around the vent as solid matter.  The solid material, together with ash and cinder, builds up higher and higher after each successive eruption, until a steep-sided mountain results.  Examples of this type are Mt. Rainier in Washington, Mt. Shasta in California, and Fujiyama in Japan.

## DISTRIBUTION

Volcanoes appear to have been widespread during the early history of the earth (See timetable, page 535).  Every era of geological history reveals volcanic activity, though some eras showed relatively little.  Volcanoes are not confined to continental areas.  Though most of the great volcanoes of the present time are located chiefly along the borders of the great continental plateaus, many are found on the floors of ocean basins. They are very numerous around the Pacific Ocean, in the Mediterranean Sea, and along the borders of continents where mountains are found.

It would seem that the distribution of volcanoes is largely determined by lines of weakness in the earth's crust. Volcanic activity and earthquakes seem to be most prevalent where diastrophism has disturbed the rocks within recent times.

## FORMS OF EXTRUSIVE ROCKS

Often the molten material reaches the surface, either through volcanic vents or great fissures, *D* (Fig. 251), and cools rapidly. Some examples of great fissure lava flows are the Columbia Plateau of Eastern Washington, 200,000 square miles, Yellowstone National Park, and the Deccan Plateau of India.

In violent eruptions the broken-up material which is forced high into the air may be portions of the crater, or lava which has solidified either before it was ejected or during its flight in the air. Much of the ejected material may become powdered and either fall back as ash or be carried great distances from the vent before settling. Still smaller broken-up portions of the lava may solidify and fall back around the crater in the form of gravel-like material called *lapilli* (pea-like). The coarser fragments are known as *cinder*, and when still larger, they are called *bombs*.

## FORMS OF INTRUSIVE LAVA

Much of the molten material which starts from deep in the earth and works its way outward solidifies before reaching the surface and is known as intrusive lava. The principal types of intrusive igneous bodies are *sill*, *dykes*, *laccoliths*, *necks*, and *bathyliths*.

*Dykes.* Dykes are lava-filled fissures, *A* (Fig. 251), which cut into or across rock layers. These fissures may be found in rocks of any kind, igneous, sedimentary, or metamorphic. Dykes may vary in thickness from a fraction of an inch to hundreds of feet.

*Sills.* Where lava is forced in between the rock layers, *B* (Fig. 251), it is known as a sill. The thickness varies from thin sheets to thick massive ones. They are much like dykes except that the intruded lava lies parallel, or nearly so, to the bedding planes.

*Laccoliths.* When molten lavas are intruded between the rock layers in a large lens-like mass so as to arch up the overlying bedrock into a dome-shaped hill or mountain, *C* (Fig. 251), it is known as a laccolith. The word *laccolith* means "lake of stone." The floor of the laccolith is flat. The Black Hills are a good illustration of this type of lava intrusion.

*Bathyliths.* Intrusions of such magnitude as not only to arch up the rocks above, but to break or fault them along the sides of

Fig. 252.  Diagram of a bathylith.

the intruded mass are called bathyliths (Fig. 252). Many of the cores of our western mountains are of this type of intrusion. The softer, fractured rocks above are soon worn away, exposing the igneous intrusions.

*Necks.* Lava-filled tubes of volcanoes which lead down to great depths are known as *necks*. After a volcano has become extinct, erosion will, in time, cut away the softer materials such as ash, cinders, and lava of the cone, leaving the more resistant material projecting up to form the neck.

In 1870, diamonds (see Chap. 29) were discovered upon a plateau located between the Vaal and Modder rivers in southern Africa. Their occurrence here is confined to limited areas, elliptical or circular in outline, and varying from 65 to 225 feet in depth. These areas are old volcanic pipes. The diamonds near the surface of the pipes are found in what is known to the miner as *yellow ground*.    At a greater depth the pipes constrict, and the yellow ground is underlain with a very hard basic magnesian rock called *kimberlite*, or blue ground.    This must be quarried and then left to weather before the diamonds can be washed from it.    Africa furnishes 95% of the world's output of diamonds.

## CAUSES OF VOLCANISM

The earth is not molten in the interior as was formerly thought.    It has been clearly proved that it is a body more rigid than steel.    One might wonder how it is possible that a substance as hot as the interior of the earth, thousands of degrees Fahrenheit, can remain solid.    The explanation is found in the tremendous pressure which must exist there.

The reason for the high temperature has not been fully determined.    It may result from the slow contraction of the earth or from the transformation of radioactive elements.    As the heat moves slowly outward, it comes in contact with certain rock material that fuses at a lower temperature than the surrounding masses.    Liquid rock impregnated with gases is lighter than solid rock, and hence, is forced upward.    The molten thread fuses its way through the rock outward toward the surface. When the lava thread reaches the fractured rock zone of the earth's surface where there is air and water, it breaks forth as a volcano.    If on the other hand the lava thread solidifies before it reaches the surface, it remains in the earth as some form of intruded lava.

# CHAPTER 36

## THE EARTH'S PAST

### INTRODUCTION

The earth of today is not what it was millions of years ago. It has ever been changing and will continue to do so into the far-distant future. The changes, however, are so slow that they are not recognizable during an individual's life span. There are many evidences here and there which reveal these changes. Waves of the sea are ceaselessly destroying coast lines; earthquakes are changing the contours of shore lines and even depressing and elevating continents and sea beds; volcanism is leaving its mark in many parts of the lithosphere; and running water, winds, and glacial ice are slowly, but surely, modifying the surface appearances of the land.

### GEOLOGY DEFINED

Geology is a history of the earth and its past inhabitants. The story is a long and complicated one. To understand and appreciate the chain of events through which our planet has passed from its very beginning on down through the long ages of the past up to the present requires a knowledge of many sciences.

Geology is an inclusive science. A knowledge of the events from the earth's very beginning as a planet and its relation to the other bodies in the solar system is a problem for astronomy. To discover how the earth secured an atmosphere and its effect upon the past and present of the earth involves a knowledge of *climatology*. The falling of moisture in the form of rain and snow and its runoff requires a knowledge of the nature of erosion and deposition of rock material in the sea. An understanding of how rocks are formed from minerals demands some knowledge of *mineralogy* and *petrology*. With the coming of an atmosphere and an ocean, life appeared on the earth. Upon the death of many of the organisms, especially those with hard parts, they were buried in the sea muds and changed into fossils. The study of these forms of ancient life is *paleontology*. After the rocks were deposited, forces within the earth twisted and deformed them so that in many places the rocks are not as they were originally deposited. A study of the causes and nature of rock deposition and deformation is *structural geology*. The investigation of the agents which are now bringing about changes on the earth's surface is known as *physiography*.

## DIVISIONS OF GEOLOGICAL TIME

The great age of the earth is clearly shown by the nature of the rocks and the evidences of life entombed in them. The earth may be compared to a book of history. History is divided into eras, periods, epochs, and ages. To acquire a knowledge of the events that have taken place in the development of civilization, the historian must go into the regions where the peoples lived and developed and there examine all traces of human life if he is to give an accurate account of their past history. In like manner the geologist must go into the field and must study the rocks and their contents if he is to give a complete and accurate picture of the earth's past. To the geologist the rocks are the pages of his history and the fossils are its inscribed characters of life development. Like history, the rocks of the earth, in terms of time, are divided into eras, periods, epochs, and ages. But these divisions are much longer than the divisions of the history of civilization.

Some of the pages are blank in the vast "nature book"—that is, no evidences of life are present in the rocks. It then becomes more difficult for the geologist to clarify the entire record of events. He uses two types of evidences in interpreting the past of the earth: the entombed fossil life, and the physical structure of the rocks.

## FOSSILS AND THEIR SIGNIFICANCE

The word *fossil* is derived from a Latin word, *fossilis*. A fossil is any evidence of past life which has been preserved by

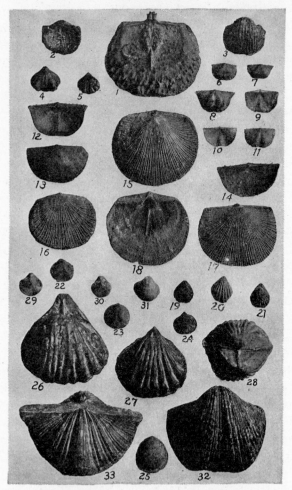

FIG. 253. Fossil brachiopods.

natural means (Fig. 253). Fossils are of great value in the study of the earth's history since they reveal something of past climates, evolution of life, shifting of seas, lakes, and rivers, and the distribution of plant and animal life on the earth.

# HOW FOSSILS ARE PRESERVED

With the advent of the atmosphere and the oceans, water vapor was carried from the oceans over the land by the winds and there deposited in the form of rain and snow. Some of the moisture penetrated into the rock material; some formed the rivers and eventually reached the sea as runoff. Weathered rock waste was thus carried and deposited in the sea. Organisms that had died and dropped to the sea bottoms became covered with sediment and later were changed into fossils. Organisms were not only buried by ocean sediments but by ash from volcanic eruptions and by winds that picked up finely weathered rock waste and deposited it in the form of *loess* (loose-material).

Fossils may be preserved in many different ways. An entire animal may become buried in sands and gravels and later frozen solidly. The flesh, hide, and hair of great hairy mammoths have recently been found intact in the cold earth of the Arctic regions. Preservation by such means is known as *refrigeration*.

Many of the organisms that live in the sea have exterior and interior hard parts. At their death, the hard parts drop to the ocean floor and, soon covered with sediment, finally become fossils. Often the entire hard parts may be removed by solution or decomposition, after the rock material surrounding them has become hardened, and then only a cavity remains where the skeleton had originally rested. The cavity is called a *mold*. Often tree trunks, twigs, and leaves fall to the ground, and if soon covered with water, their woody material is changed to carbon. This method of preserving plant life is called *carbonation*.

Along the shores of the Baltic Sea fossil resin is found in which are embedded insects and small plant seeds. As the sticky juice was exuded from the living trees, insects were attracted to it and became covered by the resin. In this way the entire organism was preserved. Fossil resin is called *amber*, and the process is known as *embalming*.

Both plant and animal life may have the material of their hard parts replaced, molecule by molecule, with some form of mineral matter, which thus reproduces the exact form and structure of the original. This method of preserving evidences of life is known as *petrification*. Footprints and tracks of prehistoric creatures have been preserved.

## WHERE TO LOOK FOR FOSSILS

Fossils occur in peat bogs, asphalt lakes, caves, and in wind, lake, river, and volcanic ash deposits. In time the sediments of the sea—sand, mud, and lime—were changed into sandstone, shale, and limestone, and then later elevated above the sea. Today we examine them for fossil remains. Some rocks are rich in fossils, while others may be entirely barren.

## PHYSICAL EVIDENCES OF GEOLOGICAL TIME

The history of the earth is measured in hundreds of millions of years. During this long expanse of time, mountain ranges, one after another, have been built up and torn down. The waste products were carried and deposited in the sea to form limestone, sandstone, and shale. The tearing down of the highlands of the earth and the building up of the sea beds bring about, in time, readjustment of the continental plateaus and ocean basins. This result initiated an up-and-down movement of the lithosphere. Portions of the sea became land, and old, worn-down lands became ocean. The period during which the rocks of the sea bed were elevated into highlands and then again worn down to sea-floor level is known as a *cycle of erosion*. There is no physical evidence of the length of time required for the elevation of the rocks and their subsequent destruction and removal to the sea.

Many times similar mountain chains have been eroded away and then elevated by an upwarp to be again washed away after each uplift. Rock strata that are deposited in the sea with no appreciable break in sedimentation are said to be "conformable." Often, after a bed of strata has accumulated to some depth in a given region, an uplift, resulting from diastrophism, may take place. Much of the elevated rock material is then eroded away. Then submergence may again take place, and younger strata will be deposited upon the eroded surface of the old rock, *ABC* (Fig. 254). This interruption in the stratigraphic succession is known as an *unconformity* or an "erosional surface" separating two sets of rocks.

Another method of determining the age of the earth is by the time it takes to wear down land masses and build up sedimentary rocks. It is estimated that 5,000 to 10,000 years are necessary to remove one foot of rock waste to the sea. The total thickness of sedimentary rock is about 50,000 feet. At this rate, the age of the earth from the beginning of the formation of sedimentary rock is placed at 500,000,000 years.

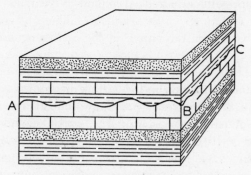

FIG. 254. Unconformity.

At one time, all the oceans were composed of fresh water. The salt which has accumulated in the sea water came originally from rocks. These were weathered and carried by rivers to the ocean. The oceans evaporated, leaving their salt behind, and their waters became saltier and saltier. It is possible to calculate the age of the oceans by determining the rate at which salt accumulates.

Still another means of estimating the great age of some of the rocks is through the study of radioactivity. Rocks have been found that contain radioactive substances such as uranium and thorium. Chemists have been able to determine the rate at which these minerals break down to form lighter elements. Such observations place the age of some of the rocks at about two billion years.

All the evidences, whether physical or organic, seem to point to the fact that the earth is of great age.

## THE GEOLOGIC ERAS

From what we have now learned, it should be apparent that the succession of events, both physical and organic, enables the geologist to divide the earth's history into a rather distinct timetable somewhat similar to human history. The longest divisions, eras, are the chapters; eras are divided into periods or paragraphs; the paragraphs into subparagraphs or epochs; and the subparagraphs into sentences or ages. (See Table 12.)

An era represents hundreds of millions of years, a period tens of millions, and an epoch thousands to millions of years. Five great eras have been recognized in the earth's book of history.

## THE ARCHEOZOIC

The first era or chapter in the earth's history is known as the Archeozoic. It is interesting to know that all era names are derived from Greek words (*archaios*—early beginning, *zoon*—life). This era is one of the longest, now estimated at 880,-000,000 years. The rocks of the era are largely igneous (fire rock) with some sedimentary which has been so greatly altered as to give it the appearance of igneous material. These greatly changed rocks are known as quartzites, slates, marbles, and schists. The Archeozoic represents the early history of the earth. No direct evidences of life have been found in these old rocks, but that does not necessarily mean that life in some form was not present on the earth during this era. Simple forms of life were, doubtless, present, but the great diastrophism which these rocks suffered may have erased all traces of it.

Some of the indirect evidences that suggest the presence of life are iron, graphite, and limestone. The presence of graphite clearly indicates the existence of plant organisms. Limestone is sometimes of chemical origin but in many cases is made from organic life.

The era was marked by volcanism, vertical up-and-down movements of the earth's surface, and widespread mountain making.   It was immediately followed by a long period of relative quiet, during which erosion was active.   Widespread distribution of waste material is found around Hudson Bay and the Great Lakes in both Canada and the United States.

## PROTEROZOIC ERA

The second chapter or era is known as the Proterozoic (*proteros*—earlier, *zoon*—life).   The rocks of this era rest unconformably upon the Archeozoic wherever the two are present. They are somewhat similar to the Archeozoic in appearance except that sedimentary rocks are more plentiful than in the first era.   The rocks are highly altered and deformed like those of the former era.   Oceans were present as evidenced by the widespread deposits of sedimentary rocks.   The rocks of this era contain fossil remains giving evidence that sea life was far advanced over that of the first era.

It was during this era that the rich iron deposits around Lake Superior, which have made the United States the leader in the iron industry, were laid down.

This long era, now estimated at 650,000,000 years, was brought to a close by widespread volcanic activity and mountain making.   The bluffs along the northern shore of Lake Superior and the mountains of northern Minnesota and Michigan were formed during this time.   Diastrophism and volcanic activity marked the close of the era.   A long period of relative quiet then followed, during which erosion and deposition were the dominant processes.

## PALEOZOIC ERA

The third era is known as the Paleozoic (*palaios*—old, *zoon*—life).   This era, while not so long as either of the first two, is estimated to have extended over 320,000,000 of years.   In many respects the Paleozoic was vastly different from the first two eras.   It is an era that can be readily differentiated from the older ones because of the nature of the rocks and the life evidences found in them.   Outstanding events of the Paleozoic included the floodings of the land by the seas, and their withdrawal.   During each period of the long era, entire continents, or large portions of them, were submerged.   In these ocean waters limestone, sandstone, and shales were deposited many times.   Aquatic animals with bony skeletons were abundant in the sea.   Their skeletal remains were later covered with sediment of the ocean floor and were preserved as fossils.   Thousands of such fossil forms are known.   With the aid of these the *paleontologist** can learn something about the advancement of life, climatic variation, and physical changes which occurred during this era.

The Paleozoic era is divided into many periods or paragraphs as you will readily discover when a study of the geological timetable is made.   In the table are recorded some of the important events of each period.   See if you can find the kinds of rocks deposited and something about the type of life present.

The Paleozoic Era was brought to a close by widespread elevation of the land out of the sea and by mountain making. It was at the close of this chapter that the Appalachian Mountains were first elevated above the sea.

## MESOZOIC ERA

The fourth chapter is known as the Mesozoic (*mesos*— middle, *zoon*—life).   The Mesozoic was a much shorter era than the Paleozoic, its length being estimated at 200,000,000 years.   Like the preceding era, it is divided into periods (see timetable).   This middle era may be thought of as a transitional time between the old and the new just as medieval history makes a transition between ancient and modern history. The earth's topography ranged from low plains to lofty mountains; its climate from torrid to frigid regions; its animals from small ratlike mammals to the dinosaurs—some giants 60 to 80 feet long and of 20 to 40 tons weight (Fig. 255).   Nonflowering plants and those bearing flowers were to be found.

The close of this era witnessed some of the greatest changes in plant and animal life that the earth has ever recorded.   The

---

*A paleontologist is one who, by means of studying fossils, deals with the life history of past geological periods.

great reptiles, the largest animals that ever roamed the earth, disappeared, and their place was taken by the modern mammals. Lower plant forms were displaced by modern ones. Thus we see why the Mesozoic era is called a *transitional time*.

*American Museum of Natural History.*

Fig. 255. Brontosaurus, the Thunder Lizard.

## CENOZOIC ERA

The Cenozoic (*kainos*—recent, *zoon*—life), is the closing chapter in the history of the earth. It is one of the shortest of chapters, the recent estimates of its duration being 60,000,000 years. This chapter, for convenience, is subdivided into two subchapters: the first, the *Tertiary*, and the second, the *Quaternary* (see timetable).

The Cenozoic was a time during which the earth was greatly changed and the present-day topography was assumed. Few of our present landscapes existed during the Mesozoic. Plains, valleys, mountains, hills, canyons, and plateaus are the gift of the Cenozoic.

Plants and animals, especially the mammals, reached their high state of development during the Cenozoic. Man, the highest of all mammals, began his physical and mental growth

long before the close of this era.   The first record of his existence was discovered in the late interglacials of the Quaternary.

American Museum of Natural History.
Fig. 256.   Cave man of the Neanderthal race.

The ape-like man (Fig. 256) had progressed to man early in the
latter part of the era.

   The Cenozoic closed by the spreading of a vast sea or "field"
of ice over much of northern North America and northern

Fig. 257.   Centers of glaciation in North America and
the southern limit of glaciation in the United States.

Europe.   For some reason, not yet
well understood, the climate became
cool and great ice sheets moved down
over the continent, not once, but in
North America, five distinct times
(Fig. 257).   Each ice invasion was followed by a warming of the climate and
a retreat of the ice.   These great ice
invasions coming in the closing stages
of our earth's history rank as one of
the greatest terrestrial events of all
time.

## THE TIMETABLE

   Table 12 gives in tabular form these
divisions of geologic time and the salient characteristics of each
arranged in chronological order with the most recent divisions
placed first.

TABLE 12
GEOLOGIC TIMETABLE

| | PERIODS AND ESTIMATED LENGTHS | ROCKS AND ECONOMIC PRODUCTS | CHIEF EVENTS | LIFE DEVELOPMENT | |
|---|---|---|---|---|---|
| QUATERNARY | Recent 25,000 | Soil<br>Sand<br>Gravel<br>Silts<br>River deposits<br>Lake deposits<br>Wind deposits | Erosion<br>Local diastrophism<br>Local volcanism | Man dominates<br>Modern plant life | Man Appears |
| QUATERNARY | Pleistocene 1,000,000 | Glacial materials<br>  Sand  Boulders<br>  Clay<br>  Gravel<br>  Peat<br>Economic products<br>  Peat  Gravel<br>  Soil  Water<br>  Sand  Water power | Changing climate—cold to warm<br>Ice invasions and retreats<br>Erosion<br>Cutting of inner gorge of Grand Canyon<br>Forming of our Great Lakes | Man first appeared<br>  Ape-like man<br>  Pithecanthropus<br>  Sinanthropus<br>  Neanderthal<br>  Heidelberg<br>  Cro Magnon<br>Modern mammals<br>Modern plant life | Man Appears |
| TERTIARY | Pliocene 10,000,000 | Uncemented materials<br>  Sand  Green sand<br>  Clays  Gravels<br>  Silts<br>Economic products<br>  Salt  Gypsum<br>  Naphtha<br>  Oil in California | Marked erosion<br>Grand Canyon forming<br>Folding and faulting in west<br>Extensive volcanism<br>Topography of west completed<br>Climate cool<br>Bad Lands forming<br>Colorado Plateau formed | Mammals dominant<br>Horse well advanced<br>Primates well advanced<br>Plant life modern<br>Intercontinental migration of mammals | Age of Mammals |
| TERTIARY | Miocene 15,000,000 | Sedimentary rocks<br>Uncemented materials<br>  Sands  Green sand<br>  Clays<br>Economic products<br>  Phosphate<br>  Gold  Bitumen<br>  Oil in Texas<br>  Iron  Fullers earth | Erosion<br>Shifting lakes in west<br>Climate cool<br>Extensive volcanism in west<br>Yellowstone Park formed<br>Columbia Plateau formed<br>Mountain making in west<br>Grand Canyon started | Mammals dominant on land<br>Horse well along<br>Elephants and camels<br>Primates present<br>Plant life changed from tropic to deciduous | Age of Mammals |
| TERTIARY | Oligocene 10,000,000 | Uncemented materials<br>  Clays  Sandstone<br>  Sands  Green sand<br>  Marls<br>Economic products<br>  Amber  Phosphate<br>  Gypsum  Lignite<br>  Salt in Texas | Extensive erosion<br>Bad Lands forming<br>Much igneous activity in west<br>Mild climate | Higher mammals<br>Carnivores present<br>Modern plant life | Age of Mammals |
| TERTIARY | Eocene 20,000,000 | Uncemented materials<br>  Clay  Green sand<br>  Sands  Gravel<br>  Boulders<br>  Shales<br>Economic products<br>  Phosphates<br>  Gold  Oil<br>  Iron  Quicksilver<br>  Coal in west Alaska | Sea invasion in west<br>Erosion and deposition<br>Starting of Bad Lands<br>Volcanism in west<br>Local diastrophism and mountain making<br>Climate mild | Ammonoids rare<br>Corals modern<br>Appearance of crabs<br>Sea urchins prominent<br>Reptiles prominent<br>Plant life advancing<br>Mammals developing<br>Ancient horse | Age of Mammals |
| MESOZOIC | Cretaceous 40,000,000 | Sedimentary rocks<br>Limestone<br>Chalk  Shales<br>Sandstone<br>Economic products<br>  Chalk<br>  Coal of west<br>  Oil and gas | Great interior sea<br>Chalk making<br>Widespread diastrophism<br>  Rocky Mountains started<br>  Appalachians uplifted<br>Great igneous activity in west<br>Glaciation in Australia | Rise of lowly mammals<br>Extinction of dinosaurs<br>Angiosperms present<br>Flying reptiles<br>Appearance of birds<br>Ammonoids diminishing | Age of Reptiles |

(CENOZOIC spans the Quaternary and Tertiary rows.)

TABLE 12
GEOLOGIC TIMETABLE (*Continued*)

| | PERIODS AND ESTIMATED LENGTHS | ROCKS AND ECONOMIC PRODUCTS | CHIEF EVENTS | LIFE DEVELOPMENTS | |
|---|---|---|---|---|---|
| **MESOZOIC** | Comanchian or Lower Cretaceous 20,000,000 | Sedimentary rocks  Limestone    Shale  Sandstone  Uncemented land   materials  Igneous rocks  Economic products   Coal    Iron   Clay    Asphalt | Mountain making in west  Local volcanism  Withdrawal of sea  Climate mild and moist | Appearance of flowering plants—angiosperms  Sponges abundant  Ammonoids much like Jurassic  Modern crabs  Reptiles at zenith | **Age of Reptiles** |
| | Jurassic 25,000,000 | Sedimentary rocks  Limestone  Sandstone  Conglomerate  Igneous material  Economic products   Salt and gypsum   Oil in California   Gold in California   Iron    Coal   Quicksilver | Marked erosion  Making of red beds in west  Semi-arid climate  Rocky Mountains started  Great igneous activity in west  Diastrophism | First reptile-like birds  Culmination of giant dinosaurs  Conifers  Cycads  at zenith  Modern insects appear  Huge sea reptiles  Zenith of ammonoids | |
| | Triassic 25,000,000 | Sedimentary rocks  Sandstone  Conglomerate  Limestone  Igneous material  Economic products   Salt and gypsum | Widespread aridity  Widespread red beds in west  Much volcanism in west  Diastrophism  Gypsum deposition  Salt | First dinosaurs  Large  coal  fern-like plants gone  Ammonoids abundant  Rise of reptile-like mammals  Cycads and conifers present  Primitive mammals | |
| **PALEOZOIC** | Permian 40,000,000 | Sedimentary rocks  Sandstone  Shale  Limestone  Igneous rocks  Economic products   Coal   Gypsum salt   Oil gas in west   Potash in Texas | Appalachians made  Great aridity in west  Salt and gypsum deposits of west  Widespread glaciation  Climate dry and cool  Red beds of west | Rise of primitive reptiles  Cycads and conifers appear  Amphibians varied  Appearance of modern corals  Trilobites disappear  Ammonoids common | **Age of Amphibians** |
| | Pennsylvanian 45,000,000 | Sedimentary rocks  Sandstones  Limestones  Shales  Mineral products   Coal    Iron   Oil and gas | Up-and-down movement of land  Coal making dominant  Warm, humid climate  Widespread sea in west  Starting of Appalachian Mountains at close  Igneous activity in Europe | Dominance of ferns  Profusion of coal-making plants   Lycopods   Horsetails  Culmination of amphibians  Earliest known insects  Scorpions  Dragonflies | |
| | Mississippian 30,000,000 | Sedimentary rocks  Sandstones  Limestones  Shales  Volcanic products  Mineral products   Salt and gypsum   Lead and zinc   Coal in Europe   Oil and gas | Two great sea invasions  Erosion and deposition  Coal making in Russia  Marked diastrophism at close  Ouachita uplift  Local volcanism | Rise of amphibians  Culmination of crinoids and blastoids  Sharks dominant in sea  Coiled cephalopods called goniatites with complex septa | **Age of Fish** |
| | Devonian 40,000,000 | Sedimentary rocks  Limestones  Sandstones  Shales  Some igneous rocks  Mineral products   Oil and gas   Phosphates   Lithographic stone   Limestone   Building stone | One great sea invasion  40% of continent under sea  Erosion and deposition  Acadian revolution in east  Volcanism in east | Ammonoids first appear  First land forests  Fishes in great variety  Great brachiopod age  Compound corals prominent  First footprints of amphibians  First spiders—air-breathing life | |

TABLE 12
GEOLOGIC TIMETABLE (*Continued*)

| PERIODS AND ESTIMATED LENGTHS | ROCKS AND ECONOMIC PRODUCTS | CHIEF EVENTS | LIFE DEVELOPMENT | |
|---|---|---|---|---|
| **PALEOZOIC** Silurian 25,000,000 | Sedimentary rocks Limestones Sandstones Shales Conglomerates Mineral products Great salt beds in east Great iron deposits Oil and gas Limestone for cement | Three great sea invasions 50 % of continent under water Great limestone making period Great period for salt making Some igneous activity in east Marked erosion and deposition Local diastrophism at close | First appearance of land plants First appearance of land life Rise of the fish Culmination of trilobites Culmination of cystids Brachiopods Pelecypods Corals abundant Coiled nautiloids dominate | Age of Fish |
| Ordovician 60,000,000 | Sedimentary rocks Sandstones Limestones Shales Some igneous rocks Minerals Oil and gas Salt and gypsum Building stone Zinc Marble Lead | Three great sea invasions Middle Ordovician greatest 66 % of continent under sea Great limestone-making period Local mountain making Taconic Mountains | Earliest known vertebrates Cephalopods and brachiopods Culmination of trilobites No known land plant life Culmination of cystids Culmination of straightshelled cephalopods, coiling marked | Age of Invertebrates |
| Cambrian 90,000,000 | Sedimentary rocks Sandstones Shales Limestones Conglomerates Igneous rocks Economic products Building stone Aquifers Gold | Great sea invasion of land 30 % of N. A. under sea Local glaciation Invertebrate life evolving Erosion and deposition Mountain making at close | Fossils abundant All kinds of animals without backbone Crustacea represented by trilobites Straight formed nautiloids mostly | |
| Proterozoic 500,000,000 | Sedimentary rocks highly metamorphosed Slates Marbles Quartzites Igneous rocks Economic products Gold Native copper Iron ore Silver Cobalt Graphite | Erosion and deposition Widespread volcanism Glaciation widespread on earth Widespread diastrophism and mountain making at close of era Life advancing | First fossils appear Low plant forms (algae) Single celled plant and animal life Water-dwelling plants Rise of cephalopods and pelecypods | Rise of Invertebrates |
| Archeozoic 850,000,000 | Igneous rocks Meta igneous Meta sedimentary Marbles Slates Schist Economic products Iron Gold Cobalt Nickel Magnetite | Marked diastrophism and mountain making Widespread volcanism Marked erosion of high lands | Indirect evidences of life Iron Limestone Carbonaceous slates Graphite No fossils found | No Fossils |
| Cosmic Time | Earth started as a nuclear knot in a spiral nebula. Grew large by gathering in small bodies called planetesimals. Hot at first but cooled and became solid. | | No life possible | |

A Refracting Telescope.  Man's powerful mechanical eye for solving some of the mysteries of the universe.

# CHAPTER 37

# ASTRONOMY, ANCIENT
# AND MODERN

## INTRODUCTION

Astronomy is one of the oldest of sciences. No one knows just when or where it began. In very ancient times man's curiosity and desire to make crude observations of heavenly bodies, to interpret their meaning, and possibly to use them as guiding facts in framing some convenient way of reckoning time, led him to study the heavenly bodies. These attempts later developed into the science of astronomy.

It was not so long ago that men thought this science was not only one of the oldest, but one of the most complete. With the advance of science, the increasingly exact methods of observing and testing, and through the great progress made in the manufacture of scientific instruments, astronomers have been forced to conclude that their science is far from complete. New fields are now opening that had never been dreamed possible a half century ago.

Astronomy first started man on the long and arduous pathway of science. In the eighteenth century it laid the foundations for the study of the laws of dynamics, which eventually led to the invention of calculus, and later, to the beginning of physics and engineering. In early times, as today, this science made possible the navigation of the seas, the establishing of boundary lines, and the determination of time.

A study of astronomy aids in developing exactness of observation, clearness in thinking, and logical expression. Man has come to know that the welfare of nations and peoples and the life history of individuals are not controlled by the motions of heavenly bodies as the ancients believed. The enormous reaches of space and time, the discovery of bodies invisible to the unaided eye, the birth of nebulae and stars, and the evolution of solar systems are just a few of the problems in astronomy that stir the popular imagination. Everyone should know something of the great truths which astronomy teaches.

## ANCIENT ASTRONOMY

Astronomy may be divided into three great periods: (1) from its very beginning to 600 B. C.; (2) 600 B. C. to 100 A. D.; and (3) 1500 A. D. to the present.

The exact date of the origin of the Babylonian calendar is not known. Authorities do not agree on dates. It is known that they used lunar months of thirty days. A month was intercalated somewhere, as the year began near the spring equinox. We find that the Sumerians were celebrating New Year's Feast during the days of the Priest King Gudea, about 2600 B. C. This does not mean that the calendar was not in existence. It is reasonable to assume that the calendar dates back to somewhere between 2350–2150 B. C.

The time of the introduction of the first Chinese calendar is not clear. In 2269 B. C., astronomers Hi and Ho reformed the calendar and adjusted the year to 365 days by adding seven days every nineteen years, so they must have had a calendar long before this.

## THE BABYLONIANS

These people erected great rectangular temples seven stories high, each story being named after some heavenly body. The first story, made of brick and painted black, was for Saturn; the second, made of orange-colored brick, was dedicated to Jupiter; the third, constructed of orange-red brick, was for Mars; the fourth, of brick gilded with gold, was for the sun, monarch of the heavens; the fifth, constructed of brick painted blue, was for Venus; the sixth, made of yellow brick, was for Mercury; and the top story of brick and covered with silver, was for the moon, the ruler of the night skies.

It was to the top story that the priests, robed in garbs of black, retired at night to study the stars.  Through their ceaseless efforts they observed the paths of the planets; accounted for the movement of the stars by assuming that they were fastened to a great dome which rotated; fixed the length of the year; and predicted the occurrence of eclipses.  This was a remarkable feat when we consider that they did all of these things without the aid of instruments.

## THE HEBREWS

This ancient race contributed very little to the knowledge of astronomy.  Their conception of the universe was very crude,

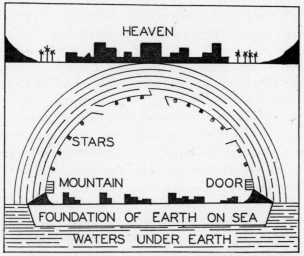

*Adapted from Blackenhorn.*

FIG. 258.  Hebrew-Babylonian Conception of the Universe.  (Reprinted by permission from Winterton C. Curtis' *Science and Human Affairs*.)

and no doubt some of their views were obtained from the Babylonians.  Fig. 258 illustrates the Hebrew-Babylonian concept of the universe.  The earth was flat and spread upon a great sea. The sky was a great dome which was supported on pillars. To the roof of the dome the stars were fastened, while great windows opening from the dome let in water to the earth. Doors in the east and west were for the rising and setting sun. Over the earth as well as under it was a vast sea, and Heaven was above the watery firmament.

## THE EGYPTIANS

These people contributed to astronomical knowledge by recording the time and occurrence of eclipses both of the moon and the sun. History assigns to them a record of 832 eclipses of the moon and 373 of the sun.

## THE BEGINNINGS OF SCIENTIFIC ASTRONOMY

Astronomy as a science began about 600 B. C. A great Grecian philosopher and scientist, Thales of Miletus, about 640 B. C. to 546 B. C., discovered the equinoxes and the solstices, and was able to account for the cause of the long, warm days of summer and the short, cold ones of winter.

Closely following Thales came Anaximander of Greece, 611 B. C. to 547 B. C., who was the first to account for the phases of the moon. He believed that the earth was a great cylinder floating in space, with man living and developing on its upper flat surface. The stars were holes in opaque hoops which were concentric around the earth and revolved with it. It was through these holes that man was able to behold the eternal fires which filled the hoops.

Eudoxus, 408 B. C. to 355 B. C., like Anaximander, proclaimed the idea that the earth was a cylinder, but he replaced the circular hoops with transparent, spherical shells. The stars, planets, moon, and the sun were openings in the shells which revolved at different rates of speed. It is this conception that gave rise to the "music of the spheres."

## PLATO AND ARISTOTLE

There arose in Athens two great schools of thought, headed by Plato, 427 B. C. to 347 B. C., and Aristotle, 384 B. C. to

322 B. C. The Academy under Plato was noted for astronomical research. Plato himself was not interested in scientific study, but was famed as a philosopher. Aristotle, on the other hand, founded the Lyceum and wrote on numerous natural scientific subjects.

## THE ALEXANDRIAN MUSEUM

At Alexandria, Egypt, there grew a university to correspond to the Lyceum of Athens. The school was founded by Ptolemy Soter, one of the noted generals under Alexander the Great. Under his influence and inspiration a great library was built up consisting of some 700,000 volumes. To this center of learning he invited famed Grecian scholars.

Aristarchus, 310 B. C. to 250 B. C., was a member of the university and was the first astronomer to set forth the heliocentric conception of the universe. He believed that all motions of the heavenly bodies could be explained by placing the sun instead of the earth at the center of the universe. His theory received little recognition in the museum because his worth as a scientist was then not recognized.

Hipparchus, 160 B. C. to 105 B. C., is best known as one of the first observational astronomers. It was he who first determined the obliquity of the ecliptic—that is, that the earth's equator in the sky is inclined to the ecliptic, the earth's orbit in the sky, at an angle of 23½ degrees. He also maintained that the equinoxes are not fixed, but moved backward slowly in the sky.

Claudius Ptolemy, the last great astronomer of the Alexandrian school, 100 A. D. to 170 A. D., was an Egyptian. In spite of the fact that both Aristarchus and Hipparchus of the same school taught that the sun was the center of the universe, Ptolemy rejected this theory. He put forth one of his own in which he placed the earth at the center of the universe and made all bodies move about it. His views, known as the *Geocentric Theory*, held unquestioned sway until the time of Copernicus. He argued that if the earth moved, as set forth by Aristarchus and Hipparchus, birds, when they attempted flight in the sky,

would be left behind.    To explain the movement of the planets
between the earth and the sun, as well as those beyond the sun,
he devised a system of small circles upon large circles, or as it
was known, a system of deferents and epicycles (Fig. 259).
Each of the planets revolved in a small circle (epicycle) around
a point, which in turn revolved around the earth in a large
circle called a deferent.    The large circles of Mercury and
Venus were located between the earth and the sun, and the

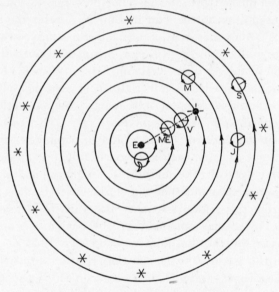

FIG. 259.    Ptolemaic idea of the universe.

centers of the small circles about which these planets moved lay
in a line connecting the earth and sun.    In these orbits, the
small circles, Mercury and Venus, oscillated back and forth,
never getting far to the right or left of the sun.    The planets
beyond the sun revolved in orbits about their centers, which in
turn moved on a large circle about the earth in such a way that
a line connecting the planet with the center of the epicycle
always kept itself parallel to the line connecting the earth and
the sun.    The moon's motion was explained by assuming that
it moved in an epicycle backward in its revolution about the

earth, while the epicycle moved forward about the earth in the same period. Ptolemy's view was generally held until about the middle of the sixteenth century.

## THE DARK PERIOD

The learning of the great Alexandrian school was followed by a period of war and conquest known as the "Dark Ages," 200 A. D. to 1500 A. D. Fierce tribes of Goths and Vandals moved out of the Baltic and Vistula River regions from northern Europe and overran the Roman Empire. Later the Saracens, Arabians from the Mesopotamia region, moved westward, conquering all of Northern Africa, Spain, and southern France. They then moved into Syria and Mesopotamia where they again settled down and put aside their fighting propensities. Soon great Arabian schools of learning sprang up in the regions where Roman and Greek centers had existed. It is not possible to say how much astronomical knowledge came from the Arabs. There seems to have been a period of about 1400 years when astronomy was all but forgotten. Independence of thought was suppressed, and the reasoning of Aristotle accepted. It was during this period that the false science, astrology, flourished. This science assumed that all human affairs are directly influenced by the position of heavenly bodies. By their position the astrologer assumed that he could predict famines, wars, pestilence, and human events, even to the birth and death of individuals.

## THE MORN OF MODERN ASTRONOMY

Modern astronomy began about the close of the Dark Ages. There was born in Thorn, Poland, a young man by the name of Nikolaus Copernicus, who later became a monk. His span of life, 1473 A. D. to 1543 A. D., witnessed a great revolution in thinking, particularly with reference to the conception of the universe. He was well educated and later became canon of the cathedral at Ermland, of which his uncle was bishop. While serving the church he received a salary sufficient to supply all his needs. Since his duties were not heavy, he devoted all his

spare time to the study of astronomy, his favorite subject.   He
had read all that had been written by the great scholars of the
past, especially the work of Ptolemy.   He could not, however,
reconcile his thinking with that of Ptolemy.   Like Pythag-
oras, he was convinced that the sun, not the earth, was the
center of the universe.   Copernicus' heliocentric theory was
set forth in a work called *On the Revolution of the Heavenly
Bodies*.   His manuscript was kept concealed for thirty years,
for fear that he might be persecuted as a heretic for his views,
which were in direct conflict with the teachings of his church.
Upon his death in 1543 his great work was published by the
church he served without a knowledge of its full contents.
After publication, a storm of opposition arose; the book was
recalled and burned.   Later the church published his thesis
after it had removed the objectionable parts.   After several
centuries the theory of Copernicus has been vindicated, and he
stands out in history as the first great contributor to modern
astronomy.

## TYCHO BRAHE

This famed scientist (1546–1601) was born at Knudstrup
in Skåne, south Sweden, then a province of Denmark.   He was
sent to the University of Copenhagen to study law.   While
there, a solar eclipse attracted his attention and awoke in him
a great desire to study astronomy.   He observed the stars at
night and began to map the heavens.   All of his spare allowance
was spent in the purchase of astronomical instruments.   He
was a remarkably accurate observer and soon discovered that
his star charts did not agree with those of his predecessors.
After reading the work of Copernicus, he was persuaded that
possibly the heliocentric theory of the universe was right.   He
reasoned that if the earth moved about the sun, the stars in
the sky should show an annular parallax.   Parallax is the
apparent displacement or difference of position of an object as
seen from two different stations or points of view.   The annual
parallax of a star is the difference in direction as seen from two
opposite points of view in the earth's orbit.   In Fig. 260, an

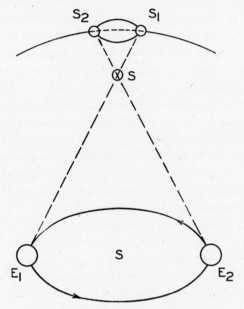

FIG. 260. Annual parallax of a star.

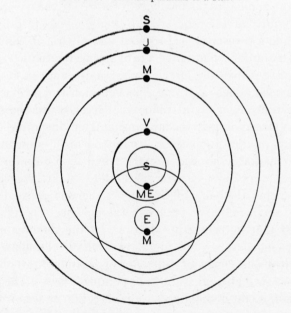

FIG. 261. Tycho Brahe's conception of the universe.

observer at $E_1$ would see a star $S$ in the sky at $S_1$, while at $E_2$ the star $S$ would be seen in the direction of $S_2$. The star's annual parallax is represented by the small circle $S_1S_2$. This small parallax he could not determine with the crude instruments of his day. On this account and because he was a good churchman, he rejected the Copernican system, placed the earth at the center of the universe, and made the sun revolve about the earth once a year. It is interesting to note that by placing the earth at the center of his system he made the sun's orbit the common deferent about which the planets moved (Fig. 261).

The work of Tycho Brahe was noted for accuracy of observation, and his famous "Rudolphine Tables" form the basis on which our present Nautical Almanacs are made.

## THE WORK OF KEPLER

Johann Kepler was born in Germany in 1571 and died in 1630. Disease in early boyhood left him with a weakened body and rendered him unfit for manual labor. He possessed a brilliant mind and was finally sent to the University of Tübingen to study for the ministry. But mathematics and astronomy made a greater appeal to him, and in these fields he progressed so rapidly that at the age of twenty-three he was made professor of astronomy at the Styrian University at Gratz.

Kepler, although a strong believer in astrology, began to study the behavior of the planets, eventually worked out the shape of their orbits, and also formulated the three laws of planetary motion. His work vindicated the Copernican conception that the sun and not the earth is the center of the universe.

## THE WORK OF GALILEO, 1564–1642

Galileo was born in Pisa, Italy, in 1564. His parents were very desirous that he study medicine, but Galileo thought otherwise. Having no love for such studies, he devoted his time to mathematics and physics. He made such rapid progress that at the age of twenty-three he was made professor of mathematics in the University at Pisa. Lippershey, a Dutch spectacle maker, had taken two spectacle lenses and placed them together in such a way that distant objects sighted through them seemed nearer. Galileo, taking the cue from Lipper-shey, immediately set about to construct a telescope of his own, and in 1609 gave to the world the first telescope used for astronomical purposes.

Galileo had studied the work of Copernicus and knew inti-mately the work of Kepler. After studying the motions of the planets through his telescope, he was convinced that Coper-nicus, and not Ptolemy, had the correct conception of the universe. But because the church was not yet ready to accept the heliocentric theory, Galileo was finally summoned to Rome and made to recant all he had taught and written. He was then banished and lived a prisoner until his death in 1642. Galileo must be looked upon as one of the real heroes of modern astronomy.

On the very day that Galileo died there was born one of the greatest scientists of all time, Sir Isaac Newton. He was noted for his work in mathematics and physics. The great question he asked of himself was: Why do the planets move around the sun, and what force keeps them in their orbits? Was there some force responsible for holding them together and keeping them moving? To this question he finally gave an answer by stating his three laws of motion and his law of universal gravita-tion. These proved that the sun is the controlling force which keeps all the other bodies in the solar system in their present orbits.

Following Newton came Sir William Herschel, Bradley, Laplace, and a long list of great men. All of these without exception were convinced that Copernicus was right in con-tending that the sun and not the earth is the center of our solar system.

# CHAPTER 38

# OUR STARRY GALAXY

What constitutes our Milky Way? Not so many years ago astronomers believed that the stars extended indefinitely in all directions. Could it be possible that their number was legion? It was no simple matter to envision an infinite universe reaching out and out including all space. Such a conception was not easy for the human mind to grasp, yet it was easier to recognize a limitless universe than one which came to an end somewhere.

The construction in recent times of large reflectors and refractors that are able to penetrate the depths of space to distances great enough to stagger the human mind has proved that our Milky Way is only one of many—possibly millions—of starry galaxies in the universe.

The nearest galaxy to our own is Andromeda (Fig. 262), 800,000 light years removed. A light year is the vast distance through which light moving *in vacuo* at 186,000 miles per second travels in one year. It is equivalent to about six trillions of miles.

In this starry galaxy of ours are billions of stars, various types of nebulae, and a solar system. Do these same kinds of bodies exist in other starry galaxies? No astronomer is yet ready to answer definitely. In Andromeda, one of the nearest starry galaxies outside of ours, are found stars and nebulae. Who dare say that there are not stars in other galaxies?

## SHAPE OF OUR STARRY GALAXY

Sir William Herschel was one of the first to indicate that this galaxy might be the shape of a disc or lens which was much

550

broader than it was thick. This view has come to be recognized as correct by modern scientists. In order to understand its vast size, it is first necessary to become familiar with

*Yerkes Observatory.*

FIG. 262. The great nebula in Andromeda.

some of the various measuring rods used by the astronomer. Within our solar system distances are usually reckoned from the sun, the central body. The mean distance of the earth from the sun is 92,870,000 miles—the measuring rod which is used in our solar system. How great is this distance? If we were to make a journey from the earth to the sun in an airplane capable of making 200 miles per hour, it would require 53 years of constant flying to cover the distance. If we were to make a journey in the plane to the nearest star, we should have to travel constantly for about 144,186 centuries. It is evident then that the measurement of distance between bodies outside our solar system demands a much larger measuring stick than is used in the solar system. Such a stick is the light year. Light, as we have already indicated, is the fastest traveling phenomenon about which we know anything. It requires but little more than one-twelfth of a second, or about the time it takes to snap the fingers, for light to travel around the earth at the equator. Some of the most distant nebulae are millions of light years away from us. For theoretical work the astronomer finds it very convenient to use a distance corresponding to a parallax of 1.″0. This unit is called a *parsec*. The word is derived by taking the first three letters of the words "parallax second." It is equal to 206,265 times the distance of the sun from the earth, or 3.258 light years.

## DIMENSIONS OF THE MILKY WAY

The distance across this vast galaxy is far greater than Sir William Herschel ever dreamed. This is not so strange, since the telescopes of Herschel's time were not powerful enough to gather light from space and to make very faint points of light visible. With the modern telescopes star "gauges" are made which reveal the galaxy to be one of immense size. Many estimates of its size have been made by astronomers, and the one most generally agreed upon is that the broad diameter of the disc is about 100,000 light years while the thickness of the lens is about 10,000 light years. It is within this great disc that we find about 30 or 40 billions of stars, nebulae, and our solar system. Our sun is not at the center or near the center, as Herschel believed, but is located some 20,000 light years from the hub or center of the galaxy.

## THE MILKY WAY

Just what is the Milky Way?  Is it real or is it only an optical illusion?  Arching across the sky from horizon to horizon may be seen a brilliant and mystic band of pearly, hazy light.  If the

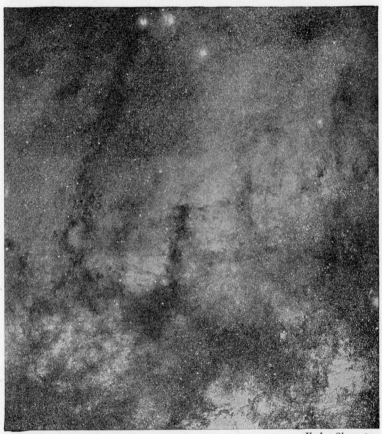

*Yerkes Observatory.*

FIG. 263.   Milky Way in Sagittarius, Ophiuchus, and Scorpius.

earth did not obstruct our view and the sky were darkened, one might see this luminous cloud encircling the entire sky.  For ages it has aroused the wonder and curiosity of both layman and astronomer.  If one were to watch the dark, clear evening sky at intervals throughout the entire year from various vantage places on the earth, he would be able to put together the separate parts of the Milky Way. In the evening during winter and summer, it appears high overhead and is very distinct and easily seen. In the spring and fall, it is low on the horizon and is not so easily seen.

Many legends have been associated with this band of light. To the Greeks it represented the path burned in the sky by the chariot of the sun which was driven by Phaeton. He attempted to drive for one day Apollo's fiery steeds, but soon lost control of them. Democritus, the Grecian philosopher, believed that the belt of light represented a great swarm of stars too faint to be detected individually. Modern telescopes have proved this theory to be correct. Today we know that this pearly, misty belt which appears as a ring is illusionary. When the band is examined with a modern telescope, it resolves itself into myriads of stars so distant and faint as to be individually invisible to the eye (Fig. 263). In looking toward the Milky Way, we behold that portion of the galaxy which extends farther and is most densely populated with stars.

## OUR STAR FAMILY

It is extremely difficult for the astronomer to determine the number of stars inhabiting the Milky Way. In ancient times man looked upon the stars as lanterns let down by the gods through openings in a metal dome to light the night sky. Today we know that each is a glowing hot body similar to our sun. Only about 30 of these incandescent suns are within 100 trillion miles from us and a few more within 500 trillions of miles. If this small number of stars occupies a space which is 200 trillions of miles across, how vast must our starry galaxy be to hold 30 to 40 billions of stars!

Each of the glowing bodies offers to the astronomer, who nightly examines it through his telescope, a complete laboratory in which he may carry on investigations so wonderful and breath-taking as to stagger the mind of man.

The stars are not distributed uniformly throughout our starry galaxy. Only 3000 to 3500 are visible to the naked eye above the horizon at any one time. The total visibility in both hemispheres is between 6000 and 7000.

*Lick Observatory.*

Fig. 264. Star cluster in Hercules.

In very ancient times, no one knows just when, the stars were separated by observers into groups and were named constellations. Forty-eight of these groups were found in Ptolemy's

*Almagest.* Since that time 40 more have been delineated and named.

In the constellation of Hercules (Fig. 264) is found one of the finest examples of a globular cluster (spherical in shape) in the northern heavens. It is estimated that it may contain as many as 50 to 100 thousand stars. They appear so close together as to make the cluster look like a snowball. But the stars in the cluster are separated by tremendous distances. They appear close together simply because they are so far away—possibly 34,000 light years. About 90 of these clusters have already been discovered. Examples of open clusters visible to the unaided eye are the Pleiades—500 light years; the Hyades— 120 light years; and Coma Berenices. The distances of the clusters vary from a few hundred to hundreds of thousands of light years.

## THE NATURE OF STARS

Stars are glowing suns. They are incandescent bodies surrounded by an atmosphere of cooler gases. They shine by means of the light they generate and not by reflected sunlight as do the planets and satellites. A planet in the night sky may be distinguished from a star by the fact that a planet does not twinkle, and if observed carefully over a sufficient period of time, it will shift its position among the stars. Stars are not fixed. They are widely scattered through space and are moving in various directions. The vast distances that intervene make their movements seem slow. Even our sun is moving rapidly forward relative to the stars around it.

All stars have proper motion, which is the rate of change in the sky of one star in relation to its neighbors. It is the shift in position of the stars after allowance for abberation, parallax, precession, and other motions of our own has been made. Proper motion does not tell us how stars are angling toward or away from us. Radial velocity is a star's speed in our line of sight. Because of the great distance of stars from us and the vast space separating them, this motion cannot be detected by the human eye except over long periods of time. To illustrate, if one were to fall asleep, as did Rip Van Winkle, and sleep for 10,000 years and then awake and search for the Great Dipper, he would be surprised to find that it had disappeared. In this time its stars would have shifted their positions sufficiently to destroy the Dipper's outline. If it be true that stars are moving at high rates, why do they not collide with one another? Such a catastrophe is possible, but not very likely. The stars are so remote and space between them is so immense that the possibility of a head-on collision is rare. Sir James Jeans, the great English astronomer, has estimated a possibility of once in a million million million years.

To the inexperienced observer all stars look alike, but not so to the astronomer. He quickly detects a difference in both brilliance and color.

Today the astronomer is very anxious to ascertain basic facts about a star such as its temperature, size, and life history. Stars vary in size greatly. Our own sun—866,000 miles in diameter—is about an average-sized member of our starry galaxy. But there are some giants. A few of these are Betelgeuse in Orion—180 to 260 million miles in diameter; Mira in Cetus—260 million; Antares in Scorpio—390 million; β Pegasi in Pegasus—150 million; Aldebaran in Taurus—37 million; Rigel in Orion—36 million; and Arcturus in Bootes—21 million.

One of the most thrilling aspects of modern astronomy is the ability the astronomer possesses of pushing back farther and farther the frontiers of the universe. The large 100-inch telescope on Mount Wilson in California has been able to gather light from space to a distance of about 500,000,000 light years. What will the future hold for the astronomer with the completion of the new 200-inch reflector? Only time can tell.

The distance of some of the most familiar stars should be of interest to all. Our sun is our nearest star—92,870,000 miles distant. But what about some of the bright stars that are visible in the heavens on a clear dark night? Table 13 will give us an answer to this question.

TABLE 13
STAR DISTANCES

| Star | Distance in Light-Years |
|---|---|
| Polaris | 1085 |
| Deneb | 465 |
| Rigel | 540 |
| Canopus | 652 |
| Betelgeuse | 296 |
| Spica | 190 |
| Antares | 390 |
| Regulus | 60 |
| Aldebaran | 71 |
| Capella | 47 |
| Castor | 45 |
| Arcturus | 38 |
| Pollux | 30 |
| Vega | 26.9 |
| Altair | 15.7 |
| Procyon | 11.2 |
| Sirius | 8.7 |
| Alpha Centauri | 4.31 |

## THE COLORS OF STARS

We have learned that all stars have temperatures sufficiently high to keep the matter in the state of an incandescent gas. Since all stars do not have the same temperature, their colors become an index of their surface temperature. A dull-red color indicates to the astronomer that the surface temperature is low —possibly around 2500° F. Orange-red stars are considerably hotter—5000° F. Yellow stars, like our own sun, have surface temperatures around 10,000° F., while bluish-white stars range from 35,000° to 70,000° F. Antares, in Scorpio, is a good example of the low-temperature star. It is a dull-red color. Rigel, in Orion, is an excellent example of a bluish-white star.

All stars have a life history, but man's span of life is far too short to discover much of it. How long stars exist as hot bodies no one knows; no one has yet been able to determine the life span of a star. Our sun has been in existence for billions of years and will continue to give light and heat for many millions of years in the future.

It was formerly believed that stars evolved through a loss of heat. Bluish-white stars were supposed to be very young, and as they lost their heat through long periods of radiation, they would pass successively through orange, yellow, and finally into a dull-red. Today the astronomer has discovered that this is not the case. The red stars are now classified into "giants" and "dwarfs." The "giants," like Antares, have low surface temperatures (6000° F.), while the "dwarfs" are small, dense, and of very low surface temperatures. Thus youthful stars are composed of huge volumes of rare gases at low temper-

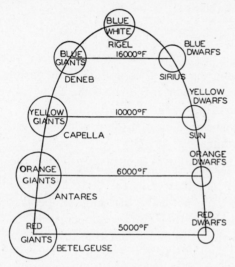

FIG. 265.   Diagram illustrating the life history of stars.   (After Russell.)

atures while the old red stars are small, dense, and also of very low surface temperatures.

The evolution of the average star seems to be about as follows: The giant-red star passes into the orange-red, then yellow, then bluish-white where it reaches its zenith of temperature, then back down the scale into yellow, orange, and to dull-red. H. N. Russell has given us a diagram showing the possible evolution, growth, and final decadence of a star (Fig. 265).

## THE DENSITIES OF STARS

The mean density of a star is found by dividing its mass by its volume. A star's density is not the same throughout, but increases as the center of the star is approached, where it may be twenty or more times greater than its average value. The range is as great as 0.000,000,2 to 64,000 times the density of our sun. The giant star Antares in Scorpio is only 0.000,000,2 the density of our sun, while Eridani $\beta$ is 64,000 times denser than our sun. In the case of Antares, the gaseous substance would be so tenuous as to offer little friction, while in a star like Eridani the density is so great as to render penetration almost impossible.

## MAGNITUDES OF STARS

If one were to examine the stars on a clear moonless night, one would soon discover that not all of the visible stars are of the same degree of brightness. Some glow as veritable diamonds, while others shine with a light so dim as to be scarcely visible. The brightness of a star is due to its temperature, size, and distance.

Long ago, astronomers arbitrarily divided the visible stars into six groups or magnitudes. The first twenty brightest they placed in the first magnitude group, and the faintest discernible without the aid of a telescope, in the sixth magnitude group. Between the first and the sixth magnitude groups, they then distributed the stars into four groups in such a way that the ratio of the brightness of a star in one group to that of a star in the next fainter group would equal the ratio of the brightness of the star in the latter group to that of a star in the next ensuing fainter group. This simply means that the brightness of a star of one magnitude is obtained from that of the next fainter magnitude by multiplying by a constant factor. This constant factor is 2.512, and is called the light ratio. It is the ratio of brightness between two stars which differ by exactly one magnitude. If a star is 2.512 times brighter than a first magnitude star, it becomes a star of zero magnitude. It should be noted that the number of the magnitudes diminishes as the brightness increases, and that the zero point makes the very brightest stars become negative magnitude stars—as, for example, Sirius in Canis Major, which is −1.58.

Before photography was applied to the study of the brightness of stars, it was the common practice to determine the brightness by visual observation. The *visual magnitude* is the expression of a star's brightness as determined by the naked eye. The human eye is very sensitive to light from the yellow-green part of the spectrum, while the photographic plate is most sensitive to light coming from the blue-violet end. If two stars, for example, were the same distance from the earth and of the same luminosity, but one was red and the other bluish-white, the red star would appear much brighter to the naked eye. The *photographic magnitude* is the expression of the brightness of a star as revealed by the photographic plate. If the equidistant red and bluish-white stars just mentioned were photographed, the bluish-white one would appear larger on the negative since the photographic plate is very sensitive to blue-violet light.

The astronomer uses another method to determine the amount of light given off by a star. It is known as the *radiometric* magnitude. By means of a very sensitive instrument called the thermocouple he is able to determine the total amount of radiant energy of all wave lengths that reach the earth, and so can determine the star's magnitude.

## NEBULAE

The layman of today is about as mystified as was Alice in Wonderland when he tries to keep pace with the astronomer in his modern-day discoveries of the various bodies that exist in our Milky Way. Some of the most beautiful and fantastic bodies that are now demanding much of the astronomer's time are the nebulae. They appear as giant islands of faint light trailing their greenish clouds in the intense darkness of space. What are nebulae? The word comes from the Latin, meaning "mist or cloud." These diffuse nebulae are of two classes: the dark and the light, with the light predominating. One of the most interesting of these bodies is the one found in the sword which hangs from the belt of Orion, the "Giant Hunter." This nebula is visible to the naked eye. However, most of these faint bodies are visible only through the large telescopes.

All of the nebulae are known to belong within the borders of our sidereal system, and for the most part, are located in or near the galactic plane. For this reason they are known as the *galactic nebulae*.

The nature of the matter composing them is not definitely known. It may consist of solids and gaseous particles making up huge, tenuous aggregations of cosmic dust or gases. Some are luminous, while others are as black as night. Why do some of them glow? This is still an unsolved problem. It may be that some are near to giant suns and appear luminous because of reflected light, while others may be hot enough to produce their own light.

There is still another type of nebula that is of supreme interest to the astronomer because it seems to possess a rather distinct form. It is known as a *planetary nebula*. About 150 of these nebulae have thus far been discovered. They are more or less circular envelopes of nebulous matter surrounding a central star (Fig. 266). Their disc-shaped form suggests that they are possibly rotating bodies. Their form and structure have inspired the idea that they may have had their genesis in the outbursts of novae, and that they are still expanding bodies. Might it not be possible that these nebulae are solar systems in the making? Why should a starry galaxy like ours be limited to one solar system?

## THE UNIVERSE

Is it infinite or is there an end to it somewhere? This is a problem that has puzzled the mind of man in the past and is yet unsolved. We have pointed out that the Milky Way does not comprise the boundary of the "universe," but that beyond our Milky Way there are possibly millions of other starry galaxies scattered throughout the vast stretches of space. Larger telescopes will, no doubt, unveil many more of these spiral aggregations of nebulae and stars. Are the galaxies unlimited then in the universe? What separates one from another?

Are they stable or are they slowly disintegrating? How do they originate? These are some of the questions for the

Mt. Wilson.

FIG. 266. A planetary nebula. The Onil Nebula in Ursa Major.

future astronomer, and no doubt answers for some of them will be found.

A study of astronomy has through the ages revealed an ever-expanding physical universe of great grandeur. From the geocentric conception of Ptolemy with the earth as the dominating feature, we have progressed to the heliocentric of Copernicus with the sun as the dominating body and the members of the solar system moving around it. We have seen that the sun is only one star among a host of stars. With the work of William Herschel a more detailed study of the stellar system began. The sun's motion in the star system, the presence of related star pairs, the vast number of star clusters and nebulae have aroused interest in a detailed study of the galactic system. The spectroscope, the refracting and reflecting telescopes, and many more precise instruments have been introduced to make it possible for man to explore the universe. Today the knowledge of our physical universe is far more advanced over that of the past. The galactic system with our sun no longer at its center stands out sharply. The mysterious spirals, and many other among the nebulae, possibly millions, now within reach of our large telescopes have been established as exterior systems many of which are gathered into greater systems. Are all of these galaxies and clusters of galaxies a super-system which form a unit in a still larger structure? This is a problem for the future.

# CHAPTER 39

# OUR SOLAR FAMILY

## THE GLOWING SUN

Our solar family consists of the sun, nine planets, satellites, asteroids, comets, and meteors.

The most important body in this great family is the sun. Most of us thoughtlessly accept the bounteous gift of sunshine and heat and give little heed to our dependence upon the sun for our very existence. The sun affects tremendously both the mind and body of man. Man plants his seeds in the fertile ground, and the heat and light of the sun, together with the rains, cause them to grow and develop into useful and beautiful plants. Many of the ills of man are healed when he exposes himself to health-giving sunshine. Plants of past ages, the gift of the sun to the earth, have been transformed into coal, and marine organisms into oil. Even the wind, which furnishes energy to drive our sail vessels over the high seas and spins the wheels of millions of windmills, is the gift of the sun. When sunshine is withdrawn from man for any length of time, he becomes mentally depressed and melancholy. There are few manifestations of energy on the earth that are not the gift of the sun. Yes, the power of the sun is, in some miraculous and mysterious way, associated with life itself.

Our sun, while it is not the largest star in our universe, is a gigantic body. If we could make a non-stop flight around it in an airplane at a speed of 200 miles per hour, it would require 565 days to encircle it at the equator. The diameter of the sun is about 866,000 miles. To appreciate this great size, if we suppose that the sun is a hollow sphere with an opening of sufficient size to admit the earth, it would require the material of 1,300,000 earths to fill this great sun shell completely.

Our sun, according to the British astronomer Sir Arthur Eddington, has a surface temperature of about 10,000° F. —about twice the temperature obtainable in an electric furnace. The interior of the sun has a temperature of possibly 70,000,-000° F. A star as hot as the sun must radiate an enormous amount of heat. Every square foot of the sun's surface radiates energy at the rate of a 9000-horsepower engine. The proportion of this heat energy received by the earth is about one part in every 2200 millions. Yet the total amount the earth receives is about 5000-thousand horsepower per square mile of surface. Here is a possible source of energy for the future. Might it not be possible for man sometime to harness this energy and turn it to his use?

## PARTS OF THE SUN

Why study the sun? We learned (Chap. 38) that there are possibly 30 or 40 billions of stars in our universe, but all except the sun are too far away to permit a detailed study of them. Our sun is near enough for the astronomer to be able to make a thorough study of its parts, and in this way to gain some knowledge of the nature of a star. The various parts of the sun are its *photosphere, reversing layer, chromosphere,* and *corona.*

## THE PHOTOSPHERE

The visible part of the sun is called the photosphere or the "light-giving sphere." The dazzling brilliance of this hot gaseous ball may be made more real if we compare it with the light of the full moon. The sun is 465,000 times as bright as the full moon. It would require six hemispherical skies massed solid with full moons to equal the light of the sun.

Through the telescope the photosphere has a mottled appearance with the dark and light areas constantly shifting. This appearance is possibly due to violent ascending and descending currents of gases at the photosphere's level. The ascending currents bring up the hotter gases from lower levels, while the descending ones carry down the cooler dark matter.

The sun's atmosphere, lying above the photosphere, is composed of two distinct parts: the reversing layer and chromo-

*Lick Observatory.*

FIG. 267.   Solar corona during an eclipse.

sphere, and the corona.   These parts can be seen only during a total eclipse of the sun.

## THE REVERSING LAYER

The reversing layer is a layer of cooler gases several hundred miles thick between the photosphere and the chromosphere,

and merging gradually into the chromosphere above. It is
this rarer and cooler gas which produces the absorption spectrum from which it is possible for the astronomer to infer the
chemical composition of the sun.

## THE CHROMOSPHERE

The chromosphere is the name given to the rose-red solar
atmosphere above the reversing layer. The chromosphere is
composed chiefly of hydrogen and calcium gases and extends
outward into space several thousands of miles. It is from this
layer that the great jets or prominences rise.

## THE CORONA

Above the chromosphere is found the mysterious corona, or
crown of light, extending from the sun's equator to a distance of
many thousands of miles. The corona is best seen during a
total eclipse of the sun (Fig. 267). This crown of light is not
of uniform thickness. During a maximum sunspot period,
long streamers extend in all directions to great distances, while
from the polar regions distinct beams may be observed stretching out thousands of miles. The nature of the material composing the corona is not fully known. In earlier days it was
thought that it was of a magnetic nature, but today it is believed
to be the more tenuous part of the solar atmosphere.

## THE SOLAR PROMINENCES

During a total eclipse of the sun, great orange-red prominences
or jets may be seen rising from the sun's periphery to a distance
of millions of miles (Fig. 268). These prominences are of two
classes, the quiescent and the eruptive. In the latter, glowing
gases appear to rush out from the sun at enormous speeds like
great tongues of fire. They seem to be more numerous in the
vicinity of sunspots and are, no doubt, great explosions in the
sun. The quiescent type spread out lazily above the sun's
surface and give the impression of a tree with a great outspread-
ing top, or of clouds floating around in the solar atmosphere.

## SUNSPOTS

Galileo's "solar clouds" are great cyclones or vortices appearing in the sun's surface, somewhat similar to funnels. They are of enormous size ranging from a few thousand to 100,000

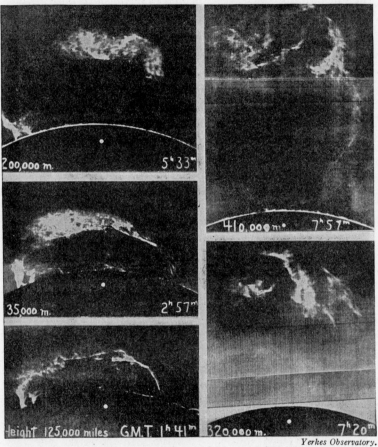

*Yerkes Observatory.*

FIG. 268.   Solar prominences during an eclipse.

miles in diameter. The average sunspot is dark at the center (*umbra*) and of a lighter shade around the margins (*penumbra*). They seldom occur near the poles of the sun, but are confined to belts about 30 degrees wide on either side of the sun's equator. The cause and nature of sunspots have been a subject for much speculation. They give the impression of great whirling cyclones moving across the sun's surface. From the central portion of a sunspot, there stream forth great masses of electrons which have been torn from the nuclei of atoms deep in the sun—atoms which are subjected to terrific heat and pressure. No doubt many of these freed electrons penetrate our atmosphere and produce magnetic disturbances which result in violent electrical storms on the earth. It has been proved that they cause interference with radio, telegraphic, and telephone reception. A severe manifestation of such disturbances occurred in March, 1940. Even our auroras or northern lights are intensified when spots are numerous on the sun.

Schwabe of Dessau, in 1843, was the first astronomer to call attention to the periodicity of sunspots. He showed that, on the average, the maximum number occurred about every 11.2 years. After this maximum was reached, the number diminished until there were times when the photosphere was free from them.

The movement of the sunspots is used to determine the sun's period of rotation. If the sun is a gas, material near the equator should have a shorter period of rotation than matter near the poles. By computing the time it takes spots to move across the sun's disc, it has been discovered that the period of rotation is 25 days at the sun's equator, while in latitude 75 degrees, it is about 75 days.

## WHAT KEEPS THE SUN HOT?

Is the sun a burning mass of carbon and oxygen? The geologist has been able to estimate roughly the age of the earth at two billions of years. Since the matter in the earth came originally from the sun, the sun must have been in existence long before the earth was formed. During all that time the sun has been radiating heat continuously and still continues to do so. To produce this great amount of heat would require the hourly burning over its entire surface of a layer of high-grade anthracite coal 16 feet thick. If coal were present in the sun, it would require an inexhaustible supply to furnish such intense heat over this great period of time.

In 1854, H. von Helmholtz, famed German physicist, was of the opinion that the heat was a result of the sun's contraction. A gaseous mass as it cools releases a great amount of heat energy. It is now known that contraction is not the chief source of the sun's long-continued heat. After a period of a few millions of years the sun would become too dense to contract further. Life has been on the earth for possibly a half-billion of years, and thus it would seem improbable that the theory of Helmholtz could explain the source of the sun's heat.

It has been suggested that some of the sun's heat might result from meteors striking its surface. No doubt some heat would result in this way, but the amount would be negligible. What then is the possible source of the sun's energy?

Recent studies by the physicist have given us a possible clue as to the heat of the sun. The great weight of the sun's upper layer tends to produce an enormous pressure on matter deep in the sun. As a result of this pressure and the intense heat, the atoms composing its gaseous material are being constantly disintegrated with the result that some of the interior mass is converted into energy—heat energy. Such "sub-atomic activity" is, no doubt, the chief source of the heat of a star. It is known that the electrons, protons, and other units of which all atoms are composed are really particles of energy; and though these units cannot be destroyed, part of the mass of the atom can be converted into energy. Thus the atoms of which a star is composed are constantly undergoing a change. The destruction of the atoms within the sun produces an unlimited amount of energy. It is estimated that the sun is losing matter at the rate of 4,620,000 tons every second, but still it remains a giant body. The sun has an estimated mass expressed in tons of 2 followed by 27 ciphers! If the present rate of loss is maintained, the sun will continue to give us heat and light for 16 with 15 ciphers of years. Thus we are relieved of all worry about our sun soon becoming a dark cold body. But it must eventually, in the far distant future, join the myriads of dark cold bodies that are parading in our starry galaxy.

## THE PLANETS

Planets, the most important bodies of the sun's family, should be of greatest interest to man, not simply because they are nearest to him, but because he lives, works, and enjoys life on one of them. If somewhere life similar to ours exists, we must look for it on planets, not on stars, comets, or meteors.

The sun has a family of nine planets moving about it in orbits that are ellipses and not circles. Their names in order from the sun are Mercury, Venus, Earth, Mars, Jupiter, Saturn, Uranus, Neptune, and Pluto.

The ancients recognized that these bodies did not remain fixed, but were constantly shifting their positions night after night, and month after month on the celestial sphere; so they named them *planets*, which means "wanderers." At first astronomers seemed to be confused by the fact that the first two planets, Mercury and Venus, appeared now on one side of the sun and then later on the other. They believed that in each case these were two different bodies. When Mercury appeared on the eastern horizon just before sunrise, it was called Apollo, but when it appeared in the west immediately after the sun had set, it was called Mercury. Likewise when Venus appeared in the east as a "morning star," it was known as Phosphorus. When it was observed in the west shortly after sunset, it was called Hesperus. It was later discovered that Mercury and Apollo were one and the same body, as were Phosphorus and Hesperus.

Planets are now classified according to their positions with reference to the earth and the sun. Those situated between the earth and the sun are known as inferior planets, while those found beyond the earth are called superior planets. They may also be classified as major and minor. The major planets are Jupiter, Saturn, Uranus, and Neptune.

## INFERIOR PLANETS

Inferior planets are best seen when near their greatest east or west elongations. The *elongation* of a planet is the angle made between lines drawn from the observer's position on the earth to a planet and to the sun. Stated simply, it is the angular distance of a planet from the sun. When Venus arrives at $V_1$ (Fig. 269), its elongation is represented by the angle $SEV_1$. The planet is now at its greatest westward elongation, and will appear in the eastern sky as a morning star just before sunrise. When the planet has arrived at $V_2$, it is at its greatest eastward

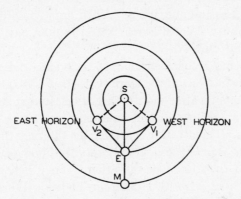

FIG. 269.   Configurations and phases of inferior and superior planets.

elongation and may be seen in the west as an evening star after the sun has set. Superior planets are best seen when they are opposite the earth from the sun, $M$ of Fig. 269. The planet is then nearest the earth and will appear on the meridian at midnight.

## BODE-TITUS LAW

In 1772 Bode worked out a series of numbers, which had been suggested to him by Titus seven years earlier, into a mathematical arrangement known as Bode's law. He took a series of nine fours; to the first four he added 0; to the second 3; to the next 6; to the next 12, etc. When these numbers are added, their sums divided by 10, and each quotient multiplied by the astronomical unit (93,000,000), they will give the relative distances of each planet from the sun.   The law is as follows:

| (1) | (2) | (3) | (4) | (5) | (6) | (7) | (8) | (9) |
|-----|-----|-----|-----|-----|-----|-----|-----|-----|
| 4 | 4 | 4 | 4 | 4 | 4 | 4 | 4 | 4 |
| 0 | 3 | 6 | 12 | 24 | 48 | 96 | 192 | 384 |
| 10) 4 | 7 | 10 | 16 | 28 | 52 | 100 | 196 | 388 |
| .4 | .7 | 1.0 | 1.6 | 2.8 | 5.2 | 10.0 | 19.6 | 38.8 |

The fifth 4 does not represent a planet, but gives the position of the "asteroids."   The term *asteroid* (star-like body) was first proposed by Sir William Herschel in the eighteenth century. He used the term, indicating that these little bodies were planets but so small as to appear like stars.

The following table gives some interesting data about the planets.

TABLE 14
PLANETS

| Planets | Diameter | Mean Distance— Million Miles | Time of Rotation | Time of Revolution | Satellites | Density of water = 1 |
|---------|----------|------------------------------|------------------|--------------------|------------|----------------------|
| Mercury | 3,100 | 36 | 88$^d$ | 88$^d$ | 0 | 3.8 |
| Venus | 7,575 | 67 | 30$^d$ | 225$^d$ | 0 | 4.86 |
| Earth | 7,926 | 93 | 23$^h$56$^m$ | 1$^y$ | 1 | 5.5 |
| Mars | 4,215 | 141 | 24$^h$37$^m$ | 1.88$^y$ | 2 | 3.95 |
| Jupiter | 88,700 | 489 | 9$^h$50$^m$ | 11.86$^y$ | 11 | 1.3 |
| Saturn | 75,060 | 866 | 10$^h$15$^m$ | 29.5$^y$ | 9 | 0.76 |
| Uranus | 30,900 | 1,782 | 10$^h$18$^m$? | 84.0$^y$ | 4 | 1.3 |
| Neptune | 32,900 | 2,793 | 15$^h$8$^m$? | 164.8$^y$ | 1 | 1.3 |
| Pluto | ? | 3,670 | ? | 248$^y$ | ? | ? |

## MERCURY

Mercury is not only the nearest planet to the sun but is, with one possible exception, the smallest of the planets.   It is the swiftest in its movement about the sun, its year consisting of 88 days.   This planet is never far from the sun and, for this reason, appears promptly above the horizon just before sunrise or lingers but a short time above the horizon after sunset at those intervals when it is far enough from the sun to be seen. Because of the difficulty of locating it in the bright twilight, it is known as the "elusive planet."

Too small to hold gases, it is an airless world. There is some dispute as to its period of rotation. The best evidence seems to indicate that it rotates once while it revolves about the sun. Thus the side that faces the sun has a surface temperature estimated at 650° F., while the opposite side must experience eternal cold. Since the planet is within the earth's orbit, it passes through the same phases as does our moon.

## VENUS

Because of its great brightness, it is the easiest of all the planets to identify. Next to the sun and the moon, Venus is the brightest object in the sky. When it appears as an evening or morning star, it shines with dazzling brilliance. It passes through phases similar to the moon. When it is full, it appears very small, being so remote from the earth. Venus is most brilliant when it is in the crescent phase—its greatest eastward or westward elongation.

We may think of Venus as the earth's twin. Its diameter is 7700 miles, only a trifle less than the diameter of the earth. The planet is surrounded with so dense an atmosphere that the telescope has not been able to penetrate through to its surface. Puzzling markings have been observed, but their real meaning is still an unsolved problem. Could it be that they are rifts in the dense clouds surrounding the planet through which occasionally the surface features become visible, or are they simply cloud phenomena? If it were possible to penetrate the atmosphere, markings might be obtained with which to prove whether the planet does or does not rotate. At present, no positive statement can be made as to the period of rotation. Some astronomers have suggested a period of thirty days. Neither is it known whether its axis is inclined to its plane of revolution about the sun.

It is probable that life may exist on Venus. It is certain that the planet has an atmosphere, since it is constantly enveloped in clouds. Little is known of its surface, since the telescope cannot penetrate to its surface. Studies made by Lyot and Mendon show the planet to be surrounded by real clouds composed of tiny water droplets, a condition which suggests water vapor in the atmosphere.

We might assume that the amount of heat received by the planet from the sun would be sufficient to make possible some form of life, but whether the proper amounts of oxygen, nitrogen, and water vapor exist to support high forms of life, no one can tell.

## THE EARTH, MAN'S HOME

Of all the planets the earth is the most important to us. It is literally beneath our feet and we can study it scientifically in greatest detail. Although we live only upon its surface, it should be possible to determine its shape, size, mass, motions, and their effects. This knowledge has been gradually accumulated.

Why is the earth not round but slightly flattened at the poles? The polar diameter is 7,899 miles, somewhat less than the equatorial, which is 7,926 miles. Why was the earth not round? Why was it formed as a nearly round ball instead of a cylinder, a cube, or some other form? The real cause for a round earth must be attributed to gravity. In its early stages, when it was in a gaseous or molten state, gravity pulled the plastic material toward a common center, causing it to assume a globular form. That it is not a true sphere is the result of rotation. Rotation exerts a centrifugal force on every object upon its surface except at the poles. This word comes from two Latin words (*centrum*— center, *fugere*—to flee). It is a force that moves objects on the earth away from its center. It should be evident that this force is greatest at the equator where the circumference is largest and then decreases poleward until at the poles it becomes zero, since there is no motion here. Under these conditions a rapidly rotating, plastic earth would bulge at the equator and flatten at the poles.

What are some of the advantages of a round earth over some other form? A round body gives rise to a uniform pull of gravity, and, therefore, all bodies of equal mass will weigh the same at sea level. Transportation is simplified, and a more uniform distribution of air and water is made possible. Only a round body can have half of its surface at any one time in sunshine. Thus the distribution of heat and light is more uniform on a round earth than an earth of some other form.

## SOME PROOFS OF A ROUND EARTH

Until the time of Columbus, many believed that the earth was a flat body, although some of the ancient Greek scholars were quite convinced that the earth was round. Eratosthenes (275–194 B. C.) was the first to attempt a measurement of the earth, and it is rather interesting to know that the results he obtained were not exceeded in accuracy until about 1600 A. D.

Today we have many proofs that the earth is nearly round. Circumnavigation of the earth in many directions with the distances always about the same proves it round. Many of us, no doubt, are familiar with the appearances of ships at sea. Ships sailing from a harbor in any direction have their hulls disappear first, the masts last; as they approach a harbor from any direction the masts are seen first and the hulls last. These phenomena could only occur on a curved surface. Man has been able to measure the curvature in different directions and in many places on the earth. The shadow of the earth cast during a lunar eclipse has always been observed to be circular. The disappearance of stars from the northern horizon, the rising higher of stars from the southern horizon to one traveling south, and the rising higher of stars from the northern horizon and the sinking of stars on the southern horizon to a north-bound traveler proves that the earth curves in a north-south direction. Owing to the rotation of the earth, one may observe the same stars in different positions in the sky in an east-west direction, proving the surface to be curved. The difference in time of sunrise and sunset for different places on the earth proves the earth curved in an east-west direction. The equal weight of equal masses at sea level for different places on the earth proves the earth must be nearly round.   These, and many more proofs, might be given to convince one that the earth is globular.

## THE EARTH'S ROTATION

The ancients believed that the earth was stationary.   This belief was little questioned until the time of Copernicus.

Many proofs may be offered to show that the earth really rotates on an axis.   One of the simplest proofs for rotation is

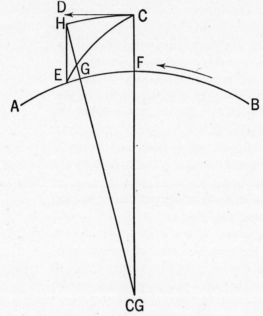

FIG. 270.   Law of falling bodies.

the law of falling bodies.   It can be demonstrated that if an object is dropped from a high prominence, it does not travel toward the center of the earth (which is the direction of a plumb line), but it is deflected in the direction of the earth's rotation (Fig. 270).   In the figure, *CF* is a high tower from the top of which an object is dropped.   The lower arrow represents the direction of the earth's rotation.   If the earth exerted no gravitational pull, an object released at *C* would move in the direction *CD*. Its speed would remain constant, and equal to that of the top of the tower. But the earth exerts a pull in the direction *CF*. This causes the object to fall, meanwhile retaining its horizontal speed. While the bottom of the tower moves from *F* to *G*, the top has moved from *C* to *D*. It will be observed that the top of the tower moves through a greater distance while the object is dropping, than does the base. The object, therefore, instead of dropping toward the base of the tower will follow the line *CE*, and when it comes to rest will appear at *E*, a little to the east of the base of the tower. This eastward deviation of falling bodies is proof that the earth is rotating in this direction.

A French physicist, M. Leon Foucault, in 1851, used a simple pendulum to demonstrate rotation. He suspended a heavy iron ball by means of a stout wire to the dome of the Pantheon in Paris. To the lower end of the ball he attached a stiff leather point so that, as the pendulum swung back and forth, it left a tracing on a pan of sand underneath the oscillating pendulum (Fig. 271). At the end of one hour he observed that the pendulum's path had changed from *AB* to *DC*, to the right of the track in which it first started. He reasoned that either the pendulum was changing its own plane of oscillation or else the earth was turning the pan of

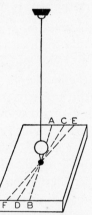

Fig. 271. Foucault's pendulum.

sand underneath the swinging pendulum. Since a pendulum cannot of itself change its plane of oscillation, he concluded that the effect was due to the earth turning the pan of sand.

W. Ferrel was convinced that the deflection of winds on the earth was a positive proof of its rotation. In 1856 he expressed his belief in a law which is as follows: *A mass of air starting to move on the earth's surface deviates to the right in the northern hemisphere (to the left in the southern hemisphere) and tends to move in a circle the radius of which depends upon the velocity of the wind and the latitude of the place.* Thus deflection of winds is a further proof of the earth's rotation.

We have another method of proving that the earth rotates. It is by means of a very interesting instrument called the *gyrocompass*. This instrument consists of a heavy wheel set spinning about an axis which is movable only in a horizontal plane. It can be proved by the laws of motion that, no matter in what direction the axis of the wheel may be pointed originally, it will eventually line itself so as to point directly toward true north. True north is in the direction of the Pole Star, and not in the direction of the magnetic pole.

## IS THE EARTH'S ROTATION UNIFORM?

We may say that the earth is the most accurate time piece we have—that is, that there is little variation in its speed of rotation. The problem of the constancy of the earth's rotation is of great importance to astronomy since the day is our most fundamental unit of measuring time. There are several natural processes at work which must surely affect the earth's rotation to some extent. If the change in size and distribution of its mass remains constant, and if it is not acted upon by exterior forces, its total quantity of motion must remain constant. But if the earth's diameter is shrinking, the day must shorten; if it is lengthening, the day must obviously increase, providing the mass remains constant.

The earth is subject to interference by outside forces, some of which have little effect on its period of rotation, while others have a more decided influence. The earth in its yearly movement about the sun passes through regions in which it encounters meteoric matter such as meteors and comets. This captured matter is constantly and slowly building up the mass of the earth. The total mass added to the earth in this way does not probably average more than 100 tons daily, yet over a long period of time it is possible that the meteoric material accumulates to an average depth of 0.3937 of an inch over the entire surface of the earth in 400,000 years. Tides produce friction not only in the ocean, but also in the atmosphere and the elastic rock material of the earth. When ocean tides beat upon the shores or surge and eddy in shallow seas, considerable friction is produced which has a retarding effect upon the earth's rotation. It has been estimated that this causes our day to increase about one second in 100,000 years. It is not a simple process to determine by observation whether the earth's period of rotation is increasing or decreasing, for it is impossible to construct a clock which is accurate enough to detect a change of one second in 100,000 years. It is only when the earth's motion is compared with the motions of other heavenly bodies, for example, the revolutions of other planets and the moon, that small changes can be detected.

## SOME RESULTS OF ROTATION

Because of the earth's rotation we have day and night on the earth. The sun, moon, and stars rise in the east and set in the west. The rising and setting of these heavenly bodies is only an apparent movement which results from rotation. All fixed points and lines such as axis, poles, equator, parallels, and meridians are also the direct result of rotation.

The equator is a line drawn around the earth midway between the poles. Parallels are lines drawn around the earth, parallel to the equator. Meridians are lines drawn from pole to pole, while a meridian circle is a line drawn around the earth through the poles; all circles that bisect the earth are called large circles.

## REVOLUTION

Revolution is the earth's yearly motion about the sun. The path which the earth pursues is called its orbit. While it is really an ellipse, it is so nearly round as to appear a true circle (Fig. 272).

The sun is not at the center of the earth's orbit, but at one of the foci. In winter in the northern hemisphere the earth arrives at its nearest position, $B$, to the sun, *perihelion* (*peri*— near, *helios*—sun)—a distance of 91,500,000 miles. Six months later, in summer, it reaches its most remote point, *aphelion*, $A$ (*apo*—away from, *helios*—sun)—a distance of 94,500,000 miles.

In 1727, James Bradley proved the earth actually moves around the sun by applying the principle of aberration of light.

Because of the finite velocity of light, there is an apparent displacement of a heavenly object when viewed from any moving station, unless the motion is directly toward or away from the object.   This principle may be illustrated by noting what

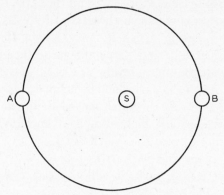

Fig. 272.   Shape of earth's orbit.

would happen in the case of falling rain drops.   If there is no wind and a stationary observer wishes to have the falling drops pass down vertically through a hollow cylinder *A* (Fig. 273) without touching the sides, he must keep the cylinder in a

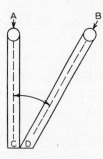

vertical position.   If he advances in any direction, the drops will no longer seem to fall vertically but will strike his face, and he must draw back the bottom of the cylinder by an amount equal to the advance he makes while the drop is passing through the tube; that is, he must tip the cylinder to the position *BD*.   The amount of tipping will depend directly upon the speed with which the drop falls, and the velocity with which the observer is moving.   The amount of angular displacement of light from stars can be measured.

Fig. 273.   Aberration of a falling raindrop.

This angular displacement is known as the star's *aberration*. Because of aberration, the telescope must, at one season of the year, be turned in one direction, and at the reverse season be turned in the opposite direction by an equal amount.   Each star's aberrational orbit, which is very small, can be calculated, and the revolution of the earth can be proved.

## SEASONS

The change of seasons experienced on the earth results mainly because the axis about which the earth rotates is not at right angles to the plane in which it moves about the sun. It is inclined 23½ degrees from a perpendicular to the plane in which it revolves about the sun. In Fig. 274, *ABC* is the plane of the earth's orbit; *EB* is the axis which is inclined 23½ degrees from the perpendicular. As the earth moves about the sun, its axis maintains this constant inclination and unchanging direction (always pointing toward the North Star).

When the plane of the earth's orbit is projected outward, it will intersect the sky in a great circle called the *ecliptic*. Since the earth's equator is at right angles to the axis, the plane of the earth's equator, if projected to the sky, will also intercept the sky in a great circle called the *celestial equa-*

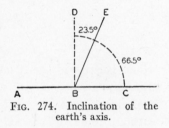

FIG. 274. Inclination of the earth's axis.

*tor*. These two planes intersect each other at an angle of 23½ degrees. The points of intersection are called the *equinoxes*, which means that when the earth reaches these positions in its annual journey around the sun, days and nights are equal. Ninety degrees from the equinoxes are the summer and winter solstices. Solstice comes from two Latin words (*sol*—sun, *stare*—to stand) and signifies that for several days the sun seems neither to approach nor to recede from the celestial equator.

If we now study Fig. 275, we will understand why days and nights vary in length during the year. On March 21 and September 23 (1 and 3, Fig. 275), the poles of the earth are tipped neither to nor away from the sun; the circle of illumination, *CI*, passes directly through the poles bisecting the equator and parallels into equal lengths of light and darkness. The vertical ray, $V$, will fall directly on the equator; thus days and nights are equal.

When the earth has moved on its orbit (counterclockwise from 1 to 2), keeping the North Pole directed to the north, the North Pole will be tipped toward the sun, while the South Pole will be tipped away from the sun. The circle of illumination, $CI$, now passes 23½ degrees beyond the North Pole but fails to

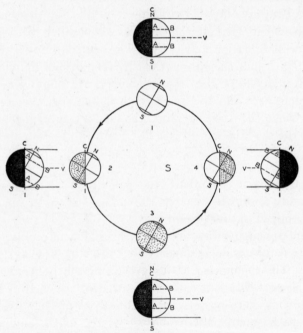

FIG. 275.   Diagram illustrating change of seasons.

reach the South Pole by the same amount. It will now be observed that the long portions of the parallels in the northern hemisphere, $AB$, that are cut by the $CI$ are in light while the shorter portions are in darkness. Thus long days and short nights will prevail in the northern hemisphere, while short days and long nights are experienced in the southern hemisphere. The vertical ray, $V$, is now 23½ degrees north of the equator.

When the earth has reached the December solstice (4, Fig. 275), the North Pole is tipped away from the sun while the South Pole is tipped toward the sun. The *CI* falls short of the North Pole and extends 23½ degrees beyond the South Pole. The South Pole is now in sunlight while the North Pole is in darkness. The *CI* cuts the parallels unequally and the long portions, *AB*, in the southern hemisphere, are in light while the short portions are in darkness; thus long days and short nights. The vertical ray, *V*, is 23½ degrees south of the equator.

It is evident that at the solstices all parallels between the circle of illumination and the poles are entirely in darkness or in sunlight, since they are not cut by the circle of illumination.

Thus it should be clear that when days are long in the northern hemisphere and the sun is high in the sky, the season is warm; when the days are short, the nights long, and the sun is low in the sky, the season is cold.

## MARS

Mars has excited more interest than any of the other planets. Of a ruddy color, when nearest the earth, as it was in July, 1939, it is an object of great beauty.

There are many ways in which this planet is similar to the earth. It rotates on an axis in about the same time as does the earth. The inclination of its axis from the perpendicular—23½ degrees—is about the same as that of the earth. Recent studies show it to possess one twentieth as much water vapor above each square foot of surface as the earth, and no free oxygen. It experiences seasons similar to the seasons on the earth except that they are nearly twice as long. Its greater distance from the sun must result, however, in wider ranges of temperature than are experienced on the earth.

On the whole the surface of the planet is much smoother than the earth's. There are no great mountain ranges or high isolated peaks.

It was the discovery of the baffling canal system that brought Mars so prominently into the public eye. Outstanding among the many students of the Martian canals was Percival Lowell of

Lowell Observatory, Flagstaff, Arizona. In 1894 this keen-eyed observer, studying through his telescope in the most ideal atmospheric conditions, made many drawings of the canals. He observed that they formed a definite pattern that could not just happen by chance. He noticed that they were straight, of uniform width, and that they criss-crossed the planet in every direction. They radiated from darker areas—oases as he termed them—in all directions like the spokes from the hub of a wheel. He observed also in the spring that in many instances the lines first appeared single and later double, and changed color. He believed that this change was due to water coming from the melting of the polar ice caps and causing the growth of vegetation.

The significance of the canals occupied his attention and led him to ask himself this question—is Mars actually inhabited by a very superior race of human beings? A canal system with such mechanical exactness could not happen by mere chance. Lowell concluded that the evidence was proof that the planet had been inhabited in some time past, if not now, by a highly intelligent race capable of performing great engineering feats and excelling any that have been attempted on the earth. In more recent time, the larger telescopes have revealed the presence of the markings as seen by Lowell, but not of the careful pattern described by him. There is considerable doubt among present-day astronomers that these markings are real canals.

We may ask the question in the light of modern investigation —can life exist on Mars? Let us first remember that plant and animal life on the earth appears in myriads of forms ranging from the microscopic to the huge elephant and the giant, towering redwoods. It thrives in all sorts of environments—in the deep sea, in dry and torrid wastes, in hot and humid lands, and in the eternal cold of the polar regions. It ranges from the single cell to the complex organism.

It may be that Mars is inhabited by some of the lower forms of both plant and animal life, but that the planet is peopled with a superior race of humans is highly improbable. Largely responsible for such a feeling is the recent discovery that the oxygen content of the atmosphere of Mars is very low—about one thousandth of that of the earth's surface. This is an amount far too small to support high forms of animal life.

Even the polar caps on Mars (Fig. 276) are not like those found on the earth. They are possibly very thin and may be mere films of hoar frost. It seems quite evident that if all the ice and snow of her pole caps were melted, the water might fill a basin no larger than that of Lake Huron. Little evidence can be found of any large amount of water vapor in the Martian atmosphere.

*Yerkes Observatory.*

FIG. 276. Polar caps of Mars.

Recent temperature measurements reveal a range from 50° F. on a summer's day to as low as −125° F. at night. The average temperature is estimated at about −22° F. This low temperature, together with the deficiency of oxygen, seems to point to the impossibility of existence for any high forms of life on the planet.

It is possible that the oxygen of the air, which may have been more abundant in past time, has combined with the rocks, oxidizing them and giving the planet its ruddy color.

Before leaving this interesting planet we should speak of its two satellites. Phobos, the inner one, and Deimos, the outer, are both small, probably not more than 10 miles in diameter. Both are very close to the planet: Phobos about 4000 miles distant, and Deimos some 13,000 miles away. While the planet gets very little light from its satellites, one of them, Phobos, is of interest because of its speed of revolution about the planet. Phobos makes its journey around Mars in 7 hours and 39 minutes, while it requires 24 hours for the planet to complete its rotation. This moon, as observed from Mars, rises in the west, passes eastward through the sky, and sets in the east.

## ASTEROIDS

These small bodies are located between the orbits of Mars and Jupiter. It is in this vast expanse of space—350,000,000 miles in width—that we should expect to find another planet. Bode's law (p. 573) shows a great break here in the sequence of orbits. Of these bodies, called "planetoids" or miniature planets, the largest is Ceres—480 miles in diameter. Those whose orbits are fairly well worked out number about 1400. No doubt more will be discovered in the future.

Why such a family of small bodies? Their origin is, as yet, not fully known. It is thought that they represent small masses of matter which were not able to combine into larger ones during the genesis of the solar family.

## JUPITER

Here is the giant among the family of planets. It has a diameter 11 times that of the earth. If you could imagine a hollow sphere the size of Jupiter, it would take the material of 1300 earths to fill it. It is next to Venus in brightness, and unlike the inferior planets, it is not confined to appearing solely in the evening and morning sky. It may be seen as a brilliant object when above the horizon.

Not only is Jupiter the largest planet, but it is really a whirling Dervish, completing a rotation every 9 hours and 55 minutes. Because of this great speed of rotation, it is one of the most oblate of all the planets. In its movement around the sun, however, it is a real sluggard. It requires almost twelve years to make a complete revolution.

Jupiter, unlike the earth, is very light and in proportion to its size its weight is about one-fourth the earth's. We might ask, why so light? This question as yet cannot be satisfactorily answered. Some astronomers think that the dense rock core of the planet is encased by a layer of ice 12,000 miles in thickness. Above the ice is a layer of atmosphere at least 6000 miles in height. The surface as seen through a telescope presents a beautiful appearance (Fig. 277). It is covered with dark and bright bands parallel to the equator of the planet. These belts are more or less permanent and show turbulent changes which are probably caused by powerful dynamic forces at work in the lower portion of the planet's atmosphere.

The temperature of this distant planet (unless the planet has some other source of heat) must be very low, possibly 200 degrees below zero. It is certain that the gases of the lower

*Yerkes Observatory.*
FIG. 277. Photograph of Jupiter.

portion of the atmosphere must be under tremendous pressure, possibly thousands of tons per square inch. This great pressure would be sufficient to liquefy them. Astronomers have recently discovered the presence of ammonia and methane in its atmosphere. If ammonia exists in large quantities, it is certain that no life could exist in this very poisonous medium.

The first celestial objects which Galileo found with his telescope, in 1610, were the satellites of this giant planet. Jupiter has a family of 11, two of them being larger than Mercury. Since the orbits of the satellites are in the plane of the planet's equator, these moons may be seen through the telescope in almost a straight line. Sometimes two will be found on one side of the planet and two on the other. Then again, one may be seen on one side and three on the other. The four brightest satellites were first discovered by Galileo in 1610.

## SATURN

Beyond Jupiter is Saturn, the second largest of the planets. To the ancients this was the outermost planet visible to the naked eye. It is the last one whose atmospheric detail is visible in a powerful telescope. It has a family of nine satellites, one of which, Titan, is larger than our moon. The outer satellite, unlike the others, moves in reverse or retrogrades as it makes its journey around the planet.

Its diameter is about nine times that of the earth, and like Jupiter, Saturn, too, is a rapidly rotating body. The day on Saturn is 10 hours and 26 minutes in length.

Of all the planets, it is the least dense. If we could find a body of water large enough in which to dump it, it would float like a cork. Is there a reason for this low density? No satisfactory answer can be given. The planet is surrounded by a dense atmosphere. The clouds are arranged in parallel belts similar to those found on Jupiter. It is believed that the atmosphere is even deeper than Jupiter's, possibly 16,000 miles. The central rock core may be coated with a layer of ice at least 6000 miles thick. If these conditions are true, they may account for its low density.

The temperature must be very low, possibly 300 degrees below zero F. The spectroscope reveals the presence of ammonia and methane. It is evident that the planet cannot support life with such atmospheric conditions.

The most impressive thing about Saturn is its ring system (Fig. 278). The rings lie like thin sheets of silver around the planet's equator. The three rings in order from the surface of the planet are the crepe or dusky ring, 11,000 miles in breadth, the inner bright ring, 17,900 miles wide, and the outer bright ring, 10,900 miles across. The outer bright ring is separated from the inner bright ring by a dark space 2300 miles in width. This dark band is known as Cassini's division, in honor of its discoverer. The rings have a probable thickness of 10 miles.

The plane of Saturn's equator is inclined 26 degrees and 45 minutes to the plane of its orbit, while the planet's orbit is inclined to the plane of the earth's orbit at an angle of 2 degrees and 29 minutes. Consequently, the maximum inclination of the plane of the ring system to the plane of the earth's orbit is about 28 degrees. As Saturn revolves about the sun once in 29.5 years, we may view the rings from many different angles.

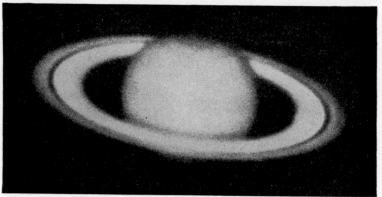

*Yerkes Observatory.*

FIG. 278.    Rings of Saturn.

Sometimes they appear tilted in one direction, and sometimes in another. Twice during the planet's journey around the sun, the rings are invisible or appear as thin wings on opposite sides of the planet.

It was formerly believed that the rings were of continuous solid or liquid structure, but it is now known that they are composed of separate bodies moving in independent orbits about the planet. It has also been proved that the particles in the inner ring move faster than those in the rings farther away from the planet.

The source of the material of the rings is still an unsolved problem. It may be that the material came from one of the inner moons of Saturn which approached so close to the planet as to be tidally disrupted into tiny particles. The rings appear bright because of reflected sunlight.

## THE DISTANT PLANETS

Little is known of the planets Uranus, Neptune, and Pluto. They are so far away that the most powerful telescope fails to reveal anything but small, illuminated bodies. Uranus and Neptune are small when compared to Jupiter and Saturn but are giants when contrasted with the earth. Uranus has two satellites and Neptune one; Pluto may not have any.

Pluto was discovered in 1930 at the Lowell Observatory at Flagstaff, Arizona. The planet was first seen by Clyde W. Tombaugh, an assistant at the observatory, although much previous work leading up to the discovery had been done by Lowell, Pickering, and others. This planet is small, possibly the size of Mercury or our own satellite. Its orbit is very elliptical. The planet's period of revolution is about 250 years. The temperature of the planet must be extremely low. It is probably so cold that the atmosphere, if it has any, is liquefied or even frozen. Are there more planets beyond Pluto? Possibly so. The search for new planets has already begun, and who knows what the future may reveal?

## THE RABBLE OF THE SOLAR FAMILY

Two classes of bodies of less significance than those which we have already discussed must be actually considered as a part of the solar family.

On a clear, moonless night one may see star-like objects appear suddenly, dart swiftly across the sky, and then just as suddenly disappear. These star-like bodies are called *meteors* or *shooting-stars*. They are in no sense stars, but may be thought of as cosmic bullets traveling with a speed far greater than bullets from a machine gun. The very faint ones last for a fraction of a second. The very bright nebulous ones are called *fire-balls*. When a meteor explodes, it is known as a *bolide*.

Meteors travel in space at the distance of the earth from the sun at 26.5 miles per second. They are generally more easily seen after midnight. Since the earth's speed in its orbit about the sun is 18.5 miles per second, meteors that collide head-on with the earth enter the atmosphere at the velocity of 45 miles per second. Those which overtake the earth before midnight may travel with a velocity as low as 7 miles per second. The swifter flight of the morning meteors through our atmosphere makes their trails brighter and more easily seen.

What are meteoric showers? When a swarm of meteors travel about the sun, each is traveling in its own orbit. Those nearest the sun are moving faster than those farther away. When the meteors are distributed quite evenly around the orbit, a shower may be expected every year when the earth runs into the swarm. Some of the noted showers are as follows: the Perseids around August 11; the Lyrids, April 20; the Andromedes, which generally last several nights, from November 20 to 27; the Aquarids, visible in early May; the Orionids, October 19; and the Geminids, December 11. If you will scan the sky on the nights of these dates, you may see many more meteors than usual.

The light and heat of meteors results from friction with the air. When meteors encounter the air, their surfaces are greatly heated, liquefied, and often entirely vaporized. The intense friction results in an envelope of incandescent gas and vapor many times larger than the meteor itself. The fused material is often swept behind the rapidly moving body in the form of an illuminated train.

It is estimated that about five billions of these cosmic bullets enter our atmosphere every 24 hours but only a few of them fall to the earth. The smaller ones are entirely consumed in the air. When the mass is large enough to withstand the loss from fusion and evaporation in the air, it falls to the earth and is known as a *meteorite*. Millions of these stones have been found, some of immense size. The largest one ever discovered weighed 50 tons.

Meteorites are classified according to their composition. They may be all-metal (*siderites*), all-stone (*aerolites*), or iron-stone (*siderolites*). Often the fall of a meteorite is accompanied by sounds as of distant thunder or the crackling of rifle fire with brilliant illumination.

The origin of these strange bodies is not certainly known. Some think they are fragments of material from which our solar system has been built but which have not yet been captured by the sun and planets, while others believe that meteorites are extraterrestrial material coming to us from outer space.

*Comets* are the most bizarre and awe-inspiring of all the heavenly bodies. They often appear suddenly, remain visible for a few days or even months, and then recede from the sun and become invisible. Throughout the ages of the past a very elaborate web of superstition has been woven around them. They have held people under their sway, and have often warped their minds with all kinds of silly nonsense. They are not omens of evil, forecasting wars, pestilences, plagues, famines, or even deaths of individuals, nor are they portents of good fortune.

Frequently when comets are first seen, they appear as hazy or nebulous masses. As they approach the sun, they manifest distinct parts as head, nucleus, and tail. They are called comets (from *coma*—hair) because when a comet is seen by the naked eye it resembles a star surrounded by a luminous fog.

Comets are Gargantuan in size. The head may vary from a few thousand to millions of miles in diameter, while the tail often extends back from the head hundreds of thousands to many millions of miles. The nucleus, the denser portion of the head, may vary from a few hundred to as large as 6000 to 8000 miles in diameter. Halley's comet, the great comet of 1628, which visits the sun once every 75 years, possessed a tail over 100 millions of miles in length and a head of 120,000 miles in diameter. The great comet of 1811, which was visible for 17 months, had a head 1,000,000 miles in diameter and a tail 100,000,000 miles in length.

Though comets are enormous in volume, they are so tenuous and substanceless as to be really "airy nothings." Very unstable, they may change their appearance with such lightning-like rapidity, that we may almost think of them as nebulous apparitions.

Many observations have revealed that when a comet passes directly between the observer and some bright star, the starlight is not dimmed in the least. It has been estimated that they may have a density of about one one-hundred-thousandth that of our atmosphere. They are less perfect vacuums than can be produced in our laboratories. If all the matter in a comet as large as Halley's could be gathered together and compacted into an iron ball with the density of steel, it might have a diameter as great as one hundred miles.

About 400 comets had been discovered before Galileo invented his telescope in 1609. Since his invention, about 500 more have been found. Today a camera attached to a telescope is used to discover these bizarre bodies. Many amateurs with homemade telescopes often discover new comets each year.

When a comet is first discovered, it is given the number of the year and a letter indicating the order of discovery—for example, 1941 $a$. Then, after its orbit has been computed, it is finally and permanently designated with the year of its perihelion passage (which may be different from the year of discovery) and a Roman numeral showing its order in the year of perihelion passage—as, for example, 1908 III (Morehouse).

Comets travel in orbits quite unlike those of the planets. Their orbits are either tipped or inclined at almost every conceivable angle and do not lie near to the plane of the earth's orbit as do those of planets. For this reason they do not follow the path of the zodiac as the planets do. Thus comets may be seen in almost any part of the sky. Though all of the planets move around the sun in the same direction, this is not true for comets. They may move in the same direction around the sun, or they may move in the opposite direction from the planets. All of the planetary orbits are slightly elliptical, but the orbits of comets may vary greatly. They may travel in one of three orbits: elliptical, parabolic, or hyperbolic. Only those that travel in the first type of orbit return periodically to visit the sun. Others visit the sun but once and then travel off into space never to return, if they are moving in parabolic or hyperbolic orbits.

Comets are dark, cold bodies composed of both solid and gaseous particles. They appear bright only when they come near to the sun. The cause and nature of their light are not yet positively known. It may be reflected light from the gaseous and solid particles; incandescency of the material when they approach the sun; or it may result from ionization of the gases in the comet's head by the violet rays of the sun.

The tails of comets are most interesting. They do not trail directly behind the head, but extend always in a direction nearly opposite the sun, lagging a little behind a line joining the sun and the comet's head. Comets whose distance from the sun is as great as the distance of Jupiter do not have appreciable tails. It is thought that the material forming the tail is matter expelled from the nucleus. After the material is ejected from the nucleus, it is probably repelled by pressure resulting from the sun's radiation. The behavior of the nucleus in some of the larger comets suggests that the repulsive force driving material from the nucleus may be electrical forces as well as the sun's radiation pressure.

There is little danger from comets. They are such rare bodies that little or no harm would result were the earth to pass through one of them. The small solid particles would fuse and disappear in the air as do meteors. The poisonous gases, if there are any, would be diffused in our dense atmosphere long before they could reach the earth's surface.

# CHAPTER 40

# LATITUDE, LONGITUDE, AND TIME

## LATITUDE

The conventional way of locating a place on the earth is to name the country in which it is found: for example, Paris in France; Mexico City in Mexico; Ottawa in Canada; and Washington, D. C., in the United States. This method of location is sufficient. But if one wishes to locate a certain individual in any one of the above cities, it is necessary to know a great deal more than the names of his city and country.

The position of any particular place on the earth is completely specified only by using the familiar terms or coordinates of latitude and longitude. The earth's rotation furnishes us with certain reference points and lines such as poles, equator, parallels, and meridians.

The accompanying diagram (Fig. 279) will make clear the meaning of coordinates. Draw $AB$ and $AC$ perpendicular to each other; then lay off equal divisions on both $AB$ and $AC$. The point $b$ is three spaces to the right on $AC$ and two up on $AB$; point $d$ is eight spaces to the right on $AC$ and four up on $AB$. This means that point $b$ is to the right of $A$ four units and above $A$ two units. The units are measured off on the lines $AB$ and $AC$, known as *coordinates*.

This same principle is employed in laying out cities and towns in level regions where rivers, valleys, and highlands do not interfere.

The next diagram (Fig. 280) will illustrate how coordinates, analogous to equator, parallels, and meridians, are used. Main

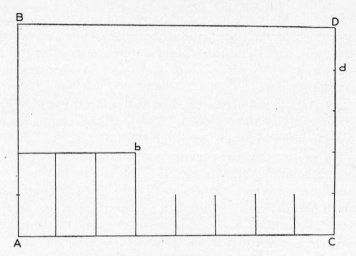

FIG. 279. Laying off distances on coordinates.

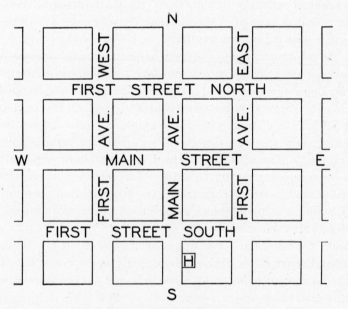

FIG. 280. Layout of streets in a city.

Avenue is the coordinate corresponding to the meridian of Greenwich or zero meridian on the earth, while avenues east and west are meridians. Main Street corresponds to the equator, and the streets north and south of Main Street to parallels.

A certain friend's home ($H$, Fig. 280) is located at 1642 First Street south on Main Avenue. This is all the information one needs in order to be able to go directly to it.

We learned that the equator is a great circle drawn around the earth midway between the poles. It is from this circle that latitude is measured. It is derived from the Latin word *latus*, which means width. Circles are divided into 360 degrees. Since the latitude of the equator is zero, that of the poles is 90 degrees or one-fourth of a circle.

Latitude is obtained from the stars and sun. It may be defined as angular distance north and south from the equator measured upon the meridians by the intersection of parallels. It is called angular distance since it is measured in terms of degrees, minutes, and seconds.

An observer in the northern hemisphere can determine his latitude on a clear, moonless night by measuring the height of the Pole Star above his northern horizon. At the North Pole the Pole Star would appear overhead; but at the equator it would be seen directly on the horizon. As one travels northward from the equator, it rises one degree for each degree traveled. The altitude of the Pole Star above the northern horizon equals the latitude of the observer. A study of Fig. 281 will make this statement clear. $O$ is the position of the observer; $N$ and $S$ are north and south points of his visible horizon; $Z$ is the zenith, the point directly overhead; $OPS$ is the earth's axis, and $OCE$ the earth's equator projected to the sky. On measuring the arc $NPS$, which is the altitude of the Polar Star above the horizon, it is found to be the latitude of the observer, or in this case 42°.

A further study of the diagram will demonstrate how the latitude of a place may be obtained by making use of the noon sun. The height of the celestial equator (earth's equator in the sky), and the altitude of the North Pole Star are at any given place complementary angles—that is, when added together they equal 90°.   The celestial equator is always 90° from the Pole Star.   An arc of the sky sphere from the northern horizon $N$, through the zenith $Z$ to the southern horizon $S$, is 180°.   Since there are 90° from the Pole Star to the celestial equator, the distance from the northern horizon, $N$, to the Pole Star and from the southern horizon, $S$, to the celestial equator, $CE$, must together equal 90°.

The *declination* of the sun is its distance north or south of the celestial equator.

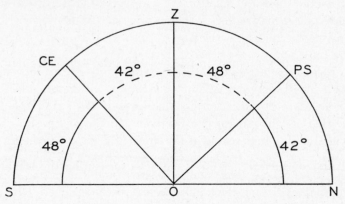

FIG. 281.   Diagram illustrating how to use the North Star and the sun to find latitude.

In the study of seasons (Chap. 39) we learned that the vertical ray of the sun is directly on the equator on March 21 and September 23.   The sun's declination is then zero.   On June 21 the vertical ray strikes the earth 23.5° north of the equator. By means of a sextant the midday altitude of the sun may be measured at any place, and for any day of the year.   By ascertaining the noonday altitude of the sun and referring to the analemma (p. 604), the declination of the sun can be found.

The following problem will illustrate how latitude of a place may be found from the above data.   The altitude of the noonday sun on June 21 is 71.5°.   Subtract 71.5° from 90°; the difference, 18.5°, is the zenith distance of the sun.   Since the sun is 23.5° north of the celestial equator, the zenith distance of the celestial equator is 42°. This is the latitude of the observer.

When the sun is south of the equator, subtract the sun's midday altitude from 90°. From this difference, subtract the sun's declination. The remainder is the observer's latitude.

The meridian of the Royal Observatory at Greenwich, England, has been arbitrarily chosen from which to measure longitude. It is called the *prime meridian*. All places on this meridian have zero longitude. The longitude of any other place is its angular distance east or west from Greenwich measured upon the equator and parallels. The greatest longitude a place may have is 180° east or west. Where the meridian crosses the equator, in the Gulf of Guinea, latitude and longitude are both zero.

Before the introduction of the radio, ships at sea determined their longitude by means of a *chronometer*. A chronometer is an accurate clock placed in a small square box. It is mounted so that it will remain constantly in an upright position notwithstanding the rocking of the ship. Each chronometer keeps Greenwich time. By observing the sun time on shipboard at the place whose longitude is desired, and comparing it with chronometer time, the longitude may be determined. It takes the sun, on the average, 24 hours to complete its apparent journey around the earth. During this time it crosses 360 degrees of longitude, or 15 degrees each hour. For example, suppose the sun indicates 12 o'clock noon, but the chronometer shows 2:00 P. M. The prime meridian is east or the longitude of the ship is 30° west from Greenwich. If, on the other hand, it is noon by the sun but 10:00 A. M. by the chronometer, the prime meridian is west or the longitude of the ship is 30° east.

## TIME

It is not easy to define time in terms that are more easily understood than the term itself. When an individual recalls past experiences in his life, he always finds it convenient to recount them in some definite order like numbers on a yard stick.  The intervals separating his experiences occupy in his mind certain intervals, and he chooses to call them time.  The universe is made up of specific events which have taken place in space and time.

Dynamical time is based upon Sir Isaac Newton's first law of motion—namely, that two intervals of time are equal, physically speaking, if a moving object not subject to outside forces passes over equal distances during those intervals of time.  Expressed in another way, it means that a rotating body not disturbed by exterior forces rotates at a uniform rate.

The most practical way of measuring time is by means of the rotating earth.  Man has not only been able to prove that the earth rotates, but has successfully determined its period of rotation.

The several units used in measuring time are the solar and sidereal days, solar and sidereal years, and synodic and sidereal months.

## SOLAR DAY

A solar day is the time intervening between two successive passages of the sun over a given meridian or from sun noon to sun noon again.

A study of Fig. 282 will make clear the meaning of solar and sidereal days.  At $E_1$ it is noon for an observer at $A$.  During one rotation on its axis, the earth moves eastward in its orbit to $E_2$.  The point $A$ has turned through 360 degrees in the direction of the arrow to $A'$.  But it is not yet noon at $A'$.  To bring the sun on the meridian, the earth must rotate through a small additional angle $A'A''$.  The time required for $A$ to rotate through $AA'A''$ is called a *solar day*.

The length of a solar day varies somewhat during the year.  This is because the earth's orbit is an ellipse with the sun at one of the foci.  The earth moves fastest at perihelion $P$ (Fig. 282) and slowest when near aphelion $A_1$.  In December and January a greater arc of its orbit, $E_1E_2$, is traversed than in June and July, $E_1E_2$.  The sun apparently moves faster along the ecliptic (the circle in which the plane of the earth's orbit cuts the celestial sphere) in the winter months, and likewise, falls farther and farther behind the stars in their rotation in the sky. As a result solar days are longer in December and January, as shown by the larger angle $A'A''$, than in June and July, angle $A'A''$.

Since solar days are not all of the same length throughout the year, it becomes necessary to use a *mean* solar day or a day which is an average of all the solar days. All mean solar days are of the same length with respect to a sidereal day as a standard. The length of a solar day is 24 h. 3 m. and 26.55 s. of mean sidereal time.

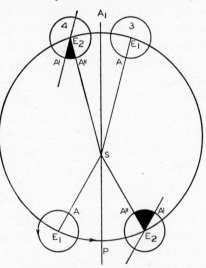

FIG. 282.   Diagram showing the length of solar days.

## THE SIDEREAL DAY

The time intervening between two passages of a given star over the observer's meridian $AA'$ is called a sidereal day (Fig. 282). Stars are so far away that the earth's daily eastward motion does not alter its position with reference to a star. The sidereal day is equal to 23 h. 56 m. 4.09 s. of mean solar time.

## THE ANALEMMA

If we were to imagine a fictitious sun moving eastward at a uniform rate we would soon discover that the *fictitious* and real sun would seldom coincide. There are four times a year when they would be very near together: December 25, April 15, June 14 or 15, and September 1. December 25 and June 14 or 15 are indicated on the analemma where the months of the year line intersects the heavy vertical line, and April 15 and September 1, where the months of the year line crosses. The difference between the true sun time and mean sun time is called *the time*

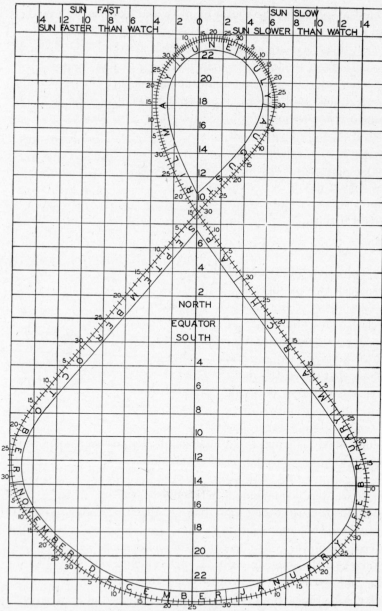

FIG. 283. The analemma.

*equation*, and is shown by means of a figure called the *analemma* (Fig. 283). The analemma indicates graphically the approximate difference between apparent sun time and mean sun time for any day of the year. It shows also the position of the vertical ray of the sun north or south of the celestial equator. The vertical lines of the figure represent the number of minutes the apparent sun is fast or slow as compared with mean sun time. The horizontal lines show the declination of the sun for any day of the year. An examination of the figure will reveal that the apparent sun and the mean sun are together on December 25, April 15, June 14, and September 1, since these dates are on the central vertical line. The time equation is then zero, and the sun is "on time." On all other days of the year the sun is either "fast" or "slow."

The time by which sundial time is faster than the average sun or watch time is usually shown by a minus sign. That by which the sundial time is slower than the average sun time or watch time is designated by a plus sign. If, for example, the apparent sun indicates noon and the analemma shows that the sun is fast 12 minutes on that date, we know that it is 11:48 A. M. by watch time. If the apparent sun indicates noon, and the analemma shows the sun to be 7 minutes slow, we know that it is 12:07 P. M. by the watch.

## STANDARD TIME

This time was adopted in the United States November 18, 1883. Prior to its adoption, the time of any specific locality was determined by setting the clock to point 12:00 noon, when the sun was exactly on the meridian of the locality. Since sun noon changes with the seasons (see analemma, p. 604), and the sun moves across 15 degrees of longitude each hour regardless of the seasons, it often happened that a single city had little agreement as to correct time. This made it very confusing to ascertain the time of train schedules. In 1869, there were about 500 railroads in the United States which involved around 8,000 different time corrections. With the expansion of the railroads and the rapid development of communication, it became apparent that some better plan of time computation must be provided. In 1869, Charles Ferdinand Dowd, a New York schoolmaster, came forward with a new proposition to correct this old state of affairs. He proposed to divide the United States, which extends through about 60 degrees of longitude, into time-belts of 15 degrees of longitude. Each belt's time was to differ by one hour from the next. The time for each belt was to be taken from a standard meridian located near the middle of the belt. The

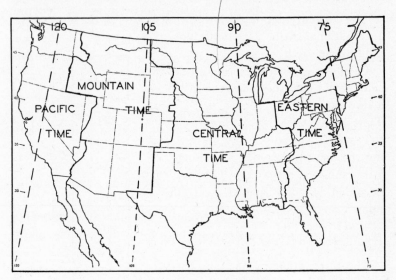

Fig. 284.　Standard time belts.

various time belts (Fig. 284) are Eastern, Central, Mountain, and Pacific time.

All places west of the time meridian in any belt have watch time faster than sun time; all places east of the meridian have sun time faster than standard or watch time.

Daylight-saving time is adopted during the summer months by many of the larger cities in the higher latitudes of northern United States. This is done to take advantage of sunshine and recreation hours after the day's work is completed. Daylight-saving time is obtained by setting the clock ahead one hour to the time of the belt directly to the east.

## CIVIL DAY

The civil day is a mean solar day which begins at midnight and ends at midnight. It is the day within which we carry on our ordinary transactions. Business is generally suspended at midnight, and the change to a new day is thus made with less confusion.

## CONVENTIONAL DAY

The conventional day is a day that begins to the west of the International Date Line and moves in a westerly direction around the earth.

Calendar dates are different on the two sides of this line; the one to the east being a day earlier than the one to the west. Thus, a ship crossing the line from west to east omits or adds a day, but in crossing the line from east to west longitude, a day must be repeated. This day that is added in correcting the calendar is known as a conventional day.

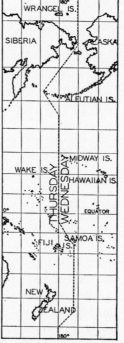

FIG. 285. Course of the International Date Line.

## THE INTERNATIONAL DATE LINE

The International Date Line has been established by international agreement on or near the 180th meridian (Fig. 285), and is as follows; from the North Pole to Bering Strait; eleven degrees into west longitude between Siberia and Alaska; seven degrees into east longitude, just to the west of the Aleutian Islands; thence back along the 180th meridian to the latitude of the Fiji and Samoan islands, where it shifts into west longitude just to the west of the Samoan Islands; thence back to the 180th meridian. This last shift gives Pago Pago, an American-owned harbor, the same time of reckoning as the United States.

## DAY LOST—WESTWARD TRAVEL

In going westward around the world in the same direction as the sun, a traveler's day is longer than the day of any fixed place. To make this statement clear, let us assume that he sails from Greenwich at noon (sun time) on Monday, January 1, and travels 15 degrees west of Greenwich. He says, "I have been out one full day by the sun," but the Greenwich clock and the chronometer indicate that it is now 1:00 P. M. According to Greenwich time the traveler has been out one day and one hour. Day after day this same experience is repeated. Each of the traveler's days is 25 hours long as measured by Greenwich time. By the time he again arrives at Greenwich he discovers that his 24 days have been, in reality, 25 days. He has lost one whole day. To keep his calendar time the same as Greenwich time he must, somewhere in his westward journey, omit a day. The day is omitted at or somewhere near the International Date Line.

## DAY GAINED—EASTWARD TRAVEL

If the traveler were to leave Greenwich on Monday noon (sun time) January 1, and were to travel eastward 15 degrees each day, he would have to set his watch ahead one hour for each 15 degrees traveled. On Tuesday noon he would say, "I have been out one day by the sun," but Greenwich time and the chronometer would indicate 11:00 o'clock A. M. or 23 hours. Each of the traveler's days would be 23 hours long. In the course of the journey he would have gained one full day. To correct his calendar he would have to repeat a day. In crossing the International Date Line from east to west longitude a day must be repeated. For example, if one arrives at the west side of the line at midnight Sunday, and immediately crosses the line, he will experience Sunday again.

## THE CALENDAR

In ancient times, the people were not so much concerned about fixed dates, seasons, or passing time as we are. They were pastoral people and did not need exacting methods of reckoning time.    In this day of intense industrialism men and women need a more accurate method of computing time than did the ancients.

The ancient farmers observed that the sun did not rise and set at the same points of the horizon during the year but with the changing season shifted north and south of an east-west line. A northerly sun signified to the Egyptians the overflow of the Nile and an abundant watering of their fields.    The priests, who were the astronomers and thinkers for the people, counted the number of solar days from one summer solstice to the next and so determined the length of the year.    Seedtime, harvest time, and feast days were governed largely by the heavenly bodies, particularly the sun and moon.

We have learned that there are two kinds of days, the solar and the sidereal.    There are also two different kinds of years, the solar or tropical and the sidereal.    Both are dependent upon the earth's motion around the sun.

*Solar Year.*    The period elapsing from the time when the earth is at the vernal equinox on March 21 until it arrives there again the following March 21 is called a *tropical* year.    The solar year does not represent a complete revolution, since the vernal equinox is not permanent.    It travels westward opposite the direction in which the earth moves in its orbit.    This westward movement, which is called "precession of the equinoxes," reduces the time between successive passages of the earth through the vernal equinox by about 20 minutes and 23 seconds. The length of the solar year is 365 d. 5 h. 48 m. 45.575 s.

*Sidereal Year.*    The time elapsing between two passages of the earth's center over a given star is known as a *sidereal* year. Its length is 365 d. 6 h. 9 m. 8.97 s.

## THE EARLY ROMAN CALENDAR

Numa Pompilius in 713 B. C. undertook the task of reconciling the Roman ten-month calendar to conform to the movements of the sun and moon.    The original ten months started the year with Martius (the first month), Aprilis, Maius, Junius, Quintilis (the fifth month), Sextilis (the sixth month), September (the seventh month), October (the eighth month), November (the ninth month), and December (the tenth month). When he decided to make March 25 the beginning of his tropical year, he added two months Januarius and Februarius to the end of his year to make a year of twelve months.

In 425 B. C. the Decemvirs rearranged the calendar, placing these two months in the position they now occupy.

The calendar as changed by the Decemvirs was as follows:

| Month | Days | Month | Days | Month | Days |
|---|---|---|---|---|---|
| Januarius | 29 | Junius | 29 | November | 29 |
| Februarius | 28 | Quintilis | 31 | December | 29 |
| Martius | 31 | Sextilis | 29 | | |
| Aprilis | 29 | September | 29 | | |
| Maius | 31 | October | 31 | | |

Since the solar year has a little more than 365 days, the year was ten days too short. On this account feast days did not occur at the same time year after year. To make a year of 365 days, Numa added a month of 22 or 23 days every second year. Because the length of this month was not fixed by law but was in the hands of the pontiffs, it often gave rise to serious corruption and fraud. A change in the number of days, or a shift in position of this month in the calendar made it possible to alter certain feast and celebration days, to lengthen the term of office of favorites, to annul debts payable at a certain time, and to carry out many other questionable practices.

## THE JULIAN CALENDAR

After the conquest of Egypt, Julius Caesar secured an astronomer, Sosigenes, and ordered him to proceed to make a calendar which would conform to the Roman requirements, and one that would comply more nearly to the movements of the earth. The year was fixed at 365¼ days, and was divided into twelve months. It was decided that all even-numbered months should have 30 days except February (dedicated to the memories of the dead), which was to be shortened to 29 days in leap years. This calendar was adopted in 46 B. C. The Roman Senate decided to honor Julius Caesar by changing the name of the fifth month from Quintilis to Julius. Upon the assassination of Julius Caesar in 44 B. C., his nephew, Augustus Caesar, desired to have something to do with the reform of the calendar. He persuaded the Roman Senate to give him a month named after himself; accordingly the month Sextilis was changed to August. A day from February was taken and added to August so that this month would have the same number of days as the month of July. Complaints made by property owners about the unequal length of the quarters forced Augustus to make further changes. A day was taken from September and added to October, and one from November and added to December.

The days in the calendars of the Caesars are as follows:

|          | Jan. | Feb. | Mar. | Apr. | May | June | July | Aug. | Sept. | Oct. | Nov. | Dec. |
|----------|------|------|------|------|-----|------|------|------|-------|------|------|------|
| Julian   | 31   | 29–30| 31   | 30   | 31  | 30   | 31   | 30   | 31    | 30   | 31   | 30   |
| Augustan | 31   | 28–29| 31   | 30   | 31  | 30   | 31   | 31   | 30    | 31   | 30   | 31   |

## POPE GREGORY XIII

What was wrong with the Caesars' calendars? Both of these calendars had the same defect. They were too long. According to these calendars the year was 365 d. 6 h. while the true solar year is 365 d. 5 h. 48 m. 45.51 s. In the course of centuries this small error would amount to several days.

When the Council of Nice in Asia Minor met in A. D. 325, the churchmen adopted a rule for fixing the time for reckoning Easter. They decided that it should come on the first Sunday after the full moon which occurs on or immediately follows the time of the vernal equinox. The council decided that Easter thereafter should fall on the first Sunday after the first full moon after March 21.

Pope Gregory XIII observed that in the centuries that had elapsed since the Council of Nicaea the long year of the calendar had had the effect of shifting the March equinox from the time agreed upon for fixing Easter. By 1582 the time gained amounted to 9.8 days. The vernal equinox occurred on March 11 instead of March 21. Pope Gregory XIII therefore decreed that ten days should be omitted from the calendar; that the day following October 4, 1582 should be called October 15, 1582. He further decreed that each centurial year divisible by 400 should be called a leap year, but any centurial year not equally divisible by 400 should not be a leap year. This device reduces the time difference to such a small amount that it would require 4,000 years to make an error of as much as one day.

## THE CALENDAR OF THE FUTURE

Our present calendar is cumbersome and unwieldy. It has many defects as a good time-measuring instrument. We might ask, why not adopt a new calendar that would measure time more accurately than does our present calendar? Julius Caesar made a new calendar which had radical changes from the old Roman calendar. The plebians were all against him and murmured among themselves about the mighty man who could defy the gods. It turned out later, however, that Julius Caesar had conferred upon his people and upon humanity a lasting benefit.

Julius Caesar introduced his improvement when the world was still in an agricultural stage. The industrial age had not yet arrived. But today, science has revolutionized the old agricultural age by the introduction of steam and electricity. There has developed, as a result, a vast and rapid expansion such as the ancient world had not experienced. The pace of civilization has been tremendously quickened, and the time element has come to have a new and a very vital relation to man's innumerable activities. This new economic age must seek to control its various activities, and if it does it justly and wisely, it must provide a better and more economic time-measurer.

Agriculture of long ago could be regulated fairly well by the accurate measurement of the time between equinox and solstice, but commerce and industry of today cannot bide the leisurely coming and going of the seasons. In man's various activities decisions must be made frequently, and the weeks and months have assumed a new and important significance.

Let us examine some of the more outstanding defects of the Caesars' calendars. (1) The divisions of the months, quarters, and half-years are of unequal length. The quarters are 90, 91, 92, and 93 days. This arrangement makes the first half of the year 2 or 3 days shorter than the second half. (2) The months, quarters, and half-years do not contain a whole number of weeks. (3) Weeks are frequently split at the beginning and close of months, quarters, and half-years. (4) The months now contain 28, 29, 30, and 31 days. This makes the calculation of salaries, pensions, rents, interest, leases, and many other business transactions inaccurate, since they must be estimated on a monthly, quarterly, and semi-yearly basis. (5) The calendar is not perpetual. The weeks do not stay put within the year. Since the days of the week shift to different dates in different years, some months have more working days than others. Comparisons based on the week—a week of this year with the "corresponding" week a year ago—are very unreliable. The Fourth of July, for instance, which came in the "corresponding" week of last year, may drift into the succeeding week this year. Dates of principal events cannot be fixed with precision.

The defects of the present calendar with its unequal months and drifting weeks cause great inconvenience to commerce, industry, and to many other of the modern agencies of our present civilization such as education, labor, modern agriculture, and government administration, and even in our homes and in our personal affairs.

It should be very obvious to all of us that the time has come in our swiftly moving human affairs to correct some of the outstanding defects of our present calendar.

The calendar of the future should have, first of all, a year consisting of 364 days instead of 365. Such a year would contain an exact number of weeks, and any particular date would always fall on the same week-day and the same date of the month. If the year in this calendar were started on Sunday (the first day of the week), it would then end on Saturday (the last day of the week). This would simplify business transactions since they could be accurately calculated in terms of the year.

Each quarter year would begin on Sunday and end on Saturday, and all quarter-years would be of equal length. Such a calendar has been proposed by the World Calendar Association, Inc., and it was hoped that it might be adopted either December 31, 1939, or not later than December 31, 1944.

TABLE 15
THE FUTURE CALENDAR

| January | | | | | | | | February | | | | | | | | March | | | | | |
|---|---|---|---|---|---|---|---|---|---|---|---|---|---|---|---|---|---|---|---|---|---|
| S | M | T | W | T | F | S | | S | M | T | W | T | F | S | | S | M | T | W | T | F | S |
| 1 | 2 | 3 | 4 | 5 | 6 | 7 | | | | | | 1 | 2 | 3 | 4 | | | | | | 1 | 2 |
| 8 | 9 | 10 | 11 | 12 | 13 | 14 | | 5 | 6 | 7 | 8 | 9 | 10 | 11 | | 3 | 4 | 5 | 6 | 7 | 8 | 9 |
| 15 | 16 | 17 | 18 | 19 | 20 | 21 | | 12 | 13 | 14 | 15 | 16 | 17 | 18 | | 10 | 11 | 12 | 13 | 14 | 15 | 16 |
| 22 | 23 | 24 | 25 | 26 | 27 | 28 | | 19 | 20 | 21 | 22 | 23 | 24 | 25 | | 17 | 18 | 19 | 20 | 21 | 22 | 23 |
| 29 | 30 | 31 | | | | | | 26 | 27 | 28 | 29 | 30 | | | | 24 | 25 | 26 | 27 | 28 | 29 | 30 |

| April | | | | | | | | May | | | | | | | | June | | | | | |
|---|---|---|---|---|---|---|---|---|---|---|---|---|---|---|---|---|---|---|---|---|---|
| S | M | T | W | T | F | S | | S | M | T | W | T | F | S | | S | M | T | W | T | F | S |
| 1 | 2 | 3 | 4 | 5 | 6 | 7 | | | | | | 1 | 2 | 3 | 4 | | | | | | 1 | 2 |
| 8 | 9 | 10 | 11 | 12 | 13 | 14 | | 5 | 6 | 7 | 8 | 9 | 10 | 11 | | 3 | 4 | 5 | 6 | 7 | 8 | 9 |
| 15 | 16 | 17 | 18 | 19 | 20 | 21 | | 12 | 13 | 14 | 15 | 16 | 17 | 18 | | 10 | 11 | 12 | 13 | 14 | 15 | 16 |
| 22 | 23 | 24 | 25 | 26 | 27 | 28 | | 19 | 20 | 21 | 22 | 23 | 24 | 25 | | 17 | 18 | 19 | 20 | 21 | 22 | 23 |
| 29 | 30 | 31 | | | | | | 26 | 27 | 28 | 29 | 30 | | | | 24 | 25 | 26 | 27 | 28 | 29 | 30 |

LEAP-YEAR DAY

| July | | | | | | | | August | | | | | | | | September | | | | | |
|---|---|---|---|---|---|---|---|---|---|---|---|---|---|---|---|---|---|---|---|---|---|
| S | M | T | W | T | F | S | | S | M | T | W | T | F | S | | S | M | T | W | T | F | S |
| 1 | 2 | 3 | 4 | 5 | 6 | 7 | | | | | | 1 | 2 | 3 | 4 | | | | | | 1 | 2 |
| 8 | 9 | 10 | 11 | 12 | 13 | 14 | | 5 | 6 | 7 | 8 | 9 | 10 | 11 | | 3 | 4 | 5 | 6 | 7 | 8 | 9 |
| 15 | 16 | 17 | 18 | 19 | 20 | 21 | | 12 | 13 | 14 | 15 | 16 | 17 | 18 | | 10 | 11 | 12 | 13 | 14 | 15 | 16 |
| 22 | 23 | 24 | 25 | 26 | 27 | 28 | | 19 | 20 | 21 | 22 | 23 | 24 | 25 | | 17 | 18 | 19 | 20 | 21 | 22 | 23 |
| 29 | 30 | 31 | | | | | | 26 | 27 | 28 | 29 | 30 | | | | 24 | 25 | 26 | 27 | 28 | 29 | 30 |

| October | | | | | | | | November | | | | | | | | December | | | | | |
|---|---|---|---|---|---|---|---|---|---|---|---|---|---|---|---|---|---|---|---|---|---|
| S | M | T | W | T | F | S | | S | M | T | W | T | F | S | | S | M | T | W | T | F | S |
| 1 | 2 | 3 | 4 | 5 | 6 | 7 | | | | | | 1 | 2 | 3 | 4 | | | | | | 1 | 2 |
| 8 | 9 | 10 | 11 | 12 | 13 | 14 | | 5 | 6 | 7 | 8 | 9 | 10 | 11 | | 3 | 4 | 5 | 6 | 7 | 8 | 9 |
| 15 | 16 | 17 | 18 | 19 | 20 | 21 | | 12 | 13 | 14 | 15 | 16 | 17 | 18 | | 10 | 11 | 12 | 13 | 14 | 15 | 16 |
| 22 | 23 | 24 | 25 | 26 | 27 | 28 | | 19 | 20 | 21 | 22 | 23 | 24 | 25 | | 17 | 18 | 19 | 20 | 21 | 22 | 23 |
| 29 | 30 | 31 | | | | | | 26 | 27 | 28 | 29 | 30 | | | | 24 | 25 | 26 | 27 | 28 | 29 | 30 |

YEAR-END DAY

How does this calendar provide for 365 days in normal years and 366 days in leap years? This will be accomplished by adding two days, Leap-year day and Year-end day. Leap-year

day is to be added between June 30 and July 1, and Year-end
day will come between December 30 and January 1.   These two
days will thus be kept out of the weeks and are to become
National Holidays.

They would serve as "peg days" to prevent the weeks from
overlapping the ends of the years.

Such a calendar will provide (1) quarter years of equal length;
(2) each half-year will be of equal length; (3) each quarter will
start on Sunday and end on Saturday; (4) each quarter will
contain 91 days with 13 Sundays and 13 Saturdays; (5) the
days will stay fixed, and the calendar becomes a perpetual one.

# CHAPTER 41

# OUR MOON A COLD DEAD WORLD

## THE MOON

Of all the celestial bodies that move night after night against the starry background of our visible celestial sphere, the moon is the swiftest. Its motion is so rapid that its changing position with reference to the stars can easily be detected within two or three hours' time. The moon was one of the first heavenly objects to attract the attention of primitive man. To the ancients, the light of the moon was endowed with supernatural powers. It could influence man's various activities, even derange his mind, and anyone so foolhardy as to sleep under its pernicious light was only inviting insanity.

The moon moves about the earth in an elliptical orbit in a period of about twenty-seven and one-third days. It is the only heavenly body that really and truly encircles the earth. During this revolution about the earth, it passes through a regular "cycle" of phases with which everyone is quite familiar.

The earth is not located in the center of the moon's orbit, but at one of the foci. When it is nearest the earth, the moon is at *perigee* (*peri*—near, *gee*—earth), approximately 224,000 miles distant. At *apogee* (*apo*—away), the distance is about 250,000 miles.

The lunar globe has a real diameter of about 2160 miles. This makes its diameter a little greater than one-fourth the diameter of the earth. This means that the earth's volume is fifty times greater than that of the moon. Since the moon's density is $3\frac{1}{3}$ times heavier than water, a person weighing 240 pounds on the earth would weigh only about 40 pounds on the moon.

## MOTIONS OF THE MOON

The moon rotates once on its axis while it makes one real revolution about the earth, but in such a way as to keep always the same side toward the earth. This explains the unchanging physical appearance of the full moon. Since the revolution and rotation of the moon take place in the same direction, from west to east, and in the same period of time, different proportions of the side presented to the observer are illuminated, causing the moon phases.

## SIDEREAL AND SYNODIC PERIODS

If the moon is observed from night to night, it will soon become evident that it shifts its position in an easterly direction

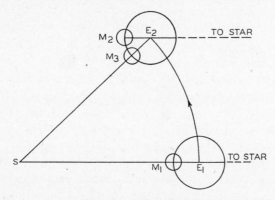

FIG. 286.   Moon phases.

to complete an entire circuit of the heavens. The time required to move from a given star, $M_1$ (Fig. 286), back to the same star again, $M_2$, is called a *sidereal* (star) month. During this time of twenty-seven and one-third days, the moon has made one complete revolution about the earth. But because the earth has moved in its orbit about the sun from $E_1$ to $E_2$, to arrive back at conjunction $M_1$, where it was at the beginning of the sidereal month, the moon must still move from $M_2$ to $M_3$. This is more than a complete revolution. The time required for the moon to move from conjunction $M_1$ back to this same position $M_3$ is known as a *synodic* or *lunar* month. The length of the lunar month is twenty-nine and one-half days.

## MOON PHASES

The side of the moon that is toward the sun is brilliantly illuminated, while the opposite side is in darkness. As the moon journeys eastward in its orbit about the earth, different portions

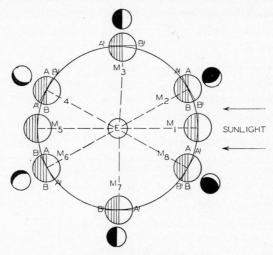

FIG. 287.   Moon phases.

of its lighted surface are presented to an observer on the earth (Fig. 287). When the moon and sun are on the same side of the earth, as at $M_1$, the dark side of the moon, represented by the parallel lines, is turned toward the earth and is invisible. It is then known as the dark of the moon, or *conjunction*. When the moon has moved eastward in the sky to $M_2$, one may see, in the early evening in the western sky, a thin crescent of light. An observer on the earth at this time cannot see beyond the line $A'B'$. Only a small portion of the front side is now in light, and it appears as a thin crescent.    The crescent is always convex to the setting sun.    When the moon has moved to $M_3$, it is at its first quarter.    One-half of the moon's surface now turned toward the earth, $A'B'$, is lighted, and the moon appears as a half-moon.    Later on, the moon appears at $M_4$.    An observer on the earth will now see more than half, and less than the full, lighted surface, $A'B'$.    The moon is now at its *gibbous* (hump) phase.    When the moon arrives at $M_5$—that is, opposite the earth from the sun—the entire lighted half is turned toward the earth, and we have full moon.    The moon is now at *opposition*.    In moving from the dark of the moon to full moon, it is seen that the lighted portion increases in size from night to night.    The moon is said to *wax*, that is, to increase in size.

After full moon, it begins to decrease in size, passing again into a gibbous moon, $M_6$, then to last quarter $M_7$, and finally, to the old crescent, $M_8$.    From full moon to the dark stage, the moon is said to *wane*, that is, to decrease in size.

## THE MOON'S RETARDATION

Because of rotation of the earth, the moon rises and sets, as do the stars, progressing steadily westward in the sky.    The moon moves eastward among the stars because of its revolution about the earth.    This eastward motion delays the moon's rising and setting from day to day, and is called its *retardation*.    The retardation amounts to 50.47 minutes in middle latitudes, but may depart greatly from this in high latitudes.

## HARVEST AND HUNTER'S MOON

The full moon that occurs nearest the autumnal equinox is called the *Harvest Moon*, while the following full moon is known as the *Hunter's Moon*.    At this time of the year the moon's orbit makes the smallest angle with the observer's eastern horizon, and the period of retardation in the latitude of New York is as little as 13 minutes.    The longer lingering of the moon in the evening skies of the northern hemisphere aided in the harvesting of the crops, hence the name Harvest Moon. The following full moon also has a shorter period of retardation than the average, hence may have been used to hunt by, with the resulting name Hunter's Moon.

## WET AND DRY MOON

Considering man's limited knowledge of the heavenly bodies and the fact that the moon is the largest astronomical body nearest the earth, it is not strange that much superstition has been associated with it. It is surprising to see how much of this old superstition has been carried over into the present.

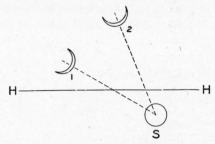

FIG. 288.—Wet and dry moon.

How frequently one hears individuals speaking jokingly, or even seriously, about a "wet" or "dry" moon, or a "warm" or "cold" moon, as if the moon actually influenced the weather.

In Fig. 288, the observer is looking toward the west with the new moon near the autumnal equinox. The moon's path now makes a small angle with $HH$, the horizon line of the observer. A line joining the cusps, that is, the horns of the new moon, is at right angles to a line from the moon to the sun, $SM_1$. The crescent is now nearly perpendicular to $HH$, and spills water. It is said by some to be "wet moon"; by others it is called "dry moon." In spring, the new moon which occurs near the vernal equinox, $M_2$, is, like a basin, right side up, and holds water. It is then known by some as "dry moon," and by others it is called "wet moon." The astronomer can predict for hundreds of years in advance the position the moon's orbit will take with reference to the horizon line $HH$, and, therefore, the position that the cusps of the moon will have with reference to the horizon line, but weather cannot be predicted scientifically with any amount of certainty for more than 24 to 48 hours in advance. While many people may still like to enjoy the superstitious belief in a "wet and dry moon," we know that it has no scientific foundation.

## LUNAR ECLIPSES

The earth, being an opaque body, casts a dark, cone-shaped shadow away from the sun. Whenever the moon enters this shadow, it is eclipsed. The moon, like the earth, also casts a dark shadow directly behind it, and when it passes directly

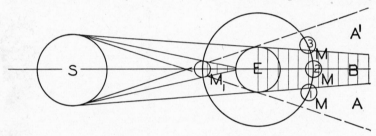

FIG. 289.—Diagram showing lunar and solar eclipses.

between the earth and the sun, $M_1$ (Fig. 289), causes an eclipse of the sun. If the shadow is long enough to reach the earth, a total eclipse will result for those directly in its path.

Lunar eclipses are of two kinds, total and partial. Total eclipses occur when the moon passes completely into the umbra, or dark part of the shadow from which all light is excluded, 2 of Fig. 289.

Partial eclipses take place when the moon goes so far north or south of the shadow as to enter it only partially, 1 and 3. The penumbra, $AA'$, is that region from which a part, but not all, of sunlight is excluded.

## NUMBER OF LUNAR ECLIPSES

If the moon's orbit were in the plane of the earth's orbit, a total eclipse would occur each synodic month; but the moon's orbit is inclined at an angle of five degrees and nine minutes to the plane of the earth's orbit (Fig. 290), and eclipses can occur only when the sun, earth, and moon are at or near the moon's *nodes* (where the moon's orbit crosses the earth's orbit). The lunar ecliptic limits are 10.5 degrees on either side of the nodes.

The solar ecliptic limits are, on the average, about 16.5 degrees on each side of the nodes.

Since the solar ecliptic limits are greater than the lunar, there are more eclipses of the sun each year than there are of the moon. There are at least two eclipses of the sun each year, either partial or total, and there may be as many as five.

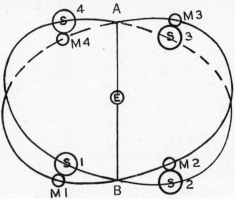

Fig. 290.—Lunar ecliptic limits.

The number of eclipses of the moon is, on the average, two each year, though this number may vary from none to three.

If the moon should be full a day or two before the earth's shadow arrives at $E_1$ (Fig. 290), no eclipse will take place, since the moon moves eastward more rapidly than does the earth. Neither will there be an eclipse a month later when the earth's shadow has reached $E_2$. In this case, no eclipse will occur in the half year during which the earth passes node $B$. Five months after the earth's shadow is at $E_2$, it will have moved along its orbit 145.5 degrees, since it moves 29.5 degrees each synodic month. But during this time, node $A$ will have retrograded (gone backward) eight degrees. The moon will pass the earth's shadow near $E_3$, at 145.5 degrees plus 10.5

degrees, or 156 degrees beyond node $B$, and 180 degrees minus 156 plus 8 degrees, or 16 degrees before it arrives at node $A$. Since the lunar ecliptic limits are 10.5 degrees, no eclipse will occur during this half of the year.    It will be seen that there is a possibility that no lunar eclipse may occur during a solar year.

## THE ATMOSPHERELESS MOON

In the distant past, the moon possibly had an atmosphere. But because it is so small, its surface gravity being about one-sixth that of the earth, it cannot hold permanently the molecules of gas such as are present in our atmosphere.    Over a long period of time the gaseous molecules have slowly escaped into space.

There are many visible evidences that the moon has little or no atmosphere.    The illuminated portion of its surface is always visible.    No haze, clouds, or dust storms have ever been observed.    When the moon passes directly between the earth and the sun, no luminous atmospheric ring is visible.    The moon's margin is sharp and black.    When the moon passes between the earth and a star, the light of the star is cut off sharply and suddenly, and not gradually.    Whatever may have been the origin of the moon, it is quite certain that if it ever possessed an atmosphere, it has lost it now.    Without air and water the moon must be devoid of life.    What a strange weird world it must be!    Imagine yourself and a friend transferred to the moon's surface.    Without air, you can have no sound, and you could not converse with your friend.    Mountains might fall, but they would do so without sound or warning.    The sky would appear inky black and gloomy.    It would be dotted everywhere with brilliant stars shining continuously.    The "lunarscape" would be made up of light and shade.    Mountains reaching into the sunlight would appear brilliantly light, while their shadows would be impenetrably black.    In daytime the surface rocks would become unbearably hot, and at night intensely cold.    No place on the surface would be free from falling meteors, unless there is a rare atmosphere around the moon.    They would fall unseen and unheard.

## THE TEMPERATURE OF THE MOON

Since the moon has little or no atmosphere, most of the heat reaching it from the sun would be absorbed at the surface, and but a small amount reflected back into space. The portion of the moon's surface exposed to the sun's rays continuously for a period of two weeks and then divested of sunlight for an equal period must experience great extremes in temperature. Recent measurements of the heat which the moon radiates to the earth have revealed for the sunlight side a temperature of 212° F., while the dark side may experience temperatures near absolute zero, −549.6° F.

It would require 400,000 to 500,000 full moons shining on the earth to equal the amount of light received from the sun.

## SURFACE OF THE MOON

The most conspicuous surface features of the moon are its volcanic craters, mountains, and dark areas called *maria* or seas. The craters of most of the volcanoes are more or less round. Some are immense—for example, Clavius, 142 miles in diameter, while many range from 20 to 50 miles. Tycho (upper right-hand side, Fig. 291) shows light streaks extending almost directly away from the center, like spokes from the hub of a wheel. The mountain chains are, with the exception of the Appenines, lower central portion of Fig. 291, very short and irregular but reach to great heights.

The dark areas appear as rather smooth, depressed plain-areas. If they were ever seas, the water has entirely disappeared.

There is some doubt as to whether the lunar craters are real volcanoes similar to those found on the earth. They seem to differ in many respects.

## INFLUENCE OF THE MOON

The moon, our nearest neighbor, is of service to man in many ways. It is the chief cause of tides, which are the alternate risings and fallings of the ocean water. Tides occur twice daily. Many years ago tides along portions of the New England coast were used to drive small water-mills (tide-mills), but today such small units of power are not practical. There are certain places along the coast of Maine, especially where the configuration of the high coast line is such as to cause a sufficient flow of water, where it might be practical to erect hydroelectric plants.

*Yerkes Observatory.*

FIG. 291.   The moon at the age of 16 days.

Flow tides make it possible for ships to enter and leave certain harbors from which shipping might be barred, as, for example, Liverpool, England.   If a harbor's communication is connected with the ocean by a narrow strait, as is the case with

New York, the passageway is scoured of its silting mud and sand by the ebb tide.

Eclipses of the sun which result because of the moon have made it possible for the astronomer to study certain parts of the sun which are not readily accessible during bright sunlight.

The moon, as well as the stars and the sun, is made use of by the mariner to find his latitude and longitude at sea. Its exact position can be accurately determined for every day in the year for years in advance, and is so recorded in nautical almanacs.

No other heavenly body has had more of superstition associated with it. In past time, these superstitious ideas prevailed more commonly than now, although there are yet many outlying rural areas where the people still believe in the moon signs.

In olden times, accidents of all kinds were ascribed to the moon. Lunacy, blindness, especially when the light of full moon fell upon the sleeper's eyes, and the hour of death were thought to be caused by the change of tides. It was believed that onions grew best after full moon; medicinal herbs were more efficacious if gathered before full moon; shingles, if not laid in the proper moon phase, would warp and curl; and meat cured in the wrong moon change would spoil.

Probably one of the most common and still prevalent superstitions is that the moon influences our weather. There are those who still believe that weather does change with the moon changes. The moon alters its phases each week, and thus the weather should change within three or four days of each change of the moon. In agricultural regions many farmers have a feeling that a "wet" or "dry" moon may be told from the position the new moon has when first seen in the western heavens shortly after sunset. When the new crescent hangs low so that a line joining the two cusps is almost perpendicular to the horizon (1, Fig. 288), the moon is called a "wet moon." Thus the farmer might expect abundant moisture for his crops. When the line connecting the cusps is very nearly horizontal with the horizon (2, Fig. 288), it is a "dry moon," and crops will wither.

No modern scientific weather forecaster will predict weather changes with any degree of accuracy beyond two or three days.

# CHAPTER 42

# WONDERS OF THE
# NIGHT SKIES

For ages the wonders of the night skies have made their stirring appeal to the mind of man. Under the canopy of the sparkling heavens man is made to sense the fact that, after all, the earth on which he lives is but a tiny speck compared with infinite space around him.

It should become a pleasure and a joy, year after year, to watch the rising and setting of the stars, to learn the names of many of the brighter ones, to know the constellations to which they belong, and to be able to locate them in the sky at various seasons of the year.

A glance at the night sky will soon convince an observer that the stars are not distributed uniformly over the heavens and are not of the same brightness and color. Many of them are grouped into rather remarkable outlines which are not difficult to distinguish one from another. The ancients had observed these outlines, some of which resembled men and women or animals which they knew; as a consequence they gave names to these star-groups or constellations and wove around them in their imaginative way beautiful and fantastic romances.

But the sky of our time is not the same as that seen centuries ago. All stars are moving, and these constellations in time must eventually disappear. Most of the names given to the constellations which were studied by the Egyptians, Babylonians, Greeks, and Romans had to do with living things. Some were patterned after birds, beasts, serpents, fish, and

men.   Others were named in honor of heroes, gods, and god-
desses.   The term *constellation* is derived from the Latin and
means literally "stars together"—a configuration of apparently
fixed stars.   It is difficult to say just when and how these
patterns were first selected.   Our first reliable record has come
to us from the Egyptians.   Ptolemy, a famed astronomer,
named, catalogued, and described 48 constellations.   Since his
time others have added new forms until we now have 88, if the
Great Ship Argo is divided into four.

When you examine the night sky for these patterns, do not
expect that you will see the outlines as they were seen or
imagined by the ancients.   It is sometimes difficult for us to
understand how they could have imagined the various objects
for which they were named.   A few of the constellations do
resemble the forms and names given them, for example: *Crater*,
the Cup; *Cetus*, the Whale; *Cygnus*, the Swan; *Aquila*, the
Eagle; *Ursa Major*, the Great Bear, or the Big Dipper as we
know it; and *Ursa Minor*, the Little Bear, or the Little Dipper.

A persistent study of the night skies should enable the
observer to locate the principal constellations together with
their important stars.   To this end, diagrams have been prepared showing the main outline of each constellation.   Not all
of the stars in each one have been given, but enough to enable
the beginner to identify the constellation.   When the outline
has once been discovered, it becomes an easy matter to locate it
readily in any position in the sky.

## THE NORTHERN CONSTELLATIONS

The polar constellations are those grouped around the Pole
Star.   They never set for an observer in middle or high latitudes, but may be seen on a clear, moonless night moving in
orbits around the Pole Star.

First study carefully the outlines of these constellations as
shown in Fig. 292 and become familiar with their forms and
names.   Then turn to Fig. 293, and see if you can locate them

as they appear in the sky.   Hold the book so that the center
of the figure is directly overhead.

## THE SPRING CONSTELLATIONS

The forms of the spring constellations are shown in Figs. 294,
and 295. Examine these figures carefully and note the
outlines for the various constellations.   Then learn their names
and the names of the principal stars in the constellation which
are indicated by the unshaded circles.   Now hold Fig. 296
directly over you in such a way that the part of the figure marked
*N* points north, and the sides marked *E* and *W* point to the
east and west respectively.   You will now find the constellations
in the sky in about the same positions they occupy at 9:00 P. M.
on March 1.

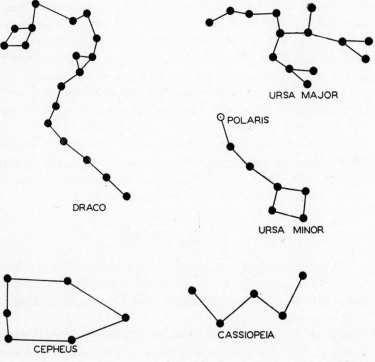

Fɪɢ. 292.

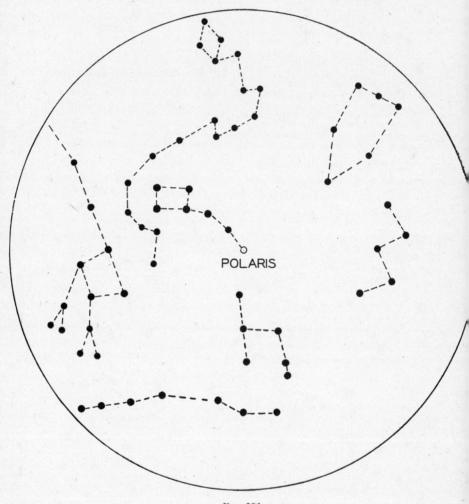

POLARIS

Fig. 293.

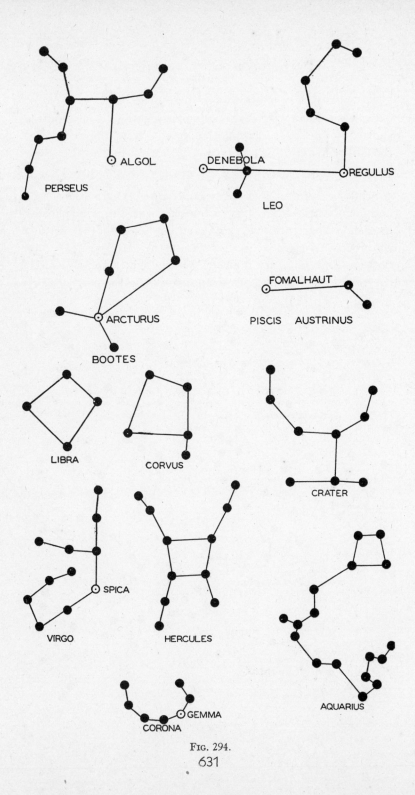

ALGOL

PERSEUS

DENEBOLA

REGULUS

LEO

ARCTURUS

BOOTES

FOMALHAUT

PISCIS   AUSTRINUS

LIBRA

CORVUS

CRATER

SPICA

VIRGO

HERCULES

AQUARIUS

GEMMA

CORONA

Fig. 294.

631

## THE SUMMER CONSTELLATIONS

On June 1, at 9:00 P. M., the constellations will appear as shown in Fig. 297. The dotted band shows the position of the Milky Way.

## THE FALL AND WINTER CONSTELLATIONS

Study carefully Figs. 298 and 299. Learn the names and forms of the constellations together with the principal stars in each. Then turn to Fig. 300 and hold it so that the letter *Z* is directly overhead. Be sure that the letters on the top, bottom, and sides are pointing in the right directions. The constellations will be shown in approximately the positions they have at 9:00 P. M., November 1.

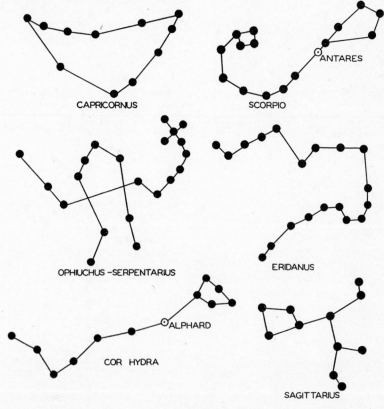

Fɪɢ. 295.

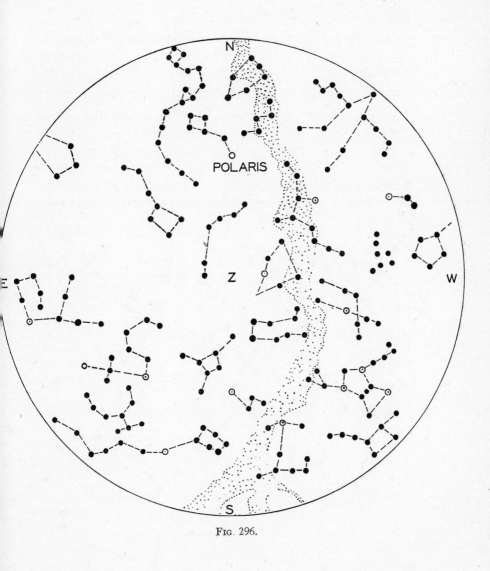

N

POLARIS

Z

W

E

S

Fig. 296.

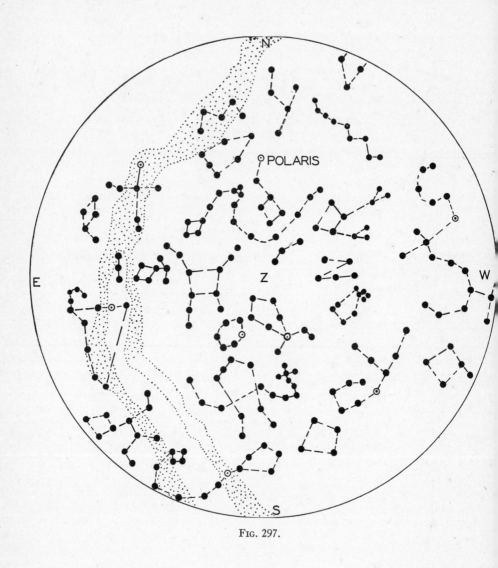

Fig. 297.

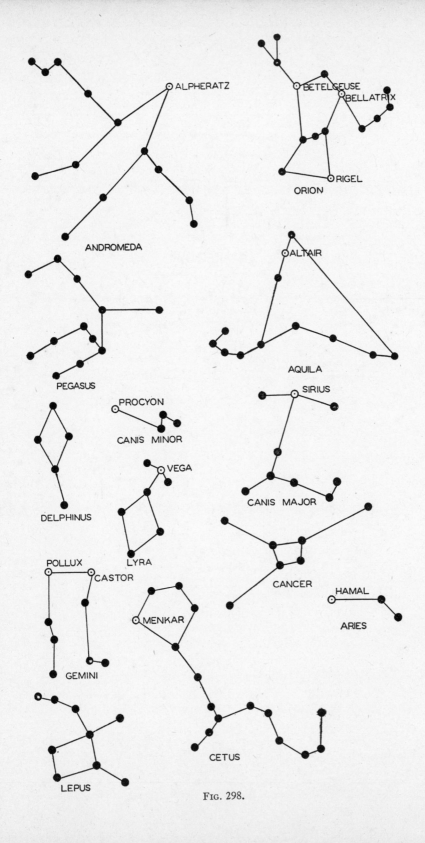

ALPHERATZ

BETELGEUSE
BELLATRIX

RIGEL

ORION

ANDROMEDA

ALTAIR

PEGASUS

AQUILA

PROCYON

CANIS MINOR

SIRIUS

DELPHINUS

VEGA

CANIS MAJOR

POLLUX
CASTOR

LYRA

CANCER

MENKAR

HAMAL

ARIES

GEMINI

CETUS

LEPUS

Fig. 298.

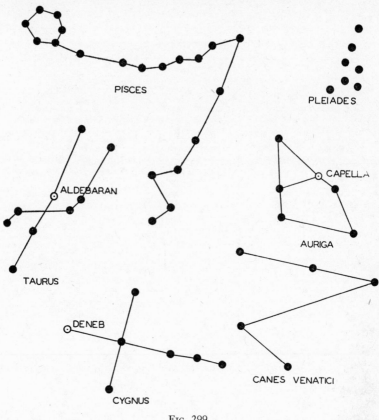

Fig. 299.

# THE PRONUNCIATIONS OF THE CONSTELLATIONS AND THEIR PRINCIPAL STARS

One should be able not only to identify the constellations but also to pronounce them properly. The pronunciations of the constellations together with their first- and second-magnitude stars are given in Table 16.

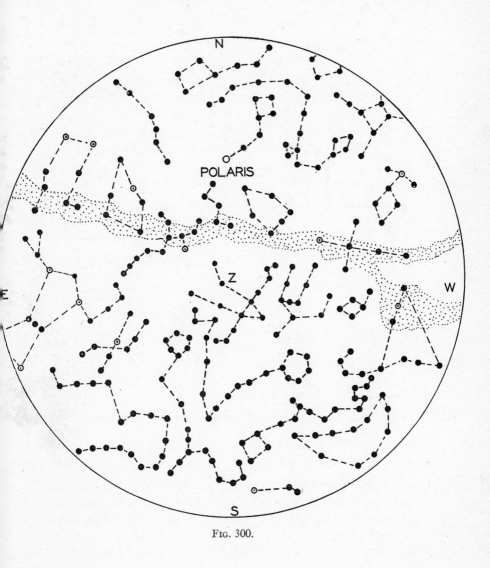

FIG. 300.

TABLE 16

## THE CONSTELLATIONS AND THEIR PRINCIPAL STARS

| Constellations | First Magnitude | Second Magnitude |
|---|---|---|
| 1. Andromeda—The Chained Maiden (ăn-drŏm′-ē-dá) | | Alpheratz (ăl′-fē-rătz) |
| 2. Aquarius—The Water Bearer (à-kwā′-rĭ-ŭs) | | |
| 3. Aquila—The Eagle (ăk′-wĭ-là) | Altair (ăl-tā′-ĭr) | |
| 4. Aries—The Ram (ā′-rĭ-ēz) | | Hamal (hăm′-ăl) |
| 5. Auriga—The Charioteer (ô-rī′-gà) | Capella (kà-pĕl′-à) | |
| 6. Piscis Austrinus—Southern Fish (pĭs′-ĭz ôs-trī′-nŭs) | Fomalhaut (fō′-măl-hôt) | |
| 7. Bootes—The Bear Driver (bō-ō′-tēz) | Arcturus (ärk-tū′-rŭs) | |
| 8. Cancer—The Crab (kăn′-sēr) | | |
| 9. Canes Venatici—The Hunting Dogs (kā′-nĕz vē-năt′-ĭ-sī) | | |
| 10. Canis Major—The Big Dog (kā′-nĭs mā′-jŏr) | | |
| 11. Canis Minor—The Little Dog (kā′-nĭs mī′-nôr) | Procyon (prō′-sĭ-ŏn) | |
| 12. Capricornus—The Sea Goat (kăp′-rĭ-kôr′-nŭs) | | |
| 13. Cassiopeia—The Queen's Chair (kăs′-ĭ-ō-pē′-yà) | | |
| 14. Cepheus—The King (sē′-fŭs or sē′-fē-ŭs) | | |
| 15. Cetus—The Whale (sē′-tŭs) | | Mira (mī′-rà) |
| 16. Corona—The Crown (kŏ-rō′-nà) | Gemma (jĕm′-à) | |
| 17. Corvus—The Crow (kôr′-vŭs) | | |
| 18. Crater—The Cup (krā′-tēr) | | |
| 19. Cygnus—The Swan (sĭg′-nŭs) | Deneb (dĕn′-ĕb) | |
| 20. Delphinus—The Dolphin (dĕl-fī′-nŭs) | | |
| 21. Draco—The Northern Dragon (drā′-kō) | | |

22. Eridanus—The River Po (ē-rĭd′-à-nŭs)
23. Gemini—The Twins (jĕm′-ĭ-nī) — Pollux (pŏl′-ŭks), Castor (kăs′-tēr)
24. Hercules—The Kneeler (hûr′-kū-lēz)
25. Cor Hydra—The Water Snake (kôr′ hī-drà) — Alphard (ăl′-färd)
26. Leo—The Lion or The Sickle (lē′-ō) — Regulus (rĕg′-ū-lŭs), Denebola (dĕ-nĕb′-ô-là)
27. Lepus—The Timid Hare (lē′-pŭs)
28. Libra—The Scales (lī′-brà)
29. Lyra—The Lyre (lī′-rà) — Vega (vē′-gà)
30. Ophiuchus—The Great Physician (ŏf-ĭ-ū′-kŭs) — Rasalhague (răs′-ăl-hä′-gwē)
31. Orion—The Giant Hunter (ō-rī′-ŏn) — Rigel (rī′-gĕl), Betelgeuse (bē′-t'l-jōoz), Bellatrix (bĕ-lā′-trĭks)

32. Pegasus—The Flying Horse (pĕg′-à-sŭs) — Markab (mär′-kăb), Scheal (shē′-ăl), Algenib (ăl-jē′-nĭb)

33. Perseus—The Champion (pûr′-sŭs or pûr′-sē′-ŭs) — Algol (ăl′-gŏl)
34. Pisces—The Fishes (pĭs′-ēz)
35. Pleiades—The Seven Virgins (plē′-à-dēz or plē′-yà-dēz)
36. Sagittarius—The Archer (săj′-ĭ-tā′-rĭ-ŭs)
37. Scorpio—The Scorpion (skôr′-pē-ō) — Antares (ăn-tär′-ēz)
38. Taurus—The Bull (tô′-rŭs) — Aldebaran (ăl-dĕb′-à-răn)
39. Ursa Major—The Big Bear (ûr′-sà mā′-jôr)
40. Ursa Minor—The Little Bear (ûr′-sà mī′-nôr)
41. Virgo—The Virgin (vûr′-gō) — Spica (spī′-ka)

639

# CHAPTER 43

# SCIENCE
AND THE WORLD
OF TOMORROW

The prediction of future events and developments has always been an intriguing subject to man. Often against his better judgment he resorts to palmistry, astrology, numerology, dope sheets, and the like. He envisions new forms of transportation and communication, strange products for food, clothing, and shelter; and conveniences and luxuries which will usher in a new Utopia. Yet, in his inconsistency, man ridicules the courageous inventive genius who offers to the world the first crude example of a new invention or product. Fulton with his steam engine, Drake and his petroleum-recovery process, Galileo and his astronomical theories—these and many others were laughed at, derided, and even persecuted for daring to offer to the world a new invention or an original idea. Dominated by his incredulity and prejudice in the presence of something new, man even refuses to believe his own eyes and ears. He declares "it isn't so," even as did the rustic who met his first sight of a giraffe with the remark, "There ain't no such animal."

Admonished by such a record of past experiences, it would be unwise for writers of books on science to attempt to forecast specific developments which might be expected to emerge from the laboratory, the study, and the factory of the future. Yet in the various fields of knowledge and invention certain trends are appearing which suggest future lines of development.

640

Popular demand, likewise, is spurring science on to intensive efforts to meet the new needs of a modern generation.   Hence it seems reasonable to anticipate that in certain fields of human interest and activity the future holds promise of great development.   We shall examine some of these possibilities.

Modern transportation demands speed and safety.   Streamlined trains, powerful automobiles, and swift airplanes are the answer.   Fast as they move, they could travel much faster and more safely except for certain limitations.   Train speeds are limited by types of road beds, structural materials, power plants, and safety devices.   Faster automobiles call for wider highways, freedom from cross traffic, numerous safety appliances, and better night-time illumination.   In the realm of air transportation we foresee successful stratosphere flying, take-off and landing devices which can utilize the back yard or the house top, and automatic equipment which will help to eliminate crashes.

Nations as well as armies "travel on their stomachs."   Food is a basic essential.   Hence we may expect marked future improvement in the cultivation and preservation and even the synthetic production of foodstuffs.   Some recent developments are fertilizers from air and water (nitrogen fixation) and soilless growth of plants (hydroponics).   Yet the balanced and proper treatment of soil for maximum crop production is still in its infancy.   In the future, perhaps not two but ten "blades of grass will grow where one grew before."

Countless tons of food are now wasted through spoilage.   In solving the problem of food preservation, we have made a beginning through the use of refrigerating rooms, gas treatment, dry ice, pasteurization, and the like.   But it is only a beginning.

The synthetic production of food offers interesting possibilities.   The need is most acute in countries of dense population and limited agricultural areas.   In some such countries, notably Germany, real progress has been made in converting carbohydrate products into edible foods.   But the field is still virtually unexplored.   Highly concentrated foods in tablet form have often been proposed.   Even if they were possible, they would be of doubtful value.    The digestive system can function properly only when supplied with considerable "roughage"—a factor which would be absent if one were to dine from the vest pocket.

A common remark is to the effect that "Everybody talks about the weather, but no one ever does anything about it." This aphorism seems to apply with considerable accuracy to football games, parades, and picnics.    In long-range weather forecasting, however, science is entering the field as a real benefactor to the farmer, the mariner, and the long-distance aviator.    Instruments for determining weather-making conditions in the upper regions of the atmosphere are being slowly evolved.    What the future holds in this promising field is still merest conjecture.

Wood, marble, and metals for construction and decoration are meeting new competitors—the plastics.    Corn stalks, casein, urea, bagasse, and numerous other raw materials are being converted into articles of utility and beauty, ranging from equipment for the dressing table and the automobile to house construction and one-piece airplanes.    Great strides in the realm of plastics are certain in the near future.

Medicine, both preventive and curative, is sending a frantic SOS to the science of tomorrow.    Cancer, infantile paralysis, common colds—to mention only a few scourges—are taking a terrible toll in human lives and comfort.    Every branch of medicine and surgery is calling for new and improved techniques and materials.    Gradually the call is being answered: for example, in the new sulfanilamid and sulfapyridine treatment for dread pneumonia.    Can we look with any assurance into a tomorrow which shall offer mankind freedom from pain, fewer "sick leaves," and longer life?

The house of tomorrow may well be a product of the laboratories of science.    The earth as a foundation for frontier houses was later replaced by rock, and it in turn by concrete.    Is concrete the last word in foundation material?    Diminishing forests are forcing the search for new materials for floors, doors, and paneling.    Wall board and plastic products offer great promise as wood substitutes.    They are easily installed and offer no asylum for dirt and vermin.    Can something even better be developed?

In many states where marked seasonal changes occur, the householder is engaged in a constant battle to keep the heat out in summer and hold it in in winter.    Insulation is the solution, but it is safe to say that our present installations will appear crude in comparison with the insulated home of the future. Present-day home lighting systems, efficient as they are, leave much to be desired.    The electric bulb is wasteful of electricity, tiring to the eyes, and often inconveniently located.    The day should not be far distant when every modern home will have an illuminating system which is economical, restful, shadowless, and convenient.

Glass as a medium for admitting daylight seems to be well established.    Yet it is a bar to the healthful ultraviolet rays and is fragile.    It is a two-way route for "seeing out" and "seeing in," and, as usually installed, it offers too free a passage for heat. A better transparent medium may some day be developed by the glass manufacturers or the makers of plastics.    The way is open to future scientists.

Air conditioning of a very efficient sort is now available to home owners in the higher income brackets.    But in the interests of health and comfort, it should be so simplified, improved, and standardized that every modern home could enjoy its benefits.    Is it safe to predict that tomorrow's science will make it as much a necessity as running water and electric lights?

Rapid methods of communication make the world seem very small.    Perhaps no modern scientific achievements are less understood by the average person than the telephone and the wireless.    It once seemed uncanny to step to a box on the wall and hear a friend's voice a thousand miles away.    Even today it seems almost miraculous that without benefit of aerial or ground wire we can bring from our radio at will voices and music from the opposite side of the earth.    We not only communicate by wireless; we direct pilotless planes by the same device.    We fly blind through darkness and fog guided by a radio beam.

With the eventual perfection of television it would seem that the utmost in communication will have been accomplished. Yet we know this is not true. Every new invention opens new fields and creates new needs. Future generations who will enjoy methods of communication yet unheard of will perhaps describe the people of today as a race who lived in unbearable isolation.

If we attempt to specify the particular machines or devices which will be greatly improved by future scientists, we find the list almost endless. It includes nearly every invention which is serving the world's needs—automobiles, airplanes, ships, printing presses, typewriters, electric shavers, permanent wavers, synthetic fabrics, engines of all types, telescopes, radios, guns, explosives, laundry washers and dryers, tractors, milking machines. In fact, an illustrated catalogue of today's products will appear as inadequate and antiquated to future generations as do our grandparents' pictures of phonographs, buggies, horse cars, scythe and cradle, and quill pens.

Scientific methods will affect the future of not only the material world, but the world of the mind as well. From the log schoolhouse to the great university, from the three R's to present-day curricula is a far cry. The public is spending huge sums on its educational institutions, and educators are making every effort to justify the investment. No group of workers is more aware of its responsibilities and shortcomings than are the educators. Scientific studies looking toward a more efficient training of the mind and a more adequate preparation for life's tasks are constantly in progress. The results are very encouraging, but the task is only well begun. Profound changes are in store for future classrooms and laboratories.

We have attempted to peer into the future of science, but not as a crystal gazer pretends to explore the unknown. We can see into the future only as it is illumined by the light of the past.

Our scientists have wrought laboriously and well. Their failures and achievements will soon be written into the pages of history. It is not the mature scientist of today who will fulfill the promise of new things to come.   The task extends beyond the span of his life time.   Rather, it is you—the reader—who must answer the challenge of the future.   As a layman, you can extend sympathetic encouragement and praise toward the efforts of an ever-advancing science.   As a scientist you can, by tireless loyalty and devotion, add your contribution to knowledge and material well-being.

# READING REFERENCES

## CHAPTER 1. THE DAWN OF SCIENCE

Cajori, Florian, *A History of Physics.* New York: The Macmillan Company, 1933.

Harvey-Gibson, R. J., *Two Thousand Years of Science.* New York: The Macmillan Company, 1929.

Heiberg, J. L., *Mathematics and Physical Science in Classical Antiquity.* London: Oxford University Press, 1922.

Mayer, Joseph, *The Seven Seals of Science.* New York: The Century Company, 1927.

Riley, Woodbridge, *From Myth to Reason.* New York: D. Appleton and Company, 1926.

Sarton, George, *The History of Science and the New Humanism.* Cambridge: Harvard University Press, 1937.

Van Wagenen, Theo. F., *Beacon Lights of Science.* New York: Thomas Y. Crowell Co., 1924.

## CHAPTER 2. MAN AND HIS MACHINES

Avery, Madalyn, *Household Physics*, Chapters III, IV. New York: The Macmillan Company, 1938.

Black, Newton Henry, *An Introductory Course in College Physics*, Chapter II. New York: The Macmillan Company, 1935.

Dreier, Thomas, *The Power of Print—and Men.* Brooklyn: Mergenthaler Linotype Company, 1936.

Heil, Louis M., *The Physical World*, Unit 3. Philadelphia: P. Blakiston's Son and Co., Inc., 1936.

Hobbie, John Remington, *Introduction to College Physics*, Chapter VII. New York: Farrar and Rinehart, Inc., 1936.

Hubert, Philip Gengembre, *Inventors.* New York: Charles Scribner's Sons, 1896.

Kilby, Clinton Maury, *Introduction to College Physics*, Second Edition, Chapter III, Section VIII. New York: D. Van Nostrand Company, Inc., 1938.

Knowlton, A. A., *Physics for College Students*, Second Edition, Chapters I–III. New York: McGraw-Hill Book Company, Inc., 1935.

Leonard, Jonathan Norton, *Tools of Tomorrow.* New York: The Viking Press, 1935.

McCormick, Cyrus, *The Century of the Reaper*.   Boston: Houghton Mifflin Company, 1931.

Millikan, Robert Andrews; Gale, Henry Gordon; and Edwards, Charles William, *A First Course in Physics for Colleges*, Revised Edition, Chapters III, IV.   New York: Ginn and Company, 1938.

Smith, Alpheus W., *Elements of Physics*, Fourth Edition, Chapter VII.   New York: McGraw-Hill Book Company, Inc., 1938.

Spinney, Louis Bevier, *A Text Book of Physics*, Fifth Edition, Chapter VII.   New York: The Macmillan Company, 1937.

Stewart, Oscar M., *Physics*, Third Edition, Chapter VIII.   New York: Ginn and Company, 1939.

Whitman, Walter G., *Household Physics*, Third Edition, Chapter II. New York: John Wiley and Sons, Inc., 1939.

## CHAPTER 3.   ENERGY UTILIZED AND WASTED

Black, Newton Henry, *An Introductory Course in College Physics*, Chapter III.   New York: The Macmillan Company, 1935.

Heil, Louis M., *The Physical World*, Unit 4.   Philadelphia: P. Blakiston's Son and Co., Inc., 1936.

Lemon, Harvey Brace, *From Galileo to Cosmic Rays*, Chapters IX, X.   Chicago: The University of Chicago Press, 1934.

Mott-Smith, Morton Churchill, *The Story of Energy*.   New York, London: D. Appleton-Century Company, 1934.

Perkins, Henry A., *College Physics*, Chapter V.   New York: Prentice-Hall, Inc., 1938.

Smith, Alpheus W., *Elements of Physics*, Fourth Edition, Chapter V. New York: McGraw-Hill Book Co., Inc., 1938.

Spinney, Louis Bevier, *A Text Book of Physics*, Fifth Edition, Chapters VI, VIII.   New York: The Macmillan Company, 1937.

Stewart, Oscar M., *Physics*, Third Edition, Chapter VII.   New York: Ginn and Company, 1939.

Whitman, Walter G., *Household Physics*, Third Edition, Chapters I, III.   New York: John Wiley and Sons, Inc., 1939.

## CHAPTER 4.   FORCE AND MOTION

Brodetsky, Selig, *Sir Isaac Newton*.   London: Methuen and Co., Ltd., 1929.

Lemon, Harvey Brace, *From Galileo to Cosmic Rays*, Chapters I–VIII. Chicago: The University of Chicago Press, 1934.

Perkins, Henry A., *College Physics*, Chapter III.   New York: Prentice-Hall, Inc., 1938.

Smith, Alpheus W., *Elements of Physics*, Fourth Edition, Chapters II, IV. New York: McGraw-Hill Book Company, Inc., 1938.

Stewart, Oscar M., *Physics*, Third Edition, Chapters IV–VI, XII. New York: Ginn and Company, 1939.

Sullivan, John William Navin, *Isaac Newton*. New York: The Macmillan Company, 1938.

Williams, Samuel Robinson, *Foundations of College Physics*, Chapter VII. New York: Ginn and Company, 1937.

## CHAPTER 5. FLUIDS AND FLUID PRESSURE

Avery, Madalyn, *Household Physics*, Chapter V. New York: The Macmillan Company, 1938.

Black, Newton Henry, *An Introductory Course in College Physics*, Chapters IV, V. New York: The Macmillan Company, 1935.

Heil, Herman G.; and Bennett, Willard H., *Fundamental Principles of Physics*, Chapter 3. New York: Prentice-Hall, Inc., 1938.

Heil, Louis M., *The Physical World*, Unit 3. Philadelphia: P. Blakiston's Son and Co., Inc., 1936.

Hobbie, John Remington, *Introduction to College Physics*, Chapters IX–XI. New York: Farrar and Rinehart, Inc., 1936.

Lemon, Harvey Brace, *From Galileo to Cosmic Rays*, Chapter XIII. Chicago: The University of Chicago Press, 1934.

Millikan, Robert Andrews; Gale, Henry Gordon; and Edwards, Charles William, *A First Course in Physics for Colleges*, Revised Edition, Chapters VI, VII. New York: Ginn and Company, 1938.

Smith, Alpheus W., *Elements of Physics*, Fourth Edition, Chapters IX–XI. New York: McGraw-Hill Book Company, Inc., 1938.

Spinney, Louis Bevier, *A Text Book of Physics*, Fifth Edition, Chapter X. New York: The Macmillan Company, 1937.

Stewart, Oscar M., *Physics*, Third Edition, Chapters I, II. New York: Ginn and Company, 1939.

## CHAPTER 6. MOLECULES AND THEIR BEHAVIOR

Cox, Richard T., *Time, Space and Atoms*. New York: The Century Company, 1933.

Eddington, A. S., *Stars and Atoms*. New Haven: Yale University Press, 1927.

Heil, Louis M., *The Physical World*, Unit 5. Philadelphia: P. Blakiston's Son and Co., Inc., 1936.

Hobbie, John Remington, *Introduction to College Physics*, Chapter XIII. New York: Farrar and Rinehart, Inc., 1936.

Knowlton, A. A., *Physics for College Students*, Second Edition, Chapter XVI. New York: McGraw-Hill Book Company, Inc., 1935.

Millikan, Robert Andrews; Gale, Henry Gordon; and Edwards, Charles William, *A First Course in Physics for Colleges*, Revised Edition, Chapters IX, XI. New York: Ginn and Company, 1938.

Rusk, Rogers D., *Atoms, Men and Stars*. New York, London: A. A. Knopf, 1937.

Smith, Alpheus W., *Elements of Physics*, Fourth Edition, Chapters VIII, XXV. New York: McGraw-Hill Book Company, Inc., 1938.

Spinney, Louis Bevier, *A Text Book of Physics*, Fifth Edition, Chapter XII. New York: The Macmillan Company, 1937.

Stewart, Oscar M., *Physics*, Third Edition, Chapter XIV. New York: Ginn and Company, 1939.

Williams, Samuel Robinson, *Foundations of College Physics*, Chapter VI. New York: Ginn and Company, 1937.

## CHAPTER 7.   BUILDING STONES OF MATTER

Brinkley, Stuart R., *Principles of General Chemistry*. New York: The Macmillan Company, 1933. Chapters 3, 10, 12.

Briscoe, Herman T., *An Introduction to College Chemistry*. Boston: Houghton Mifflin Company, 1937. Chapters 1, 3, 4, 9, 10, 12, 16, 18.

Cartledge, G. H., *Introduction to Inorganic Chemistry*. Boston: Ginn and Company, 1935. Chapters 3, 4.

Deming, Horace G., *General Chemistry*. New York: John Wiley and Sons, 1935. Chapters 2, 3, 6, 13, 22.

Holmes, Harry N., *General Chemistry*. New York: The Macmillan Company, 1936. Chapters 3, 8, 24.

Irwin, Frederick C., and Sherwood, G. Ray, *General and Inorganic Chemistry*. Philadelphia: P. Blakiston's Son and Co., Inc., 1939. Chapters 1, 2, 6, 7, 10, 11.

Jaffe, Bernard, *Crucibles*. New York: Simon and Schuster, 1930. Chapters 7, 14, 15.

———, *New World of Chemistry*. New York: Silver, Burdett and Company, 1935. Chapters 5, 9, 11.

Kendall, James, *Smith's College Chemistry*. New York: D. Appleton-Century Company, 1935. Chapters 4, 9, 27, 28.

McPherson, William, and Henderson, William Edwards, *A Course in General Chemistry*. Boston: Ginn and Company, 1933. Chapters 2, 7, 8, 13.

Norris, James F., and Young, Ralph C., *Inorganic Chemistry for Colleges*. New York: McGraw-Hill Book Company, 1938. Chapters 2, 9.

Richardson, Leon B., *General Chemistry*. New York: Henry Holt and Company, 1934. Chapters 7, 11, 21, 22.

Timm, John Arrend, *An Introduction to Chemistry*. New York: McGraw-Hill Book Company, 1930. Chapters 6, 7, 18, 19.

## CHAPTER 8.   SOME SIMPLE HEAT PHENOMENA

Avery, Madalyn, *Household Physics*, Chapters VII–XII. New York: The Macmillan Company, 1938.

Black, Newton Henry, *An Introductory Course in College Physics*, Chapters XIV–XVI. New York: The Macmillan Company, 1935.

Darrow, Floyd L., *The New World of Physical Discovery*, Chapter IV. Indianapolis: The Bobbs-Merrill Company, 1930.

Heil, Herman G.; and Bennett, Willard H., *Fundamental Principles of Physics*, Chapters 12–15. New York: Prentice-Hall, Inc., 1938.

Heil, Louis M., *The Physical World*, Unit 6. Philadelphia: P. Blakiston's Son and Co., Inc., 1936.

Knowlton, A. A., *Physics for College Students*, Second Edition, Chapter XII. New York: McGraw-Hill Book Company, Inc., 1935.

Smith, Alpheus W., *Elements of Physics*, Fourth Edition, Chapters XXII–XXIV, XXIX. New York: McGraw-Hill Book Company, Inc., 1938.

Stewart, Oscar M., *Physics*, Third Edition, Chapter XVI–XVIII, XX, XXI. New York: Ginn and Company, 1939.

Whitman, Walter G., *Household Physics*, Third Edition, Chapters IV–XIV. New York: John Wiley and Sons, Inc., 1939.

Williams, Samuel Robinson, *Foundations of College Physics*, Chapters XXI, XXII, XXIV. New York: Ginn and Company, 1937.

## CHAPTER 9.   STATES OF EXISTENCE

Brinkley, Stuart R., *Principles of General Chemistry*. New York: The Macmillan Company, 1933. Chapters 6, 8, 24.

Briscoe, Herman T., *An Introduction to College Chemistry*. Boston: Houghton Mifflin Company, 1937. Chapters 7, 23, 36.

Cartledge, G. H., *Introduction to Inorganic Chemistry*. Boston: Ginn and Company, 1935. Chapter 7.

Deming, Horace G., *General Chemistry*. New York: John Wiley and Sons, 1935. Chapters 4, 10, 35.

Holmes, Harry N., *General Chemistry*. New York: The Macmillan Company, 1936. Chapters 6, 12, 39.

Irwin, Frederick C., and Sherwood, G. Ray, *General and Inorganic Chemistry*. Philadelphia: P. Blakiston's Son and Company, 1939. Chapters 1, 41.

Jaffe, Bernard, *New World of Chemistry*. New York: Silver, Burdett and Company, 1935. Chapters 14, 18, 37.

Kendall, James, *Smith's College Chemistry*. New York: D. Appleton-Century Company, 1935. Chapters 7, 12.

McPherson, William, and Henderson, William Edwards, *A Course in General Chemistry*. Boston: Ginn and Company, 1933. Chapters 5, 9, 14, 27.

Norris, James F., and Young, Ralph C., *Inorganic Chemistry for Colleges*. New York: McGraw-Hill Book Company, 1938. Chapter 6.

Richardson, Leon B., *General Chemistry*. New York: Henry Holt and Company, 1934. Chapters 5, 9, 12, 34.

Timm, John Arrend, *An Introduction to Chemistry*. New York: McGraw-Hill Book Company, 1930. Chapters 3, 5, 27, 36.

## CHAPTER 10.  HEAT AS A FORM OF ENERGY

Black, Newton Henry, *An Introductory Course in College Physics*, Chapter XVII. New York: The Macmillan Company, 1935.

Crowther, J. G., *Men of Science*. New York: W. W. Norton and Company, 1936.

Millikan, Robert Andrews; Gale, Henry Gordon; and Edwards, Charles William, *A First Course in Physics for Colleges*, Revised Edition, Chapters XX, XXI. New York: Ginn and Company, 1938.

Mott-Smith, Morton Churchill, *Heat and Its Workings*. New York, London: D. Appleton and Company, 1933.

Smith, Alpheus W., *Elements of Physics*, Fourth Edition, Chapter XXXI. New York: McGraw-Hill Book Company, Inc., 1938.

Stewart, Oscar M., *Physics*, Third Edition, Chapters XIX, XXIII. New York: Ginn and Company, 1939.

## CHAPTER 11.  OUR ATMOSPHERE

Byers, Horace Robert, *Synoptical and Aeronautical Meteorology*. New York: McGraw-Hill Book Company, Inc., 1937.

Blair, Thomas A., *Weather Elements*. New York: Prentice-Hall, Inc., 1937.

Humphreys, W. J., *Physics of the Air*. New York: McGraw-Hill Company, Inc., 1929.

Milham, Willis I., *Meteorology*.  New York: The Macmillan Company, 1927.

Ramsay, Sir W., *The Gases of the Atmosphere*.  New York: The Macmillan Company, 1915.

Talman, C. F., *The Realm of the Air*.  Indianapolis: Bobbs-Merrill Company, 1931.

Trewartha, Glenn T., *An Introduction to Weather and Climate*. New York: McGraw-Hill Book Company, Inc., 1937.

## CHAPTER 12.  WINDS AND WEATHER

Byers, H. R., *Synoptic and Aeronautical Meteorology*.  New York: McGraw-Hill Book Company, Inc., 1937.

Blair, Thomas A., *Weather Elements*.  New York: Prentice-Hall Inc., 1937.

Brooks, C. F., *Why the Weather?*  2nd Edition.  New York: Harcourt, Brace & Company, 1935.

Brunt, D., *Meteorology*.  London: Oxford University Press, 1928.

Chamberlin, R. T., and Salisbury, Rollin D., *College Geology*, Part I. New York: Henry Holt & Company, 1928.

Humphries, W. J., *Physics of the Air*.  New York: McGraw-Hill Book Company, Inc., 1929.

Milham, Willis I., *Meteorology*.  New York: The Macmillan Company, 1927.

Moore, Willis L., *Descriptive Meteorology*.  New York: D. Appleton & Company, 1910.

Talman, C. F., *The Realm of the Air*.  Indianapolis: Bobbs-Merrill Company, 1931.

Trewartha, Glenn T., *An Introduction to Weather and Climate*. New York: McGraw-Hill Book Company, Inc., 1937.

## CHAPTER 13.  WEATHER FORECASTING

Albright, John G., *Physical Meteorology*.  New York: Prentice-Hall, Inc., 1939.

Blair, Thomas A., *Weather Elements*.  New York: Prentice-Hall, Inc., 1937.

Brooks, C. F., *Why The Weather?*  New York: Harcourt, Brace & Company, 1935.

Milham, Willis I., *Meteorology*.  New York: The Macmillan Company, 1927.

Miller, Austin A., *Climatology*.  London: Methuen & Company, Ltd., 1939.

Shaw, Sir N., *The Drama of the Weather*.  Cambridge University Press, 1934.

Talman, C. F., *Realm of the Air*. Indianapolis: Bobbs-Merrill Company, 1931.

Trewartha, Glenn T., *An Introduction to Weather*. New York: McGraw-Hill Book Company, Inc., 1937.

## CHAPTER 14. SOUND

Avery, Madalyn, *Household Physics*, Chapters XXIX–XXXII. New York: The Macmillan Company, 1938.

Black, Newton Henry, *An Introductory Course in College Physics*, Chapter XXIX, XXX. New York: The Macmillan Company, 1935.

Harrison, George Russell, *Atoms in Action*, Chapter 13. New York: William Morrow and Company, 1939.

Heil, Louis M., *The Physical World*, Unit 7. Philadelphia: P. Blakiston's Son and Co., Inc., 1936.

Hobbie, John Remington, *Introduction to College Physics*, Chapters XIX, XX. New York: Farrar and Rinehart, 1936.

Jeans, Sir James Hopwood, *Science and Music*. New York: The Macmillan Company, 1937.

Jones, Arthur Taber, *Sound*. New York: D. Van Nostrand Company, Inc., 1937.

Knowlton, A. A., *Physics for College Students*, Second Edition, Chapters XXVIII, XXIX. New York: McGraw-Hill Book Company, Inc., 1935.

McLachlan, N. W., *The New Acoustics*. London: Oxford University Press, 1936.

Lemon, Harvey Brace, *From Galileo to Cosmic Rays*, Chapter 37. Chicago: The University of Chicago Press, 1934.

Miller, Dayton Clarence, *Anecdotal History of the Science of Sound*. New York: The Macmillan Company, 1935.

——, *The Science of Musical Sounds*. New York: The Macmillan Company, 1916.

——, *Sound Waves—Their Shape and Speed*. New York: The Macmillan Company, 1939.

Mills, John, *A Fugue in Cycles and Bels*. New York: D. Van Nostrand Company, 1935.

Stewart, Oscar M., *Physics*, Third Edition, Chapter XXV. New York: Ginn and Company, 1939.

Williams, Samuel Robinson, *Foundations of College Physics*, Chapters XV–XVII. New York: Ginn and Company, 1937.

## CHAPTER 15. ILLUMINATION

Avery, Madalyn, *Household Physics*, Chapter XXXIV. New York: The Macmillan Company, 1938.

Black, Newton Henry, *An Introductory Course in College Physics*, Chapter XXXI. New York: The Macmillan Company, 1935.

Harrison, George Russell, *Atoms in Action*, Chapter 5. New York: William Morrow and Company, 1939.

Heil, Louis M., *The Physical World*, Unit 9. Philadelphia: P. Blakiston's Son and Co., Inc., 1936.

Sheard, Charles, *Life-Giving Light*. New York: The Century Co., 1933.

Smith, Alpheus W., *Elements of Physics*, Fourth Edition, Chapters XLIX–LI. New York: McGraw-Hill Book Company, Inc., 1938.

Stewart, Oscar M., *Physics*, Third Edition, Chapters XL, XLI. New York: Ginn and Company, 1939.

Tate, Alfred O., *Edison's Open Door*. New York: E. P. Dutton and Company, Inc., 1938.

Whitman, Walter G., *Household Physics*, Third Edition, Chapters XVII–XIX. New York: John Wiley and Sons, 1939.

## CHAPTER 16. THE EYE. OPTICAL INSTRUMENTS

Black, Newton Henry, *An Introductory Course in College Physics*, Chapters XXXII, XXXIII. New York: The Macmillan Company, 1935.

Bragg, Sir William, *The Universe of Light*, Chapters I, II. New York: The Macmillan Company, 1933.

Harrison, George Russell, *Atoms in Action*, Chapters 10, 11. New York: William Morrow and Company, 1939.

Heil, Louis M., *The Physical World*, Unit 9. Philadelphia: P. Blakiston's Son and Co., Inc., 1936.

Hobbie, John Remington, *Introduction to College Physics*, Chapter XXXI. New York: Farrar and Rinehart, 1936.

Ingalls, Albert G., *Amateur Telescope Making*. New York: Scientific American Publishing Co., 1928.

Knowlton, A. A., *Physics for College Students*, Second Edition, Chapter XLV. New York: McGraw-Hill Book Company, Inc., 1935.

Mees, C. E. Kenneth, *Photography*. New York: The Macmillan Company, 1937.

Millikan, Robert Andrews; Gale, Henry Gordon; and Edwards, Charles William, *A First Course in Physics for Colleges*, Revised Edition, Chapter XXXI. New York: Ginn and Company, 1938.

Namer, Emile, *Galileo, Searcher of the Heavens*. New York: R. M. McBride and Company, 1931.

Pendray, Edward, *Men, Mirrors and Stars*. New York, London: Funk and Wagnalls Company, 1935.

Smith, Alpheus W., *Elements of Physics*, Fourth Edition, Chapters LII–LIV. New York: McGraw-Hill Book Company, Inc., 1938.

Stewart, Oscar M., *Physics*, Third Edition, Chapters XLII–XLIV. New York: Ginn and Company, 1939.

Whitman, Walter G., *Household Physics*, Third Edition, Chapters XX, XXI. New York: John Wiley and Sons, Inc., 1939.

## CHAPTER 17. COLOR. SPECTRA

Avery, Madalyn, *Household Physics*, Chapter XXXVI. New York: The Macmillan Company, 1938.

Black, Newton Henry, *An Introductory Course in College Physics*, Chapter XXXIV. New York: The Macmillan Company, 1935.

Bragg, Sir William, *The Universe of Light*, Chapters III, IV. New York: The Macmillan Company, 1933.

Eddington, Sir Arthur, *The Expanding Universe*. New York: The Macmillan Company, 1933.

Harrison, George Russell, *Atoms in Action*, Chapters 8 and 11. New York: William Morrow & Company, 1939.

Heil, Louis M., *The Physical World*, Unit 9. Philadelphia: P. Blakiston's Son and Co., Inc., 1936.

Hicks, Ami Mali, and Oglesby, Catharine, *Color in Action*. New York: Funk and Wagnalls Company, 1937.

Hobbie, John Remington, *Introduction to College Physics*, Chapter XXXII. New York: Farrar and Rinehart, 1936.

Houstoun, R. A., *Light and Color*. New York: Longmans, Green and Co., 1923.

Millikan, Robert Andrews; Gale, Henry Gordon; and Edwards, Charles William, *A First Course in Physics for Colleges*, Revised Edition, Chapter XXXII. New York: Ginn and Company, 1938.

More, Louis Trenchard, *Isaac Newton*. New York, London: C. Scribner's Sons, 1934.

Smith, Alpheus W., *Elements of Physics*, Fourth Edition, Chapter LV. New York: McGraw-Hill Book Company, Inc., 1938.

Stewart, Oscar M., *Physics*, Third Edition, Chapter XLV. New York: Ginn and Company, 1939.

## CHAPTER 18. ELECTROSTATICS AND MAGNETISM

Black, Newton Henry, *An Introductory Course in College Physics*, Chapters XVIII, XIX. New York: The Macmillan Company, 1935.

Crowther, J. G., *Famous American Men of Science*. New York : W. W. Norton and Company, Inc., 1937.

Darrow, Floyd L., *The New World of Physical Discovery*, Chapter V. Indianapolis: The Bobbs-Merrill Company, 1930.

Heil, Louis M., *The Physical World*, Unit 8. Philadelphia: P. Blakiston's Son and Co., Inc., 1936.

Hobbie, John Remington, *Introduction to College Physics*, Chapters XXXIV, XXXV. New York: Farrar and Rinehart, 1936.

Knowlton, A. A., *Physics for College Students*, Second Edition, Chapters XXX, XXXII. New York: McGraw-Hill Book Company, Inc., 1935.

Lemon, Harvey Brace, *From Galileo to Cosmic Rays*, Chapters XIX–XXV. Chicago: The University of Chicago Press, 1934.

Millikan, Robert Andrews; Gale, Henry Gordon; and Edwards, Charles William, *A First Course in Physics for Colleges*, Revised Edition, Chapters XXII, XXIII. New York: Ginn and Company, 1938.

Smith, Alpheus W., *Elements of Physics*, Fourth Edition, Chapters XXXII, XXXIII. New York: McGraw-Hill Book Company, Inc., 1938.

Stewart, Oscar M., *Physics*, Third Edition, Chapters XXVI, XXVII. New York: Ginn and Company, 1939.

## CHAPTER 19. ELECTRIC CURRENTS

Black, Newton Henry, *An Introductory Course in College Physics*, Chapters XX–XXIV. New York: The Macmillan Company, 1935.

Crowther, J. A., *The Life and Discoveries of Michael Faraday*. New York: The Macmillan Company, 1920.

Darrow, Karl K., *The Renaissance of Physics*. New York: The Macmillan Company, 1936.

Heil, Herman G.; and Bennett, Willard H., *Fundamental Principles of Physics*, Chapter 25. New York: Prentice-Hall, Inc., 1938.

Heil, Louis M., *The Physical World*, Unit 8. Philadelphia: P. Blakiston's Son and Co., Inc., 1936.

Lemon, Harvey Brace, *From Galileo to Cosmic Rays*, Chapters XXVI–XXIX. Chicago: The University of Chicago Press, 1934.

Smith, Alpheus W., *Elements of Physics*, Fourth Edition, Chapters XXXV–XXXVIII, XL–XLII. New York: McGraw-Hill Book Company, Inc., 1938.

Stewart, Oscar M., *Physics*, Third Edition, Chapters XXVIII–XXXIV. New York: Ginn and Company, 1939.

Whitman, Walter G., *Household Physics*, Third Edition, Chapters XV, XVI. New York: John Wiley and Sons, 1939.

Yates, Raymond F., *These Amazing Electrons*. New York: The Macmillan Company, 1937.

## CHAPTER 20.   ELECTRICAL COMMUNICATION

Ardenne, Manfred, *Television Reception*. New York: D. Van Nostrand Company, Inc., 1936.

Black, Newton Henry, *An Introductory Course in College Physics*, Chapter XXVII. New York: The Macmillan Company, 1935.

Dunlap, Orrin E., *Marconi—The Man and His Wireless*. New York: The Macmillan Company, 1937.

Harrison, George Russell, *Atoms in Action*, Chapters 6, 7, 12. New York: William Morrow and Company, 1939.

Haslett, A. W., *Radio Around the World*. New York: The Macmillan Company, 1936.

Heil, Louis M., *The Physical World*, Unit 8. Philadelphia: P. Blakiston's Son and Co., Inc., 1936.

Mills, John, *Signals and Speech in Electrical Communication*. New York: Harcourt, Brace and Company, 1934.

Rhodes, Frederick Leland, *Beginnings of Telephony*. New York, London: Harper and Brothers, 1929.

Smith, Alpheus W., *Elements of Physics*. Fourth Edition, Chapters XL, XLVIII. New York: McGraw-Hill Book Company, Inc., 1938.

Stewart, Oscar M., *Physics*, Third Edition, Chapters XXXIV, XXXIX. New York: Ginn and Company, 1939.

Towers, Walter Kellogg, *Masters of Space*. New York, London: Harper and Brothers, 1917.

Whitman, Walter G., *Household Physics*, Third Edition, Chapter XXVIII. New York: John Wiley and Sons, Inc., 1939.

Williams, Samuel Robinson, *Foundations of College Physics*, Chapter XLI. New York: Ginn and Company, 1937.

Yates, Raymond F., *These Amazing Electrons*. New York: The Macmillan Company, 1937.

## CHAPTER 21.   X RAYS AND RADIOACTIVITY

Black, Newton Henry, *An Introductory Course in College Physics*, Chapter XXXVII. New York: The Macmillan Company, 1935.

Bragg, Sir William, *The Universe of Light*, Chapter VIII. New York: The Macmillan Company, 1933.

Curie, Eve, *Madame Curie*, translated by Vincent Sheean. Garden City: Doubleday, Doran and Company, 1937.

Darrow, Floyd L., *The New World of Physical Discovery*, Chapters VI, VII. Indianapolis: The Bobbs-Merrill Company, 1930.

Darrow, Karl K., *The Renaissance of Physics*. New York: The Macmillan Company, 1936.

Gray, George W., *The Advancing Front of Science*. New York: Whittlesey House, McGraw-Hill Book Co., 1937.

Harrison, George Russell, *Atoms in Action*, Chapter 9. New York: William Morrow and Company, 1939.

Heil, Louis M., *The Physical World*, Unit 11. Philadelphia: P. Blakiston's Son and Co., Inc., 1936.

Hobbie, John Remington, *Introduction to College Physics*, Chapters XLVII, XLIX. New York: Farrar and Rinehart, 1936.

Lemon, Harvey Brace, *From Galileo to Cosmic Rays*, Chapters XXXIV, XL. Chicago; The University of Chicago Press, 1934.

——, *Cosmic Rays Thus Far*. New York: W. W. Norton and Company, Inc., 1936.

Robertson, John K., *Atomic Artillery*. New York: D. Van Nostrand Company, 1937.

Rutherford, Lord, *The Newer Alchemy*. New York: The Macmillan Company, 1937.

Smith, Alpheus W., *Elements of Physics*, Fourth Edition, Chapters LIX, LXIII. New York: McGraw-Hill Book Company, Inc., 1938.

Stewart, Oscar M., *Physics*, Third Edition, Chapters XXXVII, XXXVIII. New York: Ginn and Company, 1939.

Whitman, Walter G., *Household Physics*, Third Edition, Chapter XXVII. New York: John Wiley and Sons, Inc., 1939.

Williams, Samuel Robinson, *Foundations of College Physics*, Chapters XL, XLIII. New York: Ginn and Company, 1937.

## CHAPTER 22.  FUNDAMENTAL CHEMICAL PROCESSES

Brinkley, Stuart R., *Principles of General Chemistry*. New York: The Macmillan Company, 1933. Chapters 2, 3, 7.

Briscoe, Herman T., *An Introduction to College Chemistry*. Boston: Houghton Mifflin Company, 1937. Chapters: Introductory, 1, 2, 5, 6, 10.

Cartledge, G. H., *Introduction to Inorganic Chemistry.* Boston: Ginn and Company, 1935. Chapters 3, 5, 16, 17.

Deming, Horace G., *General Chemistry.* New York: John Wiley and Sons, 1935. Chapters 1, 2, 5, 7.

Holmes, Harry N., *General Chemistry.* New York: The Macmillan Company, 1936. Chapters 1, 4, 5, 7.

Irwin, Frederick C., and Sherwood, G. Ray, *General and Inorganic Chemistry.* Philadelphia: P. Blakiston's Son and Co., Inc. 1939. Chapters 2, 3, 4.

Jaffe, Bernard, *Crucibles.* New York: Simon and Schuster, 1930. Chapters 4, 5, 6, 8.

———, *New World of Chemistry.* New York: Silver, Burdett and Company, 1935. Chapters 1, 2, 3, 6.

Kendall, James, *Smith's College Chemistry.* New York: D. Appleton-Century Company, 1935. Chapters 1, 2, 3, 5, 6, 8, 15.

McPherson, William, and Henderson, William Edwards, *A Course in General Chemistry.* Boston: Ginn and Company, 1933. Chapters 2, 3, 4.

Norris, James F., and Young, Ralph C., *Inorganic Chemistry for Colleges.* New York: McGraw-Hill Book Company, 1938. Chapters 4, 5.

Richardson, Leon B., *General Chemistry.* New York: Henry Holt and Company, 1934. Chapters 2, 4, 6.

Timm, John Arrend, *An Introduction to Chemistry.* New York: McGraw-Hill Book Company, 1930. Chapters 2, 8, 12, 22.

## CHAPTER 23. THE STORY OF WATER

Brinkley, Stuart R., *Principles of General Chemistry.* New York: The Macmillan Company, 1933. Chapters 2, 5, 8, 17, 29.

Briscoe, Herman T., *An Introduction to College Chemistry.* Boston: Houghton Mifflin Company, 1937. Chapters 10, 13, 19.

Cartledge, G. H., *Introduction to Inorganic Chemistry.* Boston: Ginn and Company, 1935. Chapters 5, 20.

Deming, Horace G., *General Chemistry.* New York: John Wiley and Sons, 1935. Chapters 3, 5, 8, 9, 11, 14, 17, 18, 40.

Holmes, Harry N., *General Chemistry.* New York: The Macmillan Company, 1936. Chapters 4, 9, 12, 19, 42.

Irwin, Frederick C., and Sherwood, G. Ray, *General and Inorganic Chemistry.* Philadelphia: P. Blakiston's Son and Co., Inc., 1939. Chapters 5, 12.

Jaffe, Bernard, *New World of Chemistry*. New York: Silver, Burdett and Company, 1935. Chapters 4, 8, 30.

Kendall, James, *Smith's College Chemistry*. New York: D. Appleton-Century Company, 1935. Chapters 5, 10, 17, 21, 43.

McPherson, William, and Henderson, William Edwards, *A Course in General Chemistry*. Boston: Ginn and Company, 1933. Chapters 2, 6, 8, 15, 40.

Norris, James F., and Young, Ralph C., *Inorganic Chemistry for Colleges*. New York: McGraw-Hill Book Company, 1938. Chapters 3, 6, 8, 10, 12.

Richardson, Leon B., *General Chemistry*. New York: Henry Holt and Company, 1934. Chapters 3, 7, 8, 18, 38.

Timm, John Arrend, *An Introduction to Chemistry*. New York: McGraw-Hill Book Company, 1930. Chapters 4, 9, 26.

# CHAPTER 24. IONIZATION AND EQUILIBRIUM

Brinkley, Stuart R., *Principles of General Chemistry*. New York: The Macmillan Company, 1933. Chapters 14, 25.

Briscoe, Herman T., *An Introduction to College Chemistry*. Boston: Houghton Mifflin Company, 1937. Chapters 28, 29, 30.

Cartledge, G. H., *Introduction to Inorganic Chemistry*. Boston: Ginn and Company, 1935. Chapters 7, 13.

Deming, Horace G., *General Chemistry*. New York: John Wiley and Sons, 1935. Chapters 11, 14, 19.

Holmes, Harry N., *General Chemistry*. New York: The Macmillan Company, 1936. Chapters 17, 18, 20.

Irwin, Frederick C., and Sherwood, G. Ray, *General and Inorganic Chemistry*. Philadelphia: P. Blakiston's Son and Co., Inc., 1939. Chapters 5, 22.

Jaffe, Bernard, *Crucibles*. New York: Simon and Schuster, 1930. Chapter 12.

———, *New World of Chemistry*. New York: Silver, Burdett and Company, 1935. Chapter 15.

Kendall, James, *Smith's College Chemistry*. New York: D. Appleton-Century Company, 1935. Chapters 16, 18, 19.

McPherson, William, and Henderson, William Edwards, *A Course in General Chemistry*. Boston: Ginn and Company, 1933. Chapters 12, 20.

Norris, James F., and Young, Ralph C., *Inorganic Chemistry for Colleges*. New York: McGraw-Hill Book Company, 1938. Chapter 11.

Richardson, Leon B., *General Chemistry*. New York: Henry Holt and Company, 1934. Chapters 15, 17.

Timm, John Arrend, *An Introduction to Chemistry*. New York: McGraw-Hill Book Company, 1930. Chapter 29.

## CHAPTER 25.  NITROGEN AND OTHER GASES

Brinkley, Stuart R., *Principles of General Chemistry*. New York: The Macmillan Company, 1933. Chapters 3, 20, 21.

Briscoe, Herman T., *An Introduction to College Chemistry*. Boston: Houghton Mifflin Company, 1937. Chapters 22, 31, 32.

Cartledge, G. H., *Introduction to Inorganic Chemistry.* Boston: Ginn and Company, 1935. Chapter 15.

Deming, Horace G., *General Chemistry*. New York: John Wiley and Sons, 1935. Chapters 26, 27, 32, 50.

Holmes, Harry N., *General Chemistry*. New York: The Macmillan Company, 1936. Chapters 26, 27, 28, 29, 30, 35.

Irwin, Frederick C., and Sherwood, G. Ray, *General and Inorganic Chemistry*. Philadelphia: P. Blakiston's Son and Co., Inc., 1939. Chapters 25, 26, 28.

Jaffe, Bernard, *New World of Chemistry*. New York: Silver, Burdett and Company, 1935. Chapters 7, 16, 17.

Kendall, James, *Smith's College Chemistry*. New York: D. Appleton-Century Company, 1935. Chapters 26, 29, 30, 38.

McPherson, William, and Henderson, William Edwards, *A Course in General Chemistry*. Boston: Ginn and Company, 1933. Chapters 11, 12, 19.

Norris, James F., and Young, Ralph C., *Inorganic Chemistry for Colleges*. New York: McGraw-Hill Book Company, 1938. Chapters 17, 18, 19.

Richardson, Leon B., *General Chemistry*. New York: Henry Holt and Company, 1934. Chapters 26, 27, 28, 48.

Timm, John Arrend, *An Introduction to Chemistry*. New York: McGraw-Hill Book Company, 1930. Chapters 11, 32, 37.

## CHAPTER 26.  THE HALOGENS AND THE ELEMENTS

Brinkley, Stuart R., *Principles of General Chemistry*. New York: The Macmillan Company, 1933. Chapters 5, 11, 13, 16, 18, 27.

Briscoe, Herman T., *An Introduction to College Chemistry*. Boston: Houghton Mifflin Company, 1937. Chapters 14, 24, 25, 26.

Cartledge, G. H., *Introduction to Inorganic Chemistry*. Boston: Ginn and Company, 1935. Chapters 6, 12, 14, 18.

Deming, Horace G., *General Chemistry*. New York: John Wiley and Sons, 1935. Chapters 20, 21, 22.

Holmes, Harry N., *General Chemistry*. New York: The Macmillan Company, 1936. Chapters 13, 14, 15, 23.

Irwin, Frederick C., and Sherwood, G. Ray, *General and Inorganic Chemistry*. Philadelphia: P. Blakiston's Son and Co., Inc., 1939. Chapters 6, 8, 9, 19, 32.

Jaffe, Bernard, *Crucibles*. New York: Simon and Schuster, 1930. Chapter 11.

——, *New World of Chemistry*. New York: Silver, Burdett and Company, 1935. Chapters 10, 11, 12, 29, 38.

Kendall, James, *Smith's College Chemistry*. New York: D. Appleton-Century Company, 1935. Chapters 13, 14, 20, 22, 25.

McPherson, William, and Henderson, William Edwards, *A Course in General Chemistry*. Boston: Ginn and Company, 1933. Chapters 15, 21, 22, 23.

Norris, James F., and Young, Ralph C., *Inorganic Chemistry for Colleges*. New York: McGraw-Hill Book Company, 1938. Chapters 9, 10, 21, 22.

Richardson, Leon B., *General Chemistry*. New York: Henry Holt and Company, 1934. Chapters 19, 23, 24, 25.

Timm, John Arrend, *An Introduction to Chemistry*. New York: McGraw-Hill Book Company, 1930. Chapter 16.

## CHAPTER 27.  SULFUR

Brinkley, Stuart R., *Principles of General Chemistry*. New York: The Macmillan Company, 1933. Chapter 19.

Briscoe, Herman T., *An Introduction to College Chemistry*. Boston: Houghton Mifflin Company, 1937. Chapters 33, 34.

Cartledge, G. H., *Introduction to Inorganic Chemistry*. Boston: Ginn and Company, 1935. Chapters 11, 24.

Deming, Horace G., *General Chemistry*. New York: John Wiley and Sons, 1935. Chapters 23, 24.

Holmes, Harry N., *General Chemistry*. New York: The Macmillan Company, 1936. Chapters 21, 22.

Irwin, Frederick C., and Sherwood, G. Ray, *General and Inorganic Chemistry*. Philadelphia: P. Blakiston's Son and Co., Inc., 1939. Chapters 23, 24.

Jaffe, Bernard, *New World of Chemistry*. New York: Silver, Burdett and Company, 1935. Chapters 19, 20.

Kendall, James, *Smith's College Chemistry*. New York: D. Appleton-Century Company, 1935. Chapters 23, 24.

McPherson, William, and Henderson, William Edwards, *A Course in General Chemistry*. Boston: Ginn and Company, 1933. Chapter 24.

Norris, James F., and Young, Ralph C., *Inorganic Chemistry for Colleges*. New York: McGraw-Hill Book Company, 1938. Chapters 15, 16.

Richardson, Leon B., *General Chemistry.* New York: Henry Holt and Company, 1934. Chapters 13, 16.

Timm, John Arrend, *An Introduction to Chemistry.* New York: McGraw-Hill Book Company, 1930. Chapter 32.

## CHAPTER 28.  SOME COMMON METALS

Brinkley, Stuart R., *Principles of General Chemistry.* New York: The Macmillan Company, 1933. Chapters 30, 31, 32.

Briscoe, Herman T., *An Introduction to College Chemistry.* Boston: Houghton Mifflin Company, 1937. Chapters 41, 43, 44, 47.

Cartledge, G. H., *Introduction to Inorganic Chemistry.* Boston: Ginn and Company, 1935. Chapters 8, 22, 23.

Deming, Horace G., *General Chemistry.* New York: John Wiley and Sons, 1935. Chapters 41, 43, 46, 47.

Holmes, Harry N., *General Chemistry.* New York: The Macmillan Company, 1936. Chapters 40, 43, 46, 49.

Irwin, Frederick C., and Sherwood, G. Ray, *General and Inorganic Chemistry.* Philadelphia: P. Blakiston's Son and Co., Inc. 1939. Chapters 33, 36, 37, 39.

Jaffe, Bernard, *New World of Chemistry.* New York: Silver, Burdett and Company, 1935. Chapters 24, 25, 26, 27, 28.

Kendall, James, *Smith's College Chemistry.* New York: D. Appleton-Century Company, 1935. Chapters 41, 45, 46, 47, 52.

McPherson, William, and Henderson, William Edwards, *A Course in General Chemistry.* Boston: Ginn and Company, 1933. Chapters 33, 38, 41, 42, 46.

Norris, James F., and Young, Ralph C., *Inorganic Chemistry for Colleges.* New York: McGraw-Hill Book Company, 1938. Chapters 27, 28, 34, 36, 37.

Richardson, Leon B., *General Chemistry.* New York: Henry Holt and Company, 1934. Chapters 35, 37, 39, 40, 42, 47.

Timm, John Arrend, *An Introduction to Chemistry.* New York: McGraw-Hill Book Company, 1930. Chapters 14, 15, 28, 34.

## CHAPTER 29.  CARBON AND ITS COMPOUNDS

Brinkley, Stuart R., *Principles of General Chemistry.* New York: The Macmillan Company, 1933. Chapters 23, 29, 35.

Briscoe, Herman T., *An Introduction to College Chemistry.* Boston: Houghton Mifflin Company, 1937. Chapters 20, 21, 35, 37, 44.

Cartledge, G. H., *Introduction to Inorganic Chemistry.* Boston: Ginn and Company, 1935. Chapters 9, 19.

Deming, Horace G., *General Chemistry.* New York: John Wiley and Sons, 1935. Chapters 30, 36, 42.

Ehrenfeld, Louis, *The Story of Common Things*.   New York: Minton, Balch and Company, 1932.   Chapters 3, 11.

Holmes, Harry N., *General Chemistry*.   New York: The Macmillan Company, 1936.   Chapters 10, 32, 37.

Irwin, Frederick C., and Sherwood, G. Ray, *General and Inorganic Chemistry*.   Philadelphia: P. Blakiston's Son and Co., Inc., 1939.   Chapters 13, 18.

Jaffe, Bernard, *New World of Chemistry*.   New York: Silver, Burdett and Company, 1935.   Chapters 21, 22, 23, 32.

Kendall, James, *Smith's College Chemistry*.   New York: D. Appleton-Century Company, 1935.   Chapters 32, 36, 39.

McPherson, William, and Henderson, William Edwards, *A Course in General Chemistry*.   Boston: Ginn and Company, 1933.   Chapters 10, 26, 30, 39.

Norris, James F., and Young, Ralph C., *Inorganic Chemistry for Colleges*.   New York: McGraw-Hill Book Company, 1938.   Chapters 13, 14, 25.

Read, William Thornton, *Industrial Chemistry*.   New York: John Wiley and Sons, 1933.   Chapter 13.

Richardson, Leon B., *General Chemistry*.   New York: Henry Holt and Company, 1934.   Chapters 30, 31, 33.

Timm, John Arrend, *An Introduction to Chemistry*.   New York: McGraw-Hill Book Company, 1930.   Chapter 13.

# CHAPTER 30.   ORGANIC AND FOOD CHEMISTRY

Brinkley, Stuart R., *Principles of General Chemistry*.   New York: The Macmillan Company, 1933.   Chapters 36, 37.

Briscoe, Herman T., *An Introduction to College Chemistry*.   Boston: Houghton Mifflin Company, 1937.   Chapters 37, 38, 39.

Deming, Horace G., *General Chemistry*.   New York: John Wiley and Sons, 1935.   Chapters 31, 33, 34.

Holmes, Harry N., *General Chemistry*.   New York: The Macmillan Company, 1936.   Chapters 32, 33, 34, 36, 46.

Irwin, Frederick C., and Sherwood, G. Ray, *General and Inorganic Chemistry*.   Philadelphia: P. Blakiston's Son and Co., Inc., 1939.   Chapters 14, 15, 16, 17.

Jaffe, Bernard, *Crucibles*.   New York: Simon and Schuster, 1930.   Chapter 10.

———, *New World of Chemistry*.   New York: Silver, Burdett and Company, 1935.   Chapters 33, 34, 35, 36.

Kendall, James, *Smith's College Chemistry*.   New York: D. Appleton-Century Company, 1935.   Chapters 33, 34, 37, 38.

McPherson, William, and Henderson, William Edwards, *A Course in General Chemistry*. Boston: Ginn and Company, 1933. Chapters 29, 31, 32.

Norris, James F., and Young, Ralph C., *Inorganic Chemistry for Colleges*. New York: McGraw-Hill Book Company, 1938. Chapter 26.

Richardson, Leon B., *General Chemistry*. New York: Henry Holt and Company, 1934. Chapters 32, 48, 49, 50.

Timm, John Arrend, *An Introduction to Chemistry*. New York: McGraw-Hill Book Company, 1930. Chapters 13, 38, 39, 40.

## CHAPTER 31. THE EARTH AND ITS ROCKS

Branson, E. B., and Tarr, W. A., *Introduction to Geology*. New York: McGraw-Hill Book Company, Inc., 1935.

Chamberlin, R. T., and MacClintock, Paul, *College Geology, Part I*. New York: Henry Holt & Company, 1928.

Emmons, W. H.; Thiel, George A.; Stauffer, C. R.; and Allison, Ira S., *Geology*. New York: McGraw-Hill Book Company, Inc., 1939.

Longwell, Chester R.; Knopf, Adolph; and Flint, Richard F., *A Text Book of Geology*. New York: John Wiley & Sons, Inc., 1939.

Miller, W. J., *Introduction to Physical Geology*. New York: D. Van Nostrand Company, Inc., 1935.

Pirsson, Louis V., and Schuchert, Charles, *Text Book of Geology, Part I*. New York: John Wiley & Sons, Inc., 1929.

## CHAPTER 32. THE GRADATIONAL AGENTS

Branson, E. B., and Tarr, W. A., *Introduction to Geology*. New York: McGraw-Hill Book Company, Inc., 1935.

Chamberlin, R. T., and MacClintock, Paul, *College Geology, Part I*. New York: Henry Holt & Company, 1928.

Cole, B. A. J., *Rocks and Their Origin*. New York: The Macmillan Company, 1923.

Croneis, Carey, and Krumbein, William, *Down to Earth*. Chicago: University of Chicago Press, 1936.

Emmons, William H.; Thiel, George A.; Stauffer, Clinton R.; and Allison, Ira S., *Geology*. New York: McGraw-Hill Book Company, Inc., 1939.

Hawkins, Alfred C., *The Book of Minerals*. New York: John Wiley & Sons, 1935.

Longwell, Chester R.; Knopf, Adolph; and Flint, Richard F., *A Text Book of Geology*. New York: John Wiley & Sons, Inc., 1939.

Loomis, Frederic Brewster, *Field Book on Common Rocks and Minerals*. New York: G. P. Putnam's Sons, 1923.

Miller, W. J., *Introduction to Physical Geology*. New York: D. Van Nostrand Company, Inc., 1935.

Pirsson, Louis V., and Schuchert, Charles, *Text Book of Geology*. New York: Henry Holt & Company, 1928.

Scott, William B., *An Introduction to Geology*. New York: The Macmillan Company, 1932.

## CHAPTER 33. GROUND WATER AND ITS WORK

Branson, E. B., and Tarr, W. A., *Introduction to Geology*. New York: McGraw-Hill Book Company, Inc., 1935.

Chamberlin, R. T., and MacClintock, Paul, *College Geology, Part I*. New York: Henry Holt & Company, 1928.

Emmons, W. H.; Thiel, George A.; Stauffer, C. R.; and Allison, Ira S., *Geology*. New York: McGraw-Hill Book Company, 1939.

Longwell, Chester R.; Knopf, Adolph; and Flint, Richard F., *A Text Book of Geology*. New York: John Wiley & Sons, Inc., 1939.

Miller, W. J., *Introduction to Physical Geology*. New York: D. Van Nostrand Company, Inc., 1935.

Pirsson, Louis V., and Schuchert, Charles, *Text Book of Geology, Part I*. New York: John Wiley & Sons, Inc., 1929.

## CHAPTER 34. DIASTROPHISM

Branson, E. B., and Tarr, W. A., *Introduction to Geology*. New York: McGraw-Hill Book Company, Inc., 1935.

Chamberlin, R. T., and MacClintock, Paul, *College Geology, Part I*. New York: Henry Holt & Company, 1928.

Cole, B. A. J., *Rocks and Their Origin*. New York: The Macmillan Company, 1923.

Croneis, C. G., and Krumbein, W. C., *Down to Earth*. Chicago: University of Chicago Press, 1936.

Emmons, William H.; Thiel, George A.; Stauffer, Clinton R.; and Allison, Ira S., *Geology*. New York: McGraw-Hill Book Company, Inc., 1932.

Hawkins, Alfred C., *The Book of Minerals*. New York: John Wiley & Sons, 1935.

Longwell, Chester R.; Knopf, Adolph; and Flint, Richard F., *A Text Book of Geology*. New York: John Wiley & Sons, Inc., 1939.

Loomis, Frederic Brewster, *Field Book on Common Rocks and Minerals*. New York: G. P. Putnam's Sons, 1923.

Miller, W. J., *Introduction to Physical Geology*. New York: D. Van Nostrand Company, Inc., 1935.

Pirsson, Louis V., and Schuchert, Charles, *Text Book of Geology*. New York: Henry Holt & Company, 1928.

Scott, William B., *An Introduction to Geology*. New York: The Macmillan Company, 1932.

## CHAPTER 35.  EARTHQUAKES AND VOLCANISM

Branson, E. B., and Tarr, W. A., *Introduction to Geology*. New York: McGraw-Hill Book Company, 1935.

Chamberlin, R. T., and MacClintock, Paul, *Text Book of Geology, Part I*. New York: Henry Holt & Company, 1928.

Croneis, C. G., and Krumbein, William C., *Down to Earth*. Chicago: University of Chicago Press, 1936.

Emmons, Thiel, Stauffer, and Allison, *Geology*. New York: McGraw-Hill Book Company, 1939.

Heck, N. H., *Earthquakes*. Princeton: Princeton University Press, 1936.

Hobbs, William Herbert, *Earth Features and Their Meaning*. New York: The Macmillan Company, 1933.

Mather, H. F., *Old Mother Earth*. Cambridge: Harvard University Press, 1930.

Miller, W. J., *Introduction to Physical Geology, Part I*. New York: D. Van Nostrand & Company, 1935.

Pirsson, Louis V., and Schuchert, Charles, *Text Book of Geology, Part I*. New York: John Wiley & Sons, 1929.

## CHAPTER 36.  THE EARTH'S PAST

Branson, E. B., and Tarr, W. A., *Introduction to Geology*. New York: McGraw-Hill Book Company, Inc., 1935.

Chamberlin, T. C., and Salisbury, Rollin D., *College Geology*. New York: Henry Holt & Company, 1909.

———, *Introduction to College Geology*. New York: Henry Holt & Company, 1921.

———, and others, *Text Book of Geology*. New York: Henry Holt & Company, 1930.

Croneis, C. G., and Krumbein, William C., *Down to Earth*. Chicago: University of Chicago Press, 1936.

Fabre, Jean H., *This Earth of Ours*. New York: The Century Company, 1923.

Fenton, Carroll Lane, *Our Amazing Earth*. New York: The Century Company, 1923.

Grabau, Amadeus, *A Text Book of Geology*. Boston: D. C. Heath & Company, 1921.

Miller, W. J., *Introduction to Historical Geology*. New York: D. Van Nostrand Company, 1938.

Pirsson, Louis V., and Schuchert, Charles, *An Introduction to Geology*. New York: John Wiley & Sons, Inc., 1924.

Scott, William Berryman, *An Introduction to Geology*. New York: The Macmillan Company, 1932.

## CHAPTER 37. ASTRONOMY, ANCIENT AND MODERN

Baker, Robert H., *Introduction to Astronomy*. New York: D. Van Nostrand Company, Inc., 1935.

Chase, C. T., *Frontiers of Science*. New York: D. Van Nostrand Company, 1936.

Duncan, John Charles, *Astronomy*. New York: Harper & Brothers, 1935.

Fath, Edward Arthur, *Elements of Astronomy*. New York: McGraw-Hill Book Company, Inc., 1934.

Gregory, R. A., *The Spirit and Service of Science*. New York: The Macmillan Company, 1929.

Harvey-Gibson, R. J., *Two Thousand Years of Science*. New York: The Macmillan Company, 1929.

Jastrow, Joseph, *A Story of Human Error*. New York: D. Appleton-Century Company, 1936.

McCabe, Joseph, *The Wonders of the Stars*. New York: G. P. Putnam's Sons, 1923.

Moulton, Forest R., *Astronomy*. New York: The Macmillan Company, 1931.

Murray, R. H., *Science and Scientists in the Nineteenth Century*. New York: The Century Company, 1925.

Shapley, Harlow, *Flights from Chaos*. New York: McGraw-Hill Book Company, Inc., 1930.

## CHAPTER 38. OUR STARRY GALAXY

Baker, Robert H., *Introduction to Astronomy*. New York: D. Van Nostrand Company, Inc., 1935.

Duncan, John Charles, *Astronomy*. New York: Harper & Brothers, 1935.

Fath, Edward Arthur, *Elements of Astronomy*. New York: McGraw-Hill Book Company, Inc., 1934.

Gregory, R. A., *The Spirit and Service of Science*. New York: The Macmillan Company, 1929.

Harvey-Gibson, R. J., *Two Thousand Years of Science*. New York: The Macmillan Company, 1929.

Jeans, James H., *The Stars in Their Courses*. New York: The Macmillan Company, 1931.

Moulton, Forest Ray, *Astronomy*. New York: The Macmillan Company, 1931.

## CHAPTER 39.   OUR SOLAR FAMILY

Ball, Sir Robert, *Story of the Heavens*.  England:  Cassell & Company, 1905.

Bartky, Walter, *High Lights of Astronomy*.  Chicago: University of Chicago Press, 1935.

Bergh, George van den, *Astronomy for the Millions*.  New York: E. P. Dutton & Company, Inc., 1936.

Draper, A. L., and Lockwood, Marian, *The Story of Astronomy*. New York: Dial Press, 1939.

Duncan, John Charles, *Astronomy*.  New York: Harper & Brothers, 1935.

Fath, Edward Arthur, *Elements of Astronomy*.  New York: McGraw-Hill Book Company, Inc., 1934.

Fisher, Clyde, *Exploring the Heavens*.  New York: Thomas Y. Crowell, 1937.

Jacoby, Harold, *Astronomy*.  New York: The Macmillan Company, 1922.

Jeans, Sir James H., *The Stars in Their Courses*.  New York: The Macmillan Company, 1931.

Jones, H. Spencer, *General Astronomy*.  New York: Longmans, Green & Company, 1922.

——, *Worlds Without End*.  Chicago: University of Chicago Press, 1935.

MacPherson, Hector, *A Romance of Modern Astronomy*.  London: Seeley & Company, Ltd., 1911.

Moulton, Forest R., *Astronomy*.  New York: The Macmillan Company, 1931.

——, *Consider the Heavens*.  New York: Doubleday, Doran & Company, 1931.

Smart, W. M., *Astronomy*.  London: Oxford University Press, 1937.

Todd, David, *New Astronomy*.  New York: American Book Company, 1925.

## CHAPTER 40.   LATITUDE, LONGITUDE, AND TIME

Baker, Robert H., *Introduction to Astronomy*.  New York: D. Van Nostrand Company, 1935.

Bartky, Walter, *High Lights of Astronomy*.  Chicago: Chicago University Press, 1935.

Bergh, George van den, *Astronomy for the Millions*.  New York: E. P. Dutton & Company, Inc., 1937.

Duncan, John Charles, *Astronomy*.  New York: Harper & Brothers, 1935.

Fath, Edward Arthur, *Elements of Astronomy*. New York: McGraw-Hill Book Company, Inc., 1934.

Jones, H. Spencer, *General Astronomy*. New York: Longmans, Green & Company, 1922.

Smart, W. M., *Astronomy*. London: Oxford University Press, 1937.

Todd, David, *New Astronomy*. New York: American Book Company, 1925.

## CHAPTER 41.  OUR MOON A COLD DEAD WORLD

Baker, Robert H., *Introduction to Astronomy*. New York: D. Van Nostrand Company, Inc., 1935.

Bartky, Walter, *High Lights of Astronomy*. Chicago: University of Chicago Press, 1935.

Bawden, Arthur Talbot, *Man's Physical Universe*. New York: The Macmillan Company, 1937.

Bergh, George van den, *Astronomy for the Millions*. New York: E. P. Dutton & Company, 1937.

Duncan, John Charles, *Astronomy*. New York: Harper & Brothers, 1935.

Fath, Edward Arthur, *Elements of Astronomy*. New York: McGraw-Hill Book Company, Inc., 1934.

Fletcher, Gustav L., *Earth Science*. Boston: D. C. Heath & Company, 1938.

Jacoby, Harold, *Astronomy*. New York: The Macmillan Company, 1922.

Jeans, Sir James H., *The Stars in Their Courses*. New York: The Macmillan Company, 1931.

MacPherson, Hector, *A Romance of Modern Astronomy*. London: Seeley & Company, 1911.

Moulton, Forest Ray, *Astronomy*. New York: The Macmillan Company, 1931.

Smart, W. M., *Astronomy*. London: Oxford University Press, 1937.

# QUESTIONS

## CHAPTER 2.   MAN AND HIS MACHINES

1. Name four mechanical devices widely used before the Christian era.

2. Describe briefly the methods of travel in America in colonial times.

3. Sketch the steps in the improvement of methods of transportation and travel in the 19th century.   In the 20th century.

4. What means of communication were in use in the colonies? What means were in use between 1800 and 1875?   Between 1875 and 1900?

5. Name the various kinds of simple machines.

6. Tell what is meant by the term *velocity ratio* as applied to a machine.

7. Tell what is meant by the term *mechanical advantage*.

8. A 15 ft. plank used as a teeter-totter is supported at its midpoint.   How far from one end must an 80 lb. boy sit to balance a 60 lb. boy sitting 6 inches from the other?

9. A pair of scissors has handles 4 inches long.   What force must be applied to cut a thread which is at the end of the blades, which are 6 inches long, if the thread offers a resistance of 2 ounces?

10. In loading a 200 lb. barrel into a truck 3 ft. high the barrel is rolled up a plank 12 ft. long.   Neglecting friction, how great a force acting parallel with the plank is required?

11. A 500 lb. forkful of hay is raised by a set of pulleys arranged as in Fig. 6.   Neglecting friction, how great a force is required to raise it?

12. Make a list of machines or devices in whose construction levers or their equivalent are used.   Make as long a list as you can of machines in which levers are not used.

13. What simple machines are employed in each of the following:

a. Wrench.
b. Typewriter.
c. Chisel.
d. Carpenter's saw.
e. Steering mechanism of car.
f. Hammers of a piano.
g. Scissors.

h. Can opener.
i. Playground slide.
j. Automobile jack.
k. Claw hammer in drawing a nail.
l. Bicycle pedal and sprocket wheel.

673

14. Analyze the lifting crane as used in a steam shovel, pointing out the simple machines of which it is composed and the effect of each on the mechanical advantage of the crane.

15. Analyze each of the following as in question 14:

    a. Egg beater.               d. Platform balance.
    b. Wind mill.                e. Pencil sharpener.
    c. Escalator.                 f. Lawn mower.

16. Why will an automobile climb a steeper hill in low gear than in high?

17. Draw a diagram to represent the action of the forearm as a lever. A diagram to represent the action of the foot when one rises on tiptoe.

18. Write an account of the life and achievements of one of the following:

    a. Eli Whitney.            d. Cyrus H. McCormick.
    b. Elias Howe.            e. Orville Wright.
    c. Ottmar Mergenthaler.    f. Henry Ford.

## CHAPTER 3.  ENERGY UTILIZED AND WASTED

1. State in words what is meant in mechanics by the term *work*.
2. The following units are used in measuring work.  Define each.

    a. Foot-pound.           d. Kilogram-meter.
    b. Mile-ton.              e. Erg.
    c. Gram-centimeter.     f. Joule.

3. In mechanics what is meant by the term *power?*
4. What is meant by the terms *horsepower* and *kilowatt?*
5. How many watts in 1 horsepower?  How many kilowatts?
6. What is mechanical energy?  Name two kinds and give two examples of each.
7. Name four units in terms of which energy is measured.
8. How much energy has a 200 lb. pile-driver hammer when raised 15 ft?  Of what kind is it?
9. How much potential energy has the above hammer when it has descended 10 ft.?  How much kinetic energy has it then?
10. How much kinetic energy has an 80 kg. athlete when running at a speed of 9 meters per second?
11. What is radiant energy?  Chemical energy?
12. What is meant by the term *transformation of energy.*
13. Sketch the series of transformations taking place in running a dynamo by a steam engine.  In running a dynamo by water power.

14. Can heat energy be completely converted into mechanical energy?  Give reasons for your answer.

15. State the law of conservation of energy.

16. What is meant by the term *efficiency* of a machine?  Illustrate by a numerical example.

17. Approximately how great is the efficiency of a good steam engine?

18. How great is the efficiency of a good electric motor at full load?

19. What becomes of the energy that is supplied to a machine but not delivered by it as useful work?

20. In what ways is energy lost in an automobile motor?

21. Mention two advantages gained by lubrication of a machine.

22. Why are roller bearings often used in preference to sleeve bearings (bearings in which surfaces slide over each other)?

23. Name several ways in which friction is useful to man.

24. What is a perpetual-motion machine?  How many successful kinds are there?  Explain.

25. How much work is done in raising a 250 lb. barrel 20 feet?

26. What horsepower is used in drawing a sled at a speed of 6 miles per hour if the force required to draw it is 150 lb.?

27. What is the efficiency of a pump which carries 1000 tons of water per hour to a height of 165 feet if run by an engine which supplies 300 horsepower?

28. What is the efficiency of an electric motor which receives 100 kw. of electric power and delivers 100 horsepower?

29. What is the source of the energy of a piece of coal?  Of the muscle of an ox?  Of a wind storm?  Of the tides?

30. Write a theme on the value of friction in present-day means of transportation or travel.

31. Make as long a list as you can of useful devices whose operation depends upon friction.

32. Look up and describe for the class one type of perpetual-motion machine.  Point out the reasons for its failure.

33. Assuming that the brakes offer the same constant retarding force, how far will a car travel in stopping from 60 mi. per hr. as compared with the distance traveled in stopping from 30 mi. per hr.?

34. If perpetual motion is impossible, why is it that the earth continues to rotate at the same constant speed century after century?

35. Does the continued motion of the planets in their orbits contradict the law of conservation of energy?  Explain.

36. An archer in bending his bow stores up energy which the bow will return when released.  The bow will be permanently bent,

2.54 cm in one inch.

however, if left too long in that condition. In that case what has become of the energy?

# CHAPTER 4. FORCE AND MOTION

1. State two laws of planetary motion discovered by Kepler.

2. What conclusion did Newton reach concerning the forces that hold planets in their course?

3. State the law of gravitation.

4. What is meant by the term *center of gravity?*

5. To what is the weight of objects due?

6. Why is the weight of an object slightly greater at the poles than at the equator?

7. What is the average density of the earth? Show how this is determined.

8. How are tides produced?

9. What is inertia?

10. How did Galileo show that matter has inertia?

11. Name several instruments for whose operation inertia is essential.

12. What is centripetal force? Centrifugal force?

13. Name several useful applications of centrifugal force.

14. What is meant by the term *acceleration?*

15. Upon what two factors does the acceleration of an object depend, and in what ratio does it vary with each?

16. Show what is meant by the statement, "Action is equal to reaction."

17. Why do clouds not fall?

18. An 80 lb. boy sitting on a platform scale takes hold of the platform and lifts with a force of 20 lb. What is then the reading of the scale? What would it be if he lifted with the same force on ropes fastened to the floor?

19. Why must a machine-gunner brace himself to prevent being pushed backward while firing his belt of shells?

20. Would the weight of an object as determined by a spring scale be the same at the north pole as at the equator? Would this also be true if the object were weighed by a beam balance?

21. Does the weight of a stone vary between sunrise and noon? If so, at which time is it the greater?

22. Why is it more difficult to ride a bicycle very slowly than at a moderate speed?

23. All gases show a tendency to expand without limit. Why does the atmosphere not expand indefinitely into interstellar space?

24. A smooth stream of water flowing from a faucet diminishes in diameter from the faucet downward. Why is this?

*1 cu. cm. of water weights 1 gram.*

25. Why does the nozzle of a garden hose push forcibly backward when throwing a swift stream?

26. Some lawn sprinklers rotate as they sprinkle. What causes them to do this?

27. At the street level in New York City a certain coin weighs exactly 5 standard gm. both by a sensitive spring scale and by an equal arm balance. Would it weigh the same by either instrument at the top of the Empire State building? By both instruments? If it weighs 5 gm. by only one, which one is it? Explain.

28. Mention a single process by which it is possible to accomplish all of the following:

(1) Separation of cream from milk.
(2) Extraction of honey from the comb.
(3) Removal of water from garments in a laundry.
(4) Maintaining a nearly uniform speed of a steam engine under different loads.

Does this agency also keep the planets in their course? Explain.

29. Write an account of the life and work of one of the following:

(1) Isaac Newton.          (3) Johannes Kepler.
(2) Galileo Galilei.        (4) Nikolaus Copernicus.

## CHAPTER 5.  FLUIDS AND FLUID PRESSURE

1. What distinction is made between the meanings of the terms *pressure* and *force?*

2. A liquid in an open jar exerts a pressure upon the sides and bottom of the jar. To what is this pressure due?

3. How does the pressure of a liquid in an open jar vary with depth? How with density of the liquid?

4. What is the pressure in gm. per sq. cm. at a depth of 10 meters in sea water if the density of the water is 1.02 gm. per cc.?

5. What is the pressure in lb. per sq. ft. at a depth of 100 ft. in Lake Michigan if the density of the water is 62.4 lb. per cu. ft.?

6. To what is atmospheric pressure due? How was this first demonstrated?

7. For what purpose are barometers used?

8. Describe briefly the construction of a mercurial barometer.

9. What is an altimeter? Upon what principle does it operate?

10. State Pascal's law.

11. Name three devices whose operation depends upon the transmission of pressure by fluids.

12. How is it that we are able to drink through a straw?

13. Why does a piece of wood float on water?

14. For what purposes are hydrometers used? Explain their operation.

15. What causes a balloon to rise?

16. Mention two reasons for believing that the distances between molecules are greater in gases than in liquids.

17. State Boyle's law.

18. How is the pressure in the water supply of your home town or city maintained? Describe another method of maintaining pressure in a water system.

19. Why do bubbles rising from the bottom of a pond increase in size as they ascend?

20. Why does the cream rise to the top of a bottle of milk? Does the rate of rise depend upon the temperature? Explain.

21. Why is it usually easier to swim in the ocean than in a lake?

22. Why in swimming is it desirable to keep the lungs well filled with air?

23. Why do divers wear lead on their shoes?

24. Why do steamers carry belts of cork for their passengers?

25. A fisherman in a rowboat used a 20 lb. stone as an anchor. Would a 20-lb. piece of lead or iron have been better? Explain.

26. A mountaineer on seeing smoke settle in the valley remarked that the air must be very heavy. Do you agree with him? Explain.

27. Devise a method whereby a barge load of coal can be weighed without scales.

28. If objects lose in weight with increasing elevation, why is it that a rising balloon does not ascend indefinitely?

29. Is it true, as one student contended, that the force that causes a balloon to rise has the same source as the one that causes it to return to earth? Give reasons for your answer.

30. A piece of aluminum (a very light metal) and a piece of iron weigh exactly the same in air. Will they weigh alike in a vacuum? If not, which will be the heavier in a vacuum? Explain.

31. A pitcher is level full of ice water, with 3 cu. in. of ice projecting above. How much water will overflow if the pitcher is allowed to stand until the ice all melts?

32. Does the draft of a ship remain unchanged as the ship passes from New York harbor out to sea? Explain.

33. A pan of water on a platform scale weighs 20 lb. A 3 lb. fish placed in the pan floats without touching sides or bottom. What does the scale now register? Explain.

34. Explain the action of a suction pump.

35. How long a tube would be required for a barometer in which water is used as the barometric liquid?

36. Would a barometer indicate atmospheric pressure correctly if mounted in an inclined position?   Explain.

37. Measure the dimensions of your livingroom or classroom, and compute the weight of air it contains.

38. What is the pressure in lb. per sq. ft. upon a 42 lb. stone at a depth of 10 ft. in sea water (density of water is 64 lb. per cu. ft.)? What is the pressure at a depth of 20 ft.?

39. If the stone of question 38 loses 15 lb. in weight when at a 10 ft. depth, how much will it lose when at a 20 ft. depth?   Would it sink to the bottom in the deepest part of the sea?

40. Measure the pressure of the illuminating gas in the city gas system.   Describe the gas storage tank used in this system.   How may the pressure of the gas in the tank be regulated?

41. Explain the action of an air rifle.   Of a pneumatic riveting hammer.   Of the air brake.   Of the hydraulic brake.

42. In preparing for a balloon ascension into the stratosphere which of the following plans would you adopt, and why?

      a. Make the bag enormously large and fill it to only about one eighth of its capacity?

      b. Make it smaller, and fill it to half capacity?

      c. Make it still smaller, and fill it completely?

43. Why does a liquid flow in spurts from a full jug or bottle?

44. Make a Cartesian diver.   (A pickle jar, a perfume vial, and a cork stopper will work satisfactorily.)   Observe the effects of applying pressure to the stopper.   Discover and state three laws of hydrostatics illustrated by the diver.

45. A 4 lb. bucket containing 20 lb. of water stands on a platform scale.   A 1 lb. piece of cork whose specific gravity is .25 is floated on the water.   What weight does the scale now show?   What would it show if the cork were forced under?   What if it were held under by a string fastened to the bottom of the bucket?

46. A 1 liter flask weighs about 1.2 gm. less when evacuated than when full of air at atmospheric pressure and room temperature. Would a toy balloon of the same size show the same change in weight with the removal of the air?

47. What do we mean when we say that a tire contains 30 lb. of air?   If it is a tire of average size, about what weight of air does it contain?

48. Would your tire gauge read the same at the top of a high mountain as at the base?   If not, at which place would it indicate the greater pressure?   Why?

# CHAPTER 6.   MOLECULES AND THEIR BEHAVIOR

1. About how many molecules are there in 1 cc. of air under ordinary room conditions?

2. About how many molecules are there in 1 cc. of water?   At the rate of 5 per second (one at every tick of a watch) how many years would be required to count them, counting day and night?

3. Give evidence to show that in a gas the molecules are far apart compared with the diameter of a molecule.   That in a liquid the molecules are close together.

4. Do the molecules of a liquid tend to hold together?   Give two reasons for your answer.

5. Make an experiment as follows: Let clear water fall drop by drop from a glass tube or a straw.   Note the size of the drop.   Do the same with soapy water.   Which drops are the larger?   Why?

6. In what respects do gases resemble liquids?   In what way do they differ from them?

7. What is a surface film?

8. Describe the properties of surface films.

9. What is meant by the term *surface tension?*

10. How great is the surface tension of water?   Of alcohol?   Of mercury?

11. What is capillary action?

12. In what way does the rise of liquid in a tube vary with diameter of the tube?

13. Describe the action of a blotter in taking up ink.

14. How is soil a little distance below the surface kept moist in dry weather?

15. How may evaporation of water from the soil in dry weather be reduced?

16. Make a list of ten devices in which springs are used.

17. What property of solids is most essential in a spring?   Define this property.

18. Give evidence that the molecules of fluids are constantly in motion.

19. Describe the motion of a molecule of a gas.   That of a molecule of liquid.

20. What is the average speed of the molecules of the air?

21. How heavy are hydrogen molecules as compared with those of oxygen?

22. What is the average speed of hydrogen molecules as compared with those of oxygen?

23. By what process does air in an automobile tire exert a pressure?

24. Why does a gas exert greater pressure when confined in smaller space?

25. Name six substances which exist in crystalline form.

26. What determines the crystalline form of a substance?

27. Describe three ways in which crystals may be produced.

28. Upon what does the tempering of steel depend?

29. What are cleavage planes?

30. What are amorphous substances?   Name three.

31. Which has the greater surface tension, clear water or soapy water?   Devise an experimental test of the truth of your assertion.

32. Explain the action of a towel in drying the face or hands.

33. Why is it that the ground under a loose board or large stone is usually slightly moist, even after a protracted drought?

34. What is the role of surface tension in the action of a writing pen?

35. Why is it difficult to write with ink on blotting paper?   On waxed paper?

36. Make as long a list as you can of ways in which elasticity contributes to our comfort or convenience in the home.

37. Write a theme on the subject: Elasticity of materials as a factor in transportation and travel.

38. A boy has a fish, a pound of sugar, a foot rule, and a spiral spring.   Devise two methods by which he can weigh the fish, without using any materials except those mentioned and suitable supports for them.

39. A molecule of sugar is about nineteen times as heavy as a molecule of water.   If a spoonful of sugar is dissolved in a cup of water (tea or coffee), will the sugar molecules settle to the bottom? Explain.

## CHAPTER 7.   BUILDING STONES OF MATTER

1. List the points in Dalton's atomic theory.

2. How did this theory differ from the older conception?

3. Illustrate the idea of the molecule.

4. Define the word *molecule*.

5. Explain the meaning of the word *molecule* as applied to gaseous, liquid, and solid elements.

6. Explain the meaning of the following terms:

a. diatomic.              g. neutron.
b. monatomic.             h. energy level or shell.
c. atomic weight.         i. valence.
d. molecular weight.      j. symbol.
e. electron.              k. formula.
f. proton.

7. Trace the evolution of chemical symbols.

8. What ideas may the symbols express?

9. What do the subscripts in the formula for sugar mean?

10. What three ideas can a formula represent?

11. Explain how atomic-weight ideas were arrived at.

12. Be able to compute the molecular weight of a substance if the atomic weights and the formula are known.

13. Be able to solve problems in percentage composition.

14. Compare a proton and an electron.

15. Compare the Lewis-Langmuir and the Bohr theories of atomic structure.

16. Sketch the structure of an aluminum atom, as described on page 86.

17. How does atomic structure justify our original atomic-weight system?

18. In the light of our atomic-structure theory, why do different elements have different properties?

19. Apply the atomic-structure idea to account for the formulas of sodium fluoride and magnesium fluoride.

20. Define *valence*.

21. Account for the difference between positive and negative valence.

22. Be able to derive the formulas of simple two-element compounds if the valences of the elements are known.

23. Helium, neon, and argon contain, respectively, two, ten, and eighteen planetary electrons. Sketch their structure.

24. List a few applications of our knowledge of atoms and their structure.

25. Sketch the structure of an element which contains in its atom 35 protons, 18 nuclear electrons, and 17 planetary electrons.

26. Explain why each element of Fig. 35 was associated with the planet from which it derived its symbol.

27. It has been estimated that a magnification which would make an average atom appear to have the diameter of an average common pin would magnify the pin to a diameter of about 2,873 yards. By appropriate measurements, compute the magnifying power (in diameters) of such a microscope.

28. By reference to a table of atomic weights, compute the molecular weights of the following substances: water ($H_2O$); corn sugar ($C_6H_{12}O_6$); alum ($KAl(SO_4)_2$); stearin (($C_{17}H_{35}COO)_3C_3H_5$); ozone ($O_3$).

29. Compute the percentage composition of cane sugar ($C_{12}H_{22}O_{11}$).

30. Combine each substance in the first column with each one of the second column to yield the (nine) correct formulas.   The valence of each is indicated in parentheses.

| | |
|---|---|
| Aluminum (3) | Chlorine (1) |
| Copper (2) | Carbon (4) |
| Silicon (4) | Nitrogen (3) |

# CHAPTER 8.   SOME SIMPLE HEAT PHENOMENA

1. Describe Galileo's thermometer.   What were its defects?

2. What were the advantages of Rey's water thermometer? What were its defects?

3. What were the fixed points in the original Fahrenheit thermometer?

4. What is the centigrade temperature in a room where the F. temperature is $74°$?   What is the C. temperature on a morning when the F. temperature is $-13°$?

5. What is the F. temperature in a freezing chamber in which the C. temperature is $-15°$?

6. What is the absolute scale of temperature?   What is absolute zero?

7. What are the hottest known objects?   What is their temperature?

8. Describe a type of thermometer in whose construction no liquid is used.

9. Describe the changes that take place in the volume of water when it is heated, beginning at $0°$ C.

10. What is the purpose of the breaks left at intervals in a concrete highway?

11. Describe briefly one method of automatically keeping the temperature of a room approximately constant.

12. Is a cheap watch more likely to lose time in very cold or very hot weather?   Explain.   How may variations in rate due to changes in temperature be avoided?

13. Name the common units used in measuring heat.   Define each.

14. Give approximately the heating value of anthracite coal.   Of kerosene.

15. We are told in one place that water freezes at $0°$ C. and in another that ice melts at $0°$ C.   Are both statements true?   Explain.

16. Tell what is meant by the terms *heat of fusion* and *heat of vaporization*.

17. Describe briefly the effects of large bodies of water on the climate of the surrounding region.   Explain.

18. Is it true that in winter the temperature is likely to rise during a fall of snow?   Explain.

19. Describe briefly the process of heat conduction.

20. In what respects is an aluminum frying pan preferable to one of noncorrosive steel?

21. Describe briefly the processes of heat transfer involved in heating a house by a hot water furnace.

22. Does a steam radiator heat a room only by radiation? Explain.

23. How can rock wool be employed in such a way as to reduce the cost of home heating?   Would sawdust or wood shavings serve the same purpose?   Explain.

24. Do storm sash and insulating materials really keep out the cold?

25. Air is among the poorest of heat conductors.   Why fill the air spaces in walls and under attic floors with expensive, specially prepared insulating materials?

26. When vegetables are boiling, will they cook faster if the gas is turned higher?

27. What is the advantage, if any, of a loose cover on a cooking utensil?   What is the advantage of a heavy, close-fitting cover?

28. Would water be a satisfactory liquid for thermometers which are used only for measuring temperatures between 1° C. and 80° C.?

29. Ice on a pond will often be pitted under fallen leaves. Explain.

30. Will a cloud above a balloon at noon affect the height at which the balloon will float?

31. Are automobile tires more likely to blow out in July or in January?   Are they more likely to blow out on sunny or on cloudy days?   Explain.

32. Why is it that a cold tumbler is likely to crack if quickly filled with hot water?   Is a heavy tumbler more likely to be broken in this way than a light one, or less likely?   Why?   Why is pyrex glass better able to withstand sudden changes in temperature than ordinary glass?

33. Why on a sunny day does the sand on a beach become hotter than the water adjacent?   Why does the shallow water along the shore become warmer than the deeper water farther out?

34. Why is the weather less variable in Honolulu than in Minneapolis?

35. Frost often forms on the inside surface of a window in winter, but rarely, if ever, on the outside.   Does this show that the inside surface is the colder?   Explain.

36. On a hot day a breeze may seem distinctly cool to a bather who has just come from the water.   Explain.

37. Does an electric fan cool the air of a room?

38. Does dew disappear more quickly in a breeze than in a quiet air?   More quickly on a clear than on a cloudy morning?   More quickly in the sunlight than in a shaded spot?   Explain.

39. Some distilled water poured from a bottle into a shallow pan was reported after a short time to have fallen slightly in temperature while that in the bottle remained unchanged.   Was this probably a reliable observation?   Explain.

40. Is it true that a glass of cold water loses its "coldness" more quickly when the air is hot and humid than when it is hot and dry? If so, why?

41. Would a room be warmed by a steam radiator if the water flowed from the radiator at the temperature of the entering steam? Explain.

42. Bubbles in a beaker of briskly boiling water increase markedly in size as they rise.   Why is this?

43. Why are pressure cookers more useful in Denver than in Baltimore?

44. It is claimed that water in some steam boilers is heated to a temperature above 800° F.   Can this be true?   If so, how is such intense heating made possible?   Why is it desired?

45. For what are vacuum pans used and why?

46. What weight of water vapor is contained in a living room $20' \times 10' \times 8'6''$ when the temperature is 70° F. and the relative humidity 40%?

47. Is it possible to convert ice into steam without first melting it?   If so, cite an instance in which it is done.   Cite also an instance in which the reverse change occurs; that is, a change in which water vapor is converted into a solid without first passing into the liquid state.

48. When a steam whistle is blowing, the cloud of "steam" about it may sometimes be seen not closer than a foot or two from the whistle, nor farther from it than 25 or 30 feet.   Explain.

49. What is meant by the term *heat of combustion*?   Of what interest is heat of combustion to consumers of coal?

50. What is the purpose of the layer of asbestos paper often used about the warm air pipes of domestic furnaces?   Devise a way of testing the effectiveness of such a layer for this purpose.   Make the test, and report your findings to the class.

51. The purpose of air conditioning in theaters, hotels, and elsewhere is to provide pure and relatively dust-free air at a com-

fortable temperature and of proper humidity. By visiting an air-conditioned building and examining the equipment, by correspondence with the manufacturers, or by some other satisfactory method learn the construction of such equipment, and its operation in hot, humid weather. Report your findings to the class. Learn also its operation in cold, dry weather.

## CHAPTER 9.  STATES OF EXISTENCE

1. Name the three states of matter.
2. What can be said of the shape and volume of each?
3. How does the energy content of the three states vary, for any given substance?
4. Explain the heat exchange of the refrigerating fluid in a mechanical refrigerator.
5. Sketch a Dewar flask and explain why it is efficient.
6. What practical application has been made of the Dewar-flask principle?
7. How does "dry ice" cause refrigeration?
8. State and illustrate Boyle's law.
9. Explain why the value −273 degrees centigrade is chosen as the absolute zero.
10. State Charles' law.
11. Illustrate and state Dalton's law of partial pressures.
12. What is the kinetic theory?
13. State the law of gaseous diffusion.
14. Give an illustration of diffusion in liquids.
15. Describe fully the difference between absorption and adsorption.
16. State Avogadro's law.
17. What are the nine types of solutions?
18. Name four characteristics of a solution of a solid in a liquid.
19. Explain the meaning of the terms: *solute, solvent, dilute, concentrated, saturated.*
20. Name and illustrate the factors which influence solution.
21. What effects have solutes upon their solvents?  Illustrate.
22. What can be said of the size of colloidal particles?
23. List some illustrations of colloids.
24. State the meaning of the following: effervescence, distillation, emulsoid, suspensoid, ultramicroscope.
25. State Henry's law and offer an illustration.
26. If you were seeking a chemical to use in the cooling system of a mechanical refrigerator, what properties would you specify that it should possess?

27. Suppose that a certain inferior grade of vacuum bottle fails to keep its contents hot or cold. How would you account for its inefficiency?

28. How do you explain the bubbling effect when a chunk of "dry ice" is dropped into cold water?

29. What is the likelihood of ever attaining a temperature below absolute zero?

30. In conformity with the law of partial pressures, the blood of a near-victim of drowning or asphyxiation will take up more oxygen from an oxygen inhalator than as though ordinary air were administered. Explain this statement in greater detail.

31. As Great Salt Lake continues to evaporate and becomes smaller, what will happen to the immense quantities of salts dissolved in its water? State reasons for your conclusion.

## CHAPTER 10.   HEAT AS A FORM OF ENERGY

1. What is the caloric theory of heat? Why is it no longer accepted?

2. What is the nature of heat? Give convincing evidence in support of your statement.

3. Name one thing for which each of the following is noted: Count Rumford; James Prescott Joule; Sir Humphry Davy.

4. If 1 calorie is produced by friction, how many ergs of energy have been transformed into heat to produce it? How many foot-pounds to produce 1 B.t.u.?

5. Oxygen molecules are sixteen times as massive as those of hydrogen. At the same temperature how do the kinetic energies of the two kinds of molecules compare? Explain.

6. Why is a bicycle tire pump warmed with use? Which end is warmed to the greater degree? Why?

7. It is said that expansion of air has the effect of cooling it. Is this true? Explain.

8. Can heat be converted into mechanical energy? If so, by what means is the transformation accomplished?

9. Describe briefly the operation of the steam engine.

10. Describe briefly the operation of a gasoline engine.

11. State and illustrate the law of conservation of energy.

12. Approximately how great is the efficiency of a good steam engine? Of a gasoline engine?

13. In what ways is energy wasted in a gasoline engine?

14. How much work will be done by an engine whose efficiency is 12% in consuming half a ton of coal whose heat value is 13,000 B.t.u. per lb.?

15. How much coal per hour will be used by a steam engine delivering 100 horsepower, if the engine has an efficiency of 15%, and the coal a heat value of 12,500 B.t.u. per lb.?

16. Mention an industrial application of the heating of a gas by compression.

17. What is the effect of expansion on the temperature of a gas? Of what importance in nature is this effect?

18. The water flowing over Niagara Falls is slightly warmer after passing over than before. Why is this?

19. Does rubbing the cold hands together produce warmth, or does it merely warm them by aiding the circulation of blood?

20. Describe all of the energy changes involved in the making of ice cubes in a home refrigerator.

21. How are freezing temperatures attained in large rooms of packing plants?

22. Describe a practical method of making liquid air.

23. What becomes of the kinetic energy of an automobile when it is stopped by applying the brakes? When it is allowed to stop by coasting?

## CHAPTER 11.  OUR ATMOSPHERE

1. What gases compose our atmosphere? Are they permanent?

2. Name some of the chief sources of each of these gases to the atmosphere: Nitrogen, oxygen, and carbon dioxide. Why is the carbon dioxide content larger in low places on the earth. What is mine damp? well damp?

3. Name some of the impurities that are found in the atmosphere. Are impurities necessary to life? In what respects is country air purer than city air?

4. How far above the earth does the atmosphere extend? What are several means used to determine its height?

5. What part of the atmosphere is known as the troposphere? the stratosphere? What is the meaning of each?

6. What is the meaning of tropopause? What may be said of its height in different parts of the earth?

7. Where is the ozone layer? Of what value is it to man?

8. What is a mercurial barometer? How would you go about it to make a simple barometer?

9. How does an aneroid barometer differ from a mercurial? Which is the more accurate of the two?

10. By what means is pressure represented on weather maps?

11. Which is heavier, air containing a large amount of water vapor or dry air, assuming they are at the same temperature?

12. What are the several sources of heat to the earth? Which of these sources is the most important?

13. Name all the ways in which the air secures its moisture.

14. Define the following terms: Humidity, relative humidity, absolute humidity, dew point, and saturation point.

15. What effect does change of temperature have upon the humidities?

16. Define the different forms of moisture.

17. How high has man ascended into the stratosphere? What nation has made the highest ascent? State some reasons why man is very desirous of knowing more about the stratosphere.

18. Is there a limit to which stratosphere balloons can ascend? If so, why?

19. What really makes a balloon rise? Will a balloon bag inflate or deflate as it rises? Give reasons for your answer.

20. Will it be possible for aviators to make transatlantic trips in the stratosphere? What will be some of the advantages of flying in the stratosphere?

21. If you were to use water in making a barometer, how long would the tube have to be?

22. Why is it that man cannot dive to great depths in the ocean? How deep can diving bells go? How deep has Beebe descended into the ocean depths?

23. If you were to make an airplane ascension to great heights, what type of instrument would you carry in order to determine your altitude?

24. Why would one weigh less on top of Pike's Peak than at sea level?

25. Why is the relative humidity higher in the morning and evening than it is in the middle of the day?

26. Why does an electric fan make one feel cooler?

27. Why is it that one who perspires freely on a hot summer's day feels cooler than one who does not perspire?

28. Why does frost collect more freely on windows of homes that are occupied than those not occupied? Is frost frozen dew?

29. What should be the relative humidity of furnace-heated homes in winter time where the temperature is 70 degrees? Does a high relative humidity reduce the fuel bill?

30. Why are fogs more common in winter time than in summer? Why do fogs usually collect first in low places?

31. If you were to plant delicate fruit trees, would you plant them on slopes facing north or those facing south?

32. How may clouds be used to forecast the coming weather?

33. Why do tornadoes not occur over water?

## CHAPTER 12. WINDS AND WEATHER

1. What is wind? What are air currents? In what ways are the two similar?

2. What is a *veering wind?* A *backing wind?*

3. How is wind velocity determined? Wind direction?

4. The wind has a velocity of 200 miles per hour. What is the pressure exerted on a square foot of surface?

5. What is the cause of air movement on the earth?

6. Explain how temperature, moisture, and altitude affect pressure.

7. What is the meaning of *planetary winds? Doldrums?*

8. Where are *tropical calms* or *horse latitudes* located? Why?

9. Do the poles have high or low pressure?

10. Where are the *subpolar lows?*

11. What three great classes of winds are present on the earth?

12. Why do the doldrums shift from one hemisphere to another? When are they north of the equator? South?

13. What is the meaning of *trade winds?* What is the direction of the trades in the Northern Hemisphere? The Southern Hemisphere?

14. What is meant by *migrating winds?* Where on the earth are they found?

15. What are *monsoons?* Where are they found?

16. What causes land and sea breezes? When and where do they occur?

17. What is a mountain breeze? A valley breeze? When does each occur? Why? Which is the stronger of these two winds? Why?

18. What is the meaning of diurnal?

19. Why do the planetary winds shift in latitude during the year?

20. In what latitudes are the *polar easterlies* found?

21. Name the storm winds. Are they all destructive?

22. What are *tropical cyclones?* Where are they found? What different names are given them in different parts of the world?

23. What are *extratropical cyclones?* Where are they found on the earth?

24. Compare a tropical cyclone with an extratropical cyclone. In what important respects do they differ?

25. What type of weather is experienced in an extratropical cyclone?

26. What are *anticyclones?* In what respects do they differ from extratropical cyclones? What kind of weather might one expect to experience in an anticyclone?

27. In what direction do cyclones and anticyclones travel? How fast do these storms move? What may be said of the wind velocities in each?

28. What are *tornadoes?* Why are these storms so destructive? Compare them with the extratropical cyclones.

29. What are *thunderstorms?* Why were they so named?

30. What is the meaning of a secondary circulation?

31. What was Hadley's interpretation as to the effect of rotation on the deflection of air masses?

32. In what respects did Ferrel's law differ from Hadley's?

33. Where on the oceans do the tropical cyclones originate? Why? What is their direction of travel in the Northern Hemisphere? The Southern Hemisphere?

34. If one were going to travel through a hurricane, what quadrant should he avoid? Why?

35. What causes our weather to change so suddenly?

36. A tornado is seen approaching. Suppose you could not get to a tornado cave. What directions would you take to get out of its path?

37. Why is the wind usually stronger during the middle of the day than at night?

38. Why should the winds be stronger in a tornado than in an extratropical cyclone?

39. Why do our storms always come from a westerly direction?

40. What is a blizzard? Where do they occur? Why are they more severe in the Dakotas than in Iowa? Where are they found with reference to a cyclone and anticyclone?

41. Secure a weather map and see if you can determine the shape, size, direction of movement of the winds, moisture, and temperature conditions in the cyclones and anticyclones.

## CHAPTER 13. WEATHER FORECASTING

1. Distinguish between *weather* and *climate.*

2. Name the weather-conditioning factors.

3. Write a short essay on the history of the United States Weather Bureau.

4. Name the various types of Weather Bureau stations and give the duties of each.

5. What data must each of the above stations collect? When must it be collected?

6. What divisions are made for the purpose of weather forecasting?

7. Name the center for each forecasting district.

8. How are weather data reported to Washington?

9. What is the meaning of cyclonic weather?

10. What is a *cyclone?* An *anticyclone?*

11. What is the direction of the air moving into a cyclone on the east, north, west, and south side? What differences in temperature are found?

12. What types of clouds precede this storm? How may they be told?

13. How would you go about it to tell where the center of a cyclone is located?

14. What changes in wind direction, temperature, pressure, cloud, and precipitation occur as a cyclone passes over an observer? Which side of the storm is characterized with little rain and cloud?

15. In what respects does the weather in a cyclone differ from the weather in an anticyclone?

16. What is a *blizzard?* On which side of the cyclone and the anticyclone is this storm found?

17. How far in advance may weather be forecast with some reliability?

18. What may be said of the size of cyclones and anticyclones?

19. What is the meaning of *normal weather?*

20. What sciences must the forecaster be thoroughly trained in before he is able to make accurate forecasts?

21. Why is it more difficult to forecast weather inland than along coast lines?

22. Give some reasons why you think that it was wise to divorce the Weather Bureau from the Army and place it in the Department of Agriculture.

23. Why is it difficult to forecast weather?

24. Are weather almanacs accurate? Examine one and observe how many times the forecast comes true for your community.

25. How are weather maps made at the forecasting centers? Do all centers make weather maps?

26. What methods are used today to get weather information around to the cities and people living in the country? How many times a day are such forecasts made?

27. What method does the Weather Bureau now use in collecting data high above the earth?

28. Secure a weather map and see if you can interpret its meaning.

29. Name all the ways in which the Weather Bureau is aiding agriculture, commerce, and industry.

30. How can an individual get into the Weather Bureau Service?

## CHAPTER 14.   SOUND

1. How are sounds produced?   Give evidence in support of your answer.

2. Show that sound cannot be transmitted in a vacuum.

3. Through what medium is sound usually brought to the ear?

4. At about what speed is sound transmitted in air?   In water? In steel?

5. Show that sound is a wave phenomenon.

6. Describe briefly the nature of a sound wave.

7. What is meant by the length of a sound wave?

8. What is the length of the sound wave made by a piano string vibrating 435 times per second, if the speed of sound is 1120 ft. per second?

9. What is meant by the term *pitch* of a sound?   Upon what does it depend?

10. What is meant in music by the term *harmony?*   By *discord?*

11. Describe briefly the diatonic scale.   The equally tempered scale.

12. How are beats produced?

13. Distinguish between beats and beat tones.

14. How many beats per second are made when two tones whose frequencies are 260 and 265 per second are sounded together?

15. In an organ, do the long pipes emit tones of high or of low pitch?   Why is this?

16. What is the length of an open organ pipe which emits 16 waves per second when the speed of sound is 1120 feet per second?

17. In tuning his instrument, how does the violinist raise the pitch of a string?

18. How in playing does he produce so many tones with so few strings?

19. How is it that different voices sound differently even when singing the same note at true pitch?

20. What apparent change takes place in the pitch of the horn of a passing automobile?   Why is this?

21. Describe briefly the phonograph and its operation.

22. In what respect would the sounds emitted by a cornet be altered by bringing the instrument from out of doors where the temperature is 40° F. into a room where it is 72° F.?   Why?

23. If a pipe organ and a piano in the same auditorium are tuned to the same pitch when the temperature is 55° F., will they also be so tuned when the temperature is 72° F.?   Give reasons for your answer.

24. What would be the effect on music from a distant band if sounds of different pitch were transmitted at different speeds?

25. In a motion picture what is the effect on the pitch of the sounds of speeding up the film?

26. Devise a method of measuring the wave length of the sound emitted by a tuning fork.   Measure the wave length of the sound of a fork making 256 vibrations per sec.

27. Why are words spoken in an ordinary tone sometimes heard distinctly at a considerable distance over water?

28. Write a theme on one of the following subjects:

    a. The contributions of Helmholtz to the science of acoustics.
    b. The acoustics of auditoriums.
    c. The Hammond organ.
    d. Supersonics.

# CHAPTER 15.   ILLUMINATION

1. What were the main sources of artificial light in America in colonial times?

2. How is the light produced in a kerosene wick lamp?   In an open gas jet?   In a mantle lamp?

3. Describe briefly the construction of Edison's early incandescent electric lamps.

4. In what respects do incandescent lamps of the present time differ from Edison's early types?

5. What is meant by the candle power of a lamp?

6. Define the term *foot-candle*.

7. What is the intensity of illumination from a 1000 candle power lamp 20 feet away?

8. Describe briefly a way of measuring the candle power of a lamp.

9. What is the candle power of a lamp which gives the same illumination at a distance of 10 feet as is given by a standard candle at 2 ft.?

10. Upon what factors does the candle power of an incandescent electric lamp depend?

11. Why are the bulbs of some lamps filled with nitrogen or other inert gas?

12. What intensity of light is considered desirable for reading? For sewing?

13. Describe briefly one type of foot-candle meter.   Of what aid is the foot-candle meter to a photographer?

14. Of what value are reflectors in street lighting? Of what use are they in automobile head lights?

15. State the laws of regular reflection of light.

16. What is meant by diffuse reflection of light? How is it caused? Of what value is it?

17. What is the speed of light in a vacuum? In water? In glass?

18. What effect has a window pane on the direction of a transmitted beam of light that strikes it obliquely?

19. Why are electric light bulbs "frosted"?

20. What is the purpose of a "milk glass" globe?

21. Light ordinarily travels in straight lines, yet a beam entering one end of a much bent rod of quartz or transparent plastic will follow the convolutions of the rod and pass out at the other end. Explain. Can any practical application be made of this phenomenon?

22. Describe the construction and operation of a search light. Of a system of flood lighting.

23. Investigate methods employed in producing animated lighting effects, as in street signs, and report to the class.

24. Write a brief history of the electric light—its invention and subsequent improvement.

25. Investigate one of the following:

    a. Modern methods of home illumination.
    b. Modern methods of street illumination.
    c. Polaroid and its uses.
    d. Lighthouses and their lights.
    e. Lighting in the automobile.

# CHAPTER 16.  THE EYE.  OPTICAL INSTRUMENTS

1. What is the effect on the picture of imperfect focusing of the camera? Explain.

2. What effect has increased aperture of the diaphragm? What effect has increased exposure time?

3. What is the effect on the size of the picture of bringing the camera closer to the object photographed? Explain.

4. What is nearsightedness? Farsightedness? What kind of spectacle lenses are worn by nearsighted persons? How do lenses of this type give the needed help?

5. What is astigmatism?

6. Mention three respects in which the eye and the camera are similar and three in which they are different.

7. Show how a simple pocket lens enables one to see small objects more distinctly.

8. Show how a compound microscope acts in magnifying.

9. What is a real image? A virtual image? Which kind is formed on a motion picture screen? In an ordinary mirror?

10. What is the Galilean telescope? Why are such telescopes of historic interest? Why are they of practical interest?

11. Describe the construction of a refracting astronomical telescope.

12. Mention two large refracting telescopes. Is it likely that refractors of much greater size will be constructed? Give reasons for your answer.

13. What advantages have reflecting telescopes over refractors for astronomical work?

14. Of what use to astronomy is photography?

15. Describe briefly the operation of the motion picture projector.

16. Do the pictures on the screen really move? Explain.

17. If light is projected in straight lines, why is it that every part of a room having only a west window is illuminated at least to some extent during the forenoon?

18. Why does a boy stepping into a clear pool of water find it deeper than he expected?

19. What would be the effect on the photograph of covering the lower half of the camera lens? of covering the upper half? Try both.

20. What would be the effect on the magnifying power of a compound microscope of lengthening the tube? Explain.

21. A nearsighted person was observed to take off his glasses in order to see a small object more distinctly. Did this show that the glasses were not properly adapted to his eyes? Give reasons for your answer.

## CHAPTER 17. COLOR. SPECTRA

1. Make a diagram showing the path of a beam of monochromatic (single-colored) light in passing through a triangular glass prism.

2. Make a diagram showing the path of a beam of sunlight in traversing such a prism.

3. Why does the second diagram differ from the first?

4. How did Newton show that a prism does not create the colors it discloses?

5. Explain in some detail how a rainbow is formed.

6. It is sometimes stated that the secondary (fainter, outside) bow is a reflection or image of the primary. Show that this is not the case.

7. Explain how the secondary bow is formed.

8. How may it be shown that light is a wave phenomenon?

9. How are the colors of soap bubbles produced?

10. What, approximately, is the wave length of red light? Of violet light?

11. What are ultraviolet rays? What are their effects?

12. What are infrared rays? Their effects?

13. What is meant by the term *spectrum?* What is a continuous spectrum?

14. Mention one respect in which the spectrum of sunlight differs from that of an ordinary electric lamp.

15. Astronomers tell us that the sun and stars contain many of the elements found on the earth. How is this known?

16. Tell how helium was discovered.

17. Describe an optical method of chemical analysis.

18. What information may be gained from the spectrum of the light of a star concerning the star's movement? How is this done?

19. What evidence have we that the universe is expanding?

20. What is the apparent color of a red object when illuminated by red light? By white light? By blue light? Explain.

21. Gasoline and kerosene are clear liquids, yet a trace of either on the surface of water gives a variety of colors. How are these produced?

22. Give in some detail the reasons why a mixture of yellow and blue paints is green, while a combination of yellow and blue light is white or gray.

23. Prepare a paper on one of the following topics:

    a. Color photography.
    b. How the rotogravure section of a Sunday newspaper is produced.
    c. Color in wartime camouflage.
    d. Protective coloring in nature.
    e. Color in home decoration.
    f. Photography with dark rays.

## CHAPTER 18. ELECTROSTATICS AND MAGNETISM

1. How may it be shown that there are two kinds of electrification? Why are they called positive and negative?

2. Tell how a positive charge can be produced. Is a negative charge also produced in the process? Explain.

3. What is the effect of an electric charge on a nearby metallic object?

4. What is the meaning of the term *induction?*

5. Give directions for charging an insulated metal ball positively by induction.   Give directions for charging it negatively.

6. What is a condenser?   Name one use of condensers.

7. Define *unit charge* of electricity.

8. State the laws of electrostatic attraction and repulsion.

9. What force do two charges of 40 and 50 units respectively exert upon each other when 5 cm. apart in air?

10. It is found that a charge of 30 units exerts a force of 90 dynes upon another charge when 4 cm. from it in air.   What is the magnitude of the second charge?

11. Describe Franklin's kite experiment.   What did it show?

12. How does a lightning rod protect a building from damage by lightning?

13. What are lodestones?   For what have they been used?

14. What are the poles of a magnet?   What is a north-seeking pole?   A south-seeking pole?

15. Name three paramagnetic substances.   Three diamagnetic substances.

16. What is a pole of unit strength?

17. State the laws of force exerted by magnetic poles upon each other.

18. What force is exerted upon each other by two poles, each of 40 units strength, when 10 cm. apart in air?

19. What is a magnetic field?   What are lines of force?

20. What is a field of unit strength?

21. Give all the evidence you can that magnetism is a molecular phenomenon.

22. What is the effect of a magnet on an unmagnetized piece of iron?   Explain.

23. Why will a magnet not pick up brass tacks?

24. How does a compass needle indicate direction?   Why does it not do this accurately?

25. Why in winter does a spark sometimes pass between the hand and the object when one touches a metal door knob or a light fixture?   Why does this not occur in summer?

26. Having only a fur and a piece of sealing wax could one charge two insulated metal balls, one positively and the other negatively?   If so, how?

27. Devise a method of developing a large negative charge and storing it upon an insulated metal ball, by using only a positively charged pane of glass and a metal disc provided with an insulating handle.

28. What is the purpose of the dangling chain on a gasoline truck?

29. What would be the action of a compass needle if brought along side of a steam radiator near the top? What the action if brought near the bottom? Explain.

30. Two short bars of steel are exactly alike except that one is magnetized. Devise a way of finding without the aid of any other materials which is the magnetized bar.

31. Write a theme on the scientific achievements of one of the following:

    a. William Gilbert.
    b. Benjamin Franklin.
    c. J. J. Thomson.

## CHAPTER 19.  ELECTRIC CURRENTS

1. What is the nature of an electric current in a wire? In an electrolyte?

2. Name three devices in which electric currents are used to produce heat.

3. What is an electromagnet? Name two uses of such magnets.

4. Describe the construction and operation of a direct-current electric motor.

5. Make a list of uses to which electric motors are put.

6. What is ionization? Electrolysis?

7. Mention several applications of electrolysis.

8. Mention as many points of likeness as you can between primary cells and storage cells. As many points of difference as you can.

9. Describe the operation of a dynamo.

10. What is a photoelectric cell? For what purposes are such cells used?

11. What is a thermocouple? A thermopile?

12. In what respects are an electric current and a stream of water similar? In what respects are they different?

13. Define: (1) *coulomb;* (2) *ampere.*

14. What is a galvanometer? How does the galvanometer operate?

15. Name three good conductors of electricity. Name three very poor conductors.

16. What is the meaning of the term *electrical resistance?* Define *ohm.*

17. What is an electromotive force? In what units is it measured?

18. State Ohm's law.

19. What current will flow in a lamp whose resistance is 300 ohms when connected to a 115 volt line?

20. What is the resistance of a toaster which takes 5 amperes from a 115 volt line?

21. How much power is taken by the lamp of question 19?

22. How much power is taken by the toaster of question 20?

23. What is a kilowatt hour?

24. At 5 cents per kw. hr. what is the cost of the electrical energy taken by the toaster of question 20 in ten hours of use?

25. Why are glass supports used for electric wires when these are mounted upon poles?

26. Copper is much more expensive than iron. Why is it that copper wires are used in preference to iron in constructing electric transmission lines?

27. Why is iron used in preference to copper in the pole pieces of electric motors and dynamos?

28. A famous electrical engineer once said that an electric generator (dynamo) generates no electricity. Was his statement true? Explain.

29. A certain dynamo supplies electric current to light an amusement park. What is the effect on the engine that drives the dynamo of turning on the lights? Explain.

30. Tungsten is not so good a conductor as copper and is more expensive. Why is it used in preference to copper in the filaments of electric lamps?

31. For what purposes are electric currents used in an automobile? How is this current supplied when the motor is running? How when the motor is not running?

32. Why are birds not killed when alighting on high-voltage electric wires?

33. Does an electric motor take a larger current while starting, or while running at full speed? Why is this?

34. Many Christmas tree lights are designed to operate at about 14 volts. Why is it that eight such lights are usually connected together? Are they joined in series or in parallel? Why?

35. Make diagrams to represent the following electric circuits:

(a) For ringing any one of several bells from a single battery, as in an apartment house.

(b) For ringing several bells simultaneously from a single battery, as in a school or college.

(c) For ringing one bell by pushing any one of several buttons, as in a street car.

36. Could the electric motor of a street car be made to serve as a brake? If so, how? In what respects would the performance of such a brake be unlike that of the friction brake?

37. Make a diagram to represent the proper circuits for lighting two 110 volt lamps from a 110 volt supply. Make a diagram of a circuit for lighting two 110 volt lamps from a 220 volt supply. What would be the effect of using the second wiring plan for the first case? Of using the first wiring plan for the second case?

38. Write a short essay on some large hydroelectric plant which you have visited, or concerning which you have read.

39. Write a short essay on the scientific achievements of one of the following:

a. Michael Faraday.          d. Hans Christian Oersted.
b. Joseph Henry.             e. Thomas A. Edison.
c. Alessandro Volta.

# CHAPTER 20.  ELECTRICAL COMMUNICATION

1. Who is credited with the invention of the telegraph?

2. Describe the construction and operation of a simple one-way telegraphic circuit.

3. Why is the relay used?  The sounder?

4. Of what importance is a code in telegraphy?

5. What improvements in the telegraph have been made since the first line was put in operation?

6. Why does a single wire suffice for carrying current in the telegraph?

7. Describe the construction and operation of a telephone transmitter.

8. Describe the construction and operation of a telephone receiver.

9. In what respects is the telephone superior to the telegraph? In what respects is the telegraph the better?

10. What is radiotelegraphy?

11. Describe a simple radiotelegraphic transmitter.

12. Describe a radiotelephone transmitter.

13. Describe a radio receiver.

14. What is a teletypewriter?  For what is it used?

15. Mention two ways by which talking motion pictures are produced.  Describe each briefly.

16. Describe the method of recording sound on a motion picture film.

17. Describe the method of reproducing sound from the film.

18. Are telephone booths in public places used for the purpose of confining the sound and sending it all into the line?  How far is the sound itself transmitted in the telephone?  How far in a "lover's

telephone" (a wire stretched between the bottoms of two tin cans located at the points between which the conversation takes place)?

19. In what respects has the vacuum tube extended the uses of the telephone?

20. Write an account of the life and scientific achievements of one of the following:

    a. Alexander Graham Bell.
    b. Samuel F. B. Morse.
    c. Guglielmo Marconi.
    d. Heinrich Rudolph Hertz.
    e. James Clerke Maxwell.

21. Investigate modern methods of making marine soundings.

## CHAPTER 21.  X RAYS AND RADIOACTIVITY

1. Who discovered $X$ rays?  Relate the circumstances of the discovery.

2. Why were $X$ rays so named?

3. In what respects do $X$ rays resemble light?  In what respects are they different from light?

4. Of what service are $X$ rays in medicine and surgery?

5. Of what service are $X$ rays in industry?

6. For what is Becquerel noted?  Madame Curie?

7. What is radioactivity?

8. What are alpha rays?  Describe their properties.

9. What are beta rays?  Describe their properties.

10. What is the nature of gamma rays?

11. How is an atom affected by the emission of an alpha ray?  By the emission of a beta ray?

12. How are atoms artificially disintegrated?

13. What are cosmic rays?

14. What is meant by the term "atom smashing"?  What knowledge has been gained by smashing atoms?

15. Describe briefly modern $X$ ray equipment for the treatment of cancer.

16. Write a short essay on the life and work of one of the following:

    a. William Conrad Roentgen.
    b. W. H. Bragg.
    c. Antoine Henri Becquerel.
    d. Madame Curie.
    e. Ernest Rutherford.

# CHAPTER 22. FUNDAMENTAL CHEMICAL PROCESSES

1. What was the Phlogiston Theory?
2. What overthrew the Phlogiston Theory?
3. Discuss the discovery and naming of oxygen.
4. Explain the meaning of the following terms:

| | |
|---|---|
| a. oxidation | j. reduction. |
| b. combustion. | k. combustible. |
| c. exothermic. | l. supporter of combustion. |
| d. chemical energy. | m. spontaneous combustion. |
| e. property. | n. catalysis. |
| f. physical property. | o. element. |
| g. chemical property. | p. compound. |
| h. kindling point. | q. synthesis. |
| i. endothermic. | r. hydrogenation. |

5. List five forms of energy with which chemistry deals.
6. State a definition for chemistry.
7. Where and in what proportions does oxygen occur?
8. Compare the oxygen content of ordinary and of expired air.
9. What processes are the greatest consumers of atmospheric oxygen?
10. Explain the relation of oxygen to fire extinguishers.
11. How is oxygen obtained on a commercial scale and in the laboratory?
12. List the major physical and chemical properties of oxygen.
13. Illustrate and describe the process of catalysis.
14. Distinguish between the terms, *element* and *compound*.
15. List a dozen or more, each, of the commonest elements and compounds.
16. Illustrate the loss of identity of an element when it enters into combination.
17. State the law of definite composition.
18. Indicate how hydrogen is liberated in a city water-gas plant.
19. Explain the formation of moisture from a gas flame.
20. Describe two industrial processes of hydrogenation.
21. Discuss the uses of hydrogen and helium in dirigibles.
22. Indicate the different ways in which hydrogen is utilized.
23. In what ways is hydrogen commonly produced industrially and in the laboratory?
24. Be able to give the metric tables of weight, length, and volume.
25. Be able to estimate measurements in the metric system.

26. Devise and describe an experiment to measure the length of time that a candle will burn in a limited supply of ordinary air and in the same volume of expired air.

27. Why is air bubbled through the tanks in an aquarium?

28. Calomel, a medicine, and corrosive sublimate, a deadly poison, both contain only mercury and chlorine. Is not this fact contrary to the Law of Definite Composition? Explain.

29. What fairly pure compounds can be purchased in the average grocery store?

30. What practical uses are made in the home of the following elements: silver; aluminum; copper; iodine; lead; tin; tungsten; zinc?

31. Where was Priestley's home in his later years? What events caused him to leave England?

32. Why does hydrogen burn quietly when ignited as it issues from a jet, but explode violently when mixed with air and ignited?

33. In what appropriate metric units would you record the length of this book, the thickness of a lead pencil, the distance to a neighboring town, the weight of a fly, the weight of a teaspoon, your own weight, the volume of a test tube, the volume of a milk pail?

## CHAPTER 23.  THE STORY OF WATER

1. Where and to what extent is water found?

2. What criteria should condemn water for drinking purposes?

3. List and explain all of the processes employed in complete municipal water purification.

4. Give a complete chemical explanation of how water becomes hard.

5. Explain the formation of scale.

6. Account for the stalactite formations in caves.

7. Account chemically for the effect of hard water upon soap.

8. Discuss the soda process of water softening.

9. Explain both the zeolite method of water softening and the regeneration of the softener.

10. Describe the various stages in the purification of city sewage.

11. How does the home septic tank operate?

12. Define the *small calorie, kilogram calorie, British thermal unit.*

13. Indicate the significance of the term *specific heat* and show the usefulness of the high specific heat of water.

14. Indicate the meaning and the uses (in the case of water) of the terms, *heat of fusion* and *heat of vaporization.*

15. Relate the fixed points on centigrade and Fahrenheit thermometers to the properties of water.

16. Convert each of the following values to that of the other thermometer's scale: 96° F., 7° F., −20° F., 20° C., −34° C.

17. Define the term *density* and state its value for water.

18. What is the meaning of specific gravity? What substances are used as standards of comparison for specific gravities of solids, liquids, and gases?

19. Define and illustrate the following terms:

a. Vapor pressure.
b. Vapor tension.
c. Equilibrium.
d. Deliquescence.
e. Acidic oxide.
f. Basic oxide.
g. Metallic element.
h. Nonmetal.
i. Radical.

j. Positive radical.
k. Negative radical.
l. Double decomposition.
m. Neutralization.
n. Salt.
o. Hydrate.
p. Water of hydration.
q. Dehydration.
r. Efflorescence.

20. Technically explain why calcium chloride "settles" the dust when scattered over a road.

21. How can the formulas of acids and of bases be readily identified?

22. Account for the oxidizing power of hydrogen peroxide. List some applications of this property.

23. Be able to balance simple equations.

24. Name and illustrate the four major types of inorganic chemical reactions.

25. Be able to solve problems in reaction weights.

26. One pound is equal to 453 gm. One degree C. is equal to $\frac{9}{5}$ degrees F., and one degree F. is equal to $\frac{5}{9}$ degree C. From these data compute the number of calories which are equivalent to one British thermal unit.

27. When a gram of fat is completely burned in a calorimeter, producing carbon dioxide and water, it liberates more heat than when it is oxidized in the body. Can you suggest a reason?

28. A tub of water is sometimes placed in a small, unheated vegetable cellar to reduce the danger of freezing. Explain the action.

29. Explain why burns from steam are likely to be more severe than those from hot water.

30. Magnesium chloride, a compound similar to calcium chloride, is present in much table salt. How would this explain the stickiness and tendency to caking of salt on a damp day?

31. It is claimed that certain alkaline dentifrices will correct an acid condition of saliva. Point out the fallacy of such statements.

32. It is a common belief that a wound is very dirty or badly infected if, when it is treated with hydrogen peroxide, a vigorous effervescence is observed. Indicate the error in such reasoning.

## CHAPTER 24. IONIZATION AND EQUILIBRIUM

1. List a few differences in the reactivity of certain substances when dry and when in solution.

2. What theory explains such reactivity behaviors? When and by whom was it propounded?

3. What explanation did the chemist of question 2 suggest?

4. Explain the meaning of *ion, positive ion, negative ion.*

5. How does an ion obtain its charge?

6. Explain and illustrate the following terms:

|  |  |
|---|---|
| a. Degree of ionization. | e. Electrolyte. |
| b. Highly ionized. | f. Anion and cation. |
| c. Strong acids and bases. | g. Primary product. |
| d. Weak acids and bases. | h. Secondary product. |

7. What is the difference in the mechanics of current flow in a copper wire and in an electrolyte?

8. What is the relation of extent of dilution to degree of ionization?

9. What ions in common are furnished by all acids? By all bases?

10. Offer an illustration of physical equilibrium.

11. Illustrate in some detail a case of chemical equilibrium.

12. What is meant by the statement that a certain reaction goes to completion?

13. Illustrate a completed reaction by a discussion of neutralization.

14. Under what three conditions does a reaction go to completion?

15. Illustrate a case of displacement of ionic equilibrium.

16. A 5 per cent solution of hydrochloric acid is much more sour than a 5 per cent solution of acetic acid (vinegar). Account for this difference.

17. Note the composition of a baking powder from the label on the can and then explain why a chemical action occurs when water is added to the powder.

18. Suggest in some detail a method for silver-plating iron spoons. How could the thickness of the plating be varied?

## CHAPTER 25. NITROGEN AND OTHER GASES

1. List some of the physical properties of nitrogen.

2. Discuss the value of legumes in relation to nitrogen.

3. What is the meaning of nitrogen fixation?

4. What is the Haber process of nitrogen fixation?

5. Why would a process like the Haber be valuable to a nation at war?

6. Discuss the nitrogen fixation process carried on at Muscle Shoals.

7. What is the Birkeland-Eyde method?

8. How is ammonia obtained from coal?

9. State some essential facts about ammonia water.

10. List some ammonium salts, with their practical uses.

11. Indicate how ammonia can be converted into nitric acid.

12. How can nitric oxide (NO—the Birkeland-Eyde product) be changed into nitric acid?

13. What is used to form nitric acid by the oldest process?

14. What three powerful properties does nitric acid possess?

15. How is pyroxylin prepared?

16. Discuss several valuable products made from pyroxylin.

17. What use is made of the higher nitrate (hexanitrate) of cellulose?

18. Discuss the manufacture and properties of nitroglycerine and dynamite.

19. Prepare a brief report on the Nobel Prizes.

20. Mention two products—one a nitro derivative—obtained from toluene.

21. What results from nitrating carbolic acid?

22. Account for the force of an explosion.

23. From the standpoint of atomic structure, why are the "rare elements" of the air so inactive?

24. What is the commercial source of helium?

25. Indicate the uses of helium, neon, and argon.

26. Give a number of reasons why it would (would not) be commercially profitable to establish a cyanamid nitrogen fixation plant in your home town.

27. Leguminous crops enrich the soil with nitrogenous products, even though the crop is cut for hay instead of being plowed under. State the reason.

28. List several reasons why Muscle Shoals was selected as the site for the Government's war-time nitrate plant.   In what ways is this tremendous investment now yielding financial returns?

29. Why must the steel industry have close connections with the chemical trade?

30. What part does chemistry play, directly or indirectly, in the repair of a dented automobile fender?

31. Firecrackers are exploded with a fuse and most high explosives require a detonating cap.   State the difference in these two processes. Can you explain the action of the caps?

32. How do you account for the fact that helium, neon, and argon have been discovered only recently?

33. Some of the nitrogen compounds in your body originated indirectly from the free nitrogen of the air. Trace through two series of reactions to show such transformations.

## CHAPTER 26.   THE HALOGENS AND THE ELEMENTS

1. Why are certain elements grouped into families?
2. Name the members of the halogen family.
3. What does the word signify?
4. Explain how chlorine can act as a bleacher and bactericide.
5. Describe the uses of sodium hypochlorite.
6. What is "bleaching powder" and how does it function?
7. Name two chlorates and their uses.
8. Discuss the methods of recovery of common salt (sodium chloride).
9. Describe the production of chlorine from salt.
10. Comment on toxic gases.
11. Name and discuss the uses of the chlorine compounds obtainable from marsh gas.
12. List some properties of bromine.
13. How is it recovered?
14. Discuss these methods of recovery in some detail.
15. What uses have ethyl bromide and sodium bromide?
16. Briefly outline the chemistry of the photographic processes of exposure, developing, fixing, and printing.
17. Show the relation between the object, the negative, and the positive by a simple sketch.
18. List some properties of solid and gaseous iodine.
19. What is tincture of iodine and what are its uses?
20. Mention the methods of recovery of iodine.
21. What uses have iodine compounds?
22. State a few facts about goiter.
23. What striking properties has fluorine?
24. Comment on fluorspar and the important acid derived from it.
25. What can be said about fluorides in drinking water?
26. What idea was expressed in Doebereiner's triads?
27. Explain Newlands' contribution.
28. Who gave us the Periodic Table?
29. State the Periodic law.
30. What is true of the elements of any one group?
31. How do atomic weights vary in a series?
32. Discuss Mendeleeff's vacancies and his predictions.
33. What group does not fit into the table?

34. What elements are (perhaps) missing?

35. Why did we state on page 388 that there are 92 elements?

36. Name five properties of the elements which show progressive changes in the table.

37. Of what does group VIII consist?

38. What other devices show the periodicity of the elements?

39. In what way does the table show atomic-structure relationships?

40. Why is the periodic classification fundamental to science?

41. What objection is there to the use of chlorine for bleaching silk and wool fabrics?   How is the difficulty overcome?

42. Why not employ tincture of iodine or carbolic acid for the irrigation of deep wounds?

43. Account for the fact that hydrogen gas is a by-product of the electrolytic process of chlorine manufacture.

44. If magnesium chloride—a deliquescent substance—is present in table salt, the material will become damp and cake.   This difficulty may be overcome by mixing with the salt either starch or baking soda (sodium bicarbonate).   Explain the action of each of these "driers."

45. Can you state any reasons why the use of free chlorine as a toxic gas was abandoned early in the World War?

46. Water and carbon tetrachloride when used as fire extinguishers function in entirely different ways.   Explain.

47. People are warned against using ethyl gasoline for dry-cleaning fabrics.   Why?

48. Account for the fact that overdevelopment of a film results in an almost black negative.

49. Why does a red object photograph as black on an ordinary film?   How does this account for the lighting equipment of a photographic dark room?

50. Can you cite any cases of the beneficial effects of the iodine treatment for goiter, as carried out with large groups of young people?

51. What method is commonly used for etching frosted electric light bulbs?

52. In some chemistry courses the student must practically memorize the Periodic Table.   What advantages would result from this accomplishment?

## CHAPTER 27.   SULFUR

1. Offer an explanation for the formation of Sicilian sulfur.

2. How was sulfur recovered in Sicily?

3. Where are the sulfur deposits of the United States and how may they have been formed?

4. Explain the Frasch mining process.
5. Name the three manufactured forms of sulfur.
6. Briefly outline how each is made.
7. Define *allotropy*.
8. What are the three allotropic forms of sulfur?
9. What industries consume sulfur?
10. Mention a few facts regarding hydrogen sulfide.
11. Write the equation for the burning of sulfur.
12. What uses has sulfur dioxide?
13. Briefly outline the two methods for the manufacture of sulfuric acid.
14. List the properties of sulfuric acid.
15. Explain its effect upon fabrics.
16. Relate sulfuric acid to petroleum refining.
17. How is the acid employed in the fertilizer industry?
18. Explain its use in the nitration of organic compounds.
19. How is it used in the metals industry?
20. Look up and describe the essentials of the creamery butterfat test.
21. Mention a few other uses for sulfuric acid.
22. Why is the consumption of sulfuric a good index of the degree of civilization of a people and of their prosperity?
23. Write a technical essay upon safety and "strike anywhere" matches, as described in this chapter.
24. In what ways was fire obtained before the invention of matches?
25. The specific gravity of sulfur is 2.06. What is the weight, in grams, of 1000 cubic centimeters of it? What is the volume, in cubic centimeters, of 1000 gm.?
26. Devise and describe three different ways of distinguishing between the gases, hydrogen sulfide and sulfur dioxide.
27. Why should sulfuric acid be called "oil of vitriol"?
28. Commercial sulfuric acid sometimes contains a sediment of lead sulfate. Account for it.
29. A small glass dish, nearly filled with concentrated sulfuric acid and placed in a chemical balance case to keep the air dry, will eventually overflow. How would you explain this effect?
30. Carefully examine a match from a match book and list the materials which enter into its manufacture.

## CHAPTER 28. SOME-COMMON METALS

1. List several physical properties common to metals.
2. What is the chemical test for a metal?

3. Name seven forms in which metals occur.

4. What is the meaning of the following terms:

a. Ore.                          c. Refining.
b. Metallurgy.                   d. Reduction.
                 e. Roasting.

5. Illustrate the several metallurgical processes by using the zinc ores as examples.

6. Describe the production of iron from the mine to the pig.

7. What treatment produces cast iron and wrought iron?

8. What uses do these two kinds of iron serve?

9. Describe the Bessemer process.

10. What is open hearth steel?

11. How is crucible steel produced and for what is it used?

12. Discuss alloy steels.

13. Describe automatic sprinkler systems.

14. In what ways may iron articles be protected to ensure permanency?

15. Discuss the metallurgy of aluminum.

16. What are the desirable properties of aluminum and how are they utilized?

17. What are the applications of aluminum alloys?

18. Discuss the occurrence and metallurgy of copper.

19. Describe the technique and value of the flotation process.

20. Point out the applications of metallic copper and of copper as an alloying agent.

21. Outline the methods of mining gold.

22. In what properties does gold excel other metals?

23. Explain the application of the term *carat* to gold articles.

24. What is meant by the words: solid silver; sterling silver; triple plate?

25. State the occurrence and uses of platinum.

26. What are the latest figures, in tons, on the annual production of pig iron in the United States?

27. Look up and draw a price curve, by months, for copper or aluminum in the United States during the past three years.

28. Describe the method used by some local blacksmith or other iron worker for "tempering" his iron product.

29. If samples are available, compare the prices of very similar aluminum articles of different brands to be found in local stores. Try to account for the variation in prices.

30. Write a short "human interest" type of article on Charles M. Hall's discovery of aluminum extraction.

31. Chemically, aluminum and silicon possess both metallic and nonmetallic properties. How does the Periodic Table suggest this fact?

32. What color does (bivalent) copper impart to most of its salts? Name three such salts.

33. Explain why a knife blade (iron) takes on a coating of metallic copper if it is dipped in a solution of copper sulfate.

34. What copper-containing solutions are used by the doctors and hospitals of your community in the urinary tests for diabetes?

35. Compare the densities of copper, aluminum, iron, and gold.

36. Why does a silver-plated spoon "wear out" sooner than one made of sterling silver?

## CHAPTER 29.   CARBON AND ITS COMPOUNDS

1. What qualities render diamonds valuable?

2. How were diamonds formed?

3. What is the meaning of *carat?*

4. Describe the manufacture of graphite.

5. List the uses of graphite and the properties which make it useful.

6. Discuss the composition and the analysis of coal.

7. Why does ordinary stoking result in the loss of many of the heat units of coal?

8. What is the meaning of *destructive distillation?*

9. What are the applications of the adsorptive power of certain kinds of charcoal?

10. Of what use is the carbon obtained from burning oils?

11. Why does carbon have both a positive and a negative valence of four?

12. Under what conditions is carbon monoxide formed?

13. Describe the uses of carbon monoxide.

14. Account for the asphyxiating power of carbon monoxide.

15. List the different ways in which carbon dioxide is produced.

16. Discuss rather fully its properties and uses.

17. Explain the processes of leavening by means of carbon dioxide.

18. Examine several brands of baking powder; state their composition; indicate the function of each ingredient.

19. Name five fuels which are obtained from the petroleum fields.

20. Describe the manufacture of water gas.   What kind of gas is supplied for your home community?

21. State pertinent facts about carborundum.

22. In what natural forms does silicon dioxide occur?

23. Mention a few facts about the silicates.

24. Discuss the subject of glass.

25. Indicate how a plate or a mixing bowl is made.

26. "Heat of combustion" refers to the quantity of heat liberated when 1 gm. atomic weight of a substance (12 gm. in case of carbon) is completely burned. State whether, in your judgment, equal weights of the allotropic forms of carbon, when completely burned, liberate equal quantities of heat. Verify your answer by reference to tables of heats of combustion.

27. From the standpoint of economics, what would be the best method of keeping the per carat value of diamonds at a fairly steady level?

28. Even on a fairly steady market, one-carat diamonds vary in price between $325 and $600. How do you explain this variation?

29. If an ordinary lead pencil, with its wooden sheath and its graphite-clay core, is held in a very hot gas flame for several minutes, what part or parts of the pencil will remain practically unchanged? Why?

30. How are pencils, especially drawing pencils, designated as to their degree of hardness?

31. Why can some cheap grades of coal be used efficiently in an under-feed or a chain-grate stoker furnace?

32. Carbon monoxide and hydrogen are colorless and odorless. What would be the objection to the home use of city water gas if it contained only these two substances?

33. Why are not automobile carburetors adjusted to admit sufficient air to burn the gasoline in the cylinders completely to carbon dioxide and water?

34. Suggest some reasons why dry ice is not competing with water ice in home refrigerators?

35. Explain why soda-acid fire extinguishers require recharging each time after use, while pyrene extinguishers do not.

36. What test could be applied to distinguish between two colorless, transparent plates resembling window glass—one made of glass and the other of fused quartz (silicon dioxide)?

# CHAPTER 30.  ORGANIC AND FOOD CHEMISTRY

1. Define Organic Chemistry.

2. What contribution did Wöhler make and what was its significance?

3. What are the names and formulas of the two simplest organic compounds?

4. To what series does each belong?

5. State the names and formulas of the first eight members of the methane series.

6. Define the term *homologous series*.

7. Show the formula relationship between methane, ethane, and propane.

8. Use ethane to illustrate the five kinds of formulas: empirical, simple, structural, graphic, and type.

9. For what purposes are these different kinds of formulas used?

10. Name some fuels which are composed of members of the methane series.

11. What is the significance of the "octane number"?

12. List some of the products of the fractional distillation of petroleum.

13. What is meant by the "alkyl radicals"?

14. State the names and formulas of two such radicals.

15. What are the alkyl hydroxides called?

16. State the formula, methods of preparation, and uses of wood alcohol.

17. Discuss the production and uses of ethyl alcohol.

18. What is the name, formula, and a use of a dihydroxy alcohol?

19. What is glycerine, chemically? Describe some of its uses.

20. Give the name and uses of an important phenol.

21. Discuss in some detail the different kinds of plastics.

22. Show, by means of graphic formulas, how aldehydes are related to alcohols.

23. What is formalin and what are its uses?

24. How are acids derived from aldehydes?

25. What radical is characteristic of all organic acids?

26. Name a few organic acids, together with their occurrence.

27. Discuss briefly the ethers.

28. Comment on the uses and the structure of acetone.

29. What are esters and how do they correspond to salts?

30. What uses have the simple esters?

31. How were the coal-tar dyes first discovered?

32. What definite groupings must be present in a dye?

33. What organic and inorganic classes of materials must enter into the diet?

34. What does the word *carbohydrate* signify?

35. Name the classes of carbohydrates and state their type formulas.

36. Discuss glucose—its occurrence, manufacture, formation in the body, and medical test for its presence.

37. What is fructose?

38. What formula have the disaccharides?

39. Discuss the production and the digestion of sucrose.

40. What desirable properties has lactose?

41. What can be stated about the molecular nature of the polysaccharides?

42. Discuss in some detail the subject of the starches; the dextrins.

43. What plastics and synthetic silks are produced from cellulose?

44. What use does glycogen serve?

45. What is the chemical nature of the fats?

46. Discuss saponification.

47. Explain the distinction between the high-molecular-weight fats and oils.

48. Explain how and why vegetable oils can be converted into vegetable cooking fats.

49. What is oleomargarine?

50. What elements do proteins contain?

51. Why is their molecular structure practically unknown?

52. Name some typical food proteins.

53. What are the final products of the digestion of proteins?

54. Indicate the nature of one of these products.

55. What functions do the mineral salts perform in the body?

56. What are enzymes?

57. Discuss the terminology of enzymes.

58. In what way do hormones function?

59. Discuss briefly the digestive hormones; the endocrine hormones.

60. Write the graphic formulas for (normal) butane, pentane, and hexane.

61. The first three members of the ethylene series of hydrocarbons have the formulas, $C_3H_6$, $C_4H_8$, and $C_5H_{10}$. What is their type formula?

62. Write a brief report on the classic recovery of petroleum by drilling, as first carried out by Drake at Titusville, Pa.

63. Why is "ethyl" alcohol a better technical term than "grain" alcohol?

64. Although glycerine is sweet, it is not a sugar. How does its formula verify this fact?

65. Examine a late-model automobile and list all of its parts which appear to be made of plastics.

66. Offer an explanation as to why certain soils are acid. Why does the addition of limestone (calcium carbonate, $CaCO_3$) correct this condition?

67. Why are "dime store" perfumes so much cheaper than the corresponding ones derived from flowers?

68. Can corn sugar be defined as "the sugar which is present in corn"? Explain.

69. What are the processes employed in a small-scale sorghum mill? Why does not such a mill prepare crystallized table sugar?

70. Describe as many tests as you can find for distinguishing between a cotton and a wool fabric.

71. State several reasons why a highly refined axle grease (a petroleum product) would not be a satisfactory substitute for table butter.

72. Why can not the petroleum oils, unlike vegetable oils, be saponified?

73. Can you explain why acids are alkali-forming foods while proteins are acid formers?

74. What, in general, is the composition and use of "rennet"?

75. One treatment for hypothyroidism is the administration of thyroxin; for hyperthyroidism, the operative removal of part of the thyroid gland. Why the difference in treatment?

## CHAPTER 31.  THE EARTH AND ITS ROCKS

1. Distinguish between the term *ocean* and *ocean basin*. What is the average depth of the ocean?

2. Name the several oceans. What per cent of the lithosphere is ocean?

3. What is the difference between a continent and a continental plateau?

4. Can you suggest some ways in which they have been formed? Which was the last continent to be explored? Who claims this continent?

5. What is the meaning of relief? How does the relief of the ocean floor differ from that of the land?

6. What is the meaning of *epicontinental sea?* How deep must the water be before it is part of the ocean basin?

7. Define a *plain*. In what different ways may plains be formed? Give an example of each.

8. In what ways do plateaus differ from plains? How may they be formed? Name some prominent plateaus in the United States.

9. What are mountains? How may they be formed?

10. Make clear the meaning of the following terms: element, mineral, and rock. Are air, mercury, and petroleum minerals?

11. How could you distinguish the following minerals: quartz, calcite, mica, feldspar, talc, magnetite, chalk, gypsum?

12. What is an igneous rock? Is it universal in the earth? On the earth?

13. What determines the texture of igneous rocks? What is a granite? A dolerite? A pyroxenite or hornblendite?

14. What is sedimentary rock? Of what is it composed?

15. How does the structure of an igneous rock differ from that of a sedimentary rock?

16. Is sedimentary rock the bedrock everywhere? Is it present in the earth?

17. What is a metamorphic rock? Give some examples of metamorphic rocks.

18. Give several good reasons why plains are more valuable for man to live on than plateaus.

19. Why are most of our metallic ores associated with mountainous regions?

20. List some of the ways in which mountains are valuable to man.

21. What minerals other than salt are being deposited in the sea?

22. Of what value are the oceans to man? Would it not have been better to have had three-fourths of the lithosphere land?

23. Of what value to the United States are Byrd's discoveries in Antarctica? Will this land ever be valuable for man's use?

24. Make a collection of the following rocks: granite, dolerite, basalt, pyroxenite, and felsite.

25. Quartz is one of the commonest minerals. Make a collection of the following varieties: milky, ferruginous, rose, rock crystals, geode, and amethyst.

26. Chalcedony is a fine-grained, translucent, waxy quartz. In this group there are many varieties. See if you can find agates, chert, flint, jasper.

27. Is coal a rock? How is coal formed? Is it forming on the earth today?

28. In what respects are metamorphic and igneous rocks alike?

29. What uses does man make of the igneous rocks?

30. What uses are made of sedimentary rocks? Why are not more of our homes made of these rocks?

31. List our most important economic minerals. How does the United States rank in possessing these minerals?

# CHAPTER 32. THE GRADATIONAL AGENTS

1. Make a list of all the agents you can find that aid in breaking rocks and describe how each works.

2. What chemical elements are necessary in rocks to cause them to weather by oxidation, carbonation, and hydration? In what way does a humid climate affect these processes?

3. Distinguish between weathering and erosion; abrasion and corrasion.

4. What is soil? Subsoil? What may be said of the depth of each?

5. What sort of tools does the wind use to break rocks? In what different ways does the wind secure its tools?

6. What is a *dune?* Could dunes form on a level surface? What generally starts a dune? Are they present in moist regions? What may be said as to the shape and height of dunes? What two slopes are usually present? How do they differ?

7. List all the possible sources of river water. When does a stream become permanent? Why is it that young streams are frequently intermittent?

8. How does a river secure its load? In what three ways does it carry its load? Are rivers limited in the size of the material that they can transport?

9. In what ways does a river use its tools to erode its channel?

10. List as many reasons as possible for rivers not being able to transport all of their loads.

11. What are the various types of deposits made by rivers? Where along the river's course are these deposits made, and when?

12. What are the characteristics of a young valley? An old valley? A mature valley?

13. What is the meaning of a cycle of erosion? Has a cycle ever been completed?

14. What is a snow field? The snow line? What factors determine the height of the snow line?

15. Write a statement explaining how glacial ice is formed from snow.

16. What is a glacier? In what respects are glaciers similar to rivers? Unlike rivers?

17. Name the various types of glaciers and tell how they differ.

18. Name the several ways in which glaciers secure their loads. Where do glaciers carry their load with reference to the ice? How do they differ in this respect from rivers?

19. Various types of surface features may be present on glaciers. How are the following formed: Lateral moraines, medial moraines, dust wells, crevasses, rock tables, and seracs?

20. How do glaciers use their tools to erode the surface? List some of the surface evidences of glacial erosion.

21. What is the nature of glacial motion? What factors affect the rate of motion? How fast do glaciers move?

22. Glacial deposits are of two kinds: those made from the water which comes from the melting of the ice, and those made by the ice.

Name some of the deposits made by the ice and tell how, when, and where they are made. What are the water-made deposits? How do they differ from the ice-made deposits?

23. Are glaciers limited in the size of the material that they can transport?

24. How may the farmer make soil out of subsoil? Is soil permanent?

25. What is a transported soil? What agents transport soil? What is a residual soil? How could these two soils be distinguished in the field?

26. Why should we conserve our soil? Discuss several remedies and preventives for the control of soil erosion.

27. What is a dust storm? In what parts of the United States are dust storms frequent? What is meant by the "dust bowl"? Where is it located? Can you mention some ways in which man has been responsible for producing the "dust bowl"? Can this land ever be redeemed? If so, how?

28. What are some of the means that man is using to stop the movement of dunes? Can you name some regions in the United States where dunes are covering good timber and farm land?

29. When a river's velocity becomes zero, does it deposit all of its load? Give reasons for your answer.

30. Suppose a new land surface has been elevated above the sea. When rains fall upon its surface, where will gullies first develop? Why do not all gullies become valleys?

31. Give some reasons why rivers do not make good boundary lines. What is a river system? A river basin?

32. Rivers of what age are best suited to navigation? Why? Make a list of all the uses that may be made of rivers.

33. In great hydroelectric plants, are the turbines placed under the waterfall? How does man maintain navigation in rivers that have waterfalls and rapids?

34. Why are the rivers in the eastern part of the United States more numerous and larger than those found in the western part of the country?

35. Name some famous river deltas that are used by man. What types of crops are grown on these deltas? Why do we not use the Mississippi delta to grow cotton and sugar cane?

36. Name some of the economic uses made of flood plains. Give examples.

37. What uses are made of levees, fans, and cones?

38. Why are flood plains more common in mature and old streams? In what ways is man now attempting to prevent floods? Give some examples.

39. What evidences have we that glaciers covered much of the central and northern parts of North America? How would you go about it to prove that a region has been glaciated?

40. In what ways did continental glaciation affect the drainage in the northern part of the United States?

41. Enumerate all the ways that you can find to show that continental glaciation was beneficial to man? Are there places where they were harmful? If so, where and how?

42. Are the Great Lakes a direct result of glaciation? In what ways are these lakes beneficial to man?

## CHAPTER 33.   GROUND WATER AND ITS WORK

1. What are the various sources of ground water?

2. What factors exercise control over the amount of water that gets into the ground?

3. What is the meaning of the *water table?* Is it a level table? What factors determine its height? Shape?

4. What is the maximum depth to which water can penetrate the earth? Why?

5. Is the water table a permanent thing? What may cause it to vary?

6. How does the water table in a moist region differ from one in a dry region? In what ways does the height of the water table affect farmers' crops?

7. What is the meaning of dry farming? Where is such farming carried on?

8. Can you suggest several ways whereby the water table of a region is lowered?

9. What is a spring? Distinguish between a gravity and hydro-static spring? Which of these is more common? Draw diagrams to show the conditions for each.

10. What is a well? Is it necessary to have water before it can be termed a well?

11. Through what kind of rock does water pass readily? Why? What is the meaning of "aquifer"?

12. What is a gravity well? Are they safe wells for domestic use? Where should such wells be located on the farms or near homes in the city? Why?

13. What is a hydrostatic well? How does this well differ from gravity wells?

14. Is it possible for the well driller to estimate the depth to which he must sink the well before he starts drilling? How can he find out?

15. Are hydrostatic wells flowing wells? What are the rock-structure conditions for a hydrostatic well?

16. In what different ways does ground water work to break rocks?

17. Describe in detail the forming of caves. Why are they generally found in regions where limestone is the bedrock? Name some noted caves in the United States.

18. Where are stalactites and stalagmites formed? How would you go about it to distinguish one from the other? What other deposits may be found in caverns?

19. What is a sink hole? How may they be formed? What may be said of their size?

20. What is the meaning of hard water? Soft water? Is all well water hard?

21. How could you determine whether your water supply was contaminated?

22. What is a geyser? What evidence is there that geysers and hot springs have some connection with volcanic activity?

23. Where on the earth do we find geysers? What is the probable cause of geyser eruption? Would the throwing of soap into the geyser tube cause it to erupt?

24. What is a mineral spring? What elements are easily dissolved out of rocks by water containing carbon dioxide?

25. Why do we often find fossils of men and animals in caves?

26. Do you think it practical to use the water stick to locate the place where wells should be sunk?

27. Draw a diagram of the rock-structure conditions necessary for artesian wells.

28. Why are wells less numerous in mountainous regions?

29. In what parts of the United States are artesian wells a necessity? Why?

30. Why are springs more common in a hilly or mountainous region?

31. What are some of the common sources of contamination of shallow well water? How is it possible to determine whether water is contaminated?

32. What rules should be followed in locating shallow wells on farms?

33. Name several ways in which the ground water table of a region may be lowered? Has this happened in your locality?

34. Why do we not drill wells in regions of igneous and metamorphic rocks?

35. Name some famous dams that have been constructed for irrigation purposes.

36. Why is water from deep wells superior to that of shallow wells?

37. About three-fourths of the population in the United States depend upon shallow wells for their water supply. Why have so

many cities and state legislatures passed laws to protect the water supply?

38. Is it safe to drink spring water?   Lake water?   How may it be made safe?

# CHAPTER 34.   DIASTROPHISM

1. What earth movements are involved in diastrophism?

2. What evidences may be cited to prove that the earth's surface is not stationary?

3. The hot interior of the earth is slowly losing heat by conduction.   As the outer cooler shell contracts to adjust itself to the interior portion, why does it not contract equally over all portions of the lithosphere?

4. What are some of the probable causes of diastrophism?

5. Diastrophism disturbs the position of bedrock.   Define *monocline, syncline, anticline, strike,* and *dip.*

6. What may bring about jointing in rocks?   Examine a quarry and see if you can discover joints.

7. Define a normal fault.   How does this fault differ from a thrust fault?

8. What terms are used with faults?   What is a *fault scarp?*

9. Name some of the ways in which diastrophism is valuable to man.

10. What conditions of rock structure are necessary to produce hogbacks?

11. Are strike and dip impossible in regions of horizontally bedded rocks?

12. Why is it necessary for the mining engineer to have a thorough knowledge of the rock structure before he can locate mineral veins?

13. When rocks are exposed, is it possible to tell the position of the beds?

14. Diastrophism is responsible for many mountain areas.   The Appalachian Mountains are a result of diastrophism and erosion. What must be the rock structure to have ranges so parallel?

15. The Great Basin region has mountains extending in ridges north and south.   One side is steep and the other is more gentle. Do you think they were formed by faulting?

16. In what respects do the Rocky Mountains differ from the Appalachians?

# CHAPTER 35.   EARTHQUAKES AND VOLCANISM

1. What are earthquakes?   In what regions of the earth are they of common occurrence?   In what parts of the United States are they frequent?

2. What types of tremors accompany an earthquake?

3. What warning does an earthquake give of its approach? Which is the destructive tremor?

4. What type of instrument is used to record the approach of an earthquake?

5. Are earthquakes frequent in young mountain regions, and, if so, why?

6. What makes an earthquake destructive? How much up-and-down movement of the earth particles is necessary to destroy chimneys? Buildings?

7. Are earthquakes generally associated with volcanism? Give some examples.

8. Name some of the regions of the world where earthquakes are common.

9. List some of the causes of destructive earthquakes.

10. What is a volcano? Is it correct to say that a volcano is a burning mountain? Is the mountain necessary to a volcano?

11. Two types of volcanic eruptions are found on the earth. Give an example of each type. List some famous volcanoes and tell where they are found.

12. What is the nature of the material ejected during an eruption? How far may volcanic dust travel?

13. Are there any active volcanoes in the United States? If so, where?

14. Why are some volcanic cones steep-sided while others have very gentle slopes?

15. Where on the earth are volcanoes found? Are they present on the ocean floor?

16. What is extrusive and intrusive volcanic material? Give some examples of each and tell how they are formed.

17. What form of volcanic material are the Columbia and Deccan plateaus? Where are these plateaus found?

18. What is a dyke? A sill? A laccolith? A bysmalith? Which one of these forms is represented by the Black Hills?

19. List some of the probable causes of volcanoes.

20. Enumerate some reasons why New York City has not experienced a severe earthquake in centuries.

21. Are there good reasons why earthquakes are common in Japan and southern California? Will these regions ever be free from them?

22. If one were to build a house in a region subject to severe earthquakes, where would it be more advisable to build it, on bedrock or on loose soil? Give reasons for your answer.

23. Are tall buildings common in cities along the southern coast of California? What type of structure would best withstand earthquake tremors?

24. How does the seismograph locate the center of a destructive earthquake?

25. Why do earthquakes seldom occur in the Mississippi Basin?

26. List some of the destructive effects of famous earthquakes of the past.

27. Are bysmaliths and laccoliths a type of volcano? Give reasons for your answer.

28. Find some examples of old, worn-down volcanoes? Are there any in the United States?

29. What is a dormant volcano? Have we any evidence that a dormant volcano will always remain so?

30. Is Devil's Tower in Wyoming a volcanic neck or laccolith?

31. A great sea wave, "tsunami," resulting from the violent eruption of Krakatoa destroyed 36,000 people and over 1000 villages. Where is this volcano located? Is it still eruptive?

32. What are composite cones? Why should they be more steep-sided than lava cones?

33. Name all the ways in which volcanic eruptions may cause damage to life and property?

34. Are earthquakes and volcanoes valuable? If so, why?

## CHAPTER 36.   THE EARTH'S PAST

1. What evidences can be given to prove that the earth has undergone continual change?

2. What is geology? Why is it a valuable study?

3. What sciences must the geologist be familiar with in order to interpret the past history of the earth? Is it possible to determine when the earth started? If not, why not?

4. What divisions of geological time are made? What is an era, period, epoch? In what respects do they differ? What are some of the criteria that the geologist uses to make such divisions?

5. What is a fossil? In what various ways may life be preserved? Was King Tut a fossil?

6. In what kind of rocks and rock material may fossils be found? In what way do fossils help us to interpret the physical changes and climates of the past?

7. Why are there no fossils present in the oldest rocks of the earth? Does this mean that no forms of life were present? What are some of the indirect evidences that life, in some form, was present during the formation of these old rocks?

8. What is the meaning of "unconformity"? How is it used to separate the rocks into different ages?

9. During what periods was volcanic activity widespread on the earth? In what part of North America are the oldest rocks widespread on the surface?

10. What are some of the physical and organic evidences used by the geologist to divide geological time?

11. When were the Appalachian Mountains made? Are they now old or young mountains?

12. See if you can find from the Geological Timetable some of the great salt-making periods. Great limestone-forming periods. Is salt being deposited in the sea at the present time?

13. In what period did well-preserved fossil life first appear? What form of life was it?

14. In what periods of the earth's history is oil found? Coal? Gypsum? Gold? Phosphate? Iron? Lead?

15. During what period did life reach its greatest size? See if you can find some of the types of life that reached enormous statures.

16. When did our domestic form of mammals first appear? Was this early or late in the earth's history?

17. When did man first appear on the earth? What are some of the earlier types of man?

18. What was the most outstanding event of the Pleistocene? Why was it of so much importance?

19. When were the Rocky Mountains made? Are they young or old mountains?

20. Name some of the periods when a large part of North America was under the sea. How may we tell whether the rocks of a region have been formed beneath the sea?

21. What is paleontology? Why is this a valuable study for aiding the geologist in interpreting the past history of the earth?

22. What is the meaning of evolution? In what way does the life of the later periods of the earth show great evolutionary advances?

23. What is the generally accepted theory for the origin of petroleum? In what kind of rocks is oil found? What rock structure is necessary for oil accumulation? Is it possible for the oil geologist to determine where an oil well should be drilled?

24. How does America rank with the other oil-producing nations of the earth? Will our oil supply last indefinitely? How long will it last at the present rate of consumption?

25. How did the plant life of the Pennsylvanian differ from that of today?

26. What were the first vertebrates to appear on the earth?

27. When did the reptiles dominate the earth? Are they present now? Why are they less significant now?

28. In what way does the mammal show marked advance over the earlier forms of life on the earth?

29. How would you tell a brachiopod from a pelecypod? Are these forms living at the present time?

30. In what period did the flying reptiles reach their greatest development?

31. See if you can find the names of some mammals that are now living in the sea.

32. Which great class of rocks dominates the Paleozoic? The Proterozoic? The Archeozoic?

# CHAPTER 37. ASTRONOMY, ANCIENT AND MODERN

1. What is astronomy? When and where did it first begin?

2. Why should we know something about astronomy? What are some of the things which this science has contributed to mankind?

3. Astronomy was supposed to be the oldest and most complete of all of the sciences. Is it a completed science?

4. Name some of the periods of great astronomical development. How do they differ?

5. What did the Babylonians, Hebrews, and Egyptians contribute to the knowledge of astronomy?

6. What were the specific contributions of Thales, Hipparchus, Eudoxus, Claudius Ptolemy, Copernicus, and Tycho Brahe?

7. Who founded the great Alexandrian Museum? What was the chief purpose of this school? Name some of the famous scholars who taught here.

8. What was the "Dark Period"? Who was responsible for it?

9. What was Galileo's contribution to the knowledge of astronomy? Why was he persecuted by the church? Was free speech permitted in his day?

10. What is the science of astrology? Is it a true science? Do you believe in it?

11. How did Kepler, Galileo, and Newton prove that the heliocentric conception of the universe was right? How many years did it take to prove that Copernicus was right?

12. State Kepler's three laws of motion. In what way did they support the Copernican conception?

13. What was the ancient Pythagorean notion of the "music of the spheres"?

14. What is the meaning of the *eccentricity* of the earth's orbit? The two foci of the earth's orbit are separated by one-eighth of an inch. With a radius of thirty times this distance, construct the orbit of the earth.

15. What are Newton's three laws of motion?

16. Draw a diagram that will show the meaning of *parallax*.

17. What are some of the new things that are absorbing the attention of the astronomers at the great observatories?

18. What two kinds of telescopes are now in use in the observatories? Can you name some of the noted observatories in the United States and tell where they are located?

## CHAPTER 38.   OUR STARRY GALAXY

1. What is a universe? Of what is it composed?

2. Name and define the measuring sticks used by the astronomer.

3. What is the shape and what are the possible dimensions of our starry galaxy?

4. What is the Milky Way? Does it change its position in the sky during the year?

5. In what part of our starry galaxy is our solar system?

6. How many stars are in the galaxy?

7. What is a star? How does it differ from a planet?

8. What may be said about the distribution of stars in our galaxy?

9. Why do stars differ in color? See if you can pick out some red stars.

10. What is a first-magnitude star? How are magnitudes determined?

11. Define *visual, photographic, radiometric,* and *absolute* magnitudes.

12. Who first classified stars according to brightness?

13. Compare a first-magnitude star with one of magnitude 2; 3; −2; 0; 1.4; 1.8.

14. What is meant by the proper motion of a star?

15. How may the astronomer determine the age of a star?

16. What are nebulae? What kinds are found in the universe?

17. How long would it take to fly across this galaxy of ours with an airplane capable of making 200 miles an hour if no stops were made?

18. Is our galaxy permanent? Are there galaxies beyond ours? How can the astronomer discover galaxies? Do you think it possible that there are other starry galaxies with solar systems similar to ours?

## CHAPTER 39.   OUR SOLAR FAMILY

1. What different kinds of bodies are present in our solar system? Would it be necessary to have all these types of bodies to have a solar system?

2. Name some of the reasons for the importance of the sun to the earth.

3. What parts of the sun are visible during a total eclipse? Why?

4. Why do the astronomers spend so much time and money each year to make trips to study a total eclipse of the sun?

5. What ways has the astronomer of knowing something of the composition of the sun? Why should we want to know about its composition?

6. What are sunspots? What use is made of them? Do they influence our weather? In what ways do they affect radio, telephone, and telegraphic reception?

7. How does the astronomer determine the sun's temperature?

8. List the possible sources of the sun's heat. Will our sun eventually become a cold body? When this happens, how will it affect life on the earth?

9. Name the planets in their order outward from the sun. How can we tell a planet from a star?

10. What planets besides the earth might have some form of life? Give reasons for your answer.

11. What classification of planets is made? What is the basis for such a classification?

12. What is the meaning of a morning and evening star? In what part of the sky would you look for them? Why are the planets Jupiter, Mars, and Saturn not thought of as morning and evening stars?

13. What are "shooting stars"? Is this the correct way to describe them? What is a siderite, an aerolite, a siderolite? How large may meteors become? Why does the astronomer want to study meteorites?

14. What is a comet? What are the parts of a comet? Are these parts always visible?

15. What may be said about the density of comets? The temperature of comets?

16. Give some reasons why it would not be serious to life on the earth if the earth were to pass through a comet.

17. What is the true shape of the earth?

18. Write out several proofs for the shape of the earth. Can you offer any proofs to support a belief that the earth is flat?

19. What motions does the earth have? Which one is the simplest to prove?

20. What are several results of rotation? Would it be possible for man to find his way about the earth if it did not rotate?

21. Secure a globe and see if you can identify the points and lines that result from rotation. State three points of difference between parallels and meridian circles.

22. How many parallels are there on a globe? Why? How many meridians? Why this number?

23. State the causes for the seasons found on the earth. In what way does each of these causes affect seasons?

24. Give three reasons why it is warmer in summer than in winter.

25. When are we at aphelion? Perihelion? How much nearer are we to the sun at perihelion?

26. How does the astronomer go about determining the temperature of the sun?

27. List some of the evidences to support the possibility of the existence of some form of life on Mars. What are some of the strong reasons for thinking that it possesses no high forms of life?

28. Explain how it is possible for Jupiter to capture a family of thirty comets.

29. Make a list of some of the advantages of a round earth over a flat one.

30. Why does the earth's motion of rotation and revolution remain about uniform?

31. Where would one have to go on the earth to have the sun directly overhead on June 21? December 22? March 21? Why?

32. What parts of the earth have daily sunrise and sunset throughout the year?

33. If you were located at either pole on March 21, in what direction would you look to see the sun? How high would it appear above the horizon?

34. When did Byrd attempt to reach the South Pole on his 1939 trip? In our December or June? Why did he leave when he did?

35. Why are days and nights always equal at the equator?

36. The height of the noon sun on June 21 is 70 degrees; in what latitude is the observer? The noon sun is 24 degrees high at noon on December 22; in what latitude is the observer?

## CHAPTER 40.   LATITUDE, LONGITUDE, AND TIME

1. What is the meaning of *latitude? Coordinates?*

2. On what circles is latitude measured?

3. What is the latitude of the equator? Why? What is the greatest latitude a place may have? Why?

4. Explain fully how we can use the Pole Star to determine our latitude. Draw a diagram to show the height of the North Star at the North Pole. The equator. At 45° north.

5. Explain how the captain at sea may use the noon sun to determine his latitude. The height of the noon sun on March 21 is 50°; what is the latitude? The height of the noon sun on shipboard is 70° on June 21; what is the latitude of the ship?

6. What are meridians? How many are found on a globe? What use is made of them? Where is the zero meridian? Why was it located where it is? Why do we keep it there?

7. What is the longitude of the equator? Why does a degree of longitude shorten as the pole is approached? Why do the poles have no longitude?

8. Where could one go on the earth to find no latitude and no longitude?

9. What is a chronometer? Why do ships carry chronometers? The chronometer on shipboard shows 2 P. M. when the sun indicates noon; in which longitude is the ship and how much?

10. What is the meaning of *solar time? Mean solar time?*

11. What is a solar day? Distinguish between a solar and sidereal day. Where is the conventional day used? If you were signing a contract to teach school, what kind of a day would you use?

12. What is an analemma? Is it present on globes? What uses are made of it?

13. At what time of year does the longest solar day occur? The shortest? Why should days differ in length?

14. What is standard time? When and why was it necessary to adopt this method of reckoning time in the United States? Do other countries of the world use standard time?

15. Name the standard time belts in the United States. How wide are they and why? What is the principal time meridian in each belt? Name a large city in each belt.

16. In traveling from one belt to another, where would you change your time?

17. What is daylight-saving time? When was it first used in the United States and why? Is it used at the present time?

18. Why is it necessary to have an International Date Line? Where is it located? Why does it not follow the 180th meridian?

19. Why did the ancients have less need for an economical calendar than do the peoples of the present? Did the ancients have calendars? Were they like ours?

20. What are some of the defects in our present calendar?

21. Who made our calendar? How does it differ from the early Roman calendar?

22. How and when was the method of reckoning Easter determined? When does Easter come?

23. Who was Pope Gregory? In what way did he correct the Caesars' calendars? Why was a change necessary?

24. Is the proposed calendar for the future a good one? If so, why?

25. A ship's chronometer indicates 10 A. M. When it is noon by the sun, on which side of the Greenwich meridian is the ship? It is noon by the sun on shipboard, but the chronometer indicates 4 P. M. In which longitude is the ship and how much?

26. How may radio signals be used to determine the position of a ship?

27. When it is noon by the watch in 84° west longitude, what time will the sun indicate? When it is noon by the watch in 94° west longitude, what time is it by the sun?

28. On November 10 the analemma shows the equation of time to be minus 16; this means that watch time is 16 minutes faster than sun time. When it is noon on the 94th meridian by sundial time, what will the watch indicate? When it is noon by the watch, what will sundial time show?

29. On September 30 the analemma shows the equation of time to be minus 10. This means that the watch is 10 minutes slower than the sundial time. When it is noon on the 88th meridian by sundial time, what will watch time indicate? When it is noon by the watch, what will sundial time show?

30. On which side of the International Date Line does each new day start? In what direction does it travel around the world? How long is the day for the world as a whole? If you are traveling westward, come to the International Date Line early Sunday morning and cross the line, what day will the boat take? Why? If you cross the Date Line traveling eastward and you arrive there Sunday night at midnight, when you cross the line, what day will the boat take?

31. If the earth's axis were inclined 30 degrees, what would be the width of the zones?

32. How would a greater axial inclination affect the length of our summer days?

33. Where do days and nights change in length more rapidly, at 30° N. latitude or 60° N. latitude?

34. What is the length of total darkness at the poles?

# CHAPTER 41. OUR MOON A COLD DEAD WORLD

1. Why is the moon our most important astronomical body? Compare its size with that of the earth.

2. What is the shape of the moon's orbit? What is the meaning of *apogee* and *perigee?* How near is the moon to the earth? How many times farther away is the sun?

3. In what particular way does the moon's rotation differ from that of the earth? How often does the moon rotate?

4. In what way does an eclipse of the moon help to prove the earth round? How long may a total eclipse of the moon last? Of the sun?

5. Does an observer on the earth always see the same side of the moon?

6. Why does the moon shift its position eastward in the sky night after night? What is the difference between synodic and sidereal months? Which one did the ancients use in measuring time?

7. What is meant by the moon's phases? What is a waxing moon? A waning moon? In what part of the heavens do we always see a new moon? Why?

8. Why does the moon rise about an hour later each night?

9. What is a wet moon? A dry moon? Do you think that the moon has any influence on rainfall?

10. What is a Harvest Moon? Hunter's Moon? Are they used for such purposes now?

11. What causes an eclipse of the moon? Does the shadow of the earth on the moon prove it round? What is the meaning of *umbra? Penumbra?* In which of these shadows must the moon be to be eclipsed?

12. Why do we not have a lunar eclipse with each full moon? How many eclipses of the moon occur each year? Would it be possible to have none?

13. What is a solar eclipse? What must be the relation of the sun, moon, and earth to get a total eclipse of the sun? How long does a solar eclipse last? Why cannot a total eclipse of the sun be seen over the entire earth?

14. What is the chief source of the moon's heat? How may this be determined? What must be the temperature of the dark side of the moon?

15. Are there real volcanoes on the moon?  In what ways are they unlike volcanoes on the earth?

16. What are maria?  Do they contain water now?  If they ever did, what has become of the water?  Why cannot the moon hold an atmosphere?

17. What evidences can be cited to prove that the heat and light of the moon have little influence on the time when seeds should be sown, meat cured, or wooden shingles laid on buildings?

18. Give some reasons for believing that the moon has little effect upon rainfall or changes of temperature.

19. If you could travel to the moon and utilize on its surface your normal senses, why could you not carry on a conversation with your friends?  What would be the color of your sky?  Why could you not use a radio?  Why would meteors be invisible?  In what way would the stars appear different from those seen from the earth?

20. What evidences can be given to prove that the moon has no atmosphere?

21. If you weigh 125 pounds on the earth, how much would you weigh on the moon?  How much farther could you jump?

22. In what direction do the horns of the new moon point when first seen in the west?  Why is the new moon always seen in the west soon after the sun sets?

23. Why is the moon the chief tide-producing force on the earth? Of what value are tides on the earth?

24. Explain why we see more eclipses of the moon than we do of the sun even though solar eclipses are more numerous?

25. Why do our winters occur when the earth is nearest the sun?

# INDEX